MATHEMATICAL PHYSICS RESEARCH AT THE CUTTING EDGE

MATHEMATICAL PHYSICS RESEARCH AT THE CUTTING EDGE

CHARLES V. BENTON
EDITOR

Nova Science Publishers, Inc
New York

Library of Congress Cataloging-in-Publication Data
Mathematical Physics Research at the Cutting Edge / Charles V. Benton (editor)
p.cm.
Includes bibliographical references and index.
ISBN: 1-59033-939-8
1. Mathematical physics – Research. I. Benton, Charles V.
QC20.8.M37 2003
530.15'072—dc22 2003026148

400 Oser Ave, Suite 1600
Hauppauge, New York 11788-3619
Tele. 631-231-7269 Fax 631-231-8175
e-mail: Novascience@earthlink.net
Web Site: http://www.novapublishers.com

Printed in the United States of America

Contents

Preface

Physics and mathematics have always been closely intertwined, with developments in one field frequently inspiring the other. Currently, there are many unsolved problems in physics which will likely require innovations in mathematical physics. Mathematical physics is concerned with problems in statistical mechanics, atomic and molecular physics, quantum field theory, and, in general, with the mathematical foundations of theoretical physics. This includes such subjects as scattering theory for n bodies, quantum mechanics (both nonrelativistic and relativistic), atomic and molecular physics, the existence and properties of the phases of model ferromagnets, the stability of matter, the theory of symmetry and symmetry breaking in quantum field theory (both in general and in concrete models), and mathematical developments in functional analysis and algebra to which such subjects lead. This book presents leading-edge research in this fast-moving field.

In the first chapter, *Coordinate formalism on Hilbert manifolds*, Alexey A. Kryukov illustrates the formalism by means of multiple examples. M. Botta Cantcheff establishes a basic framework in order to clarify the group structure underneath the 2-form gauge potential in the second chapter, *On the Group Structure of the Kalb-Ramond Gauge Symmetry and Spinor Representations*.

The next chapter, *Group Theoretical Interpretation of the CPT theorem*, V.V. Varlamov studies an algebraic description of basic discrete symmetries (space inversion *P*, time reversal *T*, charge conjugation *C* and their combinations *PT*, *CP*, *CT*, *CPT*). In order to understand the methods based on cross recurrence plots, Norbert Marwan and Jürgen Kurths review the concepts of phase space trajectories and recurrence plots in *Cross Recurrence Plots and Their Applications*.

In *Analytical solutions of the radiative transfer equation in one-dimensional spherical geometry with central symmetry*, Charles H Aboughantous considers the analytical solutions of the transfer equation in spherical geometry with central symmetry that are obtained on the spatial domain, in finite spheres and in infinite homogeneous and heterogeneous pure absorbing media, in LTE and for monochromatic unpolarized radiation. Matrix elements of spinor and principal series representations of the Lorentz group are studied on the basis of complex angular momentum (helicity basis) are discussed in *Hyperspherical Functions and Harmonic Analysis on the Lorentz Group* by V.V. Varlamov.

In the last chapter, *The next stage: quantum game theory*, Edward W. Piotrowski and Jan Sładkowski present the history, basic ideas and recent development in quantum game theory.

C.V. Benton
March 2004

In: Mathematical Physics Research at the Cutting Edge
Editor: C.V. Benton, pp. 1-33
ISBN 1-59033-939-8

Coordinate Formalism on Hilbert Manifolds

Alexey A. Kryukov *

Abstract

The formalism of local coordinates on infinite-dimensional Hilbert manifolds is introduced. Images of charts on the manifolds are allowed to belong to arbitrary Hilbert spaces of functions including spaces of generalized functions. The corresponding local coordinate form of algebra of tensor fields on Hilbert manifolds is constructed. A single tensor equation in the formalism is shown to produce a family of functional equations on different spaces of functions. This allows for a "covariant" approach to the theory of generalized functions and suggests a way of using generalized functions in solving linear and non-linear problems. Examples in linear algebra, differential equations, differential geometry and variational calculus are used to illustrate the results.

1 Introduction

The notion of a *vector*, or, more generally a *tensor* is one of the highlights of the 19th century science. In fact, it allows us to separate in a compact way the effects related to a particular choice of coordinates on a manifold from the coordinate independent, "absolute" properties of quantities described by tensors.

The idea of such a "relativisation" has entered physics in a significant way as a requirement that the laws of physics must be described by tensor equations. With the advances of gauge theory this idea was further extended to include gauge transformations i.e. transformations of coordinates on a fibre bundle.

Although originally tensor fields were introduced on finite dimensional manifolds, the needs of mathematics and physics have led one to consider infinite-dimensional manifolds and tensor fields on them.

The notion of an infinite-dimensional manifold is a direct generalization of its finite dimensional counterpart. Namely, such a manifold is a topological space with a differentiable structure where the charts take values in a fixed infinite-dimensional Banach space. In particular, the charts of a Hilbert manifold take values in an

*University of Wisconsin, UWC Department of Mathematics, 780 Regent Street, Madison, WI 53708. E-mail: akriouko@uwc.edu

infinite-dimensional separable Hilbert space H. In this case we also say that the manifold is modelled on (or after) H.

In the most general scenario one could assume that images of charts of a Hilbert manifold belong to a family of Hilbert spaces rather than to a fixed space. This possibility is often neglected as all infinite-dimensional separable Hilbert models are isomorphic. The situation seems to be quite similar to the case of a finite dimensional manifold. The images of charts of the latter belong to n-dimensional vector spaces each isomorphic to R^n. There is, however, an important difference. In applications of infinite-dimensional manifolds we usually work with their specific functional realizations. Unlike columns of numbers representing points of a finite dimensional manifold, functions can have very different analytic properties. As no particular space is large enough to contain all functions useful in applications it becomes important to develop a formalism which would make use of several functional models at once.

In this paper, such a formalism on Hilbert manifolds is introduced. We let images of charts on a Hilbert manifold belong to arbitrary Hilbert spaces of functions including spaces of generalized functions. Isomorphisms of these spaces are then used to define transformations of coordinates. The resulting formalism (which we call *functional coordinate*, or simply *coordinate*, or *string* formalism) seems to be the most appropriate generalization of the local coordinate approach to tensor fields in infinite-dimensional case.

The possibility of changing the model space H turns out to be essential in developing a coordinate independent approach to the theory of linear operators and in merging linear algebra on Hilbert spaces with the theory of generalized functions.

In particular, the possibility of changing Hilbert models for the abstract Hilbert space $\mathbf{S}$ means that we can alter a specific functional form of an operator $\mathbf{A}$ acting on $\mathbf{S}$. As a result, functionally different operators in the formalism may represent the same (i.e. coordinate independent) operator on $\mathbf{S}$.

Likewise, by changing a Hilbert model H we alter the analytic properties of functions representing the points of $\mathbf{S}$. In particular, the generalized functions become incorporated into the formalism on equal footing with, say, the square-integrable functions.

Moreover, the applications of the formalism are not at all restricted to linear problems. Analogously to tensor equations on manifolds, the functional tensor equations seem to provide a valuable tool for solving nonlinear problems on Hilbert spaces.

Despite the fact that the formalism requires an infinite number of dimensions, it seems at the same time to indicate a deep new connection between the finite and the infinite-dimensional manifolds. Namely, the choice of a model for an infinite-dimensional manifold (rather than the choice of a chart with values in a fixed model) turns out to be similar to the choice of coordinates on a finite dimensional manifold.

In this paper, we concentrate on illustrating the formalism by means of multiple examples. The more formal mathematical treatment of the spectral theorem discussed in section 5 and some other specific results in the paper can be found in [4]. In [5] the reader can find some applications of the formalism to quantum mechanics.

Here is the plan of the paper. In section 2 the main definitions of the functional coordinate formalism are introduced. In particular, the notions of a string manifold, string basis, coordinate structure, and a functional coordinate transformation are given and the laws of transformation of component functions of tensor fields are deduced.

The recipe of how to construct the "large" Hilbert spaces of generalized functions is obtained in section 3. In particular, a simple example of a Hilbert space containing the δ-function and all of its derivatives is introduced and the square of the norm of the δ-function is discussed.

The notion of a generalized eigenvalue problem for a linear operator is analyzed in section 4. It is shown that such a problem can be formulated in a functional tensor form i.e. in the form independent of any particular choice of functional coordinates.

In section 5 the basis of eigenvectors of an operator on the string space (the string basis of eigenvectors) is introduced and its properties are investigated. We also discuss the functional tensor approach to the theory of linear operators on Hilbert spaces and formulate the spectral theorem.

Part of the material in sections 2-5 has appeared first in the on-line publications by the author and, in the context of quantum mechanics, in [5].

In the following four sections the specific types of functional coordinate transformations are considered. In section 6 we consider coordinate transformations preserving locality of the operators. As a particular solution of the locality equations we obtain the Fourier transform.

In section 7 transformations preserving the derivative operator are analyzed. It is shown in particular that the generalized and the smooth solutions of linear differential equations with constant coefficients are related by a change of functional coordinates. This result seems to explain the root of difficulties one has when trying to define the product of generalized functions.

In section 8 we investigate coordinate transformations preserving the operator of multiplication by a function. It is shown that except for trivial cases such an operator cannot be preserved.

More general coordinate transformations are considered in section 9. The examples here show how one could use the formalism in the case of more general linear and nonlinear differential equations.

In the last two sections we discuss another interesting relationship between the finite and the infinite-dimensional manifolds. In section 10 we show how the standard formalism of finite dimensional differential geometry on a Riemannian manifold is related to the introduced coordinate formalism on Hilbert manifolds. Here singular generalized functions play an essential role.

In section 11 we deduce the equation of geodesics on a finite dimensional submanifold of a Hilbert manifold by means of the coordinate formalism.

Finally, the results and potential applications are summarized in the conclusion.

2 Coordinate formalism on abstract Hilbert space

As already discussed, we want to incorporate the arbitrary infinite-dimensional separable Hilbert spaces of functions into the structure of a Hilbert manifold. Such spaces will be simply called Hilbert spaces throughout the paper. As all separable Hilbert spaces are isomorphic, it is possible to think that there is a single abstract Hilbert space $\mathbf{S}$. Different Hilbert spaces of functions will be then *realizations* of $\mathbf{S}$. We accept the following definitions:

Definition. A *string space* $\mathbf{S}$ is an abstract infinite-dimensional linear topological space isomorphic (that is, topologically linearly isomorphic) to a separable Hilbert space.

Definition. The elements of $\mathbf{S}$ are called strings and will be denoted by the capital Greek letters $\Phi, \Psi, \ldots$.

Definition. A *Hilbert space of functions* is either a Hilbert space H, elements of which are equivalence classes of maps between two given subsets of R^n or the Hilbert space H^* dual to H. Two maps f, g are called *equivalent* if the norm of $f-g$ in H is zero.

Definition. Any Hilbert space of functions H is called a *coordinate space.* Elements of H are called *coordinates* (or *functional coordinates*) of strings and will be denoted by the small Greek letters $\varphi, \psi, \ldots$.

To identify strings with their coordinates we need a linear map $e_H : H \longrightarrow \mathbf{S}$ from a Hilbert space of functions H into the string space $\mathbf{S}$. The action of e_H on $\varphi \in H$ will be written in one of the following ways:

$$e_H(\varphi) = \int e_H(k)\varphi(k)dk = e_{Hk}\varphi^k. \tag{2.1}$$

The integral sign here is used as a notation for the action of e_H on elements of H and in general does not refer to an actual integration. We also use an obvious and convenient generalization of the Einstein's summation convention over the repeated indices k one of which is above and one below. Once again, only in special cases does this notation refer to an actual summation or integration over k.

Definition. A linear isomorphism e_H from a Hilbert space H of functions onto $\mathbf{S}$ is called a *string basis* (or a *functional basis*) on $\mathbf{S}$. The inverse map $e_H^{-1} : \mathbf{S} \longrightarrow H$ is called a *linear coordinate system on* $\mathbf{S}$ (or a *linear functional coordinate system*).

By definition any string Φ is the image of a unique element $a \in H$, i.e.

$$\Phi = e_H(a) \tag{2.2}$$

for a unique $a \in H$. Also, if

$$e_H(a) = 0, \tag{2.3}$$

then $a = 0$.

Assume for example that $H = l_2$, where l_2 is the Hilbert space of square-summable sequences. Then the action of e_H on H can be written as the matrix multiplication of a row $(e_1, e_2, ...)$ of linearly independent vectors in $\mathbf{S}$ by the column of components of $\varphi \in l_2$. In this case the string basis can be identified with the basis in the ordinary sense.

It is worth noticing that the basis e_H defines the space H itself. In fact, it acquires the meaning only as a map on H.

Let $\mathbf{S}^*$ be the dual string space. That is, $\mathbf{S}^*$ is the space of all linear continuous functionals on strings.

Definition. A linear isomorphism of H^* onto $\mathbf{S}^*$ is called a *string basis on* $\mathbf{S}^*$.

We will denote such a basis by e_{H^*}. Decomposition of an element $F \in \mathbf{S}^*$ with respect to the basis will be written in one of the following ways:

$$F = e_{H^*}(f) = \int e_{H^*}(k)f(k)dk = e^k_{H^*}f_k. \tag{2.4}$$

Definition. The basis e_{H^*} is *dual* to the basis e_H if for any string $\Phi = e_{Hk}\varphi^k$ and for any functional $F = e^k_{H^*}f_k$ the following is true:

$$F(\Phi) = f(\varphi). \tag{2.5}$$

In general case we have

$$F(\Phi) = e_{H^*}f(e_H\varphi) = e^*_H e_{H^*}f(\varphi), \tag{2.6}$$

where $e^*_H : \mathbf{S}^* \longrightarrow H^*$ is the adjoint of e_H. Therefore, e_{H^*} is the dual string basis if $e^*_H e_{H^*} : H^* \longrightarrow H^*$ is the identity operator. In this case we will also write

$$e_{Hl}{}^* e^k_{H^*} = \delta^k_l. \tag{2.7}$$

In special cases δ^k_l is the usual Krœnecker symbol or the δ- function.

Notice also that the action of F on Φ in any bases e_H on $\mathbf{S}$ and e_{H^*} on $\mathbf{S}^*$ can be written in the following way:

$$F(\Phi) = e^k_{H^*}f_k e_{Hl}\varphi^l = G(f, \varphi) = g^k_l f_k \varphi^l, \tag{2.8}$$

where G is a non-degenerate bilinear functional on $H^* \times H$.

By definition the string space $\mathbf{S}$ is isomorphic to a separable Hilbert space. We can assume then that $\mathbf{S}$ itself is an abstract Hilbert space. Respectively, we will assume that the string bases $e_H = {\pi_H}^{-1}$ are isomorphisms of Hilbert spaces. That is, a Hilbert structure on any coordinate space H will be assumed to be induced by a choice of string basis.

Let us assume that H is a real Hilbert space (generalization to the case of a complex Hilbert space will be obvious). We have:

$$(\Phi, \Psi)_S = \mathbf{G}(\Phi, \Psi) = G(\varphi, \psi) = g_{kl}\varphi^k\psi^l, \tag{2.9}$$

where $\mathbf{G} : \mathbf{S} \times \mathbf{S} \longrightarrow R$ is a bilinear form defining the inner product on $\mathbf{S}$ and $G : H \times H \longrightarrow R$ is the induced bilinear form. The expression on the right is a convenient form of writing the action of G on $H \times H$.

It is useful to notice that the choice of a coordinate Hilbert space determines the corresponding string basis up to a unitary transformation.

Definition. A string basis e_H in $\mathbf{S}$ will be called *orthogonal* if for any $\Phi, \Psi \in \mathbf{S}$

$$(\Phi, \Psi)_S = f_\varphi(\psi), \tag{2.10}$$

where $f_\varphi = (\varphi, \cdot)$ is a *regular* functional and $\Phi = e_H\varphi$, $\Psi = e_H\psi$ as before. That is,

$$(\Phi, \Psi)_S = f_\varphi(\psi) = \int \varphi(x)\psi(x)d\mu(x), \tag{2.11}$$

where $\int$ here denotes an actual integral over a μ-measurable set $D \in R^n$ which is the domain of definition of functions in H.

If the integral in (2.11) is the usual Lebesgue integral and/or a sum over a discrete index x, the corresponding coordinate space will be called an L_2-space. In this case we will also say that the basis e_H is *orthonormal.*

If the integral is a more general Lebesgue-Stieltjes integral, the coordinate space defined by (2.11) will be called an L_2-space with the weight μ.

The bilinear form $\mathbf{G} : \mathbf{S} \times \mathbf{S} \longrightarrow R$ generates a linear isomorphism $\widehat{\mathbf{G}} : \mathbf{S} \longrightarrow \mathbf{S}^*$ by $\mathbf{G}(\Phi, \Psi) = (\widehat{\mathbf{G}}\Phi, \Psi)$. In any basis e_H we have

$$(\Phi, \Psi)_S = (\widehat{\mathbf{G}}e_H\varphi, e_H\psi) = e^*_H\widehat{\mathbf{G}}e_H\varphi(\psi) = \widehat{G}\varphi(\psi), \tag{2.12}$$

where $\widehat{G} = e^*_H\widehat{\mathbf{G}}e_H$ maps H onto H^*. If e_H is orthogonal, then $\widehat{G}\varphi = f_\varphi$. In the case of an orthonormal basis e_H we will also write

$$(\Phi, \Psi)_S = \delta_{kl}\varphi^k\psi^l. \tag{2.13}$$

In a special case δ_{kl} can be the Krœnecker symbol or Dirac δ-function $\delta(k - l)$.

The form of writing in (2.13) makes it especially clear why the basis in the definition above is called orthonormal. In fact, in this case the kernel of the metric functional is a generalization of the Krœnecker symbol, which represents the Euclidean metric in an orthonormal basis.

It follows from the definition that if e_H is orthogonal, then H is a space $L_2(D, \mu)$ of square-integrable functions on a μ-measurable set $D \in R^n$. In particular, not every coordinate Hilbert space H can produce an orthogonal string basis e_H. Assume, for example, that H is a space of functions on R which contains the δ-function as a coordinate φ of a string $\Phi \in \mathbf{S}$ (an example of such a space will be given below in section 3). Then, as $\int \delta(k-l)\varphi(k)\varphi(l)dkdl$ is not defined, the basis e_H can not be orthonormal. That is, the δ-function can not be the coordinate function of a string in orthonormal basis.

On the other hand, Hilbert spaces l_2 and $L_2(R)$ are examples of coordinate spaces that admit an orthonormal string basis.

This result does not contradict the well known existence of an orthonormal basis in any separable Hilbert space. In fact, the meaning of a string basis is quite different from the meaning of an ordinary basis on a Hilbert space. Namely, a string basis on $\mathbf{S}$ permits us to represent an invariant with respect to functional transformations object (string) in terms of a function, which is an element of a Hilbert space of functions. A basis on the latter space in turn permits us to represent this function in terms of a sequence of numbers, components of the function in the basis.

Notice that formula (2.13) suggests that if H possesses an orthonormal basis e_H, then the chart $(\mathbf{S}, e_H^{-1})$ is analogous to a rectangular Cartesian coordinate systems in Euclidean space. More general formula (2.9) suggests that other string bases produce analogues of oblique Cartesian coordinate systems in Euclidean space.

Definition. A linear coordinate transformation on $\mathbf{S}$ is an isomorphism $\omega : \widetilde{H} \longrightarrow H$ of Hilbert spaces which defines a new string basis $e_{\widetilde{H}} : \widetilde{H} \longrightarrow \mathbf{S}$ by $e_{\widetilde{H}} = e_H \circ \omega$.

Let φ be coordinate of a string Φ in the basis e_H and $\widetilde{\varphi}$ its coordinate in the basis $e_{\widetilde{H}}$. Then $\Phi = e_H\varphi = e_{\widetilde{H}}\widetilde{\varphi} = e_H\omega\widetilde{\varphi}$. That is, $\varphi = \omega\widetilde{\varphi}$ by uniqueness of the decomposition. This provides the transformation law of string coordinates.

Let now $\Phi, \Psi \in \mathbf{S}$ and let $\mathbf{A}$ be a linear operator on $\mathbf{S}$. Let $\Phi = e_H\varphi$, $\Psi = e_H\psi$ with $\varphi, \psi \in H$. The scalar product $(\Phi, \mathbf{A}\Psi)_S$ is independent of a basis and in a basis e_H reduces to

$$(\varphi, A\psi)_H = (\widehat{G}\varphi, A\psi), \tag{2.14}$$

where $\widehat{G} : H \longrightarrow H^*$ defines the metric on H.

If $\omega : \widetilde{H} \longrightarrow H$ is a linear coordinate transformation and $\varphi = \omega\widetilde{\varphi}$, $\psi = \omega\widetilde{\psi}$, then

$$(\widehat{G}\varphi, A\psi) = (\widehat{G}\omega\widetilde{\varphi}, A\widetilde{\psi}) = (\omega^*\widehat{G}\omega\widetilde{\varphi}, \omega^{-1}A\omega\widetilde{\psi}) = (\widehat{G}_{\widetilde{H}}\widetilde{\varphi}, A_{\widetilde{H}}\widetilde{\psi}). \tag{2.15}$$

Therefore we have the following transformation laws:

$$\varphi = \omega\widetilde{\varphi} \tag{2.16}$$

$$\psi = \omega\widetilde{\psi} \tag{2.17}$$
$$\widehat{G}_{\widetilde{H}} = \omega^*\widehat{G}\omega \tag{2.18}$$
$$A_{\widetilde{H}} = \omega^{-1}A\omega. \tag{2.19}$$

More generally, consider an arbitrary Hilbert manifold S modelled on $\mathbf{S}$. Let (U_α, π_α) be an atlas on S.

Definition. A collection of quadruples $(U_\alpha, \pi_\alpha, \omega_\alpha, H_\alpha)$, where each H_α is a Hilbert space of functions and ω_α is an isomorphism of $\mathbf{S}$ onto H_α is called a *functional atlas* on S. A collection of all compatible functional atlases on $\mathbf{S}$ is called a *coordinate structure* on S.

Definition. Let (U_α, π_α) be a chart on S. If $p \in U_\alpha$, then $\omega_\alpha \circ \pi_\alpha(p)$ is called the *coordinate* of p. The map $\omega_\alpha \circ \pi_\alpha : U_\alpha \longrightarrow H_\alpha$ is called a *coordinate system.* The isomorphisms $\omega_\beta \circ \pi_\beta \circ (\omega_\alpha \circ \pi_\alpha)^{-1} : \omega_\alpha \circ \pi_\alpha(U_\alpha \cap U_\beta) \longrightarrow \omega_\beta \circ \pi_\beta(U_\alpha \cap U_\beta)$ are called *functional (or string) coordinate transformations.*

As S is a differentiable manifold one can also introduce the tangent bundle structure $\tau : TS \longrightarrow S$ and the bundle $\tau^r_s : T^r_s S \longrightarrow S$ of tensors of rank (r, s).

A coordinate structure on a Hilbert manifold permits one to obtain a functional description of any tensor. Namely, let $\mathbf{G}_p(F_1, ..., F_r, \Phi_1, ..., \Phi_s)$ be an (r, s)-tensor on S.

Definition. The coordinate map $\omega_\alpha \circ \pi_\alpha : U_\alpha \longrightarrow H_\alpha$ for each $p \in U_\alpha$ yields the linear map of tangent spaces $d\rho_\alpha : T_{\omega_\alpha \circ \pi_\alpha(p)} H_\alpha \longrightarrow T_p S$, where $\rho_\alpha = \pi_\alpha^{-1} \circ \omega_\alpha^{-1}$. This map is called a *local coordinate string basis on S.*

Let $e_{H_\alpha} = e_{H_\alpha}(p)$ be such a basis and $e_{H^*_\alpha} = e_{H^*_\alpha}(p)$ be the corresponding dual basis. Notice that for each p the map e_{H_α} is a string basis as defined earlier. Therefore, the local dual basis is defined for each p as before and is a function of p.

We now have $F_i = e_{H^*_\alpha} f_i$, and $\Phi_j = e_{H_\alpha}\varphi_j$ for any $F_i \in T^*_p S$, $\Phi_j \in T_p S$ and some $f_i \in H^*_\alpha, \varphi_j \in H_\alpha$. Therefore

$$\mathbf{G}_p(F_1, ..., F_r, \Phi_1, ..., \Phi_s) = G_p(f_1, ..., f_r, \varphi_1, ..., \varphi_s) \tag{2.20}$$

defines the component functions of the (r, s)-tensor $\mathbf{G}_p$ in the local coordinate basis e_{H_α}.

In the following sections our goal is to explain the formalism and its usefulness through a variety of examples.

3 Constructing "large" Hilbert spaces of functions

Our first step is to bring the generalized functions (distributions) into the picture. The most common Hilbert spaces containing some singular generalized functions are those dual to Sobolev spaces. However, these spaces are rather "meager". In particular, they do not include many of the tempered distributions standardly used in applications.

The following example shows how one can practically construct large Hilbert spaces containing standard spaces of generalized functions as topological subspaces. See [4] for details as well as for other examples of Hilbert spaces of generalized functions.

Example. Let W be the Schwartz space of infinitely differentiable rapidly decreasing functions on R with the standard topology. That is, functions $\varphi \in W$ satisfy inequalities of the form $\left|x^k\varphi^{(n)}(x)\right| \leq C_{kn}$ for some constants C_{kn} and any $k, n = 0, 1, 2, ...$. Let W^* be the dual space of continuous linear functionals on W. Let us find a Hilbert space which contains W^* as a subset. For this consider a linear transformation ρ from the space $L_2(R)$ into W given by

$$(\rho f)(x) = \int f(y)e^{-(x-y)^2-x^2}dy \tag{3.1}$$

for any $f \in L_2(R)$. One can verify that $\rho(L_2(R) \subset W$ and ρ is injective. Moreover, ρ induces the Hilbert metric on $H = \rho(L_2(R))$ by $(\varphi, \psi)_H = (\rho^{-1}\varphi, \rho^{-1}\psi)_{L_2}$. The space H with this metric is Hilbert and the embedding $H \subset W$ is continuous.

It follows in particular that $W^* \subset H^*$ as a set. In fact, any functional continuous on W will be continuous on H. Moreover, by choosing the strong topology on W^* one can show that the embedding of W^* into H^* is continuous. Notice also that one could choose the weak topology on W^* instead as the weak and strong topologies on W^* are equivalent [1].

The method used to obtain the Hilbert space H^* turns out to be quite general. It can be summarized as follows. First, find a linear injection from a standard Hilbert space (say, $L_2(R)$) into itself. This injection induces a Hilbert structure on the image H. Assume the embedding of H into the original Hilbert space is continuous. Then construct the conjugate Hilbert space H^*. By choosing the injection to a small enough subspace H, one obtains as large H^* as one wishes.

The metric on H^* induced by $\rho^* : H^* \longrightarrow L_2^*$ in the example is given by

$$(f, g)_{H^*} = \int e^{-(x-y)^2-x^2}e^{-(y-z)^2-z^2}f(x)g(z)dydxdz. \tag{3.2}$$

In particular, for the norm of the δ-function we have:

$$(\delta, \delta)_{H^*} = (\rho\rho^*\delta, \delta) = \int e^{-(x-y)^2-x^2}e^{-(y-z)^2-z^2}\delta(x)\delta(z)dydxdz = \frac{\sqrt{\pi}}{2}. \tag{3.3}$$

The fact that the norm of the δ-function in H^* is finite, is related to the fact that the metric $g_{xz} = \int e^{-(x-y)^2-x^2}e^{-(y-z)^2-z^2}dy$ is a smooth function of x and z and is capable of "compensating" singularities of the product of two δ-functions. Conversely, in case of the coordinate space $L_2(R)$ the metric g_{xz} is equal to $\delta(x-z)$.

Therefore the norm of the δ-function is not defined. That is, δ-function can not be the coordinate of a string in this case.

More generally, it is easy to see that by "smoothing" the metric we extend the class of (generalized) functions for which the norm defined by this metric is finite. The same is true if we "improve" the behavior of the metric for large $|x|$. Conversely, by "spoiling the metric" we make the corresponding Hilbert space "poor" in terms of a variety of the elements of the space.

4 Functional-tensor equations: Generalized eigenvalue problem

The usefulness of tensor equations in a finite dimensional setting is well recognized. The developed coordinate formalism permits one to introduce the analogous concept of functional tensor equations. Of course, tensor equations on infinite-dimensional manifolds are well known. However, they are ordinary understood in a simplified way as equations independent of a particular choice of a chart taking values in a fixed Hilbert space. In this sense, tensor property of equations means simply that equations can be written in a basis independent way. However, as the following example demonstrates, the notion of a string basis generalizes this understanding in a nontrivial way.

Example. Let A be a linear operator on a linear topological space V. If V is a finite-dimensional unitary space and A is, say, Hermitian, then a basis in V exists, such that each vector of it is an eigenvector of A. If V is infinite-dimensional, this statement is no longer true. Yet quite often there exists a complete system of "generalized eigenfunctions" of A in the sense of the definition below (see [2]):

Definition. A linear functional F on V, such that

$$F(A\Phi) = \lambda F(\Phi) \tag{4.1}$$

for every $\Phi \in V$, is called a *generalized eigenfunction of A corresponding to the eigenvalue λ*.

It is usually assumed that V in (4.1) is a space of test functions, i.e. a linear topological space of infinitely differentiable (and "good behaving" at infinity) functions used in the theory of generalized functions.

Notice however, that the definition above makes sense in a more general setting when F and Φ are elements of a pair of dual spaces. Assume then that V is the string space $\mathbf{S}$ and e_H is a string basis on $\mathbf{S}$. Assume F is a generalized eigenfunction of a linear operator $\mathbf{A}$ on $\mathbf{S}$. Then

$$F(\mathbf{A}\Phi) = \lambda F(\Phi), \tag{4.2}$$

that is,

$$e_H^* F(e_H^{-1} \mathbf{A} e_H \varphi) = \lambda e_H^* F(\varphi), \tag{4.3}$$

where $e_H \varphi = \Phi$ and $e_H^{-1} \mathbf{A} e_H$ is the representation of $\mathbf{A}$ in the basis e_H.

By defining $e_H^* F = f$ and $A = e_H^{-1} \mathbf{A} e_H$ we have

$$f(A\varphi) = \lambda f(\varphi). \tag{4.4}$$

Notice that the last equation describes not just one eigenvalue problem, but a family of such problems, one for each string basis e_H. As we change e_H, the operator A in general changes as well, as do the eigenfunctions f.

In particular, let $H \subset L_2(R)$ be a Hilbert space of complex-valued functions such that its dual H^* contains the functionals $f(x) = e^{ipx}$, for any $p \in R$ (see [4] for an example). Assume that the action of the operator of differentiation $A = i\frac{d}{dx}$ on H is defined. The generalized eigenvalue problem for A is

$$f(i\frac{d}{dx}\varphi) = pf(\varphi). \tag{4.5}$$

The equation (4.5) must be satisfied for every φ in H. The functionals

$$f(x) = e^{-ipx} \tag{4.6}$$

are the eigenvectors of A. Let us now consider a coordinate change $\rho : H \longrightarrow \widetilde{H}$ given by the Fourier transform. We have:

$$\psi(k) = (\rho\varphi)(k) = \int \varphi(x) e^{ikx} dx. \tag{4.7}$$

The Fourier transform induces a Hilbert structure on H. Relative to this structure ρ is an isomorphism of the Hilbert spaces $\widetilde{H}$ and H. The inverse transform is given by

$$(\omega\psi)(x) = \frac{1}{2\pi} \int \psi(k) e^{-ikx} dk. \tag{4.8}$$

Notice that as the Fourier image of e^{ipx} is the delta function, the space dual to $\widetilde{H}$ contains the functionals $\delta(k - p)$. According to (4.3) the generalized eigenvalue problem in new coordinates is

$$\omega^* f(\rho A \omega\psi) = p\omega^* f(\psi). \tag{4.9}$$

We have:

$$A\omega\psi = i\frac{d}{dx}\frac{1}{2\pi} \int \psi(k) e^{-ikx} dk = \frac{1}{2\pi} \int k\psi(k) e^{-ikx} dk. \tag{4.10}$$

Therefore,

$$(\rho A\omega\psi)(k) = k\psi(k). \tag{4.11}$$

So, the eigenvalue problem in new coordinates is as follows:

$$g(k\psi) = pg(\psi). \tag{4.12}$$

Thus, we have the eigenvalue problem for the operator of multiplication by the variable. The eigenfunctions here are given by

$$g(k) = \delta(k-p). \tag{4.13}$$

Notice that $g = \omega^* f$ is as it should be. Indeed,

$$(\omega^* f)(k) = \frac{1}{2\pi}\int f(x)e^{ikx}dx = \frac{1}{2\pi}\int e^{-ipx}e^{ikx}dx = \delta(k-p). \tag{4.14}$$

As a result, the eigenvalue problems (4.5), and (4.12) can be considered as two coordinate expressions of a single functional tensor eigenvalue problem

$$F(\mathbf{A}\Phi) = \lambda F(\Phi) \tag{4.15}$$

for an operator $\mathbf{A}$ on $\mathbf{S}$.

5 The spectral theorem

Having introduced generalized eigenvectors of an operator as elements of a Hilbert space it is natural to ask whether we can make a basis out of them. In what follows we assume that $\mathbf{A}$ is a bounded linear operator on $\mathbf{S}$.

Definition 1. A string basis e_H is the *proper basis* of a linear operator $\mathbf{A}$ on $\mathbf{S}$ with eigenvalues (eigenvalue function) $\lambda = \lambda(k)$, if

$$\mathbf{A}e_H(\varphi) = e_H(\lambda\varphi) \tag{5.1}$$

for any $\varphi \in H$.

As any string basis, the proper basis of $\mathbf{A}$ is a linear map from H onto $\mathbf{S}$ and a numeric function λ is defined on the same set as functions $\varphi \in H$.

By rewriting (5.1) as

$$e_H{}^{-1}\mathbf{A}e_H(\varphi) = \lambda\varphi \tag{5.2}$$

we see that the problem of finding a proper basis of $\mathbf{A}$ is equivalent to the problem of finding such a string basis e_H in which the action of $\mathbf{A}$ reduces to multiplication by a function λ.

The operator of multiplication by a function does not always map a Hilbert space H into itself. It is then useful to generalize the definition above.

Notice, that for any $F \in \mathbf{S}^*, \Phi \in \mathbf{S}$ and $\mathbf{A} : \mathbf{S} \longrightarrow \mathbf{S}$ we have

$$F(\mathbf{A}\Phi) = F(\mathbf{A}e_H\varphi) = F(e_{\widetilde{H}}e_{\widetilde{H}}^{-1}\mathbf{A}e_H\varphi) = e_{\widetilde{H}}^*F(e_{\widetilde{H}}^{-1}\mathbf{A}e_H\varphi) = f(A\varphi), \tag{5.3}$$

where $f = e_{\widetilde{H}}^* F \in \widetilde{H}^*$ and $A : H \longrightarrow \widetilde{H}$ is given by $A = e_{\widetilde{H}}^{-1}\mathbf{A}e_H$.

We then have the following

Definition 2. The representation $A = e_{\widetilde{H}}^{-1}\mathbf{A}e_H$ of $\mathbf{A}$ is called *proper* if for any $F \in \mathbf{S}^*$, $\Phi \in \mathbf{S}$ we have

$$F(\mathbf{A}\Phi) = f(A\varphi) = f(\lambda\varphi), \tag{5.4}$$

where $f = e_{\widetilde{H}}^* F$, $\varphi = e_H^{-1}\Phi$ and λ is a function such that the operator of multiplication by λ maps H into $\widetilde{H}$.

If $H = \widetilde{H}$ this is equivalent to the definition 1 above.

It is easy to see that when $H = l_2$ the proper basis and the ordinary basis of eigenvectors of an Hermitian operator $\mathbf{A}$ can be identified. In fact, let e_{l_2} be a proper basis of $\mathbf{A}$ existence of which at this point is assumed. Let $\varphi = (\varphi_1, \varphi_2, ...) \in l_2$. The action of e_{l_2} on φ reduces to the matrix multiplication of the matrix $e_{l_2} = (e_1, e_2, ...)$ of linearly independent vectors by the column of components of φ. That is, $e_{l_2}\varphi = e_1\varphi_1 + e_2\varphi_2 + ...$. Notice that convergence of the series is assured by the continuity of e_{l_2}. We have:

$$\mathbf{A}e_{l_2}\varphi = e_{l_2}(\lambda\varphi) = e_{l_2}(\lambda_1\varphi_1, \lambda_2\varphi_2, ...) = e_1\lambda_1\varphi_1 + e_2\lambda_2\varphi_2 + ... \quad . \tag{5.5}$$

Assume now that the ordinary basis $e_{l_2} = (e_1, e_2, ...)$ of eigenvectors of $\mathbf{A}$ exists. Then $\varphi = e_1\varphi_1 + e_2\varphi_2 + ...$ and

$$\mathbf{A}(e_1\varphi_1 + e_2\varphi_2 + ...) = \lambda_1 e_1\varphi_1 + \lambda_2 e_2\varphi_2 + ... = e_1\lambda_1\varphi_1 + e_2\lambda_2\varphi_2 + ... \quad . \tag{5.6}$$

Comparison of (5.5) and (5.6) verifies the claim.

Hermicity of $\mathbf{A}$ leads to a severe restriction on possible spaces H on which the proper basis of $\mathbf{A}$ is defined. In fact, if e_H is a proper basis of an Hermitian operator $\mathbf{A}$ on $\mathbf{S}$, then

$$(\Phi, \mathbf{A}\Psi)_S = (e_H\varphi, \mathbf{A}e_H\psi)_S = (\varphi, \lambda\psi)_H = \int g(x,y)\varphi(x)\lambda(y)\psi(y)dxdy. \tag{5.7}$$

In agreement with notations of section 2, the integral symbol is used here for the action of the bilinear metric functional G with the kernel g. Hermicity gives then

$$\int g(x,y)(\lambda(x) - \lambda(y))\varphi(x)\psi(y)dxdy = 0 \tag{5.8}$$

for any $\varphi, \psi \in H$. Therefore, the bilinear functional defined by $g(x,y)(\lambda(x)-\lambda(y))$ is equal to zero. It follows under some general assumptions that $g(x,y) = a(x)\delta(x-y)$ (see [4]).

As we have just seen, when $H = l_2$, the proper basis of an operator $\mathbf{A}$ on $\mathbf{S}$ can be identified with the ordinary basis of eigenvectors of $\mathbf{A}$. The obtained result is then equivalent to the well known orthogonality of the eigenvectors corresponding to different eigenvalues of the Hermitian operator $\mathbf{A}$.

More generally, the result means that the proper bases of Hermitian operators are orthogonal (as defined in section 2). In particular, the space H on which the proper basis of an Hermitian operator is defined must be an L_2-space.

However, many Hermitian operators do not have eigenvectors in L_2-spaces. In particular, from section 4 we recall that the eigenvectors of $A = \lambda$ acting on $L_2(R)$ can only be defined as functionals f on a space V of functions, such that

$$f(A\varphi) = \lambda_0 f(\varphi) \tag{5.9}$$

for any $\varphi \in V$ and some $\lambda_0 \in R$.

To include such functionals in the formalism we need to consider Hilbert spaces containing "more" functions than $L_2(R)$. By the above this in general requires consideration of non-Hermitian operators.

Example. We know that $A_H = x$ (operator of multiplication by the variable) has no eigenvectors on $L_2(R)$. Consider then a different Hilbert space H of functions of a real variable with a metric G. We have:

$$(G\varphi, A_H\psi) = \int g(k,m)\varphi(k)m\psi(m)dkdm. \tag{5.10}$$

By (5.8)

$$\int g(k,m)\varphi(k)m\psi(m)dkdm \neq \int g(k,m)k\varphi(k)\psi(m)dkdm, \tag{5.11}$$

that is, A_H is not Hermitian unless H is an L_2-space. On the other hand, if $g(k,m)$ is an ordinary function which defines a regular functional, then obviously

$$\int g(k,m)\varphi(k)m\psi(m)dkdm = \int mg(k,m)\varphi(k)\psi(m)dkdm. \tag{5.12}$$

So by taking

$$f = \int g(k,m)\varphi(k)dk, \tag{5.13}$$

we have:

$$f(m\psi) = (mf)(\psi). \tag{5.14}$$

If the functional $f = \int g(k,m)\varphi(k)dk$ above is not regular, we can define the action of A_H on it by taking

$$(mf)(\varphi) = f(m\varphi). \tag{5.15}$$

The resulting operator of multiplication by m is defined on H^* and is self-adjoint in the sense that (5.15) is satisfied for all possible φ, f.

To be specific, assume that H is the Hilbert subspace $H \subset L_2(R)$ of functions as in the example of section 3. The space H consists of infinitely differentiable functions only. The space H^* contains singular distributions. If $\widehat{G}$ is the metric on H, then the inner product on H^* is defined by

$$(f,g)_{H^*} = (\widehat{G}^{-1}f,g) = \int e^{-(x-y)^2-x^2}e^{-(y-z)^2-z^2}f(x)g(z)dydxdz. \tag{5.16}$$

Unlike the case of $L_2(R)$-space it is possible to find such a function $\varphi \in H$ that $f = \widehat{G}\varphi \in H^*$ in the expression

$$(f, x\psi) \tag{5.17}$$

is a (generalized) eigenvector of x. We can take, for example, $f(x) = \delta(x - \lambda_0)$. With such a choice we have:

$$(f, x\psi) = \lambda_0(f,\psi). \tag{5.18}$$

Let us recall the following definitions:

Definition. Let A be a continuous linear operator which maps a space H into a space $\widetilde{H}$. Then the *adjoint* A^* of operator A maps the space $\widetilde{H}^*$ into the space H^* according to

$$(A^*f,\varphi) = (f, A\varphi) \tag{5.19}$$

for any $\varphi \in H, f \in \widetilde{H}^*$.

Similarly,

Definition. Let A be a continuous linear operator on a Hilbert space H. Then the *Hermitian conjugate* operator A^+ of A is defined on H by

$$(A^+\varphi,\psi)_H = (\varphi, A\psi)_H, \tag{5.20}$$

for any $\varphi, \psi \in H$.

Let now A be given on H and let $\widehat{G}: H \longrightarrow H^*$ define a metric on H. Then

$$(\widehat{G}\varphi, A\psi) = (A^*\widehat{G}\varphi,\psi) = (\widehat{G}A^+\varphi,\psi) \tag{5.21}$$

and the relationship between the operators is as follows:

$$A^+ = \widehat{G}^{-1}A^*\widehat{G}. \tag{5.22}$$

Notice that the L_2-spaces are special in that the conjugate of any such space consists of the regular functionals defined by functions $f \in L_2$. It is therefore natural to identify in this case each functional with the function that defines it. Independently, this could be done on any Hilbert space as well. However, such an identification is not preserved under a general transformation of coordinates. In fact, consider a coordinate space H which is a topological subspace of an L_2-space. We then have $H \subset L_2 \subset H^*$. If we agree to identify the common elements of the spaces in the triple, then the identification $L_2 \longrightarrow L_2^*$ by $\varphi \longrightarrow (\varphi, \cdot)_{L_2}$ is inconsistent with the identification $\varphi \longrightarrow (\varphi, \cdot)_H$. The fact that H is a coordinate space shows then that the identification is not preserved under transformations of coordinates. We therefore agree to identify only the L_2-spaces with their conjugates. As for other coordinate spaces we will avoid such an identification.

If H is identified with its conjugate and $A : H \longrightarrow H$ is an operator on H, then the adjoint operator $A^* : H^* \longrightarrow H^*$ and the Hermitian conjugate $A^+ : H \longrightarrow H$ can be identified as well. As we have seen, the identification of H and H^* is not preserved under general transformations of coordinates. This forces us to distinguish between the adjoint and the Hermitian conjugate operators and, respectively, between the self-adjoint and Hermitian operators. Notice that on the L_2-spaces the distinction disappears.

In light of this, the following definition will be accepted:

Definition. Let the Hilbert space H be a topological dense subspace of an L_2-space. Let A^* be the adjoint of an operator A on H as defined by (5.19). If under the identification $L_2^* = L_2$ the action of A^* and A on their common domain $H \cap H^*$ coincide, we say that the operator A is *self-adjoint.*

It is straightforward to check that if B is a (bounded) Hermitian operator on a L_2-space and $H \subset L_2$ is a topological dense embedding than the restriction A of B onto H is a self-adjoint operator on H. In fact, A is bounded on H, $H \cap H^* \subset L_2$ and $Af(\varphi) = f(A\varphi)$ for any $f, \varphi \in H \cap H^*$.

According to the definition the operator of multiplication by the variable in the example above, when defined on the entire H, is self-adjoint. The example shows that at least in some cases there is a possibility to accommodate both the Hermicity of an operator in L_2, respectively, the self-adjointness of its restriction A onto a Hilbert subspace $H \subset L_2$ and the inclusion of generalized eigenvectors of A into the conjugate space H^*.

More generally, we have the following theorem (see [4]):

Theorem. Let B be an Hermitian operator on a Hilbert space L_2. Then there exists a topological Hilbert subspace H of L_2 which is dense in L_2 and such that the restriction A of B onto H is a self-adjoint operator and the conjugate space H^* contains the complete set of eigenvectors of A. Moreover, there exists a coordinate transformation $\rho : H \longrightarrow \widetilde{H}$ such that the transformed operator $\widetilde{A} = \rho A \rho^{-1}$ is the operator of multiplication by x.

In light of this theorem we accept the following definition:

Definition. If a proper basis e_H is such that the complete set of eigenvectors of the operator A in this basis belongs to H^* (alternatively, the complete set of eigenvectors of $\mathbf{A}$ belongs to $\mathbf{S}^*$), then the basis e_H is called the *string basis of eigenvectors of* $\mathbf{A}$ or the *string eigenbasis of* $\mathbf{A}$.

The theorem then asserts that for any Hermitian operator B on a space L_2 one can find a topological dense subspace H of L_2 such that the string eigenbasis e_H of the restriction A of B onto H exists. In particular, for *any* functional $F \in \mathbf{S}^*$ and any string Φ we have $F(\mathbf{A}\Phi) = f(\lambda\varphi_\lambda)$, where φ_λ and f are coordinates of Φ and F in the string eigenbasis e_H and its dual respectively.

The coordinate formalism therefore suggests that for a given functional form of a self-adjoint operator it is important to find an appropriate Hilbert space of functions on which the operator acts. By choosing the space appropriately, one can solve the generalized eigenvalue problem for the operator. Moreover, in this case the corresponding invariant operator $\mathbf{A}$ has a complete set of eigenvectors on $\mathbf{S}$. Respectively, the generalized eigenvalue problem for $\mathbf{A}$ in *any* basis $e_{\widetilde{H}}$ yields a complete set of (generalized) eigenvectors. Further results on the spectral theorem in light of the formalism can be found in [4].

6 Coordinate transformations preserving locality of operators

In section 4 it was shown that a single eigenvalue problem for an operator on the string space leads to a family of eigenvalue problems in particular string bases. Obviously, it is a general feature of tensor equations in the formalism: a specific functional form of an equation depends on the choice of functional coordinates. In the following four sections we will consider various special transformations of functional coordinates and analyze the effect of these transformations on functional operators and equations.

When transforming a functional equation it is often necessary to preserve some of the properties of the equation. In particular, it is often useful to preserve locality of operators in the equation.

Definition. Let H be a coordinate space of functions on R^n. We shall say that a linear operator $A : H \longrightarrow H$ is local if

$$(Af)(x) = \int \sum_{|q| \leq r} a_q(x) D^q \delta(y - x) f(y) dy. \tag{6.1}$$

Here $x, y \in R^n$, r is a nonnegative integer, $q = (q_1, ..., q_n)$ is a set of nonnegative integers, $|q| = q_1 + ... + q_n$, $D^q = \frac{\partial^{|q|}}{\partial {y_1}^{q_1} ... \partial {y_n}^{q_n}}$ and $\delta(y - x)$ denotes the δ-function of the diagonal $x = y$ in R^{2n}.

Assume first that f is an infinitely differentiable function of bounded support and $a_q(x) D^q f(x)$ is integrable. Then formula (6.1) is understood by requiring the validity of "integration by parts" which reduces (6.1) to

$$(Af)(x) = \sum_{|q|\leq r} (-1)^{|q|} a_q(x) D^q f(x). \tag{6.2}$$

More generally, let $f \in H$ be a generalized function. Then (6.1) is understood by requiring that

$$(Af, \varphi) = (f, B\varphi), \tag{6.3}$$

where φ is any smooth function of bounded support on R^n and

$$(B\varphi)(x) = \sum_{|q|\leq r} D^q(a_q(x)\varphi(x)). \tag{6.4}$$

Here we assume that a_q are smooth functions on R^n.

It is easy to see that locality of an operator is not an invariant property, that is, it depends on a particular choice of coordinates. We now want to describe such coordinate transformations that preserve locality of linear operators.

Suppose then that $A : H \longrightarrow H$ is a local linear operator, $\omega : \widetilde{H} \longrightarrow H$ is a transformation of coordinates, and $A_{\widetilde{H}} = \omega^{-1} A \omega : \widetilde{H} \longrightarrow \widetilde{H}$ is the transformed operator.

The operator $A_{\widetilde{H}}$ will be local if

$$\sum_{|q|\leq r} \omega^{-1}(x,y) a_q(y) D^q \delta(z-y) \omega(z,u) f(u) dy dz du = \sum_{|q|\leq s} b_q(x) D^q \delta(y-x) f(y) dy, \tag{6.5}$$

where notations are as above and the integral symbol is omitted. That is,

$$\sum_{|q|\leq r} a_q(x) D^q \delta(z-x) \omega(z,y) dz = \sum_{|q|\leq s} \omega(x,z) b_q(z) D^q \delta(y-z) dz. \tag{6.6}$$

In the simplest case when H and $\widetilde{H}$ are spaces of functions of one variable and the kernels of A and $A_{\widetilde{H}}$ contain only one term of the form $a_q(x)D^q\delta(y-x)$ each, the equation (6.6) reduces to

$$a(x) \frac{\partial^n}{\partial z^n} \delta(z-x) \omega(z,y) dz = \omega(x,z) b(z) \frac{\partial^m}{\partial y^m} \delta(y-z) dz. \tag{6.7}$$

If particular, when $n = 1$ and $m = 0$ (6.7) yields

$$a(x) \frac{\partial}{\partial z} \delta(z-x) \omega(z,y) dz = \omega(x,z) b(z) \delta(y-z) dz. \tag{6.8}$$

Assuming that ω is a smooth solution, "integration by parts" gives

$$-a(x) \frac{\partial \omega(x,y)}{\partial x} = \omega(x,y) b(y). \tag{6.9}$$

Solving (6.9) we obtain

$$\omega(x, y) = F(y)e^{-c(x)b(y)}, \tag{6.10}$$

where $c(x) = \int \frac{dx}{a(x)}$ and $F(y)$ is an arbitrary smooth function. To be a coordinate transformation ω must be an isomorphism as well. In particular, the Fourier transform is a solution of (6.9) with

$$\omega(x, y) = e^{ixy}. \tag{6.11}$$

Coordinate transformations satisfying (6.9) preserve locality of the first order differential operators on H by transforming them into operators of multiplication.

In the case of a more general equation (6.7), we have:

$$a(x)\frac{\partial^n \omega(x, y)}{\partial x^n} = (-1)^n \frac{\partial^m (\omega(x, y)b(y))}{\partial y^m}. \tag{6.12}$$

Solutions of (6.12) for different values of n and m produce coordinate transformations preserving locality of various operators.

7 Coordinate transformations preserving derivatives

Among solutions of (6.12) those preserving the order q of derivatives are of particular interest. To describe such transformations it is sufficient to obtain solutions of (6.12) with $n = m = 1$. Let us assume here that the coefficients a and b in (6.12) are constants equal to one. Then (6.12) gives the following equation:

$$\frac{\partial \omega(x, y)}{\partial x} + \frac{\partial \omega(x, y)}{\partial y} = 0. \tag{7.1}$$

The smooth solutions of (7.1) are given by

$$\omega(x, y) = f(x - y), \tag{7.2}$$

where f is an arbitrary infinitely differentiable function on R. In particular, the function

$$\omega(x, y) = e^{-(x-y)^2} \tag{7.3}$$

satisfies (7.1). Also, the corresponding transformation is injective (see [4]). When Hilbert structure on $\widetilde{H} = \omega^{-1}(H)$ is induced by ω, this transformation becomes an isomorphism of Hilbert spaces. Therefore, it provides an example of a coordinate transformation that preserves derivatives.

Let now H be a Hilbert space of functions on R^n. We are looking for a nontrivial transformation preserving all partial derivative operators on H. Applying equation (6.6) to this case we obtain assuming $a_q = b_q = 1$:

$$\sum_{i=1}^{n} \frac{\partial \omega(x, y)}{\partial x_i} + \frac{\partial \omega(x, y)}{\partial y_i} = 0. \tag{7.4}$$

The function

$$\omega(x, y) = e^{-(x-y)^2} \tag{7.5}$$

with $x = (x_1, ..., x_n)$ and $y = (y_1, ..., y_n)$ satisfies (7.4) and the corresponding transformation is injective inducing a Hilbert structure on the space $\widetilde{H} = \omega^{-1}(H)$.

We now have the following

Theorem. The generalized solutions of any linear differential equation with constant coefficients (either ordinary or partial) are coordinate transformations of the corresponding regular solutions (i.e. solutions given by the ordinary functions). More precisely, let L be a polynomial function of n variables. Let $u, v \in \widetilde{H}$ be functionals on the space K of functions of n variables which are infinitely differentiable and have bounded supports. Assume that u is a generalized solution of

$$L\left(\frac{\partial}{\partial x_1}, ..., \frac{\partial}{\partial x_n}\right) u = v. \tag{7.6}$$

Then there exists a regular solution φ of

$$L\left(\frac{\partial}{\partial x_1}, ..., \frac{\partial}{\partial x_n}\right) \varphi = \psi, \tag{7.7}$$

where $\varphi = \omega u$, $\psi = \omega v$ and ω is as in (7.5).

To sketch the proof consider first the case of the ordinary differential equation

$$\frac{d}{dx}u(x) = v(x). \tag{7.8}$$

Assume u is a generalized solution of (7.8). Define $\varphi = \omega u$ and $\psi = \omega v$, where ω is as in (7.3). Notice that φ, ψ are infinitely differentiable. In fact, any functional on the space K of infinitely differentiable functions of bounded support acts as follows (see [1]):

$$(f, \varphi) = \int F(x)\varphi^{(m)}(x)dx, \tag{7.9}$$

where F is a continuous function on R. Applying ω to f shows that the result is a smooth function.

As $\omega^{-1}\frac{d}{dx}\omega = \frac{d}{dx}$, we have

$$\omega^{-1}\frac{d}{dx}\omega u = v. \tag{7.10}$$

That is,

$$\frac{d}{dx}\varphi(x) = \psi(x) \tag{7.11}$$

proving the theorem in this case. The higher order derivatives can be treated similarly as

$$\omega^{-1}\frac{d^n}{dx^n}\omega = \omega^{-1}\frac{d}{dx}\omega\omega^{-1}\frac{d}{dx}\omega...\omega^{-1}\frac{d}{dx}\omega. \tag{7.12}$$

That is, transformation ω preserves derivatives of any order. Generalization to the case of several variables is straightforward.

8 Coordinate transformations preserving a product of functions

Let us now investigate changes of equations containing products of functions under transformations of string coordinates. Consider the simplest algebraic equation

$$a(x)f(x) = h(x), \tag{8.1}$$

where f is an unknown (generalized) function of a single variable x and h is an element of a Hilbert space H of functions on a set $D \subset R$. To investigate transformation properties of this equation we need to interpret it as a tensor equation on the string space **S**. The right hand side is a function. Therefore this must be a "vector equation" (i.e. both sides must be $(1,0)$-tensors on the string space). If f is to be a function as well, a must be a $(1,1)$-tensor. That is, the "correct" equation is:

$$a(x)\delta(x-y)f(y)dy = h(x). \tag{8.2}$$

To preserve the product-like form of the equation we need such a coordinate transformation $\omega : \widetilde{H} \longrightarrow H$ that

$$\omega^{-1}(u,x)a(x)\delta(x-y)\omega(y,z)dxdy = b(u)\delta(u-z). \tag{8.3}$$

In this case the equation (8.1) in new coordinates is

$$b(x)\varphi(x) = \psi(x), \tag{8.4}$$

where $h = \omega\psi$, $f = \omega\varphi$, and $\varphi, \psi \in \widetilde{H}$.

Equation (8.3) is a particular case of equation (6.12) with $n = m = 0$. It yields

$$a(x)\omega(x,y) = \omega(x,y)b(y). \tag{8.5}$$

Equation (8.5) is clearly satisfied whenever $a(x) = b(x) = C$, where C is a constant. On another hand, whenever $b'(y) \neq 0$ and H contains as a dense subset the space of smooth functions of bounded support in D, it is easy to deduce that $\omega(x,y) = a_0(x)\delta(y-x)$, where a_0 is a function (see [4]).

One could refer to the operator $a(x)\delta(x-y)$ in (8.2) as the operator of multiplication by $a(x)$. Clearly, it is a local operator. The obtained result then says that locality of this operator can be preserved only in trivial cases when $a(x) = C$ or ω itself is an operator of multiplication by a function.

In particular, the product of nonconstant functions of one and the same variable is not an invariant operation under a general transformation of coordinates.

On the other hand, consider the equation

$$a(x)f(y) = h(x,y), \tag{8.6}$$

where a and f are functions of a single variable and h is a function of two variables. This equation can be viewed as a tensor equation on the string space. The left hand side represents then a tensor product of two "vectors". The right hand side is a $(2,0)$-tensor. Therefore, any coordinate transformation preserves this form of the equation. In particular, generalized solutions f of this equation, whenever they exist, can be transformed into regular solutions by transformation of coordinates.

9 More general coordinate transformations

In section 7 we have studied coordinate transformations preserving linear differential operators with constant coefficients. Here we consider an example of a linear differential equations with non-constant coefficients. We will also begin analyzing functional coordinate transformations of nonlinear differential equations.

Example. Consider the equation (6.12) with $n = m = 1$ assuming $a(x)$ and $b(y)$ are functions. In this case the equation reads

$$a(x)\frac{\partial\omega(x,y)}{\partial x} + \frac{\partial(\omega(x,y)b(y))}{\partial y} = 0. \tag{9.1}$$

Let us look for a solution in the form

$$\omega(x,y) = e^{f(x)g(y)}. \tag{9.2}$$

Then (9.1) yields

$$a(x)f'(x)g(y) + b(y)f(x)g'(y) + b'(y) = 0. \tag{9.3}$$

If $b(y) = 1$, (9.3) is a separable equation and we have

$$\frac{a(x)f'(x)}{f(x)} = -\frac{g'(y)}{g(y)} = k, \tag{9.4}$$

where k is a constant. Solving this we obtain,

$$\omega(x,y) = e^{Ce^{\int \frac{k}{a(x)}dx}e^{-ky}}. \tag{9.5}$$

Taking for example $k = C = 1$ and $a(x) = x$, we have

$$\omega(x,y) = e^{xe^{-y}}. \tag{9.6}$$

The corresponding transformation defined on an appropriate space can be shown to be injective. As we see it transforms the operator $x\delta'(y-x)$ into the operator $\delta'(y-x)$. That is,

$$\omega^{-1} : x\psi'(x) \longrightarrow \psi'(x) \tag{9.7}$$

for *any* function ψ on the space of definition of ω.

A very important question is whether we can apply the developed coordinate formalism to nonlinear differential equations. It is known that the theory of generalized functions has been mainly successful with the linear problems. The difficulty of course lies in defining the product of generalized functions. To see what kind of solution can be offered in the new context consider the following example.

Example. Consider a differential equation containing the square of derivative of an unknown function, i.e. the term

$$\left(\varphi'(x)\right)^2, \tag{9.8}$$

where φ is an element of a Hilbert space H of functions on R. To use the coordinate formalism we need to interpret this term as a tensor. We have:

$$\varphi'(x)\cdot\varphi'(x) = \delta(x-y)\delta'(u-x)\delta'(v-y)\varphi(u)\varphi(v)dydudv, \tag{9.9}$$

where as before we omit the integral symbol. Therefore, this term is the convolution of the $(1,2)$-tensor

$$c^x_{uv} = \delta(x-y)\delta'(u-x)\delta'(v-y)dy \tag{9.10}$$

with the pair of strings $\varphi^u = \varphi(u)$. Define the function ψ by

$$c^x_{uv}\varphi^u\varphi^v = \psi^x, \tag{9.11}$$

where the meaning of notations is described in section 2. Assume that $\omega : \widetilde{H} \longrightarrow H$ is a coordinate transformation and $\omega\widetilde{\varphi} = \varphi$. Denote $\omega(x,y)$ by ω^x_y. As ψ^x is a "vector", we have

$$c^x_{uv}\omega^u_{u'}\widetilde{\varphi}^{u'}\omega^v_{v'}\widetilde{\varphi}^{v'} = \omega^x_{x'}\widetilde{\psi}^{x'}. \tag{9.12}$$

That is, the transformation properties of c^x_{uv} are as follows:

$$c^{x'}_{u'v'} = \omega^{-1}{}^{x'}_{x}\,\omega^{*v}{}_{v'}c^x_{uv}\omega^u_{u'}, \tag{9.13}$$

where ω^* is the adjoint of ω. After "integration by parts" we obtain

$$c^x_{u'v'} = \omega^{*v}{}_{v'}c^x_{uv}\omega^u_{u'} = \frac{\partial\omega(v',x)}{\partial x}\frac{\partial\omega(x,u')}{\partial x}. \tag{9.14}$$

By specifying the desired form of $c^{x'}_{u'v'}$ one obtains a nonlinear partial differential equation for the transformation ω. In particular, by solving such an equation one can make φ^u, φ^v in (9.11) singular at the expense of smoothing c^x_{uv}.

Example. Consider the equation

$$\int k(x,y)\frac{d\varphi_t(x)}{dt}\frac{d\varphi_t(y)}{dt}dxdy = 0, \tag{9.15}$$

where $\varphi_t(x)$ is an unknown function which depends on the parameter t and $k(x,y)$ is a smooth function on R^{2n}.

Let us look for a solution in the form $\varphi_t(x) = \delta(x - a(t))$. As

$$\frac{d\varphi_t(x)}{dt} = -\frac{\partial\delta(x-a(t))}{\partial x^\mu}\frac{da^\mu}{dt}, \tag{9.16}$$

we have after "integration by parts" the following equation:

$$\left.\frac{\partial^2 k(x,y)}{\partial x^\mu \partial y^\nu}\right|_{x=y=a(t)} \frac{da_t^\mu}{dt}\frac{da_t^\nu}{dt} = 0. \tag{9.17}$$

If the tensor field

$$g_{\mu\nu}(a) \equiv \left.\frac{\partial^2 k(x,y)}{\partial x^\mu \partial y^\nu}\right|_{x=y=a} \tag{9.18}$$

is symmetric and positive definite, the equation (9.17) has only the trivial solution. However, if $g_{\mu\nu}(a)$ is non-degenerate and indefinite, then there is a nontrivial solution. In particular, we can choose $g_{\mu\nu}$ to be the Minkowski tensor $\eta_{\mu\nu}$ on space-time. For this assume that x, y are space-time points and take

$$k(x,y) = e^{-\frac{1}{2}(x-y)^2} \tag{9.19}$$

where $(x-y)^2 = \eta_{\mu\nu}(x-y)^\mu(x-y)^\nu$. Then it is immediate that $g_{\mu\nu}$ is the Minkowski tensor $\eta_{\mu\nu}$. Solutions to (9.17) are then given by the null lines $a(t)$. Therefore, the original problem (9.15) has solutions of the form $\varphi_t(x) = \delta(x - a(t))$ where $a(t)$ is a null line.

Notice, that the obtained generalized function φ_t is a singular generalized solution to the nonlinear equation (9.15). Once again, such a solution becomes possible because the kernel $k(x,y)$ in (9.15) is a smooth function, so the convolution $k_{xy}\dot\varphi^x\dot\varphi^y$ is meaningful.

The last two examples suggest a way of treating generalized functions in case of nonlinear equations. The results of section 8 demonstrate that a product of functions cannot be in general preserved under functional coordinate transformations. However, by treating the product as a string-tensor quantity it becomes possible to transform it to the convolution of a "good" tensor with two or more singular generalized functions. This provides one with a systematic approach to nonlinear equations in generalized functions (see [4] for further results in this direction).

10 Embedding of a finite dimensional manifold into a Hilbert space

The constructed coordinate formalism turns out to be a useful tool in formalizing the apparatus of infinite-dimensional differential geometry and in discovering yet another interesting relationship between the finite and the infinite-dimensional manifolds.

Let us first of all apply the coordinate formalism to reconsider the main ingredients of the infinite-dimensional differential geometry. For simplicity let us assume here that the Hilbert manifold S is the string space $\mathbf{S}$ itself. Let us fix a string basis e_H on $\mathbf{S}$.

Pick a point $\Phi_0 \in \mathbf{S}$ and let $\Phi_t : R \longrightarrow \mathbf{S}$ be a differentiable path in $\mathbf{S}$ which passes through the point Φ_0 at $t = 0$. Let $\varphi = \varphi_t$ be an equation of the path in the e_H-basis (i.e. $\varphi_t = e_H^{-1}(\Phi_t)$).

The vector X *tangent* to the path Φ_t at the point Φ_0 is defined as the velocity vector of the path. In the basis e_H, X is given by

$$\xi = \left.\frac{d\varphi_t}{dt}\right|_{t=0}. \tag{10.1}$$

Given the vector X tangent to Φ_t at the point Φ_0 and a differentiable functional F on a neighborhood of Φ_0 in $\mathbf{S}$, the directional derivative of F at Φ_0 along X is defined by

$$XF = \left.\frac{dF(\Phi_t)}{dt}\right|_{t=0}. \tag{10.2}$$

By applying the chain rule we have:

$$XF = F'(\Phi)|_{\Phi=\Phi_0}\, \Phi_t'|_{t=0}, \tag{10.3}$$

where $F'(\Phi)|_{\Phi=\Phi_0} : \mathbf{S} \longrightarrow R$ is the derivative functional at $\Phi = \Phi_0$ and $\Phi_t'|_{t=0} \in \mathbf{S}$ is the derivative of Φ_t at $t = 0$.

The last expression can be also written in the coordinate form. For this notice that as $\Phi_t'|_{t=0} \in \mathbf{S}$, we also have $\varphi_t'|_{t=0} \in H$. Then

$$XF = \int \left.\frac{\delta f(\varphi)}{\delta \varphi(x)}\right|_{\varphi=\varphi_0} \xi(x)dx, \tag{10.4}$$

where the linear functional $\left.\frac{\delta f(\varphi)}{\delta \varphi(x)}\right|_{\varphi=\varphi_0}$, which is an element of the dual space H^*, can be thought of as the derivative functional F' in the basis e_{H^*}. As before, the integral sign is understood here in the sense of action of $\frac{\delta f(\varphi)}{\delta \varphi(x)}$ on ξ. In these notations we can also write

$$X = \int \xi(x)\frac{\delta}{\delta\varphi(x)}dx, \tag{10.5}$$

where $\xi \in H$ and the right hand side acts on functionals f defined by

$$f(\varphi) = F(\Phi), \tag{10.6}$$

where F is as before and $e_H\varphi = \Phi$. In particular, we see that in these notations tangent vectors are represented symbolically as "linear combinations" of the "partial" derivatives. Let us remark, however, that one must be careful in using this symbolic expression as on the infinite-dimensional manifolds a vector field cannot be identified with a derivation (i.e. with a satisfying the product rule R-linear map acting on functions on the manifold).

The space $\mathbf{T_0S}$ of all tangent at a point Φ_0 vectors X with an appropriate topology is isomorphic to $\mathbf{S}$. In fact, it is easy to see that the map $\omega : \mathbf{T_0S} \longrightarrow \mathbf{S}$ which in the basis e_H is given by $\int \xi(x) \left.\frac{\delta}{\delta\varphi(x)}\right|_{\varphi_0} dx \longrightarrow \int e_H(x)\xi(x)dx$ is one-to-one. Therefore, ω induces a Hilbert structure on the space $\mathbf{T_0S}$. Relative to this structure ω is an isomorphism of Hilbert spaces.

The space $\mathbf{T_0S}$ with the above Hilbert structure will be called the *tangent space* to $\mathbf{S}$ at the point Φ_0. Notice that the isomorphism ω makes it possible to identify the functional basis e_H with the symbol $\frac{\delta}{\delta\varphi}$.

Let us now investigate an interesting relationship between the finite and the infinite-dimensional differential geometries in light of the coordinate formalism.

Assume we are given a specific realization of $\mathbf{S}$ as a coordinate space H. We will further assume that H contains the delta-functions $\delta(x-a)$ for various possible $a \in R^n$ (see section 3 for an example of such a realization).

Let M be the subset of H consisting of all delta-functions (without linear combinations). Notice first of all that as a subset of H, M is a topological space with the induced (subset) topology. We will further assume that the inclusion map $i : M \longrightarrow H$ is an embedding. In particular, M will be a submanifold of H.

Clearly, M is not a linear subspace of H. Nevertheless, in the simplest case the space M may have a linear structure (different than the one on H).

We will see now that the tangent bundle structure and the Riemannian structure on M are naturally induced by the embedding of M into H.

The notion of "naturality" requires some clarification. Clearly, the embedding of any finite dimensional manifold into H is always possible. Moreover, it is possible to ensure an *isometric* embedding, i.e. such that the Riemannian metric on M is a restriction (pull-back) of the Hilbert metric on H. This is due to the fact that H has "enough room" for any finite dimensional submanifold.

What distinguishes the embedding i is that $i(M)$ consists of functions concentrated at a point (delta-functions). Respectively, vectors tangent to $i(M)$ are also given by functions concentrated at a point (directional derivatives of delta-functions). It will be shown that under such an embedding the variational derivatives associated with vectors tangent to $\mathbf{S}$ according to (10.4), naturally reduce to the partial derivatives that can be identified with vectors tangent to M. Respectively, the induced Riemannian metric on M is obtained from the kernel $k(x, y)$ of the Hilbert metric on H by means of a *local* transformation (differentiation). Moreover, the entire local coordinate approach to differential geometry on M appears as a special case of the developed coordinate formalism on infinite-dimensional manifolds.

To verify this, let us select from all paths in H the paths laying in M. For each value of the parameter t any such path φ_t reduces to a delta-function. That is,

$$\varphi_t(x) = \delta(x - a(t)) \tag{10.7}$$

for some function $a(t)$ which takes values in R^n.

It is easy to see that vectors tangent to such paths can be identified with the ordinary 4-vectors. In fact, assume f is an analytic functional on H, i.e. on a neighborhood $\|\varphi - \varphi_0\|_H < \epsilon$ of φ_0 the functional f can be represented by a uniformly convergent in a ball $\|\varphi - \varphi_0\|_H \leq \delta < \epsilon$ power series

$$f(\varphi) = f_0 + \int f_1(x)\varphi(x)dx + \int\int f_2(x,y)\varphi(x)\varphi(y)dxdy + ... \quad . \tag{10.8}$$

Then

$$\left.\frac{df(\varphi_t)}{dt}\right|_{t=0} = \left.\frac{\partial f(x)}{\partial x^\mu}\right|_{x=a(0)} \left.\frac{da^\mu}{dt}\right|_{t=0}, \tag{10.9}$$

where $f(x)$ is defined by the uniformly convergent in a ball $\|a - a_0\|_{R^4} \leq \delta_1$ in R^n series

$$f(x) = f_0 + f_1(x) + f_2(x,x) + ... \quad . \tag{10.10}$$

In particular, the expression on the right of (10.9) can be immediately identified with the action of a 4-vector on the function $f(x)$.

To be more specific assume now that H is a real Hilbert space with the metric $K : H \times H \longrightarrow R$ given by a smooth kernel $k(x,y)$. Then the norm of a vector $\delta\varphi \in H$ can be written as

$$\|\delta\varphi\|_H^2 = \int k(x,y)\delta\varphi(x)\delta\varphi(y)dxdy. \tag{10.11}$$

If $\varphi = \varphi_t(x) = \delta(x - a(t))$ is a path in M, then $\delta\varphi(x) \equiv \left.\frac{d\varphi_t(x)}{dt}\right|_{t=0} = -\nabla_\mu\delta(x - a) \left.\frac{da^\mu}{dt}\right|_{t=0}$, where $a = a(0)$ and derivatives are understood in a generalized sense. Therefore,

$$\|\delta\varphi\|_H^2 = \int k(x,y)\nabla_\mu\delta(x-a) \left.\frac{da^\mu}{dt}\right|_{t=0} \nabla_\nu\delta(y-a) \left.\frac{da^\nu}{dt}\right|_{t=0} dxdy. \tag{10.12}$$

"Integration by parts" in the last expression gives

$$\int k(x,y)\delta\varphi(x)\delta\varphi(y)dxdy = \left.\frac{\partial^2 k(x,y)}{\partial x^\mu \partial y^\nu}\right|_{x=y=a} \left.\frac{da^\mu}{dt}\right|_{t=0} \left.\frac{da^\nu}{dt}\right|_{t=0}. \tag{10.13}$$

By defining $\frac{da^\mu}{dt}|_{t=0} = dx^\mu$, we have

$$\int k(x,y)\delta\varphi(x)\delta\varphi(y)dxdy = g_{\mu\nu}(a)dx^\mu dx^\nu, \tag{10.14}$$

where

$$g_{\mu\nu}(a) = \left.\frac{\partial^2 k(x,y)}{\partial x^\mu \partial y^\nu}\right|_{x=y=a}. \quad (10.15)$$

As the functional K is symmetric, the tensor $g_{\mu\nu}(a)$ can be assumed symmetric as well. If in addition $\left.\frac{\partial^2 k(x,y)}{\partial x^\mu \partial y^\nu}\right|_{x=y=a}$ is positive definite at every a, the tensor $g_{\mu\nu}(a)$ can be identified with the Riemannian metric on M. Moreover, as shown in [6], [7], an arbitrary Riemannian metric on M can be locally written in the form (10.15).

In particular, consider the Hilbert space H with the metric given by the kernel $k(x,y) = e^{-\frac{1}{2}(x-y)^2}$. Using (10.15) and assuming $(x-y)^2 = \delta_{\mu\nu}(x-y)^\mu(x-y)^\nu$, we immediately conclude that $g_{\mu\nu}(a) = \delta_{\mu\nu}$.

The case of a complex Hilbert space H leads in a similar way to the Kähler metric on the complex extension M^c of M. Moreover, an arbitrary Kähler metric on M^c can be obtained in such a way.

Let us also remark here that the transformations on M are in this setting just the M-preserving functional transformations on H. In particular, Lorentz transformations on Minkowski space can be identified with the special functional transformations on the appropriate Hilbert space H. The reader is referred to [7] for details.

Finally, notice that the submanifold M of H is locally parameterized by the elements $a \in R^n$ which serve as abstract parameters needed to define the elements of H. The manifold structure on M is *not* the same as on the space of parameters, but rather appears as a restriction (pull-back) of the manifold structure on H. It is therefore defined by a specific realization H of the abstract Hilbert space $\mathbf{S}$. After the space H and the submanifold M are chosen, the parameters a^μ can be identified with coordinates on M.

As a clarifying example consider a Hilbert space which contains the delta-functions $\delta(\theta - a)$ on R with functions $\delta(\theta - a)$ and $\delta(\theta - (a + 2\pi))$ identified for any $a \in R$. The space of parameters here is R. The space H is a space of generalized functions on the circle S^1. The space M consists of all delta-functions on S^1 and by the formalism of this section is naturally identified with the unit circle itself. The parameter a becomes then identified with the angular coordinate on S^1.

11 The equation of geodesics on M

In the last section we saw how the formalism of local coordinates on finite dimensional manifolds has naturally appeared as a special case of the developed functional formalism on infinite-dimensional manifolds. Here we will further extend this correspondence to demonstrate how the equation of geodesics on M can be obtained by variation of the energy functional on $\mathbf{S}$. This will also provide an example of a variational problem within the formalism.

Assume that $\mathbf{S}$ is a complex Hilbert space and let $e_H : H \longrightarrow \mathbf{S}$ be any realization of $\mathbf{S}$ as a space of functions (i.e. a functional basis on $\mathbf{S}$). The inner product on $\mathbf{S}$ can be expressed in terms of the inner product on H and will be written in one of the following ways:

$$(\varphi, \psi)_H = \int k(z, \overline{z})\varphi(z)\overline{\psi}(z)dzd\overline{z} = k_{z\overline{z}}\varphi^z\psi^{\overline{z}}. \tag{11.1}$$

As always, the integral is understood as the action of the Hermitian form K given by the kernel $k(z, \overline{z})$ and the expression on the right is a convenient form of writing this action.

Consider a curve on $\mathbf{S}$ which in the basis e_H is given by $\varphi = \varphi_t(z) \equiv \varphi_t^z$, with $t \in [a, b]$. Let us define the *square-length* (or *energy*) action functional on $\mathbf{S}$ by

$$l = \int_a^b dt k_{z\overline{z}} \frac{d\varphi_t^z}{dt}\frac{d\varphi_t^{\overline{z}}}{dt}. \tag{11.2}$$

The corresponding Lagrangian L depends only on $\frac{d\varphi}{dt} \equiv \dot{\varphi}$ and $\frac{d\overline{\varphi}}{dt} \equiv \dot{\overline{\varphi}}$, i.e. $L = L(\dot{\varphi}, \dot{\overline{\varphi}})$. For variation of l we then have:

$$\delta l = \int_a^b dt k_{z\overline{z}} \left(\ddot{\varphi}_t^z \delta\varphi_t^{\overline{z}} + \ddot{\varphi}_t^{\overline{z}}\delta\varphi_t^z\right). \tag{11.3}$$

Therefore the pair of complex conjugate equations of motion is

$$k_{z\overline{z}}\ddot{\varphi}_t^z = 0, \quad k_{z\overline{z}}\ddot{\varphi}_t^{\overline{z}} = 0. \tag{11.4}$$

If $k_{z\overline{z}}$ is an integral operator acting on integrable functions, it follows that φ_t must be a linear function of time. This is consistent with the fact that the shortest line in a Hilbert space is a straight line.

Assume that the kernel $k(z, \overline{z})$ is a smooth function. The resulting complex Hilbert space H contains then singular generalized functions, in particular, delta-functions. As in the previous section let us form a complex n-dimensional submanifold M^c of H consisting of all delta-functions in H. An arbitrary path in M^c is given by

$$\varphi_t(z) = \delta(z - a(t)), \quad \varphi_t(\overline{z}) = \delta(\overline{z} - \overline{a}(t)). \tag{11.5}$$

Variation of l with constraints (11.5) gives the equation (11.4) in the form

$$\int k(z, \overline{z})\frac{d^2}{dt^2}\delta(z - a(t))dz = 0 \tag{11.6}$$

as well as the complex conjugate equation. Notice that in a generalized sense

$$\frac{d^2}{dt^2}\delta(z - a(t)) = \frac{\partial^2}{\partial z^\nu \partial z^\mu}\delta(z - a(t))\frac{da^\nu}{dt}\frac{da^\mu}{dt} - \frac{\partial}{\partial z^\mu}\delta(z - a(t))\frac{d^2 a^\mu}{dt^2}. \tag{11.7}$$

"Integration by parts" in (11.6) gives then

$$\int \left(\frac{\partial^2 k(z,\overline{z})}{\partial z^\nu \partial z^\mu} \frac{da^\nu}{dt} \frac{da^\mu}{dt} + \frac{\partial k(z,\overline{z})}{\partial z^\mu} \frac{d^2 a^\mu}{dt^2} \right) \delta(z - a(t)) dz = 0. \tag{11.8}$$

Let us now differentiate the last equation with respect to $\overline{z}^\alpha \equiv z^{\overline{\alpha}}$ and change the order of partial derivatives. This yields

$$\int \left(\frac{\partial}{\partial z^\mu} \frac{\partial^2 k(z,\overline{z})}{\partial z^\nu \partial z^{\overline{\alpha}}} \frac{da^\nu}{dt} \frac{da^\mu}{dt} + \frac{\partial^2 k(z,\overline{z})}{\partial z^\mu \partial z^{\overline{\alpha}}} \frac{d^2 a^\mu}{dt^2} \right) \delta(z - a(t)) dz = 0. \tag{11.9}$$

Using the notation

$$g_{\mu\overline{\alpha}} = \left. \frac{\partial^2 k(z,\overline{z})}{\partial z^\mu \partial z^{\overline{\alpha}}} \right|_{z=a, \overline{z}=\overline{a}}, \tag{11.10}$$

we have

$$g_{\mu\overline{\alpha}} \frac{d^2 a^\mu}{dt^2} + \frac{\partial g_{\nu\overline{\alpha}}}{\partial z^\mu} \frac{da^\nu}{dt} \frac{da^\mu}{dt} = 0. \tag{11.11}$$

Assume now that the matrix $(g_{\mu\overline{\alpha}})$ is non-degenerate. Then, multiplying (11.11) by the inverse matrix $(g^{\overline{\alpha}\beta})$, we obtain

$$\frac{d^2 a^\beta}{dt^2} + g^{\overline{\alpha}\beta} \frac{\partial g_{\nu\overline{\alpha}}}{\partial z^\mu} \frac{da^\nu}{dt} \frac{da^\mu}{dt} = 0. \tag{11.12}$$

In a similar way the equation complex conjugate to (11.6) gives the complex conjugate of (11.12).

It is known that the metric given by (11.10) is Kähler. Conversely, any Kähler metric can be locally written in the form (11.10). Moreover, the symbols

$$\Gamma^\beta_{\nu\mu} = g^{\overline{\alpha}\beta} \frac{\partial g_{\nu\overline{\alpha}}}{\partial z^\mu} \tag{11.13}$$

are the connection coefficients for the Kähler metric (see for example [3]). That is, the equation (11.12) and the complex conjugate equation are equations of geodesics on the Kähler manifold M^c.

12 Conclusion

The passage from differentiable structure on a finite dimensional manifold to its infinite-dimensional counterpart offers an essentially new type of coordinate transformations consisting of changing Hilbert models for the manifold.

While this fact is obvious, it is rarely used because the manifold structure does not depend on a choice of the model.

Consider for example a passage from the space R^n of n-tuples to the Hilbert space l_2 of sequences. The crucial new entity on the space l_2, directly related to the infinite number of dimensions, is the notion of convergence needed to identify a sequence of numbers as an element of l_2. However, in setting up a differentiable structure on an infinite-dimensional manifold we do not pay attention to the kind of convergence available on the model space l_2. Even when, say, several Hilbert spaces of sequences are simultaneously considered as models of a Hilbert manifold, differentiable structure is not affected by the difference between them. It is concerned only with the differentiability of maps.

It is advocated here that a more productive approach to infinite-dimensional manifolds is to use the difference between Hilbert models even if the differentiable structure itself is not altered by changing a model.

The functional coordinate formalism that follows from such an approach leads to a merging of linear algebra on Hilbert spaces with the theory of generalized functions. It also provides us with an invariant functional tensor approach to linear and nonlinear problems on manifolds.

The formalism suggests that the existing approach to functional analysis overemphasizes singling out a particular functional space appropriate for a problem in hand. In the coordinate formalism such a space appears as a result of a particular (possibly, especially convenient) choice of coordinates on a manifold.

By considering several models for a manifold at once and by relating these models by isomorphisms it becomes possible to reduce the seemingly unrelated problems on different spaces of functions to a single problem on the string space. The generalized eigenvalue problem considered in section 4 provides an example.

We also obtain the possibility of reformulating a problem given on one space in terms of another space. A good example of the usefulness of such a reformulation is provided by the theory of generalized functions. In this theory operations that could not be defined directly on spaces containing singular distributions are defined first on the fundamental spaces of "good" functions. Then they are "transplanted" to the larger dual spaces. In the approach advocated here this passage from a space to its dual is a coordinate transformation and the operations themselves could be defined in an invariant manner on the string space $\mathbf{S}$.

Moreover, all Hilbert spaces of functions including spaces of generalized functions enter the formalism on equal footing. As a result, the theory of generalized functions and linear algebra on Hilbert spaces become naturally synthesized in the formalism. It was shown in section 5 that this permits us to formulate the spectral theorem and to treat the generalized eigenvalue problems for self-adjoint operators without needing to use the rigged Hilbert space structure as in [2].

Choosing appropriate coordinates on $\mathbf{S}$ for a problem in hand is as useful (if not more) as choosing canonical coordinates for a finite dimensional problem. The simplest example of this is the Fourier transform which provides an algebraic approach to solving differential equations. Whenever useful, one can apply a coordinate change to alter analytic properties of elements of the coordinate space. The example of section 3 shows that in such a way one can transform singular distributions to infinite differentiable functions and vice versa.

We also see that in the developed approach the finite and infinite-dimensional manifolds become related in a new way. The notions of a string basis, orthogonal string basis, string eigenbasis of an operator, etc. are clear analogues of their finite dimensional counterparts. Simultaneously they provide us with the power of changing coordinate spaces and the corresponding functional description of invariant objects (tensors).

The entire approach turns out to be very similar in spirit to the nineteenth century introduction of vectors. However, it can *not* be reduced to consideration of elements of an infinite-dimensional Hilbert space as vectors. In fact, given a Hilbert space of functions elements of such space *are* vectors. The objects that we call strings are more general. They are defined for *all* Hilbert spaces of functions (i.e. coordinate spaces) at once and do not depend on a particular choice of such a space.

Preservation of various properties of operators under transformations of coordinates leads to various special types of transformations. For example, preserving locality of operators in the simplest case leads to the Fourier-like transformation as in (6.10). By finding a transformation that preserves the derivative operator we were able to relate the generalized and the regular solutions to linear partial differential equations with constant coefficients.

The results of the section 9 suggest that the nonlinear problems can be approached in the same fashion. For this it must be possible to interpret a given nonlinear equation as a tensor equation on the string space. Then various "nonlinearities" are interpreted as convolutions of tensors on the space. This seems to open a systematic way of using generalized functions in nonlinear problems.

The results of the last two sections demonstrate another unexpected relationship between the finite and the infinite-dimensional manifolds. We have seen that the coordinate formalism on the Hilbert space **S** naturally reduces to the local coordinate formalism on a (specially chosen) finite dimensional Riemannian submanifold M of **S**. Moreover, under the appropriate constraints, the variational problem for a geodesic on **S** yields a geodesic on M. This seems to indicate that the finite and the infinite-dimensional manifolds can be treated together within the same local functional coordinate formalism.

The presented results provide only the first steps in applications of the formalism. A systematic approach to linear and nonlinear problems in light of the formalism is still lacking. It is the author's hope that his interest in the formalism and its applications will be shared and that a complete understanding of the formalism will be eventually obtained.

Acknowledgments. This work originated in the author's research while a graduate student at St. Petersburg University. I would like to express my warmest feelings toward the people of Mathematical Physics and High Energy Physics departments of the university. I would like to dedicate this work to the memory of Yu. A. Yappa.

References

[1] Gel'fand I M and Shilov G E 1968 *Generalized Functions* vol 2 (New York and London, Academic Press)

[2] Gel'fand I M and Vilenkin N V *Generalized Functions* vol 4 (New York and London, Academic Press)

[3] Kobayashi S and Nomizu K 1969 *Foundations of Differential Geometry* vol 2 (New York, London and Sydney: Interscience Publishers)

[4] Kryukov A *Linear algebra on abstract Hilbert space* To appear

[5] Kryukov A 2003 *Found. Phys.* **33** No 3 pp 407-443

[6] Kryukov A 1997 *Nonlin. Anal.Theor. Meth. and Appl.* **30** pp 819-24

[7] Kryukov A *On the problem of emergence of classical space-time* Submitted

In: Mathematical Physics Research at the Cutting Edge
Editor: C.V. Benton, pp. 35-50
ISBN 1-59033-939-8

On the Group Structure of the Kalb-Ramond Gauge Symmetry and Spinor Representations

M. Botta Cantcheff*
Centro Brasileiro de Pesquisas Fisicas (CBPF)
Departamento de Teoria de Campos e Particulas (DCP)
Rua Dr. Xavier Sigaud, 150 - Urca
22290-180 - Rio de Janeiro - RJ - Brasil
Grupo de Física Teórica Jose Leite Lopes, Petrópolis, RJ, Brazil.

Abstract

The transformation properties of a Kalb-Ramond field are those of a gauge field; however, it is not clear which group structure these transformations are associated with. Our main purpose is to establish a basic framework in order to clarify the group structure underneath the 2-form gauge potential.

By using a specific spinorial group representation, extensions of the Lie groups are built. We also obtain a (Abelian) two-form field as a connection on a flat space-time and its corresponding canonical curvature tensor.

1 Introduction.

The so-called (Abelian) Kalb-Ramond field [2], $B_{\mu\nu}$, is a two-form field which appears in the low energy limit of String Theory and in several other frameworks in Particle Physics [3]; for instance, most of the attempts to incorporate topological mass in four dimensional field theories take into account this object [4, 5]. Its dynamics is governed by an action which remains invariant under transformations whose form are extremely similar to those of a one-form gauge field [6]. The Kalb-Ramond (KR) field transforms according with the following rule:

$$B_{\mu\nu} \rightarrow B_{\mu\nu} + \partial_{[\mu}\beta_{\nu]}, \tag{1}$$

where β_ν is a one form parameter. The question is, may this be systematically generated from a group element? In other words, how can we associate the parameter β_μ to the manifold of some gauge group? [7, 8]. The first observation one can do is that the set of parameters, namely $\Gamma \equiv \{\beta_\mu\}$, is not isomorphic to a group algebra

*e-mail: botta@cbpf.br

in itself; however, we shall show here how it encodes this information. The main purpose of this chapter is to shed some light into this question.

This work is organized as follows: in the Section 2, we deal with the conditions to parametrize a group with an one-form parameter In Section 3, we discuss these conditions in the context of spinorial representations from several point of view. In the Section 4, we construct a Lie group such that a two form field may be recovered from the connection, the covariant derivative and the curvature tensor for an Abelian Lie group are defined and the two-form field appears in the connection. Concluding Remarks are collected in Section 4; finally, in an Appendix, we prove a proposition which which is a technical detail for our arguments.

2 A One-Form Group Parameter and Spectral Theorem.

Let us assume a four-dimensional Minkowski space-time $(M, \eta_{\mu\nu})$ and some Lie group denoted by G, whose associated algebra is $\mathcal{G}$; τ^a are the matrices representing the generators of the group with $a = 1, \ldots, \dim G$; τ_{abc} are the structure constants. Let us take the gauge parameter to be an adjoint-one-form which can be expanded as below:

$$\beta_\mu = \beta^a_\mu \tau^a. \tag{2}$$

Consider also a vector space $\mathcal{S} = \{\psi_I\}$ being a representation for G, where I, J denote the internal indices of this space [1]. Which is its transformation law under a group element parametrized by the object β^a_μ?. Let us take an infinitesimal transformation $\epsilon^a_\mu \in \Gamma$. We shall get

$$\psi'_I = g_\epsilon \psi = (I_{IJ} + i\epsilon^a_\mu \tau^a \rho^\mu_{IJ} + o^2(\epsilon))\psi_J \tag{3}$$

where $\{\rho^\mu\}^3_{\mu=0}$ are four linearly independent matrices which must transform as space-time vectors under the Lorentz Group. For an arbitrary one form β_μ, $\beta_\mu\rho^\mu$ must be a linear operator from $\mathcal{S}$ into itself; which implies that $\mathcal{S}$ may be taken to be a spinor space. This is the possibility which will be explored throgout this paper due to the obvious physical interest; i.e, an eventual minimal KR-fermion interaction would have applications in several physical models [9].

With the first order expression (3), we may build up a group element corresponding to a non-infinitesimal parameter, β; by considering $\beta^a_\mu = N\,\epsilon^a_\mu$ for a large integer number N.

Thus, we have

$$g_\beta = \exp(i\beta^a_\mu \tau^a \rho^\mu). \tag{4}$$

For the moment, we will not worry about the unitarity of these groups and their representations.

[1]Actually, ψ_I is an N-component object, where N is the dimension of the group representation.

The key point in this construction arises from the analysis of the group property

$$g_{\beta_1} g_{\beta_2} = g_{\beta_3} \,, \tag{5}$$

where $\beta_{1,2,3} \in \Gamma$.

The question here is to identify under which conditions the parameters β_1 and β_2 are such that g_{β_3} is also a group element.

Thus, one must have that $[\beta_{1\mu}\rho^{\mu}; \beta_{2\nu}\rho^{\nu}]$ is some linear combination of the group generators τ^a (i.e, it remains in the algebra). This condition may be written explicitly as

$$[\beta_1, \beta_2] = \frac{1}{2}\beta^a_{1\mu}\beta^b_{2\nu}\left([\tau^a, \tau^b]\{\rho^{\mu}, \rho^{\nu}\}_{IJ} + \{\tau^a, \tau^b\}[\rho^{\mu}, \rho^{\nu}]_{IJ}\right) = \beta^a_3 \tau^a, \tag{6}$$

where in principle, β^a_3 also has to be a one-form. Since we cannot extend the algebraic structure to be larger than that of the group G and the space-time symmetries (Lorentz group [2]), in general, the third term is not in the algebra, i.e, $[\rho^{\mu}, \rho^{\nu}]$ is not a linear combination of the matrices ρ^{μ}, as well as the anti-commutators $\{\tau^a, \tau^b\}$ do not lye in $\mathcal{G}$ in general.

Thus, it becomes clear that the group property (5) *is not* satisfied for arbitrary pairs of parameters β_1, β_2. Therefore, we must determine which are the sub-families (sections of Γ) of parameters, denoted by $P_{\mathcal{G}}$, such that it satisfy two basic requirements:

(i) For all pair β_1, β_2 in the same $P_{\mathcal{G}}$, eq. (5) is satisfied for some $b_3 \in P_{\mathcal{G}}$.

(ii) Each $P_{\mathcal{G}}$ is large enough to cover (parametrize) the group manifold.

For a better understanding of the conditions implied by the requirements (i) and (ii), let us first consider the case of a Abelian group, if we assume this to be also unitary ($G \sim U(1)$) [3], one may consider this problem from other point of view: let $M(\beta)$ the matrix corresponding to the parameter β in the representation $\mathcal{S}$, assumed to be a complex vector space with an internal product. In other words, M is a linear map from Λ_1 into some matrices space and

$$\delta\psi = iM(\beta)\psi \,. \tag{7}$$

By virtue of the unitarity, M is Hermitian and then diagonalizes. Therefore, we can make use of the well-known Spectral Theorem (ST) which states that if it has K different eigenvalues then there exist linear operators $E_1, ..., E_K$ on $\mathcal{S}$, such that

1) $M(\beta) = \sum_{i=1}^{K} c_i(\beta)E_i$, where c_i are scalars.

2) $I = \sum_{i=1}^{K} E_i$

3) $E_iE_j = 0$, $i \neq j$

4) $E_iE_i = E_i$ (E_i is a projector).

[2] Clearly, we must restrict our discussion to space-time point-preserving transformations.

[3] Later, we shall see that unitarity is related to the Euclidean character of the space time; thus, in order to avoid a question of this type at this point, we assume a Riemanian space time metric, since this does not represent some conceptual or technical inconvenient in field theories.

5) $\mathcal{S} = \oplus_{i=1}^{K} \mathcal{S}_i$ (direct orthogonal sum), where E_i is the identity on the vector subspace $\mathcal{S}_i$.

Notice that only the eigenvalues c_i depend of β, but not the projectors E_i, because for all arbitrary pair of parameters β_1, β_2, the $[M(\beta_1), M(\beta_2)] = 0$ (since we are considering a representation for an Abelian group), then both diagonalize in the same basis E_i.

It is clear then from 1)... 5) that for all pair β_1, β_2, the commutators vanish:

$$[M(\beta_1), M(\beta_2)] = \Sigma_{i,j} c_i(\beta_1) c_j(\beta_2)[E_i, E_j] = \Sigma_i c_i(\beta_1) c_i(\beta_2)(E_i - E_i) = 0\,. \tag{8}$$

Going on with our construction, M is a first order function of β, then $c_i(\beta)$ must be linear scalar functions of the one form β. Therefore, by definition, there exist K space time vectors, e_i such that $c_i =< e_i; \beta >$.

Next, if we require that the full one form β be recovered from the matrix $M(\beta)$, i.e that the mapping $\beta \to M(\beta)$ be invertible, thus at least four (if this is the space time dimension) e_i are linearly independents (otherwise it would be impossible to recover the full information of β); so, we shall verify that the dimension of the representation shall satisfy $D \geq 4$. We are considering a generic β, then it is obvious that the dimension of the representation $D \equiv \dim \mathcal{S}$ must satisfy $D \geq K$, for all β. On the other hand, there exists at least one β such that $K \geq 4$. Therefore we get the first important conclusion on this group structure: the dimension of the representation shall satisfy the constraint $D \geq 4$, we leave for a forthcoming work to show that in fact, $D = 4$ constitutes the minimal (i.e fundamental) representation.

Notice, in addition, that each E_i is associated to the vector e_i: let us take $\beta = e_i$[4]; then, since $c_i = 1, c_{j \neq i} = 0$, we obtain that the projector must be given in terms of this unit vector.

$$M(e_i) = E_i \ . \tag{9}$$

By virtue of this, notice that the set of matrices $\mathcal{M}$ is a closed algebra which can be decomposed in a direct sum of invariant spaces, each one associated with a single space time direction:

$$\mathcal{M} = \bigoplus_i \mathcal{M}_i \,. \tag{10}$$

Clearly, there is a natural non-Abelian generalization of this structure which may be thought as the extension of the Lie algebra, however we will not analyze this point here in more detail despite throughout the work, we discuss some aspects related to the non-Abelian generalizations.

---

[4]Rigorously speaking, one should say: the one form (dual) corresponding to the vector e_i, however this is not necessary since we are considering the existence of a flat metric in the space time.

3 Spinor representations.

A non-trivial algebraic structure compatible with the space-time symmetries we can count on, is the well-known Dirac's matrices algebra [5]:

$$\{\gamma^\mu, \gamma^\nu\}_{IJ} = \eta^{\mu\nu} I_{IJ}. \tag{11}$$

We are going to explore now the representations we may build related to this structure due to its important possible applications in quantum field theories as mentioned; so for concreteness, all we can do is to identify the ρ^μ-matrices with the elements of this algebra and the spinorial representation, $\mathcal{S}$, with a Dirac spinor space. We shall carry out a more detailed discussion about these points in the next section.

Notice that due to relation (11), it is natural to introduce an additional scalar group parameter α associated with I_{IJ}; however, since the commutators $[\alpha, \beta] = \alpha^a \beta^b_\mu [\tau^a, \tau^b] \rho^\mu$ and $[\alpha, \alpha'] = \alpha^a \alpha'^b [\tau^a, \tau^b]$, remain in the algebra: no restrictions to this scalar parameters will arise. So, in order to simplify our analysis, we stand for (5), (30) and the following expressions involving the parameter $\beta = \beta^a_\mu \tau^a \rho^\mu_{IJ}$ *up to* the component associated to the identity.

Since no extra algebraic structure (of the type $[\gamma^\mu, \gamma^\nu]_{IJ} = c^{\mu\nu} I_{IJ} + c^{\mu\nu}_\rho \gamma^\mu_{IJ}$, for certain tensors $c^{\mu\nu}, c^{\mu\nu}_\rho$[6]) can be required, the condition (30) may simply be expressed as,

$$\beta_{1\,\mu} \beta_{2\,\nu} [\gamma^\mu, \gamma^\nu]_{IJ} = 0. \tag{12}$$

Then, we obtain a constraint on the parameters expressed by:

$$\beta_{1\,[\mu} \beta_{2\,\nu]} = 0 \tag{13}$$

This clearly implies that $\beta_{1\,\mu}$ and $\beta_{2\,\nu}$ are *parallel.*

Of course, this condition is also sufficient to satisfy (i), (ii): if $\beta_{1\,\mu} \propto \beta_{2\,\nu}$ the algebra closes and the composition law (5) is satisfied. The other group properties are automatically satisfied too. Then, we get that, for each (fixed) direction in Λ^1 we choose, say v_μ, we have a group structure, and each straight line (a *dimG*-dimensional plane in Γ) passing through the origin is isomorphic to the group algebra $\mathcal{G}$ [7]. Let us remark finally that the choice of v is completely arbitrary; so, this must not be interpreted as a sort of gauge choice nor a breaking of the Lorentz symmetry. For each direction v, one have the full structure of the group algebra.

For a more general Lie group, G, the second term of (30) must be vanish, therefore, the constraint on the group parameters reads [8]:

$$\beta^{(a}_{1\,[\mu} \beta^{b)}_{2\,\nu]} = 0\,. \tag{14}$$

[5]Where the matrices γ^μ are linear maps on the Dirac spinor space in itself.

[6]In particular, $I, \gamma^\mu, [\gamma^\mu, \gamma^\nu]$ are linearly independents.

[7]Below, this shall be confirmed for general Lie groups.

[8]Since this must not involve the generators, but only the parameters.

One can give a proof (see appendix) that there are two families of parameters which are solutions to these equations; the first one reads

$$\beta^a_{1\,\mu} \propto \beta^a_{2\,\mu}. \tag{15}$$

Nevertheless, this does not satisfy a basic condition of the group parametrization (requirement (ii)); this is a one-dimensional set of parameters, while $dimG > 1$. The second family of solutions is actually the appropriate one for us,

$$\beta^a_\mu = \beta^a\ v_\mu\,, \tag{16}$$

where $\beta^a \in \mathcal{G}$, while $v_\mu \in \Lambda_1$ has to be *fixed* for each group parametrization.

Recalling the presence of an arbitrary term proportional to I_{IJ}, the general form of an element of the algebra is $(\alpha^a I + \beta^a_\mu (= \beta^a v_\mu)\gamma^\mu)$ for a v fixed. This algebra is: $\bar{\mathcal{G}} = \mathcal{G} \oplus \mathcal{G}$, the direct sum of two copies of $\mathcal{G}$ associated with the matrices I and $\not{v}$ respectively.

So, our final result is that

$$g(\alpha,\beta) = \exp i\,(\alpha^a + (\beta^a v_\mu)\gamma^\mu))\,\tau^a \tag{17}$$

is a well-defined (generic) representative of a element of the Lie group $\bar{G}$ which results from the exponentiation of $\bar{\mathcal{G}}$ [11]. In the Abelian case this simply reduces to $\bar{G} \sim G_{(I)} \circ G_{(\not{v})}$, the *composition* of two copies of G associated with I and $\not{v}$ respectively.

For simplicity, it has been assumed up to now that only the five matrices $\{I, \rho^\mu\}$, appearing in (3), can be used to close the algebra (eq (30)); but, since only a structure compatible with the Lorentz symmetry may be considered, this constitutes a strong restriction to the parameters as it has been shown. However, one also relies on the structure of the Clifford Algebra (CA) which closes by construction: so in principle, one may consider additional independent gauge parameters (with other tensorial ranks) apart from β_μ. We are going to see in the following section that, even if we start off with such a more general situation, one *necessarily* falls back to essentially the same results, and the framework described above is actually not too restrictive.

3.1 Multi-tensorial Lie parameters via Clifford's Algebras and fixed directions.

Let us consider an ordered basis of the Clifford Algebra $\mathcal{C}$:

$$\{\rho^A\} \equiv \{I, \gamma_5, \gamma^\mu, \gamma_5\gamma^\mu, [\gamma^\mu, \gamma^\nu]\}, \tag{18}$$

where A is a multi-index running over this multi-tensorial basis. Thus we may represent infinitesimal group transformations as

$$\psi'_I = g_\epsilon \psi = (I + \epsilon^a_A \tau^a \rho^A_{IJ} + o^2(\epsilon))\psi_J, \tag{19}$$

where $\epsilon^a_A = (\epsilon^a, \epsilon'^a, \epsilon^a_\mu, \epsilon'^a_\mu, \epsilon^a_{\mu\nu}\}$ [9]. The Clifford algebra satisfies a crucial property: there exist a set of tensors, C^{AB}_C, such that $(\rho^A)_{IK}(\rho^B)_{KJ} = C^{AB}_C(\rho^C)_{IJ}$.

Notice once more that the component β^a, associated with the first element of the Clifford basis (I_{IJ}) does need not some restriction, since $[I, \rho^B] \equiv 0$; thus, in order to simplify our analysis as before, we stand for all the expressions involving the multi-parameter $\beta = \beta^a_A \tau^a \rho^A_{IJ}$ through this section, *up to* the component associated to the identity.

Let us first consider an Abelian (one-dimensional) group like $U(1)$: by construction, the commutator $[\beta_1; \beta_2]$ remains in $\mathcal{C}$. So, in principle, one would have a $4 \times 4(= 16)$-parametric representation of the group. However, an important point has to be taken in account: if no restrictions are imposed, these *are not* Abelian representations. In fact, $\exp\beta_1 \exp\beta_2 \neq \exp\beta_2 \exp\beta_1$, unless precisely $[\beta_1, \beta_2] = 0$, which leads to the extension of the conclusion of the previous section:

$$\beta_{(1,2)\,A} = \beta_{(1,2)}\,V_A\,, \tag{20}$$

for a same (fixed) $V_A \in \mathcal{C}$. This is a central result in this work: it states that, despite considering a full aggregate structure for the parameters, we may only consider families of parameters described by (20), such as it was understood in the first part of the article. In particular, if we wish to involve only a one-form parameter as in the initial formulation of the problem, one must to choose $V_A \equiv (0, 0, v_\mu, 0, 0)$. Recalling once more the presence of an arbitrary term proportional to I_{IJ}, the more general form of the multi-parameter involving a one-form is:

$$\beta = (\alpha I + \beta_\mu \gamma^\mu)\,, \tag{21}$$

where the direction of β_μ is fixed, in coincidence with our previous result.

Notice that, if we consider an more general (non-Abelian) group G, the conclusion above cannot be stated in the same way because, by construction, the commutator

$$2[\beta_1, \beta_2] \equiv \beta^a_{1\,A}\beta^b_{2\,B}\left([\tau^a, \tau^b]\{\rho^A, \rho^B\} + \{\tau^a, \tau^b\}[\rho^A, \rho^B]\right)_{IJ} \tag{22}$$

does not vanish. However, it may be extended also to the non-Abelian case by observing that $\{\tau^a, \tau^b\}$ is representation-dependent and in general, it is out of the algebra, thus the constraint must be imposed is similar to (14):

$$\beta^{(a}_{1\,[A}\beta^{b)}_{2\,B]} = 0\,, \tag{23}$$

whose solutions are also similar (see Appendix):

$$\beta^a_A = \beta^a\;V_A\,, \tag{24}$$

---

[9]These objects are also known in the literature as *aggregates*

where $\beta^a \in \mathcal{G}$, while $V_A \in \mathcal{C}$ has to be *fixed* for each group parametrization. This is a *dimG*-dimensional manifold of parameters such as it was understood in the first part of the article. Again, we may choose $V_A \equiv (0, 0, v_\mu, 0, 0)$ and due to the presence of an arbitrary scalar gauge parameter, a generic group element writes as in (17).

4 The Kalb-Ramond field as a connection on a flat space time.

As it has been learned in the previous part of this work , the gauge parameter needs to be separable: $\beta^a_\mu = \beta^a\, v_\mu$; where $v_\mu \in \Lambda_1$ is *fixed* and $\beta^a \in \mathcal{G}$. So, for each fixed direction in Λ_1, one have a parametrization of the Lie group. A natural scalar (algebra valued), α, must be introduced and the general form of a group parameter is $\rho \equiv (\alpha^a I + \beta^a_\mu (= \beta^a v_\mu)\gamma^\mu)\tau^a$ for a v_μ fixed [11]. The commutators algebra for two of these arbitrary parameters is given by:

$$[\rho, \rho'] = [\alpha, \alpha'] + [\beta, \beta']v^2 + ([\alpha, \beta'] + [\beta, \alpha'])\not{v} \tag{25}$$

Given this situation, the question is how may we define the covariant derivative in such a way that the KR field be obtained in the connection. This is the main purpose of this section.

Notice that the group formed by the collection of the elements (17) is not enough to recover the KR field from the corresponding connection: as usual, one would have a one-form connection $A^{(v)}_\mu$, associated with the direction v in the space-time; *however*, the transformation law (Abelian for simplicity) would be $\delta A^{(v)}_\mu = \partial_\mu \beta^{(v)}$. This reveals that $A^{(v)}_\mu$ *is not* a one-form but a component of a *rank-two* tensor field; since the gauge parameter $\beta^{(v)}$ is not a scalar but a component of a one form. In addition, it is clear that a two-form may be thought as a *collection* of four one-forms; each one associated with an element of an orthonormal basis of the space-time, i.e

$$B_{\mu\nu} \sim \{B^{\underline{\nu}}_\mu\}_{\underline{\nu}}. \tag{26}$$

These are main mathematical motivations to propose the algebraic structure considered below as an ansatz to recover a two form field in the connection on some group manifold [12].

Let us assume a four-dimensional oriented Minkowski space-time $(M, \eta_{\mu\nu}(\equiv diag[1, 1, 1, -1])$. The Dirac's matrices satisfy the well known algebra: $\{\gamma^\mu, \gamma^\nu\}_{IJ} = \eta^{\mu\nu} I_{IJ}$ Therefore $\{\gamma^i\}^3_{i=1}$ are hermitian while γ^4 is anti-hermitian; thus, if τ^a are hermitian and v is time-like, ρ^a must thus be anti-hermitian and α^a, purely imaginary numbers. The group manifold one is considering in this case is the one obtained from G by replacing the Lie parameter α by $i\alpha$. The unitarity or not of the groups is not determinant for our discussion; however, in order to avoid this type of considerations one may to Euclideanize the space-time metric. The ordering of the cartesian basis implies that we uniquely may define the extensions

$$\Gamma^{\underline{\mu}} \equiv \underbrace{I \otimes \ldots \otimes I}_{\mu-1} \otimes \gamma^{\underline{\mu}} \otimes \underbrace{I \otimes \ldots \otimes I}_{4-\mu}, \tag{27}$$

The underlined $\underline{\mu}$ manifestly refers only to the component μ of a tensor (Ex. $\langle dx^{\underline{\mu}}; V\rangle = V^{\underline{\mu}}$ for a vector V), where $\{dx^{\underline{\mu}}\}_{\mu=0}^{3}$ is a cartesian (coordinate) basis for Λ_1 [10]; furthermore, repetitions of these indices do not indicate summation over. This objects are operators on a spinor $\Psi \in \otimes_{\mu} \mathcal{S}_{(\mu)} \equiv \mathcal{S}_4$ where $\mathcal{S} = \{\psi_I\}$ is the Dirac's spinor space $\mathcal{S} = \{\psi_I\}$ used above (which represents G). I denotes the identity on $\mathcal{S}$.

Notice that $\Gamma^{\underline{\mu}}$ consists in inserting $\gamma^{\underline{\mu}}$ in the position $\underline{\mu}$ between tensor products of the identities.

Thus, let us adopt the notation:

$$\beta_{\underline{\mu}}\Gamma^{\underline{\mu}} \equiv \underbrace{I \otimes \ldots \otimes I}_{\mu-1} \otimes \beta_{\underline{\mu}}\gamma^{\underline{\mu}} \otimes \underbrace{I \otimes \ldots \otimes I}_{4-\mu}, \tag{28}$$

then,

$$\beta_{\mu}\Gamma^{\mu} = \sum_{\mu=1}^{4} \beta_{\underline{\mu}}\Gamma^{\underline{\mu}} \tag{29}$$

for an arbitrary one-form β_{μ}.

Given an *ordered* basis in space time, $\{\frac{\partial}{\partial x^{\mu}}\}_{\mu=0}^{3}$ and a one form, β_{μ}, the map: $\beta_{\mu} \longmapsto \beta_{\mu}\Gamma^{\mu}$, is uniquely defined.

Due to (34) and the properties of the tensor product, we get the commutation relations

$$[\Gamma^{\mu}; \Gamma^{\nu}] = 0, \tag{30}$$

It is crucial to notice the position of γ^{μ} in the tensor product of eq. (34) determines the commutation relation above.

Defining also the extended identity

$$\mathcal{I} \equiv \underbrace{I \otimes \ldots \otimes I}_{4}, \tag{31}$$

we can consider exponentials of linear combinations of these operators. We shall prove that they form a well-defined group which actually is a *tensor product* of (four) of those groups determined in previous section. If we define the generic one form: $\beta \equiv \sum_{\underline{\mu}=1}^{4} \beta_{\underline{\mu}} dx^{\underline{\mu}}$, we have $\beta_{\underline{\mu}} = \langle \beta; \frac{\partial}{\partial x^{\underline{\mu}}}\rangle$ (where $\langle dx^{\mu}; \frac{\partial}{\partial x^{\nu}}\rangle = \delta^{\mu}_{\nu}$). In fact, let us consider a group element as being a *tensor product* of (four) elements of the respective groups, $\bar{G}_{\underline{\mu}} \equiv \bar{G}_{v \equiv dx^{\underline{\mu}}}$:

$$g \equiv \otimes_{\mu=1}^{4} \left(g_{\underline{\mu}} \in G_{\underline{\mu}}\right), \tag{32}$$

[10] An *inertial* orthonormal frame on flat space-time.

where $g_{\underline{\mu}}$ is a well defined group element associated with the direction $dx^{\underline{\mu}} \in \Lambda_1$, i.e

$$g_{\underline{\mu}} = \exp i \left(\alpha^a_{(\underline{\mu})} + \beta^a_{\underline{\mu}} \gamma^{\underline{\mu}}) \right) \tau^a, \tag{33}$$

where $\alpha_{(\underline{\mu})}$ is an algebra valued scalar parameter and $\beta_{\underline{\mu}} dx^{\underline{\mu}}$ is a one form pointing in the direction of $dx^{\underline{\mu}}$; if we define the generic one form: $\beta \equiv \sum_{\underline{\mu}=1}^{4} \beta_{\underline{\mu}} dx^{\underline{\mu}}$, we have $\beta_{\underline{\mu}} = \langle \beta; \frac{\partial}{\partial x^{\underline{\mu}}} \rangle$ (where $\langle dx^{\mu}; \frac{\partial}{\partial x^{\nu}} \rangle = \delta^{\mu}_{\nu}$). We may denote this group as $G \sim \otimes^4_{\underline{\mu}=1} G_{\underline{\mu}}$.

In what follows, we restrict ourselves to Abelian groups. Since for general (non-Abelian) Lie groups some technical details must be particularly discussed, we shall analyze this separately.

Next, in order to re-express g in a more convenient form for algebraic manipulations, we need to define some extra structure. The ordering of the cartesian basis implies that we univocally may define the extensions

$$\Gamma^{\underline{\mu}} \equiv \underbrace{I \otimes \ldots \otimes I}_{\mu-1} \otimes \gamma^{\underline{\mu}} \otimes \underbrace{I \otimes \ldots \otimes I}_{4-\mu}, \tag{34}$$

where I is the identity on the spinor space $\mathcal{S}$. Notice that $\Gamma^{\underline{\mu}}$ consists in inserting $\gamma^{\underline{\mu}}$ in the position $\underline{\mu}$ between tensor products of the identities.

Then, from (32) the generic group element may be written:

$$g(\alpha, \beta) = \exp i \, (\alpha \mathcal{I} + \beta_\mu \Gamma^\mu), \tag{35}$$

where, all the parameters $\alpha_{(\underline{\mu})}$ have been absorbed in a only scalar α [11].

A crucial property of these objects is the linear independence:

$$\alpha \mathcal{I} + \beta_\mu \Gamma^\mu = 0 \Longrightarrow \alpha = \beta_\mu = 0. \tag{37}$$

In the Abelian case, a group element may be separated as

$$g(\alpha, \beta) = \exp i \alpha \mathcal{I} \; \exp i \, \beta_\mu \Gamma^\mu. \tag{38}$$

The factor $e^{i\alpha}$ is not interesting for us because this generates the usual one form connection and the Maxwell field strength. Thus, for more simplicity, we drop it out from the construction presented below.

We define the covariant derivative as

$$\nabla_\mu \equiv \partial_\mu - i B_\mu \tag{39}$$

[11] This is verified by using the property of tensor products among the identities of the different spaces:

$$a\mathcal{I} = aI \otimes I \otimes I \otimes I = I \otimes aI \otimes I \otimes I = I \otimes I \otimes aI \otimes I = I \otimes I \otimes I \otimes aI = \mathcal{I}a \tag{36}$$

for all scalar a.

acting on a spinor $\Psi \in \otimes_\mu \mathcal{S}_{(\mu)} \equiv \mathcal{S}_4$. Thus, by assuming that under a gauge transformation $\Psi \to \Psi' = g(\beta)\Psi = e^{i\beta_\mu \Gamma^\mu}\Psi$, its covariant derivative transforms in according with $\nabla'_\mu \Psi' = g(\beta)\nabla_\mu \Psi$, and $\nabla'_\mu = \partial_\mu - iB'_\mu$,we get that the connection transforms according to

$$B'_\mu = e^{-i\beta_\nu \Gamma^\nu}(B_\mu + \partial_\mu \beta_\nu \Gamma^\nu)e^{i\beta_\nu \Gamma^\nu}. \tag{40}$$

Furthermore, for a coordinate basis in a flat space-time, we have the property $\partial_\mu(dx^\nu) = 0$, in virtue of this property and (30), we obtain the transformation law for the connection reduces to

$$B'_\mu - B_\mu = (\partial_\mu \beta_\nu)\, \Gamma^\nu \tag{41}$$

as expected.

This means that the manifest form of the connection is $B_\mu = B_{\mu\nu}\Gamma^\nu$, since it must be an object whose nature is preserved under gauge transformation. Of course, this connection may be decomposed in its symmetric and anti-symmetric part, as $b_{\mu\nu} \equiv B_{[\mu\nu]}$ and $G_{\mu\nu} \equiv B_{(\mu\nu)}$. We identify the Kalb Ramond gauge (Abelian) field with $b_{\mu\nu}$.

Now, we define the curvature tensor for the B-connection as usual by :

$$[\nabla_\mu, \nabla_\nu]\Psi = -i\mathcal{F}_{\mu\nu}\Psi\, ; \tag{42}$$

we thus obtain

$$\mathcal{F}_{\mu\nu} = 2\partial_{[\mu}B_{\nu]}\, . \tag{43}$$

Using that

$$\mathcal{F}_{\mu\nu} = \mathcal{F}_{\mu\nu\rho}\Gamma^\rho\, , \tag{44}$$

we get the final result:

$$\mathcal{F}_{\mu\nu\rho} = 2\partial_{[\mu}B_{\nu]\rho}\, . \tag{45}$$

It is very useful to define the totally antisymmetric part of this tensor, $H_{\mu\nu\rho} \equiv \mathcal{F}_{[\mu\nu\rho]}$, because the commonly studied Abelian gauge actions (for instance, the so-called Cremer-Sherk-Kalb-Ramond model [1, 4]) are quadratic in the dual of the field strength, $\epsilon^{\sigma\mu\nu\rho}\mathcal{F}_{2\mu\nu\rho} = \epsilon^{\sigma\mu\nu\rho}H_{\mu\nu\rho}$; notice also that H only involves derivatives of Kalb-Ramond field b, the antisymmetric component of B.

Finally, let us mention that this construction may be expressed in a covariant notation: let us define the matrices

$$\Gamma^\mu_{(i)} \equiv \underbrace{I \otimes \ldots \otimes I}_{i-1} \otimes \gamma^\mu \otimes \underbrace{I \otimes \ldots \otimes I}_{4-i}\, , \tag{46}$$

which consists in inserting γ^μ in the position $i = 1, 2, 3, 4$ (note that here, the vectorial index μ does not appear underlined since these matrices are not referred to specific basis elements). These matrices are manifestly independent of the reference system; under Lorentz transformations, they transform as: $\Gamma'^\mu_{(i)} = \Lambda^\mu_\nu\, \sigma(\Lambda)\Gamma^\nu_{(i)}\sigma^{-1}(\Lambda) =$

$\Gamma^\mu_{(i)}$ (Pauli theorem), where $\sigma(\Lambda) \equiv S(\Lambda) \otimes S(\Lambda) \otimes S(\Lambda) \otimes S(\Lambda)$, and S is the usual unitary transformation induced by the Lorentz transformation (Λ^μ_ν) on the Dirac spinor space.

Notice that a group element (17), corresponds to the Lorentz transformed, $g^\Lambda(\alpha,\beta) = \exp i\left(\alpha^a + S(\beta^a v_\mu)\gamma^\mu)S^{-1}\right)\tau^a$, in the representation $\mathcal{S}^\Lambda = \{S(\Lambda)\Psi \,/\, \Psi \in \mathcal{S}\}$.

On the other hand, given a particular orthonormal basis of the space-time $\{e^\mu_{(i)}\}_{i=1}^4$ (such that $\partial_\alpha e^\mu_{(i)} = 0$), there exists a unique way of writing an arbitrary one-form:

$$\beta_\mu = \sum_i \beta^{(i)}_\mu \qquad (\Lambda^1 = \oplus_{(i)}\Lambda^1_{(i)}). \tag{47}$$

Thus, for all one form β_μ, the group parameter,

$$\mathcal{B} \equiv \sum_i \beta^{(i)}_\mu \Gamma^\mu_{(i)}, \tag{48}$$

is uniquely defined. This is a geometric object which transforms as: $\mathcal{B} \to \sigma\mathcal{B}\sigma^{-1}$.

5 Consistency with the Spectral Theorem.

Here, we shall to verify that the representation presented here fits into the ST. As mentioned, when we consider an Euclidean space time we have an unitary (Abelian) group G as required for using the ST in Section 2; then, the matrices γ^μ are Hermitian and their eigenvalues are ± 1. Let $S \equiv S_0 \otimes S_1 \otimes S_2 \otimes S_3$, and S_μ is the unitary transformation which diagonalizes γ^μ into γ^μ_D, thus obviously, $S_0 = I$, therefore

$$\Gamma^\mu_D = S\,\Gamma^\mu\,S^{-1} = \underbrace{I \otimes \ldots \otimes I}_{\mu-1} \otimes \gamma^\mu_D \otimes \underbrace{I \otimes \ldots \otimes I}_{4-\mu} \tag{49}$$

is a diagonal matrix. Let the basis f_i [12] such that $\gamma^\mu_D f_i = s_{i_\mu} f_i$, where $s_{i_\mu} = \pm 1$ are the corresponding eigenvalues of γ^μ, then $\gamma^\mu_D = \Sigma_{i=1}^4\, s_{i_\mu}\, (f_i \otimes f_i)$, and of course $I = \Sigma_{i=1}^4 (f_i \otimes f_i)$. Therefore, defining $\mathcal{E}_{i_1,i_2,i_3,i_4} = (f_{i_1} \otimes f_{i_1}) \otimes \ldots \otimes (f_{i_4} \otimes f_{i_4})$, we may write:

$$\Gamma^\mu_D = \Sigma_{i_1,i_2,i_3,i_4}\; s_{i_\mu}\; \mathcal{E}_{i_1,i_2,i_3,i_4} \quad \mu = 1,\ldots,4; \tag{51}$$

thus a general parameter $\Sigma_\mu \beta_\mu \Gamma^\mu_D$ Finally, using that each $f_{i_\mu} \otimes f_{i_\mu}$ is a projector and the properties of the tensor product, it is straightforward to show that $\mathcal{E}_{i_1,i_2,i_3,i_4}$ are projectors; thus, a general parameter $\mathcal{B} = \Sigma_\mu \beta_\mu \Gamma^\mu_D$ can be written as a linear combination of these ones, which in according with the ST.

---

[12] In this already diagonal form this is a standard basis:

$$f_i = (\underbrace{0,\ldots,0}_{i-1}, 1, \underbrace{0,\ldots,0}_{4-i}), \tag{50}$$

Notice furthermore that, as claimed by the ST, in this representation the space of parameters have a spectral structure (see eq. (47)), is a direct sum of subspaces (subalgebras) each one associated with a single space time direction.

6 Final comments.

The possible group structure associated with the KR symmetry was determined and well-defined together with its spinorial representations. We saw that, by considering the largest multi-tensorial parameter space (Clifford Algebra), the result is basically the same: the tensorial direction of the parameter is *fixed*, and tensorially *separated* from the group parameter (Eq.(16)). This separation condition for the Lie parameter is a bit unexpected, since it does not seem to be a restriction arising from the transformation properties of a KR-field; however, we have shown in a special spinorial representation that, by considering direct sum of these algebras, one can to construct a covariant derivative extracting the Kalb-Ramond two-form field from the connection [12].

We conclude this article by stressing that this construction is an initial step, the fundamental starting point in order to construct well-defined Abelian and non-Abelian gauge theories involving KR fields.

It is often claimed that the Kalb Ramond symmetry is associated to the Cech cohomology rather than a group structure; however, this approach open up the possibility for a stimulating mathematical investigation: the relation of this structure with the Cech cohomology, its possible group structure.

Acknowledgements: The author is specially indebted to Alvaro L. M. A. Nogueira for many invaluable discussions, relevant comments and criticisms. Special thanks are due to Prof. A. Lahiri for pertinent and estimulating comments on the approach developed here. Prof. S. Alves Días is acknowledged for discussions and Prof. J. A. Helayel-Neto for clarifying technical questions on Group Theory and for the helpful corrections on the original manuscript. Prof. Helayel-Neto pointed out essential questions and motivations on an earlier work and observed the relation with the structure of aggregates.

7 Appendix: On the possible families of group parameters.

Here, we study the solutions to equation (23) which define a group parametrization. In the second section we found the eq. (14) whose form is identical and the solutions are of the same type, the single difference is that Λ_1 must be considered in behalf of the Clifford Algebra $\mathcal{C}$ analyzed here; thus, the statement proved here applies to the proposal of the Section 2.

Let us denote by $P_{\mathcal{G}}$ a family of parameters, β, corresponding to a same group representation; as has been argued before, if two parameters are in $P_{\mathcal{G}}$ then they are related by the equation (23). Here we shall show that only class of solutions to this equation actually constitutes a group parametrization.

Contracting this equation with generic objects $X_a \in \mathcal{G}^\star$ and $Y^A \in \mathcal{C}^\star$, where $\mathcal{C}$ denotes the CA and *, the corresponding *dual space*, one obtains the following relation between two elements of $P_{\mathcal{G}}$, b_1 and b_2:

$$\beta^a_{2\,A} = \frac{b_2}{b_1}\,\beta^a_{1\,A} + u^a\,U_A + w^a\,W_A\,, \tag{52}$$

for certain $u^a, w^a \in \mathcal{G}$ and $U_A, W_A \in \mathcal{C}$. Here, we also have the complex numbers, $b_{1,2} \equiv X_a Y^A \beta^a_{(1,2)\,A}$.

Next, we make two suppositions which shall define a particular class of solutions to (23):

I- u^a, w^a are not proportional. Then, they may form, together with $(dim(\mathcal{G})-2)$-linearly independent elements of $\mathcal{G}$, say $\{e_{i'}\}_{i'=1}^{dim(\mathcal{G})-2}$, a basis for it.

II- U_A, W_A are not proportional. Then, they may form, together with $(dim(\mathcal{C})-2(=14))$-linearly independent elements of $\mathcal{C}$, say $\{C_{iA}\}_{i=1}^{14}$, a basis for it.

Clearly, we may write

$$\beta^a_{1\,A} = \Sigma_{i=1}^{14} a^a_i C_{iA} + a^a_U U_A + a^a_W W_A. \tag{53}$$

Substituting this into the equation (23), and using the identity $\beta^{(a}_{1\,[A}\beta^{b)}_{1\,B]} \equiv 0$, we get the equation

$$\Sigma_{i=1}^{14}[a^{(a}_i u^{b)} C_{i[A}U_{B]} + a^{(a}_i w^{b)} C_{i[A}W_{B]}] + [a^{(a}_W u^{b)} - a^{(a}_U w^{b)}]W_{[A}U_{B]} = 0, \tag{54}$$

which, due to the linear independence implies $a^{(a}_i u^{b)} = 0$, $a^{(a}_i w^{b)} = 0$ and

$$a^{(a}_W u^{b)} - a^{(a}_U w^{b)} = 0. \tag{55}$$

Contracting the first two equations with an arbitrary element of $\mathcal{G}$, one obtains that a^a_i must be proportional to both u^a, w^a; since they are not parallel by hypothesis, we conclude $a^a_i = 0$.

So, we shall finally solve only the equation (55). Due to the assumption **I**, one may write

$$a^a_U = \Sigma_{i=1}^{dim\mathcal{G}-2} a^{i'}_U e^a_{i'} + a^u_U u^a + a^w_U w^a \tag{56}$$

and

$$a^a_W = \Sigma_{i=1}^{dim\mathcal{G}-2} a^{i'}_W e^a_{i'} + a^u_W u^a + a^w_W w^a \tag{57}$$

where $a^{i'}_U, a^{i'}_W, a^u_U, a^w_U, a^u_W, a^w_W$ are complex numbers. Putting these expressions back into eq. (55) we get

$$\Sigma_{i=1}^{dim\mathcal{G}-2}[a^{i'}_U e^{(a}_{i'} w^{b)} - a^{i'}_W e^{(a}_{i'} u^{b)}] + [a^u_U - a^w_U] u^{(a} w^{b)} + a^w_U w^{(a} w^{b)} + a^u_W u^{(a} u^{b)} = 0. \tag{58}$$

Due to **I**, we conclude that $a^{i'}_U = 0, a^{i'}_W = 0, a^w_U = 0, a^u_W = 0$ and $a \equiv a^u_U = a^w_U$. Then, our multi-parameter initial must have the form

$$\beta^a_{1\,A} = a[u^a\, U_A + w^a\, W_A]; \tag{59}$$

which, by virtual of eq. (52), implies

$$\beta^a_{2\,A} \propto \beta^a_{1\,A} \tag{60}$$

However, as it has already been argued, this class of solutions do not constitute a group parametrization because it is a one-parametric family of parameters; therefore, it is not isomorphic to $\mathcal{G}$ (unless it is a one-dimensional group, which was excluded from this discussion).

So, we only can consider some of the hypotheses **I**, **II** to be false; in both cases, eq. (52) may be rewritten as

$$\beta^a_{2\,A} = \frac{b_2}{b_1}\,\beta^a_{1\,A} + v^a\, V_A\,, \tag{61}$$

for certain $v^a \in \mathcal{G}$ and $V_A \in \mathcal{C}$. Then, we may write

$$\beta^a_{1\,A} = \Sigma^{15}_{i=1} a^a_i C_{iA} + \beta^a_1 V_A\,, \tag{62}$$

where $\{\{C_{iA}\}^{dim(\mathcal{C})-1(=15)}_{i=1}\,; V_A\}$ constitutes a basis for $\mathcal{C}$. Thus, using this in the equation (23), one gets

$$\Sigma^{15}_{i=1} a^{(a}_i v^{b)} C_{i[A} V_{B]} = 0. \tag{63}$$

Therefore,

$$a^{(a}_i v^{b)} = 0. \tag{64}$$

Contracting this equation with an arbitrary element of $\mathcal{G}$: $a^a_i = a_i\, v^b$; plugging this back into (64), we get $a^a_i = 0$. Then, the complete solution results as below:

$$\beta^a_{1\,A} = \beta^a_1 V_A\,. \tag{65}$$

From (23), $\beta^a_{2\,A} = \beta^a_2 V_A$, which shows that all parameter in this family writes as $\beta^a_A = \beta^a V_A$, where V_A is fixed. This is a $dim\mathcal{G}$-parametric family of parameters, as expected.

This completes the argument.

References

[1] M. Kalb and P. Ramond, *Phys. Rev.* D **9**, 2273 (1974).

[2] D. Z. Freedman, CALT-68-624. K. Seo, M. Okawa and A. Sugamoto, *Phys. Rev.* D **19**, 3744 (1979).

D. Z. Freedman and P. K. Townsend, *Nucl. Phys.* B **177**, 282 (1981).

[3] A. S. Schwarz, *Lett. Math. Phys.* **2**, 247 (1978).

A. S. Schwarz, *Commun. Math. Phys.* **67**, 1 (1979).

E. Witten, *Commun. Math. Phys* **117**, 353 (1988).

D. Birmingham, M. Blau, M. Rakowski and G. Thompson, *Phys. Rept.* **209**, 129 (1991).

[4] E. Cremmer and J. Scherk, *Nucl. Phys.* B **72**, 117 (1974).

[5] A. Aurilia and Y. Takahashi, *Prog. Theor. Phys.* **66**, 693 (1981).

T. R. Govindarajan, *J. Phys.* G **8**, L17 (1982).

T. J. Allen, M. J. Bowick and A. Lahiri, *Phys. Lett.* B **237**, 47 (1990).

T. J. Allen, M. J. Bowick and A. Lahiri, *Mod. Phys. Lett.* A **6**, 559 (1991).

[6] A. Lahiri, Mod.Phys.Lett.A17 (2002) 1643; *J. Phys.*A35 (2002) 8779, and references therein.

[7] P.G.O. Freund and R.I. Nepomechie, *Nucl. Phys.* B199 (1982) 482.

[8] C. Hofman, *Nonabelian 2 Forms*, e-Print Archive: hep-th/0207017.

[9] C.N. Ferreira, M.B.D.S.M. Porto, J.A. Helayel-Neto ; *Nucl. Phys.* B 620 (2002) 181.

H.R. Christiansen, M.S. Cunha, J.A. Helayel-Neto, L.R.U. Manssur, A.L.M.A. Nogueira; *Int. J. Mod. Phys.* A 14 (1999) 1721.

Winder A. Moura-Melo, N. Panza , J.A. Helayel-Neto; *Int. J. Mod. Phys.* A 14 (1999) 3949.

[10] M. Botta Cantcheff, *Phys. Lett.* B 533 (2002) 126 and *Eur. Phys. Jour.* C6 vol.4 (2002)1-14 (e-Print Archive: hep-th/0107123).

[11] M. Botta Cantcheff, *On the Group Structure of the Kalb-Ramond Gauge Symmetry.*, e-Print Archive: hep-th/0211239 .

[12] M. Botta Cantcheff, *The Kalb-Ramond Field as a Connection on a Flat Space Time.*, e-Print Archive: hep-th/0212180

In: Mathematical Physics Research at the Cutting Edge
Editor: C.V. Benton, pp. 51-100
ISBN 1-59033-939-8

Group Theoretical Interpretation of the CPT-Theorem

V. V. Varlamov
Department of Mathematics, Siberia State University,
Kirova 42, Novokuznetsk 654007, Russia

Abstract

An algebraic description of basic discrete symmetries (space inversion P, time reversal T, charge conjugation C and their combinations PT, CP, CT, CPT) is studied. Discrete subgroups $\{1, P, T, PT\}$ of orthogonal groups of multidimensional spaces over the fields of real and complex numbers are considered in terms of fundamental automorphisms of Clifford algebras. The fundamental automorphisms form a finite group of order 4. The charge conjugation is represented by a pseudoautomorphism of the Clifford algebra. Such a description allows one to extend the automorphism group. It is shown that an extended automorphism group (CPT-group) forms a finite group of order 8. The group structure and isomorphisms between the extended automorphism groups and finite groups are studied in detail. It is proved that there exist 64 different realizations of the CPT-group. An extension of universal coverings (Clifford-Lipschitz groups) of the orthogonal groups is given in terms of CPT-structures which include the well-known Shirokov-Dąbrowski PT-structures as a particular case.

MSC 2000: **15A66, 15A90, 20645**
PACS numbers: **02.10.Tq, 11.30.Er, 11.30.Cp**

1 Introduction

The importance of discrete transformations is well–known. Many textbooks on quantum theory began with description of the discrete symmetries, and famous Lüders–Pauli CPT–Theorem is a keystone of quantum field theory. A fundamental notion of antimatter immediately relates with the charge conjugation C. The requirement of invariance concerning the each of the discrete transformations gives rise to certain consequences which can be verified in experience. So, from the invariance concerning the CPT-transformation it follows an identity of the masses and full life times of particles and antiparticles, from the invariance concerning the time reversal T we have certain relations between the forward and reverse reaction cross-sections. In turn, from the invariance concerning the charge conjugation C it follows an absence of the reactions forbidden by the conservation law of charge parity, and from the invariance concerning the space inversion P and time reversal T it follows an absence of the electric dipole moment of particles. As follows from experience, for the processes defined by strong and electromagnetic interactions there exists an invariance with respect to the all discrete transformations. In contrast to strong and electromagnetic interactions, for the weak interaction, as shown by experiment, there is no invariance concerning space inversion P, but there is invariance with respect to CP–transformation. Moreover, there are experimental evidences confirming CP–violation (a decay of the neutral K–mesons). It is clear that the analysis of the discrete symmetries allows us to reveal the most profound structural characteristics of the matter.

However, usual practice of definition of the discrete symmetries from the analysis of relativistic wave equations does not give a full and consistent theory of the discrete transformations. In the standard approach, except a well studied case of the spin $j = 1/2$ (Dirac equation), a situation with the discrete symmetries remains unclear for the fields of higher spin $j > 1/2$. It is obvious that a main reason of this is an absence of a fully adequate formalism for description of higher–spin fields (all widely accepted higher–spin formalisms such as Rarita–Schwinger approach [20], Bargmann–Wigner [1] and Gel'fand–Yaglom [10] multispinor theories, and also Joos–Weinberg $2(2j+1)$–component formalism [14, 31] have many intrinsic contradictions and difficulties). The first attempt of going out from this situation was initiated by Gel'fand, Minlos and Shapiro in 1958 [11]. In the Gel'fand–Minlos–Shapiro approach, the discrete symmetries are represented by outer involutory automorphisms of the Lorentz group (there are also other realizations of the discrete symmetries via the outer automorphisms, see [17, 15, 27]). At present, the Gel'fand–Minlos–Shapiro ideas have been found further development in the works of Buchbinder, Gitman and Shelepin [5, 12], where the discrete symmetries are represented by both outer and inner automorphisms of the Poincaré group.

Discrete symmetries P and T transform (reflect) space and time (two the most fundamental notions in physics), but in the Minkowski 4–dimensional space–time continuum [18] space and time are not separate and independent. By this reason a transformation of one (space or time) induces a transformation of another. Therefore, discrete symmetries should be expressed by such transformations of the continuum, that transforms all its structure totally with a full preservation of discrete nature. The only possible candidates on the role of such transformations are automorphisms. In such a way, the idea of representation of the discrete symmetries via the automorphisms of the Lorentz group ('rotation' group of the 4–dimensional continuum) is appeared in the Gel'fand–Minlos–Shapiro approach, or via the automorphisms of the Poincaré group (motion group of the 4–dimensional continuum) in the Buchbinder–Gitman–Shelepin approach.

In 1909, Minkowski showed [18] that a causal structure of the world is described by a 4–dimensional pseudo–Euclidean geometry. In accordance with [18] the quadratic form $x^2 + y^2 + z^2 - c^2t^2$ remains invariant under the action of linear transformations of the four variables x, y, z and t, which form a general Lorentz group G. As known, the general Lorentz group G consists of a proper orthochronous Lorentz group G_0 and three reflections (discrete transformations) P, T, PT, where P and T are space and time reversal, and PT is a so–called full reflection. The discrete transformations P, T and PT added to an identical transformation form a finite group. Thus, the general Lorentz group may be represented by a semidirect product $G_0 \odot \{1, P, T, PT\}$.

In 1958, Shirokov pointed out [25, 26] that an universal covering of the inhomogeneous Lorentz group has eight inequivalent realizations. Later on, in the eighties this idea was applied to a general orthogonal group $O(p,q)$ by Dąbrowski [9]. As known, the orthogonal group $O(p,q)$ of the real space $\mathbb{R}^{p,q}$ is represented by the semidirect product of a connected component $O_0(p,q)$ and a discrete subgroup $\{1, P, T, PT\}$. Further, a double covering of the orthogonal group $O(p,q)$ is a Clifford–Lipschitz group $\mathbf{Pin}(p,q)$ which is completely constructed within a Clifford algebra $C\!\ell_{p,q}$. In accordance with squares of elements of the discrete subgroup ($a = P^2$, $b = T^2$, $c = (PT)^2$) there exist eight double coverings (Dąbrowski groups [9]) of the orthogonal group defining by the signatures (a, b, c), where $a, b, c \in \{-, +\}$. Such in brief is a standard description scheme of the discrete transformations. However, in this scheme there is one essential flaw. Namely, the Clifford–Lipschitz group is an intrinsic notion of the algebra $C\!\ell_{p,q}$ (a set of the all invertible elements of $C\!\ell_{p,q}$), whereas the discrete subgroup is introduced into the standard scheme in an external way, and the choice of the signature (a, b, c) of the discrete subgroup is not determined by the signature of the space $\mathbb{R}^{p,q}$. Moreover, it is suggest by default that for any signature (p,q) of the vector space there exist the all eight kinds of the discrete subgroups. It is obvious that a consistent description of the double coverings of $O(p,q)$ in terms of the Clifford–Lipschitz groups $\mathbf{Pin}(p,q) \subset C\!\ell_{p,q}$ can be obtained only in the case when the discrete subgroup $\{1, P, T, PT\}$ is also defined within the algebra $C\!\ell_{p,q}$. Such a description has been given in the works [28, 29, 30], where the discrete symmetries are represented by fundamental automorphisms of the Clifford algebras. So, the space inversion P, time reversal T and their combination PT correspond to an automorphism $\star$ (involution), an antiautomorphism $\widetilde{\ }$ (reversion) and an antiautomorphism $\widetilde{\star}$ (conjugation), respectively. Group theoretical structure of the discrete transformations is a central point in this work. The fundamental automorphisms of the Clifford algebras are compared to elements of the finite group formed by the discrete transformations. In its turn, a set of the fundamental automorphisms, added by an identical automorphism, forms a finite group $\mathrm{Aut}(C\!\ell)$, for which in virtue of the Wedderburn–Artin Theorem there exists a matrix representation. In such a way, an isomorphism $\{1, P, T, PT\} \simeq \mathrm{Aut}(C\!\ell)$ plays a central role and allows us to use methods of the Clifford algebra theory at the study of a group theoretical structure of the discrete transformations. First of all, it allows us to classify the discrete groups into Abelian $\mathbb{Z}_2 \otimes \mathbb{Z}_2$, $\mathbb{Z}_4$ and non–Abelian D_4, Q_4 finite groups, and also to establish a dependence between the finite groups and signature of the spaces in case of real numbers. It is shown that the division ring structure of $\mathcal{C}\ell_{p,q}$ imposes hard restrictions on existence and choice of the discrete subgroup, and the signature (a, b, c) depends upon the signature of the underlying space $\mathbb{R}^{p,q}$. Moreover, this description allows one to incorporate the Gel'fand–Minlos–Shapiro automorphism theory into Shirokov–Dąbrowski scheme and further to unite them on the basis of the Clifford algebra theory.

Other important discrete symmetry is the charge conjugation C. In contrast with the transformations P, T, PT, the operation C is not space–time discrete symmetry. This transformation first appeared on the representation spaces of the Lorentz group and its nature is strongly different from other discrete symmetries. By this reason in the Chapter 3 the charge conjugation C is represented by a pseudoautomorphism $\mathcal{A} \rightarrow \overline{\mathcal{A}}$ which is not fundamental automorphism of the Clifford algebra. All spinor representations of the pseudoautomorphism $\mathcal{A} \rightarrow \overline{\mathcal{A}}$ are given in Theorem 9. An introduction of the transformation $\mathcal{A} \rightarrow \overline{\mathcal{A}}$ allows us to extend the automorphism group $\mathrm{Aut}(\mathcal{C}\ell)$ of the Clifford algebra. It is shown that automorphisms $\mathcal{A} \rightarrow \mathcal{A}^\star$, $\mathcal{A} \rightarrow \widetilde{\mathcal{A}}$, $\mathcal{A} \rightarrow \widetilde{\mathcal{A}^\star}$, $\mathcal{A} \rightarrow \overline{\mathcal{A}}$, $\mathcal{A} \rightarrow \overline{\mathcal{A}^\star}$, $\mathcal{A} \rightarrow \overline{\widetilde{\mathcal{A}}}$ and $\mathcal{A} \rightarrow \overline{\widetilde{\mathcal{A}^\star}}$ form a finite group of order 8 (an extended automorphism group $\mathrm{Ext}(\mathcal{C}\ell) = \{\mathrm{Id}, \star, \widetilde{\ }, \widetilde{\star}, \overline{\ }, \overline{\star}, \overline{\widetilde{\ }}, \overline{\widetilde{\star}}\}$). The group $\mathrm{Ext}(\mathcal{C}\ell)$ is isomorphic to a CPT-group $\{1, P, T, PT, C, CP, CT, CPT\}$. There exist isomorphisms between $\mathrm{Ext}(\mathcal{C}\ell)$ and finite groups of order 8. A full number of different realizations of $\mathrm{Ext}(\mathcal{C}\ell)$ is equal to 64. This result allows us to define extended universal coverings (CPT-structures) of the orthogonal groups. It is shown that the eight Shirokov-Dąbrowski PT-structures present a particular case of general CPT-structures.

2 Clifford–Lipschitz groups

Theory of spinors and spinor representations (universal coverings of the groups) is closely related with the foundations of quantum mechanics. As known, any quantized system S corresponds to a complex separable Hilbert space $\mathcal{H}$. At this point, a physical state is represented by a vector $\mid x\rangle \in \mathcal{H}$ and $\langle x \mid x\rangle = 1$. In turn, any physical observable a (for example, energy, electric charge and so on) corresponds to a self-conjugated operator A in the space $\mathcal{H}$. The spectrum of A coincides with a set of all possible values of a. Quantum mechanics does not give a definite value of the magnitude a in the state $\mid x\rangle$. We have here only a mathematical expectation of a:

$$\langle x \mid A \mid x\rangle = \mathrm{Sp}AP_x,$$

where P_x is a Hermitean projection operator ($P^+_x = P_x$) on the state $\mid x\rangle$. The unit eigenvectors of P_x are distinguished by the scalar phase factor. All these vectors give rise to identical physical predictions and, therefore, they describe one and the same state. In turn, the operators P_x in itself are observables. Indeed, the magnitude

$$\mathrm{Sp}P_xP_y = |\langle x \mid y\rangle|^2 \tag{1}$$

is a location probability of the physical system S in the state $\mid x\rangle$ (or $\mid y\rangle$).

For the each quantized system S there exists an invariance group G. It means that G acts on the system S and there exists an isomorphism between S and $g(S)$, $g \in G$. Let P_{gx_i} be the state obtained from P_{x_i} via the transformation $g \in G$. Then, the group G is the invariance group if all probabilities in (1) are invariant:

$$\forall \mid x\rangle \in \mathcal{H}, \quad \forall g \in G, \quad \mathrm{Sp}P_{gx_1}P_{gx_2} = \mathrm{Sp}P_{x_1}P_{x_2},$$

or

$$|\langle gx_1 \mid gx_2\rangle|^2 = |\langle x_1 \mid x_2\rangle|^2.$$

It means that G acts on $\mathcal{H}$ isometrically. As it shown in [32, 33, 2], the mapping $\mid x\rangle \rightarrow\mid gx\rangle$ is either unitary operator $U(g)$ or antiunitary operator $V(g)$ on the Hilbert space $\mathcal{H}$. Let $\mathcal{V}(\mathcal{H})$ be a group of both unitary and antiunitary operators on $\mathcal{H}$, and let $\mathcal{U}(\mathcal{H})$ be a subgroup of unitary operators. The group $\mathcal{U}(\mathcal{H})$ is a subgroup of index 2 of the group $\mathcal{V}(\mathcal{H})$, and by this reason $\mathcal{U}(\mathcal{H})$ is an invariant subgroup of $\mathcal{V}(\mathcal{H})$. The transformations $\mathcal{U}(g)$ for $g \in G$ generate a subgroup $\mathcal{E}(G)$ of the group $\mathcal{V}(\mathcal{H})$, which is an extension of G by means of the group U (multiplication of the vectors of $\mathcal{H}$ by the phase factor $e^{i\alpha}$, where α is a real number; at this point the state remains unaltered), that is,

$$G \xrightarrow{f} \mathrm{Aut}\, U,$$

where a kernel of the mapping $\mathrm{Ker}\, f$ is an invariant subgroup $G_+ \subset G$ of index 2, which acts as the group of unitary transformations, and a nontrivial element of the mapping image $\mathrm{Im} f$ is the complex conjugation. Therefore, one can say that G_+ acts as a linear unitary projective representation. For example, if G_+ is a rotation group $SO(3)$, then its projective representations are coincide with linear irreducible unitary representations of the group $SU(2)$ (the group $SU(2)$ is an universal covering of $SO(3)$). In turn, universal coverings of the orthogonal groups are completely defined within Clifford–Lipschitz groups.

The Lipschitz group $\boldsymbol{\Gamma}_{p,q}$, also called the Clifford group, introduced by Lipschitz in 1886 [16], may be defined as the subgroup of invertible elements s of the algebra $\mathcal{C}\!\ell_{p,q}$:

$$\boldsymbol{\Gamma}_{p,q} = \left\{ s \in \mathcal{C}\!\ell^+_{p,q} \cup \mathcal{C}\!\ell^-_{p,q} \mid \forall \mathbf{x} \in \mathbb{R}^{p,q},\ s\mathbf{x}s^{-1} \in \mathbb{R}^{p,q} \right\}.$$

The set $\boldsymbol{\Gamma}^+_{p,q} = \boldsymbol{\Gamma}_{p,q} \cap \mathcal{C}\!\ell^+_{p,q}$ is called *special Lipschitz group* [7].

Let $N : \mathcal{C}\!\ell_{p,q} \rightarrow \mathcal{C}\!\ell_{p,q}$, $N(\mathbf{x}) = \mathbf{x}\widetilde{\mathbf{x}}$. If $\mathbf{x} \in \mathbb{R}^{p,q}$, then $N(\mathbf{x}) = \mathbf{x}(-\mathbf{x}) = -\mathbf{x}^2 = -Q(\mathbf{x})$. Further, the group $\boldsymbol{\Gamma}_{p,q}$ has a subgroup

$$\mathbf{Pin}(p, q) = \{ s \in \boldsymbol{\Gamma}_{p,q} \mid N(s) = \pm 1 \}. \tag{2}$$

Analogously, *a spinor group* $\mathbf{Spin}(p, q)$ is defined by the set

$$\mathbf{Spin}(p, q) = \left\{ s \in \boldsymbol{\Gamma}^+_{p,q} \mid N(s) = \pm 1 \right\}. \tag{3}$$

It is obvious that $\mathbf{Spin}(p,q)=\mathbf{Pin}(p,q)\cap C\!\ell^+_{p,q}$. The group $\mathbf{Spin}(p,q)$ contains a subgroup

$$\mathbf{Spin}_+(p,q)=\{s\in\mathbf{Spin}(p,q)\mid N(s)=1\}\,. \tag{4}$$

It is easy to see that the groups $O(p,q)$, $SO(p,q)$ and $SO_+(p,q)$ are isomorphic, respectively, to the following quotient groups

$$O(p,q)\simeq\mathbf{Pin}(p,q)/\mathbb{Z}_2,\quad SO(p,q)\simeq\mathbf{Spin}(p,q)/\mathbb{Z}_2,\quad SO_+(p,q)\simeq\mathbf{Spin}_+(p,q)/\mathbb{Z}_2,$$

where the kernel $\mathbb{Z}_2=\{1,-1\}$. Thus, the groups $\mathbf{Pin}(p,q)$, $\mathbf{Spin}(p,q)$ and $\mathbf{Spin}_+(p,q)$ are the double coverings of the groups $O(p,q)$, $SO(p,q)$ and $SO_+(p,q)$, respectively.

Further, since $C\!\ell^+_{p,q}\simeq C\!\ell^+_{q,p}$, then

$$\mathbf{Spin}(p,q)\simeq\mathbf{Spin}(q,p).$$

In contrast with this, the groups $\mathbf{Pin}(p,q)$ and $\mathbf{Pin}(q,p)$ are non–isomorphic. Denote $\mathbf{Spin}(n)=\mathbf{Spin}(n,0)\simeq\mathbf{Spin}(0,n)$.

Theorem 1 ([8]). *The spinor groups*

$$\mathbf{Spin}(2),\ \ \mathbf{Spin}(3),\ \ \mathbf{Spin}(4),\ \ \mathbf{Spin}(5),\ \ \mathbf{Spin}(6)$$

are isomorphic to the unitary groups

$$U(1),\ \ Sp(1)\sim SU(2),\ \ SU(2)\times SU(2),\ \ Sp(2),\ \ SU(4).$$

Over the field $\mathbb{F}=\mathbb{R}$ in the case of $p-q\equiv 1,5\pmod 8$ the algebra $C\!\ell_{p,q}$ is isomorphic to a direct sum of two mutually annihilating simple ideals $\frac{1}{2}(1\pm\omega)C\!\ell_{p,q}$: $C\!\ell_{p,q}\simeq\frac{1}{2}(1+\omega)C\!\ell_{p,q}\oplus\frac{1}{2}(1-\omega)C\!\ell_{p,q}$, where $\omega=\mathbf{e}_{12\ldots p+q}$, $p-q\equiv 1,5\pmod 8$. At this point, the each ideal is isomorpic to $C\!\ell_{p,q-1}$ or $C\!\ell_{q,p-1}$. Therefore, for the Clifford–Lipschitz groups we have the following isomorphisms

$$\begin{aligned}\mathbf{Pin}(p,q) &\simeq \mathbf{Pin}(p,q-1)\bigcup\mathbf{Pin}(p,q-1)\\ &\simeq \mathbf{Pin}(q,p-1)\bigcup\mathbf{Pin}(q,p-1).\end{aligned} \tag{5}$$

Or, since $C\!\ell_{p,q-1}\simeq C\!\ell^+_{p,q}\subset C\!\ell_{p,q}$, then according to (4)

$$\mathbf{Pin}(p,q)\simeq\mathbf{Spin}(p,q)\bigcup\mathbf{Spin}(p,q)$$

if $p-q\equiv 1,5\pmod 8$.

Further, when $p-q\equiv 3,7\pmod 8$, the algebra $C\!\ell_{p,q}$ is isomorphic to a complex algebra $\mathbb{C}_{p+q-1}$. Therefore, for the **Pin** groups we obtain

$$\begin{aligned}\mathbf{Pin}(p,q) &\simeq \mathbf{Pin}(p,q-1)\bigcup\mathbf{e}_{12\ldots p+q}\,\mathbf{Pin}(p,q-1)\\ &\simeq \mathbf{Pin}(q,p-1)\bigcup\mathbf{e}_{12\ldots p+q}\,\mathbf{Pin}(q,p-1)\end{aligned} \tag{6}$$

if $p-q\equiv 1,5 \pmod 8$ and correspondingly

$$\mathbf{Pin}(p,q)\simeq \mathbf{Spin}(p,q)\cup \mathbf{e}_{12\ldots p+q}\,\mathbf{Spin}(p,q). \qquad (7)$$

In case of $p-q\equiv 3,7 \pmod 8$ we have isomorphisms which are analogous to (6)-(7), since $\omega C\!\ell_{p,q}\sim C\!\ell_{p,q}$. Generalizing these results, we obtain the following

Theorem 2. *Let* $\mathbf{Pin}(p,q)$ *and* $\mathbf{Spin}(p,q)$ *be the Clifford-Lipschitz groups of the invertible elements of the algebras* $C\!\ell_{p,q}$ *with odd dimensionality,* $p-q\equiv 1,3,5,7 \pmod 8$. *Then*

$$\begin{aligned}\mathbf{Pin}(p,q) &\simeq \mathbf{Pin}(p,q-1)\bigcup \omega\,\mathbf{Pin}(p,q-1)\\ &\simeq \mathbf{Pin}(q,p-1)\bigcup \omega\,\mathbf{Pin}(q,p-1)\end{aligned}$$

and

$$\mathbf{Pin}(p,q)\simeq \mathbf{Spin}(p,q)\bigcup \omega\,\mathbf{Spin}(p,q),$$

where $\omega=\mathbf{e}_{12\ldots p+q}$ *is a volume element of* $C\!\ell_{p,q}$.

In case of low dimensionalities from Theorem 1 and Theorem 2 it immediately follows

Theorem 3. *For* $p+q\leq 5$ *and* $p-q\equiv 3,5 \pmod 8$,

$$\begin{aligned}\mathbf{Pin}(3,0) &\simeq SU(2)\cup iSU(2),\\ \mathbf{Pin}(0,3) &\simeq SU(2)\cup eSU(2),\\ \mathbf{Pin}(5,0) &\simeq Sp(2)\cup eSp(2),\\ \mathbf{Pin}(0,5) &\simeq Sp(2)\cup iSp(2).\end{aligned}$$

Proof. Indeed, in accordance with Theorem 2 $\mathbf{Pin}(3,0)\simeq \mathbf{Spin}(3)\cup \mathbf{e}_{123}\,\mathbf{Spin}(3)$. Further, from Theorem 1 we have $\mathbf{Spin}(3)\simeq SU(2)$, and a square of the element $\omega=\mathbf{e}_{123}$ is equal to -1, therefor,e $\omega\sim i$. Thus, $\mathbf{Pin}(3,0)\simeq SU(2)\cup iSU(2)$. For the group $\mathbf{Pin}(0,3)$ a square of ω is equal to $+1$, therefore, $\mathbf{Pin}(0,3)\simeq SU(2)\cup eSU(2)$, e is a double unit. As expected, $\mathbf{Pin}(3,0)\not\simeq \mathbf{Pin}(0,3)$. The isomorphisms for the groups $\mathbf{Pin}(5,0)$ and $\mathbf{Pin}(0,5)$ are analogously proved.

□

In turn, over the field $\mathbb{F}=\mathbb{C}$ there exists a complex Clifford–Lipschitz group

$$\mathbf{\Gamma}_n=\left\{s\in \mathbb{C}_n^+\cup \mathbb{C}_n^-\mid \forall \mathbf{x}\in \mathbb{C}^n,\ s\mathbf{x}s^{-1}\in \mathbb{C}^n\right\}.$$

The group $\mathbf{\Gamma}_n$ has a subgroup

$$\mathbf{Pin}(n,\mathbb{C})=\{s\in \mathbf{\Gamma}_n\mid N(s)=\pm 1\}. \qquad (8)$$

$\mathbf{Pin}(n, \mathbb{C})$ is an universal covering of the complex orthogonal group $O(n, \mathbb{C})$. When $n \equiv 1 \pmod 2$ we have

$$\mathbf{Pin}(n, \mathbb{C}) \simeq \mathbf{Pin}(n-1, \mathbb{C}) \bigcup \mathbf{e}_{12\cdots n} \mathbf{Pin}(n-1, \mathbb{C}). \tag{9}$$

On the other hand, there exists a more detailed version of the **Pin**–group (2) proposed by Dąbrowski in 1988 [9]. In general, there are eight double coverings of the orthogonal group $O(p, q)$ [9, 4]:

$$\rho^{a,b,c}: \ \mathbf{Pin}^{a,b,c}(p, q) \longrightarrow O(p, q),$$

where $a, b, c \in \{+, -\}$. As known, the group $O(p, q)$ consists of four connected components: identity connected component $O_0(p, q)$, and three components corresponding to space inversion P, time reversal T, and the combination of these two PT, i.e., $O(p, q) = (O_0(p, q)) \cup P(Q_0(p, q)) \cup T(O_0(p, q)) \cup PT(O_0(p, q))$. Further, since the four–element group (reflection group) $\{1, P, T, PT\}$ is isomorphic to the finite group $\mathbb{Z}_2 \otimes \mathbb{Z}_2$ (Gauss–Klein viergruppe [23, 24]), then $O(p, q)$ may be represented by a semidirect product $O(p, q) \simeq O_0(p, q) \odot (\mathbb{Z}_2 \otimes \mathbb{Z}_2)$. The signs of a, b, c correspond to the signs of the squares of the elements in $\mathbf{Pin}^{a,b,c}(p, q)$ which cover space inversion P, time reversal T and a combination of these two PT ($a = -P^2$, $b = T^2$, $c = -(PT)^2$ in Dąbrowski's notation [9] and $a = P^2$, $b = T^2$, $c = (PT)^2$ in Chamblin's notation [6] which we will use below). An explicit form of the group $\mathbf{Pin}^{a,b,c}(p, q)$ is given by the following semidirect product

$$\mathbf{Pin}^{a,b,c}(p, q) \simeq \frac{(\mathbf{Spin}_+(p, q) \odot C^{a,b,c})}{\mathbb{Z}_2}, \tag{10}$$

where $C^{a,b,c}$ are the four double coverings of $\mathbb{Z}_2 \otimes \mathbb{Z}_2$. All the eight double coverings of the orthogonal group $O(p, q)$ are given in the following table:

$a\ b\ c$	$C^{a,b,c}$	Remark
$+\ +\ +$	$\mathbb{Z}_2 \otimes \mathbb{Z}_2 \otimes \mathbb{Z}_2$	$PT = TP$
$+\ -\ -$	$\mathbb{Z}_2 \otimes \mathbb{Z}_4$	$PT = TP$
$-\ +\ -$	$\mathbb{Z}_2 \otimes \mathbb{Z}_4$	$PT = TP$
$-\ -\ +$	$\mathbb{Z}_2 \otimes \mathbb{Z}_4$	$PT = TP$
$-\ -\ -$	Q_4	$PT = -TP$
$-\ +\ +$	D_4	$PT = -TP$
$+\ -\ +$	D_4	$PT = -TP$
$+\ +\ -$	D_4	$PT = -TP$

Here $\mathbb{Z}_4$, Q_4, and D_4 are complex, quaternion, and dihedral groups, respectively. According to [9] the group $\mathbf{Pin}^{a,b,c}(p, q)$ satisfying the condition $PT = -TP$ is called *Cliffordian*, and respectively *non–Cliffordian* when $PT = TP$.

3 Discrete symmetries and Clifford algebras

In Clifford algebra $C\ell$ there exist four fundamental automorphisms.

1) **Identity**: An automorphism $\mathcal{A} \rightarrow \mathcal{A}$ and $\mathbf{e}_i \rightarrow \mathbf{e}_i$.
This automorphism is an identical automorphism of the algebra $C\ell$. $\mathcal{A}$ is an arbitrary element of $C\ell$.

2) **Involution**: An automorphism $\mathcal{A} \rightarrow \mathcal{A}^\star$ and $\mathbf{e}_i \rightarrow -\mathbf{e}_i$.
In more details, for an arbitrary element $\mathcal{A} \in C\ell$ there exists a decomposition $\mathcal{A} = \mathcal{A}' + \mathcal{A}''$, where $\mathcal{A}'$ is an element consisting of homogeneous odd elements, and $\mathcal{A}''$ is an element consisting of homogeneous even elements, respectively. Then the automorphism $\mathcal{A} \rightarrow \mathcal{A}^\star$ is such that the element $\mathcal{A}''$ is not changed, and the element $\mathcal{A}'$ changes sign: $\mathcal{A}^\star = -\mathcal{A}' + \mathcal{A}''$. If $\mathcal{A}$ is a homogeneous element, then

$$\mathcal{A}^\star = (-1)^k \mathcal{A}, \tag{11}$$

where k is a degree of the element. It is easy to see that the automorphism $\mathcal{A} \rightarrow \mathcal{A}^\star$ may be expressed via the volume element $\omega = \mathbf{e}_{12\ldots p+q}$:

$$\mathcal{A}^\star = \omega \mathcal{A} \omega^{-1}, \tag{12}$$

where $\omega^{-1} = (-1)^{\frac{(p+q)(p+q-1)}{2}} \omega$. When k is odd, the basis elements $\mathbf{e}_{i_1 i_2 \ldots i_k}$ the sign changes, and when k is even, the sign is not changed.

3) **Reversion**: An antiautomorphism $\mathcal{A} \rightarrow \widetilde{\mathcal{A}}$ and $\mathbf{e}_i \rightarrow \mathbf{e}_i$.
The antiautomorphism $\mathcal{A} \rightarrow \widetilde{\mathcal{A}}$ is a reversion of the element $\mathcal{A}$, that is the substitution of each basis element $\mathbf{e}_{i_1 i_2 \ldots i_k} \in \mathcal{A}$ by the element $\mathbf{e}_{i_k i_{k-1} \ldots i_1}$:

$$\mathbf{e}_{i_k i_{k-1} \ldots i_1} = (-1)^{\frac{k(k-1)}{2}} \mathbf{e}_{i_1 i_2 \ldots i_k}.$$

Therefore, for any $\mathcal{A} \in C\ell_{p,q}$ we have

$$\widetilde{\mathcal{A}} = (-1)^{\frac{k(k-1)}{2}} \mathcal{A}. \tag{13}$$

4) **Conjugation**: An antiautomorpism $\mathcal{A} \rightarrow \widetilde{\mathcal{A}^\star}$ and $\mathbf{e}_i \rightarrow -\mathbf{e}_i$.
This antiautomorphism is a composition of the antiautomorphism $\mathcal{A} \rightarrow \widetilde{\mathcal{A}}$ with the automorphism $\mathcal{A} \rightarrow \mathcal{A}^\star$. In the case of a homogeneous element from the formulae (11) and (13), it follows

$$\widetilde{\mathcal{A}^\star} = (-1)^{\frac{k(k+1)}{2}} \mathcal{A}. \tag{14}$$

One of the most fundamental theorems in the theory of associative algebras is

Theorem 4 (Wedderburn–Artin). *Any finite-dimensional associative simple algebra $\mathfrak{A}$ over the field $\mathbb{F}$ is isomorphic to a full matrix algebra $\mathsf{M}_n(\mathbb{K})$, where a natural number n defined unambiguously, and a division ring $\mathbb{K}$ defined with an accuracy of isomorphism.*

In accordance with this theorem all properties of the initial algebra $\mathfrak{A}$ are isomorphically transferred to the matrix algebra $\mathsf{M}_n(\mathbb{K})$. Later on we will widely use this theorem. In its turn, for the Clifford algebra $C\!\ell_{p,q}$ over the field $\mathbb{F}=\mathbb{R}$ we have an isomorphism $C\!\ell_{p,q}\simeq\mathrm{End}_{\mathbb{K}}(I_{p,q})\simeq\mathsf{M}_{2^m}(\mathbb{K})$, where $m=\frac{p+q}{2}$, $I_{p,q}=C\!\ell_{p,q}f$ is a minimal left ideal of $C\!\ell_{p,q}$, and $\mathbb{K}=fC\!\ell_{p,q}f$ is a division ring of $C\!\ell_{p,q}$. The primitive idempotent of the algebra $C\!\ell_{p,q}$ has a form

$$f=\frac{1}{2}(1\pm\mathbf{e}_{\alpha_1})\frac{1}{2}(1\pm\mathbf{e}_{\alpha_2})\cdots\frac{1}{2}(1\pm\mathbf{e}_{\alpha_k}),$$

where $\mathbf{e}_{\alpha_1},\mathbf{e}_{\alpha_2},\ldots,\mathbf{e}_{\alpha_k}$ are commuting elements with square 1 of the canonical basis of $C\!\ell_{p,q}$ generating a group of order 2^k. The values of k are defined by a formula $k=q-r_{q-p}$, where r_i are the Radon–Hurwitz numbers [19, 13], values of which form a cycle of the period 8: $r_{i+8}=r_i+4$. The values of all r_i are

i	0	1	2	3	4	5	6	7
r_i	0	1	2	2	3	3	3	3

The all Clifford algebras $C\!\ell_{p,q}$ over the field $\mathbb{F}=\mathbb{R}$ are divided into eight different types with a following division ring structure:

I. Central simple algebras.

1) Two types $p-q\equiv 0,2 \pmod 8$ with a division ring $\mathbb{K}\simeq\mathbb{R}$.

2) Two types $p-q\equiv 3,7 \pmod 8$ with a division ring $\mathbb{K}\simeq\mathbb{C}$.

3) Two types $p-q\equiv 4,6 \pmod 8$ with a division ring $\mathbb{K}\simeq\mathbb{H}$.

II. Semi–simple algebras.

4) The type $p-q\equiv 1 \pmod 8$ with a double division ring $\mathbb{K}\simeq\mathbb{R}\oplus\mathbb{R}$.

5) The type $p-q\equiv 5 \pmod 8$ with a double quaternionic division ring $\mathbb{K}\simeq\mathbb{H}\oplus\mathbb{H}$.

Over the field $\mathbb{F}=\mathbb{C}$ there is an isomorphism $\mathbb{C}_n\simeq\mathsf{M}_{2^{n/2}}(\mathbb{C})$ and there are two different types of complex Clifford algebras $\mathbb{C}_n$: $n\equiv 0 \pmod 2$ and $n\equiv 1 \pmod 2$.

In virtue of the Wedderburn–Artin theorem the all fundamental automorphisms of $C\!\ell$ are transferred to the matrix algebra. Matrix representations of the fundamental automorphisms of $\mathbb{C}_n$ were first obtained by Rashevskii in 1955 [21]: 1) Involution: $\mathsf{A}^\star=\mathsf{W}\mathsf{A}\mathsf{W}^{-1}$, where W is a matrix of the automorphism $\star$ (matrix representation of the volume element ω); 2) Reversion: $\widetilde{\mathsf{A}}=\mathsf{E}\mathsf{A}^{\mathsf{T}}\mathsf{E}^{-1}$, where E is a matrix of the antiautomorphism $\widetilde{\ }$ satisfying the conditions $\mathcal{E}_i\mathsf{E}-\mathsf{E}\mathcal{E}_i^{\mathsf{T}}=0$ and $\mathsf{E}^{\mathsf{T}}=(-1)^{\frac{m(m-1)}{2}}\mathsf{E}$, here $\mathcal{E}_i=\gamma(\mathbf{e}_i)$ are matrix representations of the units of the algebra $C\!\ell$; 3) Conjugation: $\widetilde{\mathsf{A}^\star}=\mathsf{C}\mathsf{A}^{\mathsf{T}}\mathsf{C}^{-1}$, where $\mathsf{C}=\mathsf{E}\mathsf{W}^{\mathsf{T}}$ is a matrix of the antiautomorphism $\widetilde{\star}$ satisfying the conditions $\mathsf{C}\mathcal{E}^{\mathsf{T}}+\mathcal{E}_i\mathsf{C}=0$ and $\mathsf{C}^{\mathsf{T}}=(-1)^{\frac{m(m+1)}{2}}\mathsf{C}$.

In the recent paper [28] it has been shown that space reversal P, time reversal T and combination PT are correspond respectively to the fundamental automorphisms $\mathcal{A}\rightarrow\mathcal{A}^\star$, $\mathcal{A}\rightarrow\widetilde{\mathcal{A}}$ and $\mathcal{A}\rightarrow\widetilde{\mathcal{A}^\star}$.

Proposition 1. *Let $\mathcal{C}\!\ell_{p,q}$ $(p+q=2m)$ be a Clifford algebra over the field $\mathbb{F}=\mathbb{R}$ and let $\mathbf{Pin}(p,q)$ be a double covering of the orthogonal group $O(p,q)=O_0(p,q)\odot\{1,P,T,PT\}\simeq O_0(p,q)\odot(\mathbb{Z}_2\otimes\mathbb{Z}_2)$ of transformations of the space $\mathbb{R}^{p,q}$, where $\{1,P,T,PT\}\simeq\mathbb{Z}_2\otimes\mathbb{Z}_2$ is a group of discrete transformations of $\mathbb{R}^{p,q}$, $\mathbb{Z}_2\otimes\mathbb{Z}_2$ is the Gauss–Klein group. Then there is an isomorphism between the group $\{1,P,T,PT\}$ and an automorphism group $\{\mathrm{Id},\star,\widetilde{\ },\widetilde{\star}\}$ of the algebra $\mathcal{C}\!\ell_{p,q}$. In this case, space inversion P, time reversal T and combination PT are correspond to the fundamental automorphisms $\mathcal{A}\rightarrow\mathcal{A}^\star$, $\mathcal{A}\rightarrow\widetilde{\mathcal{A}}$ and $\mathcal{A}\rightarrow\widetilde{\mathcal{A}^\star}$.*

An equivalence of the multiplication tables of the groups $\{1,P,T,PT\}$ and $\mathrm{Aut}(\mathcal{C}\!\ell)=\{\mathrm{Id},\star,\widetilde{\ },\widetilde{\star}\}$ proves this isomorphism (in virtue of the commutativity $\widetilde{(\mathcal{A}^\star)}=(\widetilde{\mathcal{A}})^\star$ and the involution conditions $(\star)^2=(\widetilde{\ })^2=\mathrm{Id}$):

	Id	$\star$	$\widetilde{\ }$	$\widetilde{\star}$
Id	Id	$\star$	$\widetilde{\ }$	$\widetilde{\star}$
$\star$	$\star$	Id	$\widetilde{\star}$	$\widetilde{\ }$
$\widetilde{\ }$	$\widetilde{\ }$	$\widetilde{\star}$	Id	$\star$
$\widetilde{\star}$	$\widetilde{\star}$	$\widetilde{\ }$	$\star$	Id

$\sim$

	1	P	T	PT
1	1	P	T	PT
P	P	1	PT	T
T	T	PT	1	P
PT	PT	T	P	1

Further, in the case $P^2=T^2=(PT)^2=\pm1$ and $PT=-TP$ there is an isomorphism between the group $\{1,P,T,PT\}$ and an automorphism group $\mathsf{Aut}(\mathcal{C}\!\ell)=\{\mathsf{I},\mathsf{W},\mathsf{E},\mathsf{C}\}$. So, for the Dirac algebra $\mathbb{C}_4$ in the canonical γ–basis there exists a standard (Wigner) representation $P=\gamma_0$ and $T=\gamma_1\gamma_3$ [3], therefore, $\{1,P,T,PT\}=\{1,\gamma_0,\gamma_1\gamma_3,\gamma_0\gamma_1\gamma_3\}$. On the other hand, in the γ–basis an automorphism group of $\mathbb{C}_4$ has a form $\mathsf{Aut}(\mathbb{C}_4)=\{\mathsf{I},\mathsf{W},\mathsf{E},\mathsf{C}\}=\{\mathsf{I},\gamma_0\gamma_1\gamma_2\gamma_3,\gamma_1\gamma_3,\gamma_0\gamma_2\}$. It has been shown [28] that $\{1,P,T,PT\}=\{1,\gamma_0,\gamma_1\gamma_3,\gamma_0\gamma_1\gamma_3\}\simeq\mathsf{Aut}(\mathbb{C}_4)\simeq\mathbb{Z}_4$, where $\mathbb{Z}_4$ is a complex group with the signature $(+,-,-)$. Generalizations of these results onto the algebras $\mathbb{C}_n$ are contained in the following two theorems:

Theorem 5 ([28]). *Let $\mathsf{Aut}=\{\mathsf{I},\mathsf{W},\mathsf{E},\mathsf{C}\}$ be the automorphism group of the algebra $\mathbb{C}_{p+q}$ $(p+q=2m)$, where $\mathsf{W}=\mathcal{E}_1\mathcal{E}_2\cdots\mathcal{E}_m\mathcal{E}_{m+1}\mathcal{E}_{m+2}\cdots\mathcal{E}_{p+q}$, and $\mathsf{E}=\mathcal{E}_1\mathcal{E}_2\cdots\mathcal{E}_m$, $\mathsf{C}=\mathcal{E}_{m+1}\mathcal{E}_{m+2}\cdots\mathcal{E}_{p+q}$ if $m\equiv1\pmod 2$, and $\mathsf{E}=\mathcal{E}_{m+1}\mathcal{E}_{m+2}\cdots\mathcal{E}_{p+q}$, $\mathsf{C}=\mathcal{E}_1\mathcal{E}_2\cdots\mathcal{E}_m$ if $m\equiv0\pmod 2$. Let Aut_- and Aut_+ be the automorphism groups, in which the all elements correspondingly commute $(m\equiv0\pmod 2)$ and anticommute $(m\equiv1\pmod 2)$. Then over the field $\mathbb{F}=\mathbb{C}$ there are only two non–isomorphic groups: $\mathsf{Aut}_-\simeq\mathbb{Z}_2\otimes\mathbb{Z}_2$ for the signature $(+,+,+)$ if $n\equiv0,1\pmod 4$ and $\mathsf{Aut}_+\simeq Q_4/\mathbb{Z}_2$ for the signature $(-,-,-)$ if $n\equiv2,3\pmod 4$.*

Theorem 6 ([28]). *Let $\mathbf{Pin}^{a,b,c}(p,q)$ be a double covering of the complex orthogonal group $O(n,\mathbb{C})$ of the space $\mathbb{C}^n$ associated with the complex algebra $\mathbb{C}_n$. Squares of the symbols $a,b,c\in\{-,+\}$ are correspond to squares of the elements of the finite group $\mathsf{A}=\{\mathsf{I},\mathsf{W},\mathsf{E},\mathsf{C}\}:$ $a=\mathsf{W}^2$, $b=\mathsf{E}^2$, $c=\mathsf{C}^2$, where W,E and C are correspondingly*

the matrices of the fundamental automorphisms $\mathcal{A} \to \mathcal{A}^\star$, $\mathcal{A} \to \widetilde{\mathcal{A}}$ *and* $\mathcal{A} \to \widetilde{\mathcal{A}^\star}$ *of* $\mathbb{C}_n$. *Then over the field* $\mathbb{F} = \mathbb{C}$ *for the algebra* $\mathbb{C}_n$ *there exist two non–isomorphic double coverings of the group* $O(n, \mathbb{C})$*:*
1) Non–Cliffordian groups

$$\mathbf{Pin}^{+,+,+}(n, \mathbb{C}) \simeq \frac{(\mathbf{Spin}_+(n, \mathbb{C}) \odot \mathbb{Z}_2 \otimes \mathbb{Z}_2 \otimes \mathbb{Z}_2)}{\mathbb{Z}_2},$$

if $n \equiv 0 \pmod 4$ *and*

$$\mathbf{Pin}^{+,+,+}(n, \mathbb{C}) \simeq \mathbf{Pin}^{+,+,+}(n-1, \mathbb{C}) \bigcup \mathbf{e}_{12\ldots n} \mathbf{Pin}^{+,+,+}(n-1, \mathbb{C}),$$

if $n \equiv 1 \pmod 4$.
2) Cliffordian groups

$$\mathbf{Pin}^{-,-,-}(n, \mathbb{C}) \simeq \frac{(\mathbf{Spin}_+(n, \mathbb{C}) \odot Q_4)}{\mathbb{Z}_2},$$

if $n \equiv 2 \pmod 4$ *and*

$$\mathbf{Pin}^{-,-,-}(n, \mathbb{C}) \simeq \mathbf{Pin}^{-,-,-}(n-1, \mathbb{C}) \bigcup \mathbf{e}_{12\ldots n} \mathbf{Pin}^{-,-,-}(n-1, \mathbb{C}),$$

if $n \equiv 3 \pmod 4$.

A consideration of the discrete symmetries over the field of real numbers is a much more complicated problem. First of all, in contrast to the field of complex numbers over the field $\mathbb{F} = \mathbb{R}$ there exist eight different types of the Clifford algebras and five division rings, which, in virtue of the Wedderburn–Artin Theorem, impose hard restrictions on existence and choice of the matrix representations for the fundamental automorphisms.

Theorem 7. *Let* $C\!\ell_{p,q}$ *be a Clifford algebra over a field* $\mathbb{F} = \mathbb{R}$ *and let* $\mathsf{Aut}(C\!\ell_{p,q}) = \{\mathsf{I}, \mathsf{W}, \mathsf{E}, \mathsf{C}\}$ *be a group of fundamental automorphisms of the algebra* $C\!\ell_{p,q}$. *Then for eight types of the algebras* $C\!\ell_{p,q}$ *there exist, depending upon a division ring structure of* $C\!\ell_{p,q}$, *following isomorphisms between finite groups and groups* $\mathsf{Aut}(C\!\ell_{p,q})$ *with different signatures* (a, b, c), *where* $a, b, c \in \{-, +\}$*:*

1) $\mathbb{K} \simeq \mathbb{R}$, *types* $p - q \equiv 0, 2 \pmod 8$.
If $\mathsf{E} = \mathcal{E}_{p+1}\mathcal{E}_{p+2}\cdots\mathcal{E}_{p+q}$ *and* $\mathsf{C} = \mathcal{E}_1\mathcal{E}_2\cdots\mathcal{E}_p$, *then Abelian groups* $\mathsf{Aut}_-(C\!\ell_{p,q}) \simeq \mathbb{Z}_2 \otimes \mathbb{Z}_2$ *with the signature* $(+, +, +)$ *and* $\mathsf{Aut}_-(C\!\ell_{p,q}) \simeq \mathbb{Z}_4$ *with the signature* $(+, -, -)$ *exist at* $p, q \equiv 0 \pmod 4$ *and* $p, q \equiv 2 \pmod 4$, *respectively, for the type* $p - q \equiv 0 \pmod 8$, *and also Abelian groups* $\mathsf{Aut}_-(C\!\ell_{p,q}) \simeq \mathbb{Z}_4$ *with the signature* $(-, -, +)$ *and* $\mathsf{Aut}_-(C\!\ell_{p,q}) \simeq \mathbb{Z}_4$ *with the signature* $(-, +, -)$ *exist at* $p \equiv 0 \pmod 4$, $q \equiv 2 \pmod 4$ *and* $p \equiv 2 \pmod 4$, $q \equiv 0 \pmod 4$ *for the type* $p - q \equiv 2 \pmod 8$, *respectively.*
If $\mathsf{E} = \mathcal{E}_1\mathcal{E}_2\cdots\mathcal{E}_p$ *and* $\mathsf{C} = \mathcal{E}_{p+1}\mathcal{E}_{p+2}\cdots\mathcal{E}_{p+q}$, *then non–Abelian groups*

$\mathsf{Aut}_+(C\!\ell_{p,q}) \simeq D_4/\mathbb{Z}_2$ *with the signature* $(+,-,+)$ *and* $\mathsf{Aut}_+(C\!\ell_{p,q}) \simeq D_4/\mathbb{Z}_2$ *with the signature* $(+,+,-)$ *exist at* $p,q \equiv 3 \pmod 4$ *and* $p,q \equiv 1 \pmod 4$*, respectively, for the type* $p-q \equiv 0 \pmod 8$*, and also non–Abelian groups* $\mathsf{Aut}_+(C\!\ell_{p,q}) \simeq Q_4/\mathbb{Z}_2$ *with* $(-,-,-)$ *and* $\mathsf{Aut}_+(C\!\ell_{p,q}) \simeq D_4/\mathbb{Z}_2$ *with* $(-,+,+)$ *exist at* $p \equiv 3 \pmod 4$, $q \equiv 1 \pmod 4$ *and* $p \equiv 1 \pmod 4$, $q \equiv 3 \pmod 4$ *for the type* $p-q \equiv 2 \pmod 8$*, respectively.*

2) $\mathbb{K} \simeq \mathbb{H}$*, types* $p-q \equiv 4, 6 \pmod 8$.
If $\mathsf{E} = \mathcal{E}_{j_1}\mathcal{E}_{j_2}\cdots\mathcal{E}_{j_k}$ *is a product of* k *skewsymmetric matrices (among which* l *matrices have a square* $+\mathsf{I}$ *and* t *matrices have a square* $-\mathsf{I}$*) and* $\mathsf{C} = \mathcal{E}_{i_1}\mathcal{E}_{i_2}\cdots\mathcal{E}_{i_{p+q-k}}$ *is a product of* $p+q-k$ *symmetric matrices (among which* h *matrices have a square* $+\mathsf{I}$ *and* g *have a square* $-\mathsf{I}$*), then at* $k \equiv 0 \pmod 2$ *for the type* $p-q \equiv 4 \pmod 8$ *there exist Abelian groups* $\mathsf{Aut}_-(C\!\ell_{p,q}) \simeq \mathbb{Z}_2 \otimes \mathbb{Z}_2$ *with* $(+,+,+)$ *and* $\mathsf{Aut}_-(C\!\ell_{p,q}) \simeq \mathbb{Z}_4$ *with* $(+,-,-)$ *if* $l-t,\ h-g \equiv 0,1,4,5 \pmod 8$ *and* $l-t,\ h-g \equiv 2,3,6,7 \pmod 8$*, respectively. And also at* $k \equiv 0 \pmod 2$ *for the type* $p-q \equiv 6 \pmod 8$ *there exist* $\mathsf{Aut}_-(C\!\ell_{p,q}) \simeq \mathbb{Z}_4$ *with* $(-,+,-)$ *and* $\mathsf{Aut}_-(C\!\ell_{p,q}) \simeq \mathbb{Z}_4$ *with* $(-,-,+)$ *if* $l-t \equiv 0,1,4,5 \pmod 8$, $h-g \equiv 2,3,6,7 \pmod 8$ *and* $l-t \equiv 2,3,6,7 \pmod 8$, $h-g \equiv 0,1,4,5 \pmod 8$*, respectively.*
Inversely, if $\mathsf{E} = \mathcal{E}_{i_1}\mathcal{E}_{i_2}\cdots\mathcal{E}_{i_{p+q-k}}$ *is a product of* $p+q-k$ *symmetric matrices and* $\mathsf{C} = \mathcal{E}_{j_1}\mathcal{E}_{j_2}\cdots\mathcal{E}_{j_k}$ *is a product of* k *skewsymmetric matrices, then at* $k \equiv 1 \pmod 2$ *for the type* $p-q \equiv 4 \pmod 8$ *there exist non–Abelian groups* $\mathsf{Aut}_+(C\!\ell_{p,q}) \simeq D_4/\mathbb{Z}_2$ *with* $(+,-,+)$ *and* $\mathsf{Aut}_+(C\!\ell_{p,q}) \simeq D_4/\mathbb{Z}_2$ *with* $(+,+,-)$ *if* $h-g \equiv 2,3,6,7 \pmod 8$, $l-t \equiv 0,1,4,5 \pmod 8$ *and* $h-g \equiv 0,1,4,5 \pmod 8$, $l-t \equiv 2,3,6,7 \pmod 8$*, respectively. And also at* $k \equiv 1 \pmod 2$ *for the type* $p-q \equiv 6 \pmod 8$ *there exist* $\mathsf{Aut}_+(C\!\ell_{p,q}) \simeq Q_4/\mathbb{Z}_2$ *with* $(-,-,-)$ *and* $\mathsf{Aut}_+(C\!\ell_{p,q}) \simeq D_4/\mathbb{Z}_2$ *with* $(-,+,+)$ *if* $h-g,\ l-t \equiv 2,3,6,7 \pmod 8$ *and* $h-g,\ l-t \equiv 0,1,4,5 \pmod 8$*, respectively.*

3) $\mathbb{K} \simeq \mathbb{R} \oplus \mathbb{R}$, $\mathbb{K} \simeq \mathbb{H} \oplus \mathbb{H}$*, types* $p-q \equiv 1, 5 \pmod 8$.
For the algebras $C\!\ell_{0,q}$ *of the types* $p-q \equiv 1,5 \pmod 8$ *there exist Abelian automorphism groups with the signatures* $(-,-,+)$, $(-,+,-)$ *and non–Abelian automorphism groups with the signatures* $(-,-,-)$, $(-,+,+)$*. Correspondingly, for the algebras* $C\!\ell_{p,0}$ *of the types* $p-q \equiv 1,5 \pmod 8$ *there exist Abelian groups with* $(+,+,+)$, $(+,-,-)$ *and non–Abelian groups with* $(+,-,+)$, $(+,+,-)$*. In general case for* $C\!\ell_{p,q}$*, the types* $p-q \equiv 1,5 \pmod 8$ *admit all eight automorphism groups.*

4) $\mathbb{K} = \mathbb{C}$*, types* $p-q \equiv 3, 7 \pmod 8$.
The types $p-q \equiv 3,7 \pmod 8$ *admit the Abelian group* $\mathsf{Aut}_-(C\!\ell_{p,q}) \simeq \mathbb{Z}_2 \otimes \mathbb{Z}_2$ *with the signature* $(+,+,+)$ *if* $p \equiv 0 \pmod 2$ *and* $q \equiv 1 \pmod 2$*, and also non–Abelian group* $\mathsf{Aut}_+(C\!\ell_{p,q}) \simeq Q_4/\mathbb{Z}_2$ *with the signature* $(-,-,-)$ *if* $p \equiv 1 \pmod 2$ *and* $q \equiv 0 \pmod 2$.

Theorem 8. *Let* $\mathbf{Pin}^{a,b,c}(p,q)$ *be a double covering of the orthogonal group* $O(p,q)$ *of the real space* $\mathbb{R}^{p,q}$ *associated with the algebra* $C\!\ell_{p,q}$*. The squares of symbols* $a,b,c \in \{-,+\}$ *correspond to the squares of the elements of a finite group* $\mathsf{Aut}(C\!\ell_{p,q}) =$

$\{\mathsf{I},\mathsf{W},\mathsf{E},\mathsf{C}\}:\ a=\mathsf{W}^2,\ b=\mathsf{E}^2,\ c=\mathsf{C}^2$, *where* W,E *and* C *are the matrices of the fundamental automorphisms* $\mathcal{A}\rightarrow\mathcal{A}^\star$, $\mathcal{A}\rightarrow\widetilde{\mathcal{A}}$ *and* $\mathcal{A}\rightarrow\widetilde{\mathcal{A}^\star}$ *of the algebra* $C\!\ell_{p,q}$*, respectively. Then over the field* $\mathbb{F}=\mathbb{R}$ *in dependence on a division ring structure of the algebra* $C\!\ell_{p,q}$*, there exist eight double coverings of the orthogonal group* $O(p,q)$*:*

1) A non–Cliffordian group

$$\mathbf{Pin}^{+,+,+}(p,q)\simeq\frac{(\mathbf{Spin}_0(p,q)\odot\mathbb{Z}_2\otimes\mathbb{Z}_2\otimes\mathbb{Z}_2)}{\mathbb{Z}_2},$$

exists if $\mathbb{K}\simeq\mathbb{R}$ *and the numbers* p *and* q *form the type* $p-q\equiv 0\pmod 8$ *and* $p,q\equiv 0\pmod 4$*, and also if* $p-q\equiv 4\pmod 8$ *and* $\mathbb{K}\simeq\mathbb{H}$*. The algebras* $C\!\ell_{p,q}$ *with the rings* $\mathbb{K}\simeq\mathbb{R}\oplus\mathbb{R}$, $\mathbb{K}\simeq\mathbb{H}\oplus\mathbb{H}$ ($p-q\equiv 1,5\pmod 8$) *admit the group* $\mathbf{Pin}^{+,+,+}(p,q)$ *if in the direct sums there are addendums of the type* $p-q\equiv 0\pmod 8$ *or* $p-q\equiv 4\pmod 8$*. The types* $p-q\equiv 3,7\pmod 8$, $\mathbb{K}\simeq\mathbb{C}$ *admit a non–Cliffordian group* $\mathbf{Pin}^{+,+,+}(p+q-1,\mathbb{C})$ *if* $p\equiv 0\pmod 2$ *and* $q\equiv 1\pmod 2$*. Further, non–Cliffordian groups*

$$\mathbf{Pin}^{a,b,c}(p,q)\simeq\frac{(\mathbf{Spin}_0(p,q)\odot(\mathbb{Z}_2\otimes\mathbb{Z}_4)}{\mathbb{Z}_2},$$

with $(a,b,c)=(+,-,-)$ *exist if* $p-q\equiv 0\pmod 8$, $p,q\equiv 2\pmod 4$ *and* $\mathbb{K}\simeq\mathbb{R}$*, and also if* $p-q\equiv 4\pmod 8$ *and* $\mathbb{K}\simeq\mathbb{H}$*. Non–Cliffordian groups with the signatures* $(a,b,c)=(-,+,-)$ *and* $(a,b,c)=(-,-,+)$ *exist over the ring* $\mathbb{K}\simeq\mathbb{R}$ ($p-q\equiv 2\pmod 8$) *if* $p\equiv 2\pmod 4$, $q\equiv 0\pmod 4$ *and* $p\equiv 0\pmod 4$, $q\equiv 2\pmod 4$*, respectively, and also these groups exist over the ring* $\mathbb{K}\simeq\mathbb{H}$ *if* $p-q\equiv 6\pmod 8$*. The algebras* $C\!\ell_{p,q}$ *with the rings* $\mathbb{K}\simeq\mathbb{R}\oplus\mathbb{R}$, $\mathbb{K}\simeq\mathbb{H}\oplus\mathbb{H}$ ($p-q\equiv 1,5\pmod 8$) *admit the group* $\mathbf{Pin}^{+,-,-}(p,q)$ *if in the direct sums there are addendums of the type* $p-q\equiv 0\pmod 8$ *or* $p-q\equiv 4\pmod 8$*, and also admit the groups* $\mathbf{Pin}^{-,+,-}(p,q)$ *and* $\mathbf{Pin}^{-,-,+}(p,q)$ *if in the direct sums there are addendums of the type* $p-q\equiv 2\pmod 8$ *or* $p-q\equiv 6\pmod 8$*.*

2) A Cliffordian group

$$\mathbf{Pin}^{-,-,-}(p,q)\simeq\frac{(\mathbf{Spin}_0(p,q)\odot Q_4)}{\mathbb{Z}_2},$$

exists if $\mathbb{K}\simeq\mathbb{R}$ ($p-q\equiv 2\pmod 8$) *and* $p\equiv 3\pmod 4$, $q\equiv 1\pmod 4$*, and also if* $p-q\equiv 6\pmod 8$ *and* $\mathbb{K}\simeq\mathbb{H}$*. The algebras* $C\!\ell_{p,q}$ *with the rings* $\mathbb{K}\simeq\mathbb{R}\oplus\mathbb{R}$, $\mathbb{K}\simeq\mathbb{H}\oplus\mathbb{H}$ ($p-q\equiv 1,5\pmod 8$) *admit the group* $\mathbf{Pin}^{-,-,-}(p,q)$ *if in the direct sums there are addendums of the type* $p-q\equiv 2\pmod 8$ *or* $p-q\equiv 6\pmod 8$*. The types* $p-q\equiv 3,7\pmod 8$, $\mathbb{K}\simeq\mathbb{C}$ *admit a Cliffordian group* $\mathbf{Pin}^{-,-,-}(p+q-1,\mathbb{C})$*, if* $p\equiv 1\pmod 2$ *and* $q\equiv 0\pmod 2$*. Further, Cliffordian groups*

$$\mathbf{Pin}^{a,b,c}(p,q)\simeq\frac{(\mathbf{Spin}_0(p,q)\odot D_4)}{\mathbb{Z}_2},$$

with $(a,b,c) = (-,+,+)$ *exist if* $\mathbb{K} \simeq \mathbb{R}$ $(p-q \equiv 2 \pmod 8)$ *and* $p \equiv 1 \pmod 4$, $q \equiv 3 \pmod 4$, *and also if* $p - q \equiv 6 \pmod 8$ *and* $\mathbb{K} \simeq \mathbb{H}$. *Cliffordian groups with the signatures* $(a,b,c) = (+,-,+)$ *and* $(a,b,c) = (+,+,-)$ *exist over the ring* $\mathbb{K} \simeq \mathbb{R}$ $(p-q \equiv 0 \pmod 8)$ *if* $p, q \equiv 3 \pmod 4$ *and* $p, q \equiv 1 \pmod 4$, *respectively, and also these groups exist over the ring* $\mathbb{K} \simeq \mathbb{H}$ *if* $p - q \equiv 4 \pmod 8$. *The algebras* $\mathcal{C}\!\ell_{p,q}$ *with the rings* $\mathbb{K} \simeq \mathbb{R} \oplus \mathbb{R}$, $\mathbb{K} \simeq \mathbb{H} \oplus \mathbb{H}$ $(p - q \equiv 1, 5 \pmod 8)$ *admit the group* $\mathbf{Pin}^{-,+,+}(p,q)$ *if in the direct sums there are addendums of the type* $p - q \equiv 2 \pmod 8$ *or* $p - q \equiv 6 \pmod 8$, *and also admit the groups* $\mathbf{Pin}^{+,-,+}(p,q)$ *and* $\mathbf{Pin}^{+,+,-}(p,q)$ *if in the direct sums there are addendums of the type* $p - q \equiv 0 \pmod 8$ *or* $p - q \equiv 4 \pmod 8$.

4 Pseudoautomorphism $\mathcal{A} \longrightarrow \overline{\mathcal{A}}$ and charge conjugation

As known, the algebra $\mathbb{C}_n$ is associated with a complex vector space $\mathbb{C}^n$. Let $n = p+q$, then an extraction operation of the real subspace $\mathbb{R}^{p,q}$ in $\mathbb{C}^n$ forms the foundation of definition of the discrete transformation known in physics as *a charge conjugation* C. Indeed, let $\{\mathbf{e}_1, \ldots, \mathbf{e}_n\}$ be an orthobasis in the space $\mathbb{C}^n$, $\mathbf{e}_i^2 = 1$. Let us remain the first p vectors of this basis unchanged, and other q vectors multiply by the factor i. Then the basis

$$\{\mathbf{e}_1, \ldots, \mathbf{e}_p, i\mathbf{e}_{p+1}, \ldots, i\mathbf{e}_{p+q}\} \tag{15}$$

allows us to extract the subspace $\mathbb{R}^{p,q}$ in $\mathbb{C}^n$. Namely, for the vectors $\mathbb{R}^{p,q}$ we take the vectors of $\mathbb{C}^n$ which decompose on the basis (15) with real coefficients. In such a way, we obtain a real vector space $\mathbb{R}^{p,q}$ endowed (in general case) with a non–degenerate quadratic form

$$Q(x) = x_1^2 + x_2^2 + \ldots + x_p^2 - x_{p+1}^2 - x_{p+2}^2 - \ldots - x_{p+q}^2,$$

where $x_1, \ldots, x_{p+q}$ are coordinates of the vector $\mathbf{x}$ in the basis (15). It is easy to see that the extraction of $\mathbb{R}^{p,q}$ in $\mathbb{C}^n$ induces an extraction of *a real subalgebra* $\mathcal{C}\!\ell_{p,q}$ in $\mathbb{C}_n$. Therefore, any element $\mathcal{A} \in \mathbb{C}_n$ can be unambiguously represented in the form

$$\mathcal{A} = \mathcal{A}_1 + i\mathcal{A}_2,$$

where $\mathcal{A}_1, \mathcal{A}_2 \in \mathcal{C}\!\ell_{p,q}$. The one-to-one mapping

$$\mathcal{A} \longrightarrow \overline{\mathcal{A}} = \mathcal{A}_1 - i\mathcal{A}_2 \tag{16}$$

transforms the algebra $\mathbb{C}_n$ into itself with preservation of addition and multiplication operations for the elements $\mathcal{A}$; the operation of multiplication of the element $\mathcal{A}$ by the number transforms to an operation of multiplication by the complex conjugate number. Any mapping of $\mathbb{C}_n$ satisfying these conditions is called *a pseudoautomorphism*. Thus, the extraction of the subspace $\mathbb{R}^{p,q}$ in the space $\mathbb{C}^n$ induces in the algebra $\mathbb{C}_n$ a pseudoautomorphism $\mathcal{A} \rightarrow \overline{\mathcal{A}}$ [21, 22].

Let us consider a spinor representation of the pseudoautomorphism $\mathcal{A} \to \overline{\mathcal{A}}$ of the algebra $\mathbb{C}_n$ when $n \equiv 0 \pmod 2$. In the spinor representation the every element $\mathcal{A} \in \mathbb{C}_n$ should be represented by some matrix A, and the pseudoautomorphism (16) takes a form of the pseudoautomorphism of the full matrix algebra $\mathsf{M}_{2^{n/2}}$:

$$\mathsf{A} \longrightarrow \overline{\mathsf{A}}.$$

On the other hand, a transformation replacing the matrix A by the complex conjugate matrix, $\mathsf{A} \to \dot{\mathsf{A}}$, is also some pseudoautomorphism of the algebra $\mathsf{M}_{2^{n/2}}$. The composition of the two pseudoautomorpisms $\dot{\mathsf{A}} \to \mathsf{A}$ and $\mathsf{A} \to \overline{\mathsf{A}}$, $\dot{\mathsf{A}} \to \mathsf{A} \to \overline{\mathsf{A}}$, is an internal automorphism $\dot{\mathsf{A}} \to \overline{\mathsf{A}}$ of the full matrix algebra $\mathsf{M}_{2^{n/2}}$:

$$\overline{\mathsf{A}} = \Pi\dot{\mathsf{A}}\Pi^{-1}, \tag{17}$$

where Π is a matrix of the pseudoautomorphism $\mathcal{A} \to \overline{\mathcal{A}}$ in the spinor representation. The sufficient condition for definition of the pseudoautomorphism $\mathcal{A} \to \overline{\mathcal{A}}$ is a choice of the matrix Π in such a way that the transformation $\mathsf{A} \to \Pi\dot{\mathsf{A}}\Pi^{-1}$ transfers into itself the matrices $\mathcal{E}_1, \ldots, \mathcal{E}_p, i\mathcal{E}_{p+1}, \ldots, i\mathcal{E}_{p+q}$ (the matrices of the spinbasis of $\mathcal{C}\!\ell_{p,q}$), that is,

$$\mathcal{E}_i \longrightarrow \mathcal{E}_i = \Pi\dot{\mathcal{E}}_i\Pi^{-1} \quad (i = 1, \ldots, p+q). \tag{18}$$

Theorem 9. *Let $\mathbb{C}_n$ be a complex Clifford algebra for $n \equiv 0 \pmod 2$ and let $\mathcal{C}\!\ell_{p,q} \subset \mathbb{C}_n$ be its subalgebra with a real division ring $\mathbb{K} \simeq \mathbb{R}$ when $p - q \equiv 0, 2 \pmod 8$ and quaternionic division ring $\mathbb{K} \simeq \mathbb{H}$ when $p - q \equiv 4, 6 \pmod 8$, $n = p + q$. Then in dependence on the division ring structure of the real subalgebra $\mathcal{C}\!\ell_{p,q}$ the matrix Π of the pseudoautomorphism $\mathcal{A} \to \overline{\mathcal{A}}$ has the following form:*

1) $\mathbb{K} \simeq \mathbb{R}$, $p - q \equiv 0, 2 \pmod 8$.
The matrix Π for any spinor representation over the ring $\mathbb{K} \simeq \mathbb{R}$ is proportional to the unit matrix.

2) $\mathbb{K} \simeq \mathbb{H}$, $p - q \equiv 4, 6 \pmod 8$.
$\Pi = \mathcal{E}_{\alpha_1}\mathcal{E}_{\alpha_2}\cdots\mathcal{E}_{\alpha_a}$ when $a \equiv 0 \pmod 2$ and $\Pi = \mathcal{E}_{\beta_1}\mathcal{E}_{\beta_2}\cdots\mathcal{E}_{\beta_b}$ when $b \equiv 1 \pmod 2$, where a complex matrices $\mathcal{E}_{\alpha_t}$ and b real matrices $\mathcal{E}_{\beta_s}$ form a basis of the spinor representation of the algebra $\mathcal{C}\!\ell_{p,q}$ over the ring $\mathbb{K} \simeq \mathbb{H}$, $a + b = p + q$, $0 < t \leq a$, $0 < s \leq b$. At this point,

$$\begin{aligned} \Pi\dot{\Pi} &= \mathsf{I} \quad \text{if } a, b \equiv 0, 1 \pmod 4, \\ \Pi\dot{\Pi} &= -\mathsf{I} \quad \text{if } a, b \equiv 2, 3 \pmod 4, \end{aligned}$$

where I is the unit matrix.

Proof. The algebra $\mathbb{C}_n$ ($n \equiv 0 \pmod 2$, $n = p + q$) in virtue of $\mathbb{C}_n = \mathbb{C} \otimes \mathcal{C}\!\ell_{p,q}$ and definition of the division ring $\mathbb{K} \simeq f\mathcal{C}\!\ell_{p,q}f$ (f is a primitive idempotent of the algebra $\mathcal{C}\!\ell_{p,q}$) has four different real subalgebras: $p - q \equiv 0, 2 \pmod 8$ for the real division ring $\mathbb{K} \simeq \mathbb{R}$ and $p - q \equiv 4, 6 \pmod 8$ for the quaternionic division ring $\mathbb{K} \simeq \mathbb{H}$.

1) $\mathbb{K} \simeq \mathbb{R}$.

Since for the types $p - q \equiv 0, 2 \pmod 8$ there is an isomorphism $C\!\ell_{p,q} \simeq \mathsf{M}_{2^{\frac{p+q}{2}}}(\mathbb{R})$ (Wedderburn–Artin Theorem), then all the matrices $\mathcal{E}_i$ of the spinbasis of $C\!\ell_{p,q}$ are real and $\dot{\mathcal{E}}_i = \mathcal{E}_i$. Therefore, in this case the condition (18) can be written as follows

$$\mathcal{E}_i \longrightarrow \mathcal{E}_i = \Pi\mathcal{E}_i\Pi^{-1},$$

whence $\mathcal{E}_i\Pi = \Pi\mathcal{E}_i$. Thus, for the algebras $C\!\ell_{p,q}$ of the types $p - q \equiv 0, 2 \pmod 8$ the matrix Π of the pseudoautomorphism $\mathcal{A} \to \overline{\mathcal{A}}$ commutes with all the matrices $\mathcal{E}_i$. It is easy to see that $\Pi \sim \mathsf{I}$.

2) $\mathbb{K} \simeq \mathbb{H}$.

In turn, for the quaternionic types $p - q \equiv 4, 6 \pmod 8$ there is an isomorphism $C\!\ell_{p,q} \simeq \mathsf{M}_{2^{\frac{p+q}{2}}}(\mathbb{H})$. Therefore, among the matrices of the spinbasis of the algebra $C\!\ell_{p,q}$ there are matrices $\mathcal{E}_\alpha$ satisfying the condition $\dot{\mathcal{E}}_\alpha = -\mathcal{E}_\alpha$. Let a be a quantity of the complex matrices, then the spinbasis of $C\!\ell_{p,q}$ is divided into two subsets. The first subset $\{\dot{\mathcal{E}}_{\alpha_t} = -\mathcal{E}_{\alpha_t}\}$ contains complex matrices, $0 < t \leq a$, and the second subset $\{\dot{\mathcal{E}}_{\beta_s} = \mathcal{E}_{\beta_s}\}$ contains real matrices, $0 < s \leq p + q - a$. In accordance with a spinbasis structure of the algebra $C\!\ell_{p,q} \simeq \mathsf{M}_{2^{\frac{p+q}{2}}}(\mathbb{H})$ the condition (18) can be written as follows

$$\mathcal{E}_{\alpha_t} \longrightarrow -\mathcal{E}_{\alpha_t} = \Pi\mathcal{E}_{\alpha_t}\Pi^{-1}, \quad \mathcal{E}_{\beta_s} \longrightarrow \mathcal{E}_{\beta_s} = \Pi\mathcal{E}_{\beta_s}\Pi^{-1}.$$

Whence

$$\mathcal{E}_{\alpha_t}\Pi = -\Pi\mathcal{E}_{\alpha_t}, \quad \mathcal{E}_{\beta_s}\Pi = \Pi\mathcal{E}_{\beta_s}. \tag{19}$$

Thus, for the quaternionic types $p - q \equiv 4, 6 \pmod 8$ the matrix Π of the pseudoautomorphism $\mathcal{A} \to \overline{\mathcal{A}}$ anticommutes with a complex part of the spinbasis of $C\!\ell_{p,q}$ and commutes with a real part of the same spinbasis. From (19) it follows that a structure of the matrix Π is analogous to the structure of the matrices E and C of the antiautomorphisms $\mathcal{A} \to \widetilde{\mathcal{A}}$ and $\mathcal{A} \to \widetilde{\mathcal{A}^\star}$, correspondingly (see Theorem 7), that is, the matrix Π of the pseudoautomorphism $\mathcal{A} \to \overline{\mathcal{A}}$ of the algebra $\mathbb{C}_n$ is a product of only complex matrices, or only real matrices of the spinbasis of the subalgebra $C\!\ell_{p,q}$.

So, let $0 < a < p + q$ and let $\Pi = \mathcal{E}_{\alpha_1}\mathcal{E}_{\alpha_2}\cdots\mathcal{E}_{\alpha_a}$ be a matrix of $\mathcal{A} \to \overline{\mathcal{A}}$, then permutation conditions of the matrix Π with the matrices $\mathcal{E}_{\beta_s}$ of the real part $(0 < s \leq p + q - a)$ and with the matrices $\mathcal{E}_{\alpha_t}$ of the complex part $(0 < t \leq a)$ have the form

$$\Pi\mathcal{E}_{\beta_s} = (-1)^a\mathcal{E}_{\beta_s}\Pi, \tag{20}$$

$$\begin{aligned} \Pi\mathcal{E}_{\alpha_t} &= (-1)^{a-t}\sigma(\alpha_t)\mathcal{E}_{\alpha_1}\mathcal{E}_{\alpha_2}\cdots\mathcal{E}_{\alpha_{t-1}}\mathcal{E}_{\alpha_{t+1}}\cdots\mathcal{E}_{\alpha_a}, \\ \mathcal{E}_{\alpha_t}\Pi &= (-1)^{t-1}\sigma(\alpha_t)\mathcal{E}_{\alpha_1}\mathcal{E}_{\alpha_2}\cdots\mathcal{E}_{\alpha_{t-1}}\mathcal{E}_{\alpha_{t+1}}\cdots\mathcal{E}_{\alpha_a}, \end{aligned} \tag{21}$$

that is, when $a \equiv 0 \pmod 2$ the matrix Π commutes with the real part and anticommutes with the complex part of the spinbasis of $\mathcal{C}\ell_{p,q}$. Correspondingly, when $a \equiv 1 \pmod 2$ the matrix Π anticommutes with the real part and commutes with the complex part. Further, let $\Pi = \mathcal{E}_{\beta_1}\mathcal{E}_{\beta_2}\cdots\mathcal{E}_{\beta_{p+q-a}}$ be a product of the real matrices, then

$$\begin{aligned} \Pi\mathcal{E}_{\beta_s} &= (-1)^{p+q-a-s}\sigma(\beta_s)\mathcal{E}_{\beta_1}\mathcal{E}_{\beta_2}\cdots\mathcal{E}_{\beta_{s-1}}\mathcal{E}_{\beta_{s+1}}\cdots\mathcal{E}_{\beta_{p+q-a}}, \\ \mathcal{E}_{\beta_s}\Pi &= (-1)^{s-1}\sigma(\beta_s)\mathcal{E}_{\beta_1}\mathcal{E}_{\beta_2}\cdots\mathcal{E}_{\beta_{s-1}}\mathcal{E}_{\beta_{s+1}}\cdots\mathcal{E}_{\beta_{p+q-a}}, \end{aligned} \tag{22}$$

$$\Pi\mathcal{E}_{\alpha_t} = (-1)^{p+q-a}\mathcal{E}_{\alpha_t}\Pi, \tag{23}$$

that is, when $p+q-a \equiv 0 \pmod 2$ the matrix Π anticommutes with the real part and commutes with the complex part of the spinbasis of $\mathcal{C}\ell_{p,q}$. Correspondingly, when $p+q-a \equiv 1 \pmod 2$ the matrix Π commutes with the real part and anticommutes with the complex part.

The comparison of the conditions (20)–(21) with the condition (19) shows that the matrix $\Pi = \mathcal{E}_{\alpha_1}\mathcal{E}_{\alpha_2}\cdots\mathcal{E}_{\alpha_a}$ exists only at $a \equiv 0 \pmod 2$, that is, Π is a product of the complex matrices $\mathcal{E}_{\alpha_t}$ of the even number. In turn, a comparison of (22)–(23) with (19) shows that the matrix $\Pi = \mathcal{E}_{\beta_1}\mathcal{E}_{\beta_2}\cdots\mathcal{E}_{\beta_{p+q-a}}$ exists only at $p+q-a \equiv 1 \pmod 2$, that is, Π is a product of the real matrices $\mathcal{E}_{\beta_s}$ of the odd number.

Let us calculate now the product $\Pi\dot{\Pi}$. Let $\Pi = \mathcal{E}_{\beta_1}\mathcal{E}_{\beta_2}\cdots\mathcal{E}_{\beta_{p+q-a}}$ be a product of the $p+q-a$ real matrices. Since $\dot{\mathcal{E}}_{\beta_s} = \mathcal{E}_{\beta_s}$, then $\dot{\Pi} = \Pi$ and $\Pi\dot{\Pi} = \Pi^2$. Therefore,

$$\Pi\dot{\Pi} = (\mathcal{E}_{\beta_1}\mathcal{E}_{\beta_2}\cdots\mathcal{E}_{\beta_{p+q-a}})^2 = (-1)^{\frac{(p+q-a)(p+q-a-1)}{2}}\cdot \mathsf{I}. \tag{24}$$

Further, let $\Pi = \mathcal{E}_{\alpha_1}\mathcal{E}_{\alpha_2}\cdots\mathcal{E}_{\alpha_a}$ be a product of the a complex matrices. Then $\dot{\mathcal{E}}_{\alpha_t} = -\mathcal{E}_{\alpha_t}$ and $\dot{\Pi} = (-1)^a\Pi = \Pi$, since $a \equiv 0 \pmod 2$. Therefore,

$$\Pi\dot{\Pi} = (\mathcal{E}_{\alpha_1}\mathcal{E}_{\alpha_2}\cdots\mathcal{E}_{\alpha_a})^2 = (-1)^{\frac{a(a-1)}{2}}\cdot \mathsf{I}. \tag{25}$$

Let $p+q-a = b$ be a quantity of the real matrices $\mathcal{E}_{\beta_s}$ of the spinbasis of $\mathcal{C}\ell_{p,q}$, then $p+q = a+b$. Since $p+q$ is always even number for the quaternionic types $p-q \equiv 4, 6 \pmod 8$, then a and b are simultaneously even or odd numbers. Thus, from (24) and (25) it follows

$$\Pi\dot{\Pi} = \begin{cases} \mathsf{I}, & \text{if } a, b \equiv 0, 1 \pmod 4, \\ -\mathsf{I}, & \text{if } a, b \equiv 2, 3 \pmod 4, \end{cases}$$

which required to be proved. □

In the present form of quantum field theory complex fields correspond to charged particles. Thus, the extraction of the subalgebra $\mathcal{C}\ell_{p,q}$ with the real ring $\mathbb{K} \simeq \mathbb{R}$ in $\mathbb{C}_n$, $p-q \equiv 0, 2 \pmod 8$, corresponds to physical fields describing *truly neutral particles* such as photon and neutral mesons (π^0, η^0, ρ^0, ω^0, φ^0, K^0). In turn, the subalgebras $\mathcal{C}\ell_{p,q}$ with the ring $\mathbb{K} \simeq \mathbb{H}$, $p-q \equiv 4, 6 \pmod 8$ correspond to charged or neutral fields.

5 Extended automorphism groups

An introduction of the pseudoautomorphism $\mathcal{A} \rightarrow \overline{\mathcal{A}}$ allows us to extend the automorphism set of the complex Clifford algebra $\mathbb{C}_n$. Namely, we add to the four fundamental automorphisms $\mathcal{A} \rightarrow \mathcal{A}$, $\mathcal{A} \rightarrow \mathcal{A}^\star$, $\mathcal{A} \rightarrow \widetilde{\mathcal{A}}$, $\mathcal{A} \rightarrow \widetilde{\mathcal{A}^\star}$ the pseudoautomorphism $\mathcal{A} \rightarrow \overline{\mathcal{A}}$ and following three combinations:
1) A pseudoautomorphism $\mathcal{A} \rightarrow \overline{\mathcal{A}^\star}$. This transformation is a composition of the pseudoautomorphism $\mathcal{A} \rightarrow \overline{\mathcal{A}}$ with the automorphism $\mathcal{A} \rightarrow \mathcal{A}^\star$.
2) A pseudoantiautomorphism $\mathcal{A} \rightarrow \overline{\widetilde{\mathcal{A}}}$. This transformation is a composition of $\mathcal{A} \rightarrow \overline{\mathcal{A}}$ with the antiautomorphism $\mathcal{A} \rightarrow \widetilde{\mathcal{A}}$.
3) A pseudoantiautomorphism $\mathcal{A} \rightarrow \overline{\widetilde{\mathcal{A}^\star}}$ (a composition of $\mathcal{A} \rightarrow \overline{\mathcal{A}}$ with the antiautomorphism $\mathcal{A} \rightarrow \widetilde{\mathcal{A}^\star}$).

Thus, we obtain an automorphism set of $\mathbb{C}_n$ consisting of the eight transformations. Let us show that the set $\{\mathrm{Id}, \star, \widetilde{\ }, \widetilde{\star}, \overline{\ }, \overline{\star}, \overline{\widetilde{\ }}, \overline{\widetilde{\star}}\}$ forms a finite group of order 8 and let us give a physical interpretation of this group.

Proposition 2. *Let* $\mathbb{C}_n$ *be a Clifford algebra over the field* $\mathbb{F} = \mathbb{C}$ *and let* $\mathrm{Ext}(\mathbb{C}_n) = \{\mathrm{Id}, \star, \widetilde{\ }, \widetilde{\star}, \overline{\ }, \overline{\star}, \overline{\widetilde{\ }}, \overline{\widetilde{\star}}\}$ *be an extended automorphism group of the algebra* $\mathbb{C}_n$. *Then there is an isomorphism between* $\mathrm{Ext}(\mathbb{C}_n)$ *and the full CPT–group of the discrete transformations,* $\mathrm{Ext}(\mathbb{C}_n) \simeq \{1, P, T, PT, C, CP, CT, CPT\} \simeq \mathbb{Z}_2 \otimes \mathbb{Z}_2 \otimes \mathbb{Z}_2$. *In this case, space inversion* P, *time reversal* T, *full reflection* PT, *charge conjugation* C, *transformations* CP, CT *and the full* CPT*–transformation correspond to the automorphism* $\mathcal{A} \rightarrow \mathcal{A}^\star$, *antiautomorphisms* $\mathcal{A} \rightarrow \widetilde{\mathcal{A}}$, $\mathcal{A} \rightarrow \widetilde{\mathcal{A}^\star}$, *pseudoautomorphisms* $\mathcal{A} \rightarrow \overline{\mathcal{A}}$, $\mathcal{A} \rightarrow \overline{\mathcal{A}^\star}$, *pseudoantiautomorphisms* $\mathcal{A} \rightarrow \overline{\widetilde{\mathcal{A}}}$ *and* $\mathcal{A} \rightarrow \overline{\widetilde{\mathcal{A}^\star}}$, *respectively.*

Proof. The group $\{1, P, T, PT, C, CP, CT, CPT\}$ at the conditions $P^2 = T^2 = (PT)^2 = C^2 = (CP)^2 = (CT)^2 = (CPT)^2 = 1$ and commutativity of all the elements forms an Abelian group of order 8, which is isomorphic to a cyclic group $\mathbb{Z}_2 \otimes \mathbb{Z}_2 \otimes \mathbb{Z}_2$. The Cayley tableau of this group has a form

	1	P	T	PT	C	CP	CT	CPT
1	1	P	T	PT	C	CP	CT	CPT
P	P	1	PT	T	CP	C	CPT	CT
T	T	PT	1	P	CT	CPT	C	CP
PT	PT	T	P	1	CPT	CT	CP	C
C	C	CP	CT	CPT	1	P	T	PT
CP	CP	C	CPT	CT	P	1	PT	T
CT	CT	CPT	C	CP	T	PT	1	P
CPT	CPT	CT	CP	C	PT	T	P	1

In turn, for the extended automorphism group $\{\mathrm{Id}, \star, \widetilde{}, \tilde{\star}, \overline{}, \bar{\star}, \overline{\widetilde{}}, \bar{\tilde{\star}}\}$ in virtue of commutativity $\widetilde{(\mathcal{A}^\star)} = \left(\widetilde{\mathcal{A}}\right)^\star$, $\overline{(\mathcal{A}^\star)} = (\overline{\mathcal{A}})^\star$, $\overline{\left(\widetilde{\mathcal{A}}\right)} = \widetilde{(\overline{\mathcal{A}})}$, $\overline{\left(\widetilde{\mathcal{A}^\star}\right)} = \widetilde{(\overline{\mathcal{A}})}^\star$ and an involution property $\star\star = \widetilde{}\widetilde{} = \overline{}\,\overline{} = \mathrm{Id}$ we have a following Cayley tableau

	Id	$\star$	$\sim$	$\tilde{\star}$	$-$	$\bar{\star}$	$\overline{\sim}$	$\bar{\tilde{\star}}$
Id	Id	$\star$	$\sim$	$\tilde{\star}$	$-$	$\bar{\star}$	$\overline{\sim}$	$\bar{\tilde{\star}}$
$\star$	$\star$	Id	$\tilde{\star}$	$\sim$	$\bar{\star}$	$-$	$\bar{\tilde{\star}}$	$\overline{\sim}$
$\sim$	$\sim$	$\bar{\star}$	Id	$\star$	$\overline{\sim}$	$\bar{\tilde{\star}}$	$-$	$\bar{\star}$
$\tilde{\star}$	$\tilde{\star}$	$\sim$	$\star$	Id	$\bar{\tilde{\star}}$	$\overline{\sim}$	$\bar{\star}$	$-$
$-$	$-$	$\bar{\star}$	$\overline{\sim}$	$\bar{\tilde{\star}}$	Id	$\star$	$\sim$	$\tilde{\star}$
$\bar{\star}$	$\bar{\star}$	$-$	$\bar{\tilde{\star}}$	$\overline{\sim}$	$\star$	Id	$\tilde{\star}$	$\sim$
$\overline{\sim}$	$\overline{\sim}$	$\bar{\tilde{\star}}$	$-$	$\bar{\star}$	$\sim$	$\tilde{\star}$	Id	$\star$
$\bar{\tilde{\star}}$	$\bar{\tilde{\star}}$	$\overline{\sim}$	$\bar{\star}$	$-$	$\tilde{\star}$	$\sim$	$\star$	Id

The identity of multiplication tables proves the group isomorphism

$$\{1, P, T, PT, C, CP, CT, CPT\} \simeq \{\mathrm{Id}, \star, \widetilde{}, \tilde{\star}, \overline{}, \bar{\star}, \overline{\widetilde{}}, \bar{\tilde{\star}}\} \simeq \mathbb{Z}_2 \otimes \mathbb{Z}_2 \otimes \mathbb{Z}_2.$$

□

Further, in the case of $P^2 = T^2 = \ldots = (CPT)^2 = \pm 1$ and anticommutativity of the elements we have an isomorphism between the CPT–group and a group $\mathsf{Ext}(\mathbb{C}_n)$. The elements of $\mathsf{Ext}(\mathbb{C}_n)$ are spinor representations of the automorphisms of the algebra $\mathbb{C}_n$. The Wedderburn–Artin Theorem allows us to define any spinor representations for the automorphisms of $\mathbb{C}_n$.

5.1 Pseudoautomorphism $\mathcal{A} \to \overline{\mathcal{A}^\star}$

Let us find a spinor representation of the pseudoautomorphism $\mathcal{A} \to \overline{\mathcal{A}^\star}$. The transformation $\mathcal{A} \to \overline{\mathcal{A}^\star}$ is a composition of the pseudoautomorphism $\mathcal{A} \to \overline{\mathcal{A}}$ and the automorphism $\mathcal{A} \to \mathcal{A}^\star$. Under action of $\mathcal{A} \to \mathcal{A}^\star$ we have $\mathbf{e}_i \to -\mathbf{e}_i$, where $\mathbf{e}_i$ are the units of $C\kern-0.3em\ell_{p,q}$. In turn, under action of $\mathcal{A} \to \overline{\mathcal{A}}$ the units $\mathbf{e}_i$ remain unaltered, $\mathbf{e}_i \to \mathbf{e}_i$. Therefore, under action of the pseudoautomorphism $\mathcal{A} \to \overline{\mathcal{A}^\star}$ we obtain $\mathbf{e}_i \to -\mathbf{e}_i$.

As it shown previously, the transformations $\mathcal{A} \to \mathcal{A}^\star$ and $\mathcal{A} \to \overline{\mathcal{A}}$ in the spinor representation are defined by the expressions $\mathsf{A}^\star = \mathsf{W}\mathsf{A}\mathsf{W}^{-1}$ and $\overline{\mathsf{A}} = \Pi\dot{\mathsf{A}}\Pi^{-1}$. The order of the composition of these transformations is not important ($\overline{\mathcal{A}^\star} = \left(\overline{\mathcal{A}}\right)^\star = \overline{(\mathcal{A}^\star)}$). Indeed, if W is a real matrix, then

$$\overline{\mathsf{A}^\star} = \mathsf{W}\Pi\dot{\mathsf{A}}\Pi^{-1}\mathsf{W}^{-1} = \Pi\left(\mathsf{W}\mathsf{A}\mathsf{W}^{-1}\right)^{\cdot}\Pi^{-1},$$

or

$$\overline{\mathsf{A}^\star} = (\mathsf{W}\Pi)\dot{\mathsf{A}}(\mathsf{W}\Pi)^{-1} = (\Pi\mathsf{W})\dot{\mathsf{A}}(\Pi\mathsf{W})^{-1}. \tag{26}$$

Otherwise, we have $\overline{(\mathsf{A}^\star)} = \Pi\dot{\mathsf{W}}\dot{\mathsf{A}}\dot{\mathsf{W}}^{-1}\Pi^{-1}$. Let us assume that W is a complex matrix, then $\dot{\mathsf{W}} = -\mathsf{W}$ and, therefore, $\overline{(\mathsf{A}^\star)} = \Pi(-\mathsf{W})\dot{\mathsf{A}}(-\mathsf{W}^{-1})\Pi^{-1} = (\Pi\mathsf{W})\dot{\mathsf{A}}(\Pi\mathsf{W})^{-1}$. Thus, the relation (26) is always fulfilled.

Let $\mathsf{K} = \Pi\mathsf{W}$ be a matrix of the pseudoautomorphism $\mathcal{A} \to \overline{\mathcal{A}^\star}$. Then (26) can be written as follows

$$\overline{\mathsf{A}^\star} = \mathsf{K}\dot{\mathsf{A}}\mathsf{K}^{-1}. \tag{27}$$

Since under action of the pseudoautomorphism $\mathcal{A} \to \overline{\mathcal{A}^\star}$ we have $\mathbf{e}_i \to -\mathbf{e}_i$, in the spinor representation we must demand $\mathcal{E}_i \to -\mathcal{E}_i$ also, or

$$\mathcal{E}_i \longrightarrow -\mathcal{E}_i = \mathsf{K}\dot{\mathcal{E}}_i\mathsf{K}^{-1}. \tag{28}$$

In the case of real subalgebras $\mathcal{C}\!\ell_{p,q}$ with the ring $\mathbb{K} \simeq \mathbb{R}$ we have $\dot{\mathcal{E}}_i = \mathcal{E}_i$ and the relation (28) takes a form

$$\mathcal{E}_i \longrightarrow -\mathcal{E}_i = \mathsf{K}\mathcal{E}_i\mathsf{K}^{-1},$$

whence

$$\mathcal{E}_i\mathsf{K} = -\mathsf{K}\mathcal{E}_i,$$

that is, the matrix K is always anticommutes with the matrices of the spinbasis. However, for the ring $\mathbb{K} \simeq \mathbb{R}$ the matrix Π of $\mathcal{A} \to \overline{\mathcal{A}}$ is proportional to the unit matrix, $\Pi \sim \mathsf{I}$ (Theorem 9). Therefore, in this case we have $\mathsf{K} \sim \mathsf{W}$.

In the case of real subalgebras $\mathcal{C}\!\ell_{p,q}$ with the quaternionic ring $\mathbb{K} \simeq \mathbb{H}$ the spinbasis is divided into two parts: a complex part $\left\{\dot{\mathcal{E}}_{\alpha_t} = -\mathcal{E}_{\alpha_t}\right\}$, $(0 < t \leq a)$, where a is a number of the complex matrices of the spinbasis, and a real part $\left\{\dot{\mathcal{E}}_{\beta_s} = \mathcal{E}_{\beta_s}\right\}$, where $p+q-a$ is a number of the real matrices, $(0 < s \leq p+q-a)$. Then, in accordance with the spinbasis structure of the algebra $\mathcal{C}\!\ell_{p,q} \simeq \mathsf{M}_{2^{\frac{p+q}{2}}}(\mathbb{H})$, the relation (28) can be written as follows

$$\mathcal{E}_{\alpha_t} \longrightarrow \mathcal{E}_{\alpha_t} = \mathsf{K}\mathcal{E}_{\alpha_t}\mathsf{K}^{-1}, \quad \mathcal{E}_{\beta_s} \longrightarrow -\mathcal{E}_{\beta_s} = \mathsf{K}\mathcal{E}_{\beta_s}\mathsf{K}^{-1}.$$

Whence

$$\mathcal{E}_{\alpha_t}\mathsf{K} = \mathsf{K}\mathcal{E}_{\alpha_t}, \quad \mathcal{E}_{\beta_s}\mathsf{K} = -\mathsf{K}\mathcal{E}_{\beta_s}. \tag{29}$$

Thus, for the quaternionic types $p-q \equiv 4, 6 \pmod 8$ the matrix K of the pseudoautomorphism $\mathcal{A} \to \overline{\mathcal{A}^\star}$ commutes with the complex part and anticommutes with the real part of the spinbasis of $\mathcal{C}\!\ell_{p,q}$. Hence it follows that a structure of the matrix K is analogous to the structure of the matrix Π of the pseudoautomorphism $\mathcal{A} \to \overline{\mathcal{A}}$ (see Theorem 9), that is, the matrix K of $\mathcal{A} \to \overline{\mathcal{A}^\star}$ is a product of only complex or only real matrices.

So, let $0 < a \leq p+q$ and let $\mathsf{K} = \mathcal{E}_{\alpha_1}\mathcal{E}_{\alpha_2}\cdots\mathcal{E}_{\alpha_a}$ be the matrix of the pseudoautomorphism $\mathcal{A} \to \overline{\mathcal{A}^\star}$, then permutation conditions of the matrix K with the matrices

$\mathcal{E}_{\beta_s}$ of the real part $(0 < s \leq p+q-a)$ and the matrices $\mathcal{E}_{\alpha_t}$ of the complex part $(0 < t \leq a)$ have the form

$$\mathsf{K}\mathcal{E}_{\beta_s} = (-1)^a \mathcal{E}_{\beta_s}\mathsf{K}, \tag{30}$$

$$\begin{aligned} \mathsf{K}\mathcal{E}_{\alpha_t} &= (-1)^{a-t}\sigma(\alpha_t)\mathcal{E}_{\alpha_1}\mathcal{E}_{\alpha_2}\cdots\mathcal{E}_{\alpha_{t-1}}\mathcal{E}_{\alpha_{t+1}}\cdots\mathcal{E}_{\alpha_a}, \\ \mathcal{E}_{\alpha_t}\mathsf{K} &= (-1)^{t-1}\sigma(\alpha_t)\mathcal{E}_{\alpha_1}\mathcal{E}_{\alpha_2}\cdots\mathcal{E}_{\alpha_{t-1}}\mathcal{E}_{\alpha_{t+1}}\cdots\mathcal{E}_{\alpha_a}, \end{aligned} \tag{31}$$

that is, at $a \equiv 0 \pmod 2$ K commutes with the real part and anticommutes with the complex part of the spinbasis. Correspondingly, at $a \equiv 1 \pmod 2$ K anticommutes with the real and commutes with the complex part. Further, let $\mathsf{K} = \mathcal{E}_{\beta_1}\mathcal{E}_{\beta_2}\cdots\mathcal{E}_{\beta_{p+q-a}}$ be a product of the real matrices of the spinbasis, then

$$\begin{aligned} \mathsf{K}\mathcal{E}_{\beta_s} &= (-1)^{p+q-a-s}\sigma(\beta_s)\mathcal{E}_{\beta_1}\mathcal{E}_{\beta_2}\cdots\mathcal{E}_{\beta_{s-1}}\mathcal{E}_{\beta_{s+1}}\cdots\mathcal{E}_{\beta_{p+q-a}}, \\ \mathcal{E}_{\beta_s}\mathsf{K} &= (-1)^{s-1}\sigma(\beta_s)\mathcal{E}_{\beta_1}\mathcal{E}_{\beta_2}\cdots\mathcal{E}_{\beta_{s-1}}\mathcal{E}_{\beta_{s+1}}\cdots\mathcal{E}_{\beta_{p+q-a}}, \end{aligned} \tag{32}$$

$$\mathsf{K}\mathcal{E}_{\alpha_t} = (-1)^{p+q-a}\mathcal{E}_{\alpha_t}\mathsf{K}, \tag{33}$$

that is, at $p+q-a \equiv 0 \pmod 2$ the matrix K anticommutes with the real part and commutes with the complex part of the spinbasis. Correspondingly, at $p+q-a \equiv 1 \pmod 2$ K commutes with the real and anticommutes with the complex part.

A comparison of the conditions (30)–(31) with (29) shows that the matrix $\mathsf{K} = \mathcal{E}_{\alpha_1}\mathcal{E}_{\alpha_2}\cdots\mathcal{E}_{\alpha_a}$ exists only if $a \equiv 1 \pmod 2$. In turn, a comparison of the conditions (32)–(33) with (29) shows that the matrix $\mathsf{K} = \mathcal{E}_{\beta_1}\mathcal{E}_{\beta_2}\cdots\mathcal{E}_{\beta_{p+q-a}}$ exists only if $p+q-a \equiv 0 \pmod 2$.

Let us find now squares of the matrix K. In accordance with obtained conditions there exist two possibilities:

1) $\mathsf{K} = \mathcal{E}_{\alpha_1}\mathcal{E}_{\alpha_2}\cdots\mathcal{E}_{\alpha_a}$, $a \equiv 1 \pmod 2$.

$$\mathsf{K}^2 = \begin{cases} +\mathsf{I}, & \text{if } a_+ - a_- \equiv 1, 5 \pmod 8, \\ -\mathsf{I}, & \text{if } a_+ - a_- \equiv 3, 7 \pmod 8, \end{cases}$$

where a_+ and a_- are numbers of matrices with +- and −-squares in the product $\mathcal{E}_{\alpha_1}\mathcal{E}_{\alpha_2}\cdots\mathcal{E}_{\alpha_a}$.

2) $\mathsf{K} = \mathcal{E}_{\beta_1}\mathcal{E}_{\beta_2}\cdots\mathcal{E}_{\beta_{p+q-a}}$, $p+q-a \equiv 0 \pmod 2$.

$$\mathsf{K}^2 = \begin{cases} +\mathsf{I}, & \text{if } b_+ - b_- \equiv 0, 4 \pmod 8, \\ -\mathsf{I}, & \text{if } b_+ - b_- \equiv 2, 6 \pmod 8, \end{cases}$$

where b_+ and b_- are numbers of matrices with '+'- and '−'-squares in the product $\mathcal{E}_{\beta_1}\mathcal{E}_{\beta_2}\cdots\mathcal{E}_{\beta_{p+q-a}}$, respectively.

5.2 Pseudoantiautomorphism $\mathcal{A} \rightarrow \overline{\widetilde{\mathcal{A}}}$

The pseudoantiautomorphism $\mathcal{A} \rightarrow \overline{\widetilde{\mathcal{A}}}$ is the composition of the pseudoautomorphism $\mathcal{A} \rightarrow \overline{\mathcal{A}}$ with the antiautomorphism $\mathcal{A} \rightarrow \widetilde{\mathcal{A}}$. Under action of $\mathcal{A} \rightarrow \widetilde{\mathcal{A}}$ the units $\mathbf{e}_i$ remain unaltered, $\mathbf{e}_i \rightarrow \mathbf{e}_i$. Analogously, under action of $\mathcal{A} \rightarrow \overline{\mathcal{A}}$ we have $\mathbf{e}_i \rightarrow \mathbf{e}_i$. Therefore, under action of the pseudoantiautomorphism $\mathcal{A} \rightarrow \overline{\widetilde{\mathcal{A}}}$ the units $\mathbf{e}_i$ remain unaltered also, $\mathbf{e}_i \rightarrow \mathbf{e}_i$.

The spinor representations of the transformations $\mathcal{A} \rightarrow \widetilde{\mathcal{A}}$ and $\mathcal{A} \rightarrow \overline{\mathcal{A}}$ are defined by the expressions $\widetilde{\mathsf{A}} = \mathsf{E}\mathsf{A}^{\mathsf{T}}\mathsf{E}^{-1}$ and $\overline{\mathsf{A}} = \Pi\dot{\mathsf{A}}\Pi^{-1}$, respectively. Let us find a spinor representation of the transformation $\mathcal{A} \rightarrow \overline{\widetilde{\mathcal{A}}}$. The order of the composition of these transformations is not important, $\overline{\widetilde{\mathcal{A}}} = \widetilde{(\overline{\mathcal{A}})} = \overline{\left(\widetilde{\mathcal{A}}\right)}$. Indeed,

$$\overline{\widetilde{\mathsf{A}}} = \mathsf{E}\left(\Pi\dot{\mathsf{A}}\Pi^{-1}\right)^{\mathsf{T}}\mathsf{E}^{-1} = \Pi\left(\mathsf{E}\mathsf{A}^{\mathsf{T}}\mathsf{E}^{-1}\right)^{\cdot}\Pi^{-1}$$

or,

$$\overline{\widetilde{\mathsf{A}}} = (\mathsf{E}\Pi)\left(\dot{\mathsf{A}}\right)^{\mathsf{T}}(\mathsf{E}\Pi)^{-1} = (\Pi\mathsf{E})\left(\mathsf{A}^{\mathsf{T}}\right)^{\cdot}(\Pi\mathsf{E})^{-1}, \tag{34}$$

since $\Pi^{-1} = \Pi^{\mathsf{T}}$ and $\overline{\widetilde{\mathsf{A}}} = \Pi\dot{\mathsf{E}}\left(\mathsf{A}^{\mathsf{T}}\right)^{\cdot}\dot{\mathsf{E}}^{-1}\Pi^{-1} = \Pi\mathsf{E}\left(\mathsf{A}^{\mathsf{T}}\right)^{\cdot}\mathsf{E}^{-1}\Pi^{-1}$ in the case when $\dot{\mathsf{E}} = \mathsf{E}$ is a real matrix and $\overline{\widetilde{\mathsf{A}}} = \Pi\dot{\mathsf{E}}\left(\mathsf{A}^{\mathsf{T}}\right)^{\cdot}\dot{\mathsf{E}}^{-1}\Pi^{-1} = \Pi(-\mathsf{E})\left(\mathsf{A}^{\mathsf{T}}\right)^{\cdot}(-\mathsf{E}^{-1})\Pi^{-1} = \Pi\mathsf{E}\left(\mathsf{A}^{\mathsf{T}}\right)^{\cdot}(\Pi\mathsf{E})^{-1}$ in the case when $\dot{\mathsf{E}} = -\mathsf{E}$ is a complex matrix. Let $\mathsf{S} = \Pi\mathsf{E}$ be a matrix of the pseudoantiautomorphism $\mathcal{A} \rightarrow \overline{\widetilde{\mathcal{A}}}$ in the spinor representation. Then (34) can be rewritten as follows

$$\overline{\widetilde{\mathsf{A}}} = \mathsf{S}\left(\mathsf{A}^{\mathsf{T}}\right)^{\cdot}\mathsf{S}^{-1}. \tag{35}$$

Since under action of the transformation $\mathcal{A} \rightarrow \overline{\widetilde{\mathcal{A}}}$ we have $\mathbf{e}_i \rightarrow \mathbf{e}_i$, in the spinor representation we must demand $\mathcal{E}_i \rightarrow \mathcal{E}_i$ also, or

$$\mathcal{E}_i \longrightarrow \mathcal{E}_i = \mathsf{S}\dot{\mathcal{E}}_i^{\mathsf{T}}\mathsf{S}^{-1}. \tag{36}$$

In the case of real subalgebras $\mathcal{C}\!\ell_{p,q}$ with the ring $\mathbb{K} \simeq \mathbb{R}$ we have $\dot{\mathcal{E}}_i = \mathcal{E}_i$ and, therefore, the relation (36) takes a form

$$\mathcal{E}_i \longrightarrow \mathcal{E}_i = \mathsf{S}\mathcal{E}_i^{\mathsf{T}}\mathsf{S}^{-1}. \tag{37}$$

Let $\{\mathcal{E}_{\gamma_i}\}$ be a set of symmetric matrices $\left(\mathcal{E}_{\gamma_i}^{\mathsf{T}} = \mathcal{E}_{\gamma_i}\right)$ and let $\{\mathcal{E}_{\delta_j}\}$ be a set of skewsymmetric matrices $\left(\mathcal{E}_{\delta_j}^{\mathsf{T}} = -\mathcal{E}_{\delta_j}\right)$ of the spinbasis of the algebra $\mathcal{C}\!\ell_{p,q}$. Then from the relation (37) it follows

$$\mathcal{E}_{\gamma_i} \longrightarrow \mathcal{E}_{\gamma_i} = \mathsf{S}\mathcal{E}_{\gamma_i}\mathsf{S}^{-1}, \quad \mathcal{E}_{\delta_j} \longrightarrow \mathcal{E}_{\delta_j} = -\mathsf{S}\mathcal{E}_{\delta_j}\mathsf{S}^{-1}.$$

Whence

$$\mathcal{E}_{\gamma_i}\mathsf{S} = \mathsf{S}\mathcal{E}_{\gamma_i}, \quad \mathcal{E}_{\delta_j}\mathsf{S} = -\mathsf{S}\mathcal{E}_{\delta_j},$$

that is, the matrix S of the pseudoantiautomorphism $\mathcal{A} \to \widetilde{\overline{\mathcal{A}}}$ in the case of $\mathbb{K} \simeq \mathbb{R}$ commutes with the symmetric part and anticommutes with the skewsymmetric part of the spinbasis of $C\!\ell_{p,q}$. In virtue of Theorem 9, over the ring $\mathbb{K} \simeq \mathbb{R}$ the matrix Π of the pseudoautomorphism $\mathcal{A} \to \overline{\mathcal{A}}$ is proportional to the unit matrix, $\Pi \sim \mathsf{I}$. Therefore, in this case we have $\mathsf{S} \sim \mathsf{E}$ and an explicit form of S coincides with E.

Further, in case of the quaternionic ring $\mathbb{K} \simeq \mathbb{H}$, $p - q \equiv 4, 6 \pmod 8$, a spinbasis of $C\!\ell_{p,q}$ contains both complex matrices $\mathcal{E}_{\alpha_t}$ and real matrices $\mathcal{E}_{\beta_s}$, among which there are symmetric and skewsymmetric matrices. It is obvious that the sets of complex and real matrices do not coincide with the sets of symmetric and skewsymmetric matrices. Let $\{\mathcal{E}_{\alpha_t}\}$ be a complex part of the spinbasis, then the relation (36) takes a form

$$\mathcal{E}_{\alpha_t} \longrightarrow \mathcal{E}_{\alpha_t} = -\mathsf{S}\mathcal{E}^{\mathsf{T}}_{\alpha_t}\mathsf{S}^{-1}. \tag{38}$$

Correspondingly, let $\{\mathcal{E}_{\alpha_\gamma}\}$ and $\{\mathcal{E}_{\alpha_\delta}\}$ be the sets of symmetric and skewsymmetric matrices of the complex part. Then the relation (38) can be written as follows

$$\mathcal{E}_{\alpha_\gamma} \longrightarrow \mathcal{E}_{\alpha_\gamma} = -\mathsf{S}\mathcal{E}_{\alpha_\gamma}\mathsf{S}^{-1}, \quad \mathcal{E}_{\alpha_\delta} \longrightarrow \mathcal{E}_{\alpha_\delta} = \mathsf{S}\mathcal{E}_{\alpha\delta}\mathsf{S}^{-1}.$$

Whence

$$\mathcal{E}_{\alpha_\gamma}\mathsf{S} = -\mathsf{S}\mathcal{E}_{\alpha_\gamma}, \quad \mathcal{E}_{\alpha_\delta}\mathsf{S} = \mathsf{S}\mathcal{E}_{\alpha_\delta}. \tag{39}$$

Therefore, the matrix S of the pseudoantiautomorphism $\mathcal{A} \to \widetilde{\overline{\mathcal{A}}}$ anticommutes with the complex symmetric matrices and commutes with the complex skewsymmetric matrices of the spinbasis of $C\!\ell_{p,q}$.

Let us consider now the real part $\{\mathcal{E}_{\beta_s}\}$ of the spinbasis of $C\!\ell_{p,q}$, $p - q \equiv 4, 6 \pmod 8$. In this case the relation (36) takes a form

$$\mathcal{E}_{\beta_s} \longrightarrow \mathcal{E}_{\beta_s} = \mathsf{S}\mathcal{E}^{\mathsf{T}}_{\beta_s}\mathsf{S}^{-1}. \tag{40}$$

Let $\{\mathcal{E}_{\beta_\gamma}\}$ and $\{\mathcal{E}_{\beta_\delta}\}$ be the sets of real symmetric and real skewsymmetric matrices, respectively. Then the relation (40) can be written as follows

$$\mathcal{E}_{\beta_\gamma} \longrightarrow \mathcal{E}_{\beta_\gamma} = \mathsf{S}\mathcal{E}_{\beta_\gamma}\mathsf{S}^{-1}, \quad \mathcal{E}_{\beta_\delta} \longrightarrow \mathcal{E}_{\beta_\delta} = -\mathsf{S}\mathcal{E}_{\beta_\delta}\mathsf{S}^{-1}.$$

Whence

$$\mathcal{E}_{\beta_\gamma}\mathsf{S} = \mathsf{S}\mathcal{E}_{\beta_\gamma}, \quad \mathcal{E}_{\beta_\delta}\mathsf{S} = -\mathsf{S}\mathcal{E}_{\beta_\delta}. \tag{41}$$

Thus, the matrix S of the transformation $\mathcal{A} \to \widetilde{\overline{\mathcal{A}}}$ commutes with the real symmetric matrices and anticommutes with the real skewsymmetric matrices of the spinbasis of $C\!\ell_{p,q}$.

Let us find now an explicit form of the matrix $\mathsf{S} = \Pi\mathsf{E}$. In accordance with Theorem 9 for the quaternionic types $p-q \equiv 4, 6 \pmod 8$ the matrix Π takes the two different forms: 1) $\Pi = \mathcal{E}_{\alpha_1}\mathcal{E}_{\alpha_2}\cdots\mathcal{E}_{\alpha_a}$ is the product of complex matrices at $a \equiv 0 \pmod 2$; 2) $\Pi = \mathcal{E}_{\beta_1}\mathcal{E}_{\beta_2}\cdots\mathcal{E}_{\beta_b}$ is the product of real matrices at $b \equiv 1 \pmod 2$. In turn, for the matrix E of the antiautomorphism $\mathcal{A} \to \widetilde{\mathcal{A}}$ over the ring $\mathbb{K} \simeq \mathbb{H}$ (see Theorem 7) we have the following two forms: 1) $\mathsf{E} = \mathcal{E}_{j_1}\mathcal{E}_{j_2}\cdots\mathcal{E}_{j_k}$ is the product of skewsymmetric matrices at $k \equiv 0 \pmod 2$; 2) $\mathsf{E} = \mathcal{E}_{i_1}\mathcal{E}_{i_2}\cdots\mathcal{E}_{i_{p+q-k}}$ is the product of symmetric matrices at $k \equiv 1 \pmod 2$. Thus, in accordance with definition $\mathsf{S} = \Pi\mathsf{E}$ we have four different products: $\mathsf{S} = \mathcal{E}_{\alpha_1\alpha_2\cdots\alpha_a}\mathcal{E}_{j_1j_2\cdots j_k}$, $\mathsf{S} = \mathcal{E}_{\alpha_1\alpha_2\cdots\alpha_a}\mathcal{E}_{i_1i_2\cdots i_{p+q-k}}$, $\mathsf{S} = \mathcal{E}_{\beta_1\beta_2\cdots\beta_b}\mathcal{E}_{j_1j_2\cdots j_k}$, $\mathsf{S} = \mathcal{E}_{\beta_1\beta_2\cdots\beta_b}\mathcal{E}_{i_1i_2\cdots i_{p+q-k}}$. It is obvious that in the given products there are identical matrices.

Let us examine the first product $\mathsf{S} = \mathcal{E}_{\alpha_1\alpha_2\cdots\alpha_a}\mathcal{E}_{j_1j_2\cdots j_k}$. Since in this case Π contains all the complex matrices of the spinbasis, among which there are symmetric and skewsymmetric matrices, and E contains all the skewsymmetric matrices of the spinbasis, then Π and E contain a quantity of identical matrices (complex skewsymmetric matrices). Let m be a number of the complex skewsymmetric matrices of the spinbasis of the algebra $\mathcal{C}\ell_{p,q}$, $p - q \equiv 4, 6 \pmod 8$. Then the product $\mathsf{S} = \Pi\mathsf{E}$ takes a form

$$\mathcal{E}_{\alpha_1}\mathcal{E}_{\alpha_2}\cdots\mathcal{E}_{j_1}\mathcal{E}_{j_2}\cdots\mathcal{E}_{j_k} = (-1)^{\mathcal{N}}\sigma(i_1)\sigma(i_2)\cdots\sigma(i_m)\mathcal{E}_{c_1}\mathcal{E}_{c_2}\cdots\mathcal{E}_{c_s},$$

where the indices $c_1, \ldots, c_s$ present itself a totality of the indices $\alpha_1, \ldots, \alpha_a, j_1, \ldots, j_k$ obtained after removal of the indices occured twice; $\mathcal{N}$ is a number of inversions.

First of all, let us remark that $\mathcal{E}_{c_1}\mathcal{E}_{c_2}\cdots\mathcal{E}_{c_s}$ is an even product, since the original product $\Pi\mathsf{E}$ is the even product also. Besides, the product $\mathcal{E}_{c_1}\mathcal{E}_{c_2}\cdots\mathcal{E}_{c_s}$ contains all the complex symmetric matrices and all the real skewsymmetric matrices of the spinbasis.

Let us find now permutation conditions between the matrix $\mathsf{S} = \mathcal{E}_{c_1}\mathcal{E}_{c_2}\cdots\mathcal{E}_{c_s}$ and the units of the spinbasis of $\mathcal{C}\ell_{p,q}$, $p - q \equiv 4, 6 \pmod 8$. For the complex symmetric matrices $\mathcal{E}_{\alpha_\gamma}$ and complex skewsymmetric matrices $\mathcal{E}_{\alpha_\delta}$ we have

$$\begin{aligned} \mathsf{S}\mathcal{E}_{\alpha_\gamma} &= (-1)^{s-\gamma}\mathcal{E}_{c_1}\mathcal{E}_{c_2}\cdots\mathcal{E}_{c_{s-2}}, \\ \mathcal{E}_{\alpha_\gamma}\mathsf{S} &= (-1)^{\gamma-1}\mathcal{E}_{c_1}\mathcal{E}_{c_2}\cdots\mathcal{E}_{c_{s-2}}, \end{aligned} \tag{42}$$

$$\mathsf{S}\mathcal{E}_{\alpha_\delta} = (-1)^{s}\mathcal{E}_{\alpha_\delta}\mathsf{S}, \tag{43}$$

that is, the matrix S always anticommutes with the complex symmetric matrices and always commutes with the complex skewsymmetric matrices, since $s \equiv 0 \pmod 2$. Further, for the real symmetric matrices $\mathcal{E}_{\beta_\gamma}$ and real skewsymmetric matrices $\mathcal{E}_{\beta_\delta}$ we have

$$\mathsf{S}\mathcal{E}_{\beta_\gamma} = (-1)^{s}\mathcal{E}_{\beta_\gamma}\mathsf{S}, \tag{44}$$

$$\begin{aligned} \mathsf{S}\mathcal{E}_{\beta_\delta} &= (-1)^{s-\delta}\mathcal{E}_{c_1}\mathcal{E}_{c_2}\cdots\mathcal{E}_{c_{s-2}}, \\ \mathcal{E}_{\beta_\delta}\mathsf{S} &= (-1)^{\delta-1}\mathcal{E}_{c_1}\mathcal{E}_{c_2}\cdots\mathcal{E}_{c_{s-2}}. \end{aligned} \tag{45}$$

Therefore, S always commutes with the real symmetric matrices and always anticommutes with the real skewsymmetric matrices.

A comparison of the obtained conditions (42)–(45) with (39) and (41) shows that $\mathsf{S} = \mathcal{E}_{c_1}\mathcal{E}_{c_2}\cdots\mathcal{E}_{c_s}$ automatically satisfies the conditions, which define the matrix of the pseudoantiautomorphism $\mathcal{A} \rightarrow \widetilde{\overline{\mathcal{A}}}$.

Let examine the second product $\mathsf{S} = \mathcal{E}_{\alpha_1\alpha_2\cdots\alpha_a}\mathcal{E}_{i_1i_2\cdots i_{p+q-k}}$. In this case Π contains all the complex matrices of the spinbasis, among which there are symmetric and skewsymmetric matrices, and E contains all the symmetric matrices of the spinbasis. Thus, Π and E contain a quantity of identical complex symmetric matrices. Let l be a number of the complex symmetric matrices, then for the product $\mathsf{S} = \Pi\mathsf{E}$ we obtain

$$\mathcal{E}_{\alpha_1}\mathcal{E}_{\alpha_2}\cdots\mathcal{E}_{\alpha_a}\mathcal{E}_{i_1}\mathcal{E}_{i_2}\cdots\mathcal{E}_{i_{p+q-k}} = (-1)^{\mathcal{N}}\sigma(i_1)\sigma(i_2)\cdots\sigma(i_l)\mathcal{E}_{d_1}\mathcal{E}_{d_2}\cdots\mathcal{E}_{d_g},$$

where $d_1, \ldots, d_g$ present itself a totality of the indices $\alpha_1, \ldots, \alpha_a, i_1, \ldots, i_{p+q-k}$ obtained after the removal of the indices occured twice. The product $\mathsf{S} = \mathcal{E}_{d_1}\mathcal{E}_{d_2}\cdots\mathcal{E}_{d_g}$ is odd, since the original product $\Pi\mathsf{E}$ is odd also. Besides, $\mathcal{E}_{d_1}\mathcal{E}_{d_2}\cdots\mathcal{E}_{d_g}$ contains all the complex skewsymmetric matrices and all the real symmetric matrices of the spinbasis.

Let us find permutation conditions of the matrix $\mathsf{S} = \mathcal{E}_{d_1}\mathcal{E}_{d_2}\cdots\mathcal{E}_{d_g}$ with the units of the spinbasis of $C\!\ell_{p,q}$. For the complex part of the spinbasis we have

$$\mathsf{S}\mathcal{E}_{\alpha_\gamma} = (-1)^g\mathcal{E}_{\alpha_\gamma}\mathsf{S}, \tag{46}$$

$$\begin{aligned}\mathsf{S}\mathcal{E}_{\alpha_\delta} &= (-1)^{g-\delta}\mathcal{E}_{d_1}\mathcal{E}_{d_2}\cdots\mathcal{E}_{d_{g-2}},\\ \mathcal{E}_{\alpha_\delta}\mathsf{S} &= (-1)^{\delta-1}\mathcal{E}_{d_1}\mathcal{E}_{d_2}\cdots\mathcal{E}_{d_{g-2}},\end{aligned} \tag{47}$$

that is, the matrix S anticommutes with the complex symmetric matrices and commutes with the complex skewsymmetric matrices, since $g \equiv 1 \pmod 2$. For the real part of the spinbasis of $C\!\ell_{p,q}$ we obtain

$$\begin{aligned}\mathsf{S}\mathcal{E}_{\beta_\gamma} &= (-1)^{g-\gamma}\mathcal{E}_{d_1}\mathcal{E}_{d_2}\cdots\mathcal{E}_{d_{g-2}},\\ \mathcal{E}_{\beta_\gamma}\mathsf{S} &= (-1)^{\gamma-1}\mathcal{E}_{d_1}\mathcal{E}_{d_2}\cdots\mathcal{E}_{d_{g-2}},\end{aligned} \tag{48}$$

$$\mathsf{S}\mathcal{E}_{\beta_\delta} = (-1)^g\mathcal{E}_{\beta_\delta}\mathsf{S}. \tag{49}$$

Therefore, S commutes with the real symmetric matrices and anticommutes with the real skewsymmetric matrices.

Comparing the obtained conditions (46)–(49) with the conditions (39) and (41) we see that $\mathsf{S} = \mathcal{E}_{d_1}\mathcal{E}_{d_2}\cdots\mathcal{E}_{d_g}$ automatically satisfies the conditions which define the matrix of the transformation $\mathcal{A} \rightarrow \widetilde{\overline{\mathcal{A}}}$.

Let us consider now the third product $\mathsf{S} = \mathcal{E}_{\beta_1\beta_2\cdots\beta_b}\mathcal{E}_{j_1j_2\cdots k}$. In this product the matrix Π of the pseudoautomorphism $\mathcal{A} \rightarrow \overline{\mathcal{A}}$ contains all the real matrices of the spinbasis, among which there are symmetric and skewsymmetric matrices, and the matrix E of $\mathcal{A} \rightarrow \widetilde{\mathcal{A}}$ contains all the skewsymmetric matrices of the spinbasis, among which there are both the real and complex matrices. Therefore, S contains a quantity of identical real skewsymmetric matrices. Let u be a number of the real skewsymmetric matrices of the spinbasis of the algebra $\mathcal{C}\!\ell_{p,q}$, $p-q\equiv 4,6 \pmod 8$, then for the product S we obtain

$$\mathcal{E}_{\beta_1}\mathcal{E}_{\beta_2}\cdots\mathcal{E}_{\beta_b}\mathcal{E}_{j_1}\mathcal{E}_{j_2}\cdots\mathcal{E}_{j_k}=(-1)^{\mathcal{N}}\sigma(i_1)\sigma(i_2)\cdots\sigma(i_u)\mathcal{E}_{e_1}\mathcal{E}_{e_2}\cdots\mathcal{E}_{e_h},$$

where the indices $e_1, e_2, \ldots, e_n$ present itself a totality of the indices $\beta_1, \ldots, \beta_b, j_1, \ldots, j_k$ obtained after the removal of the indices occurred twice. The product $\mathsf{S}=\mathcal{E}_{e_1}\mathcal{E}_{e_2}\cdots\mathcal{E}_{e_h}$ is odd, since the original product $\Pi\mathsf{E}$ is odd also. It is easy to see that $\mathcal{E}_{e_1}\mathcal{E}_{e_2}\cdots\mathcal{E}_{e_h}$ contains all the real symmetric matrices and all the complex skewsymmetric matrices of the spinbasis. Therefore, the matrix $\mathsf{S}=\mathcal{E}_{e_1}\mathcal{E}_{e_2}\cdots\mathcal{E}_{e_h}$ is similar to the matrix $\mathsf{S}=\mathcal{E}_{d_1}\mathcal{E}_{d_2}\cdots\mathcal{E}_{d_g}$, and its permutation conditions with the units of the spinbasis of $\mathcal{C}\!\ell_{p,q}$ are equivalent to the relations (46)–(49).

Finally, let us examine the fourth product $\mathsf{S}=\mathcal{E}_{\beta_1\beta_2\cdots\beta_b}\mathcal{E}_{i_1i_2\cdots i_{p+q-k}}$. In turn, this product contains a quantity of identical real symmetric matrices. Let v be a number of the real symmetric matrices of the spinbasis of $\mathcal{C}\!\ell_{p,q}$, then

$$\mathcal{E}_{\beta_1}\mathcal{E}_{\beta_2}\cdots\mathcal{E}_{\beta_b}\mathcal{E}_{i_1}\mathcal{E}_{i_2}\cdots\mathcal{E}_{i_{p+q-k}}=(-1)^{\mathcal{N}}\sigma(i_1)\sigma(i_2)\cdots\sigma(i_v)\mathcal{E}_{f_1}\mathcal{E}_{f_2}\cdots\mathcal{E}_{f_w},$$

where $f_1, \ldots, f_w$ present itself a totality of the indices $\beta_1, \ldots, \beta_b, i_1, \ldots, i_{p+q-k}$ obtained after the removal of the indices occurred twice. The product $\mathsf{S}=\mathcal{E}_{f_1}\mathcal{E}_{f_2}\cdots\mathcal{E}_{f_w}$ is even, since the original product $\Pi\mathsf{E}$ is even also. It is easy to see that $\mathcal{E}_{f_1}\mathcal{E}_{f_2}\cdots\mathcal{E}_{f_w}$ contains all the real skewsymmetric matrices and all the complex symmetric matrices of the spinbasis. Therefore, the matrix $\mathsf{S}=\mathcal{E}_{f_1}\mathcal{E}_{f_2}\cdots\mathcal{E}_{f_w}$ is similar to the matrix $\mathsf{S}=\mathcal{E}_{c_1}\mathcal{E}_{c_2}\cdots\mathcal{E}_{c_s}$, and its permutation conditions with the units of the spinbasis are equivalent to the relations (42)–(45).

Thus, from the four products we have only two non-equivalent products. The squares of the non-equivalent matrices $\mathsf{S}=\mathcal{E}_{c_1}\mathcal{E}_{c_2}\cdots\mathcal{E}_{c_s}$ ($s\equiv 0 \pmod 2$) and $\mathsf{S}=\mathcal{E}_{d_1}\mathcal{E}_{d_2}\cdots\mathcal{E}_{d_g}$ ($g\equiv 1 \pmod 2$) are

$$\mathsf{S}^2=(\mathcal{E}_{c_1}\mathcal{E}_{c_2}\cdots\mathcal{E}_{c_s})^2=\begin{cases}+\mathsf{I}, & \text{if } u+l\equiv 0,4 \pmod 8,\\ -\mathsf{I}, & \text{if } u+l\equiv 2,6 \pmod 8;\end{cases}\tag{50}$$

$$\mathsf{S}^2=(\mathcal{E}_{d_1}\mathcal{E}_{d_2}\cdots\mathcal{E}_{d_g})^2=\begin{cases}+\mathsf{I}, & \text{if } m+v\equiv 1,5 \pmod 8,\\ -\mathsf{I}, & \text{if } m+v\equiv 3,7 \pmod 8.\end{cases}\tag{51}$$

5.3 Pseudoantiautomorphism $\mathcal{A}\rightarrow\overline{\widetilde{\mathcal{A}^\star}}$

The pseudoantiautomorphism $\mathcal{A}\rightarrow\overline{\widetilde{\mathcal{A}^\star}}$, that defines the CPT-transformation, is a composition of the pseudoautomorphism $\mathcal{A}\rightarrow\overline{\mathcal{A}}$, antiautomorphism $\mathcal{A}\rightarrow\widetilde{\mathcal{A}}$ and automorphism $\mathcal{A}\rightarrow\mathcal{A}^\star$. Under action of the automorphism $\mathcal{A}\rightarrow\mathcal{A}^\star$ the units of $\mathcal{C}\!\ell_{p,q}$ change the sign, $\mathbf{e}_i\rightarrow-\mathbf{e}_i$. In turn, under action of the transformations $\mathcal{A}\rightarrow\overline{\mathcal{A}}$ and $\mathcal{A}\rightarrow\widetilde{\mathcal{A}}$ the units remain unaltered, $\mathbf{e}_i\rightarrow\mathbf{e}_i$. Therefore, under action of the pseudoantiautomorphism $\mathcal{A}\rightarrow\overline{\widetilde{\mathcal{A}^\star}}$ the units change the sign, $\mathbf{e}_i\rightarrow-\mathbf{e}_i$.

The spinor representations of the transformations $\mathcal{A} \to \mathcal{A}^\star$, $\mathcal{A} \to \widetilde{\mathcal{A}}$ and $\mathcal{A} \to \overline{\mathcal{A}}$ have the form: $\mathsf{A}^\star = \mathsf{W}\mathsf{A}\mathsf{W}^{-1}$, $\widetilde{\mathsf{A}} = \mathsf{E}\mathsf{A}^{\mathsf{T}}\mathsf{E}^{-1}$ and $\overline{\mathsf{A}} = \Pi\dot{\mathsf{A}}\Pi^{-1}$. Let us find a matrix of the transformation $\mathcal{A} \to \overline{\widetilde{\mathcal{A}^\star}}$. We will consider the pseudoantiautomorphism $\mathcal{A} \to \overline{\widetilde{\mathcal{A}^\star}}$ as a composition of the pseudoautomorphism $\mathcal{A} \to \overline{\mathcal{A}}$ with the antiautomorphism $\mathcal{A} \to \widetilde{\mathcal{A}^\star}$. The spinor representation of $\mathcal{A} \to \widetilde{\mathcal{A}^\star}$ is $\widetilde{\mathcal{A}^\star} = \mathsf{C}\mathsf{A}^{\mathsf{T}}\mathsf{C}^{-1}$, where $\mathsf{C} = \mathsf{E}\mathsf{W}$. Since $\overline{\widetilde{\mathcal{A}^\star}} = \left(\widetilde{\overline{\mathcal{A}}}\right)^\star = \overline{\left(\widetilde{\mathcal{A}^\star}\right)}$, then

$$\overline{\widetilde{\mathsf{A}^\star}} = \mathsf{C}\left(\Pi\dot{\mathsf{A}}\Pi^{-1}\right)^{\mathsf{T}}\mathsf{C}^{-1} = \Pi\left(\mathsf{C}\mathsf{A}^{\mathsf{T}}\mathsf{C}^{-1}\right)^{\cdot}\Pi^{-1},$$

or

$$\overline{\widetilde{\mathsf{A}^\star}} = (\mathsf{C}\Pi)\dot{\mathsf{A}}^{\mathsf{T}}(\mathsf{C}\Pi)^{-1} = (\Pi\mathsf{C})\dot{\mathsf{A}}^{\mathsf{T}}(\Pi\mathsf{C})^{-1}, \tag{52}$$

since $\Pi^{-1} = \Pi^{\mathsf{T}}$ and $\overline{\widetilde{\mathsf{A}^\star}} = \Pi\dot{\mathsf{C}}\left(\mathsf{A}^{\mathsf{T}}\right)^{\cdot}\dot{\mathsf{C}}^{-1}\Pi^{-1} = \Pi\mathsf{C}\dot{\mathsf{A}}^{\mathsf{T}}\mathsf{C}^{-1}\Pi^{-1}$ in the case when $\dot{\mathsf{C}} = \mathsf{C}$ is a real matrix, and also $\overline{\widetilde{\mathsf{A}^\star}} = \Pi\dot{\mathsf{C}}\left(\mathsf{A}^{\mathsf{T}}\right)^{\cdot}\dot{\mathsf{C}}^{-1}\Pi^{-1} = \Pi(-\mathsf{C})\left(\mathsf{A}^{\mathsf{T}}\right)^{\cdot}\left(-\mathsf{C}^{-1}\right)\Pi^{-1} = \Pi\mathsf{C}\dot{\mathsf{A}}^{\mathsf{T}}\mathsf{C}^{-1}\Pi^{-1}$ in the case when $\dot{\mathsf{C}} = -\mathsf{C}$ is a complex matrix.

Let $\mathsf{F} = \Pi\mathsf{C}$ (or $\mathsf{F} = \Pi\mathsf{E}\mathsf{W}$) be a matrix of the pseudoantiautomorphism $\mathcal{A} \to \overline{\widetilde{\mathcal{A}^\star}}$. Then the relation (52) can be written as follows

$$\overline{\widetilde{\mathsf{A}^\star}} = \mathsf{F}\dot{\mathsf{A}}^{\mathsf{T}}\mathsf{F}^{-1}. \tag{53}$$

Since under action of the transformation $\mathcal{A} \to \overline{\widetilde{\mathcal{A}^\star}}$ we have $\mathbf{e}_i \to -\mathbf{e}_i$, in the spinor representation we must demand $\mathcal{E}_i \to -\mathcal{E}_i$ also, or

$$\mathcal{E}_i \longrightarrow -\mathcal{E}_i = \mathsf{F}\dot{\mathcal{E}}_i^{\mathsf{T}}\mathsf{F}^{-1}. \tag{54}$$

In case of the real subalgebras $C\!\ell_{p,q}$ with the ring $\mathbb{K} \simeq \mathbb{R}$, $p - q \equiv 0, 2 \pmod 8$, we have $\dot{\mathcal{E}}_i = \mathcal{E}_i$ for all matrices of the spinbasis and, therefore, the relation (54) takes a form

$$\mathcal{E}_i \longrightarrow -\mathcal{E}_i = \mathsf{F}\mathcal{E}_i^{\mathsf{T}}\mathsf{F}^{-1}. \tag{55}$$

Let $\{\mathcal{E}_{\gamma_i}\} \cup \{\mathcal{E}_{\delta_j}\}$ be a spinbasis of the algebra $C\!\ell_{p,q}$ over the ring $\mathbb{K} \simeq \mathbb{R}$, ($\mathcal{E}_{\gamma_i}^{\mathsf{T}} = \mathcal{E}_{\gamma_i}$, $\mathcal{E}_{\delta_j}^{\mathsf{T}} = -\mathcal{E}_{\delta_j}$). Then the relation (55) can be written in the form

$$\mathcal{E}_{\gamma_i} \longrightarrow -\mathcal{E}_{\gamma_i} = \mathsf{F}\mathcal{E}_{\gamma_i}\mathsf{F}^{-1}, \quad \mathcal{E}_{\delta_j} \longrightarrow \mathcal{E}_{\delta_j} = \mathsf{F}\mathcal{E}_{\delta_j}\mathsf{F}^{-1}.$$

Whence

$$\mathcal{E}_{\gamma_i}\mathsf{F} = -\mathsf{F}\mathcal{E}_{\gamma_i}, \quad \mathcal{E}_{\delta_j}\mathsf{F} = \mathsf{F}\mathcal{E}_{\delta_j},$$

that is, the matrix F of the pseudoantiautomorphism $\mathcal{A} \to \overline{\widetilde{\mathcal{A}^\star}}$ in case of the ring $\mathbb{K} \simeq \mathbb{R}$ anticommutes with the symmetric part of the spinbasis of $C\!\ell_{p,q}$ and commutes with the skewsymmetric part. In virtue of Theorem 9 the matrix Π of the pseudoautomorphism $\mathcal{A} \to \overline{\mathcal{A}}$ over the ring $\mathbb{K} \simeq \mathbb{R}$ is proportional to the unit matrix,

$\Pi \simeq \mathsf{I}$. Therefore, in this case $\mathsf{F} \sim \mathsf{C}$ ($\mathsf{F} \sim \mathsf{EW}$) and an explicit form of the matrix F coincides with C (see Theorem 7).

In case of the quaternionic ring $\mathbb{K} \simeq \mathbb{H}$, $p - q \equiv 4, 6 \pmod 8$, the spinbasis of $\mathcal{C}\!\ell_{p,q}$ contains both complex matrices $\mathcal{E}_{\alpha_t}$ and real matrices $\mathcal{E}_{\beta_r}$. For the complex part the relation (54) takes a form

$$\mathcal{E}_{\alpha_t} \longrightarrow \mathcal{E}_{\alpha_t} = \mathsf{F}\mathcal{E}^{\mathsf{T}}_{\alpha_t}\mathsf{F}^{-1},$$

Or, taking into account complex symmetric and complex skewsymmetric components of the spinbasis, we obtain

$$\mathcal{E}_{\alpha_\gamma} \longrightarrow \mathcal{E}_{\alpha_\gamma} = \mathsf{F}\mathcal{E}_{\alpha_\gamma}\mathsf{F}^{-1}, \quad \mathcal{E}_{\alpha_\delta} \longrightarrow \mathcal{E}_{\alpha_\delta} = -\mathsf{F}\mathcal{E}_{\alpha_\delta}\mathsf{F}^{-1}.$$

Whence

$$\mathcal{E}_{\alpha_\gamma}\mathsf{F} = \mathsf{F}\mathcal{E}_{\alpha_\gamma}, \quad \mathcal{E}_{\alpha_\delta}\mathsf{F} = -\mathsf{F}\mathcal{E}_{\alpha_\delta}. \tag{56}$$

For the real part of the spinbasis of $\mathcal{C}\!\ell_{p,q}$ from (54) we obtain

$$\mathcal{E}_{\beta_r} \longrightarrow -\mathcal{E}_{\beta_r} = \mathsf{F}\mathcal{E}^{\mathsf{T}}_{\beta_r}\mathsf{F}^{-1},$$

or, taking into account symmetric and skewsymmetric components of the real part of the spinbasis, we find

$$\mathcal{E}_{\beta_\gamma} \longrightarrow -\mathcal{E}_{\beta_\gamma} = \mathsf{F}\mathcal{E}_{\beta_\gamma}\mathsf{F}^{-1}, \quad \mathcal{E}_{\beta_\delta} \longrightarrow \mathcal{E}_{\beta_\delta} = \mathsf{F}\mathcal{E}_{\beta_\delta}\mathsf{F}^{-1}.$$

Whence

$$\mathcal{E}_{\beta_\gamma}\mathsf{F} = -\mathsf{F}\mathcal{E}_{\beta_\gamma}, \quad \mathcal{E}_{\beta_\delta}\mathsf{F} = \mathsf{F}\mathcal{E}_{\beta_\delta}. \tag{57}$$

Therefore, the matrix F of the pseudoantiautomorphism $\mathcal{A} \rightarrow \overline{\widetilde{\mathcal{A}^\star}}$ commutes with the complex symmetric and real skewsymmetric matrices, and also F anticommutes with the complex skewsymmetric and real symmetric matrices of the spinbasis of $\mathcal{C}\!\ell_{p,q}$, $p - q \equiv 4, 6 \pmod 8$.

Let us find an explicit form of the matrix $\mathsf{F} = \Pi\mathsf{C}$. It is easy to see that in virtue of $\mathsf{F} = \Pi\mathsf{C} = (\Pi\mathsf{E})\mathsf{W} = \mathsf{SW}$ the matrix F is a dual with respect to the matrix S of the pseudoantiautomorphism $\mathcal{A} \rightarrow \overline{\widetilde{\mathcal{A}}}$. In accordance with Theorem 9 for the quaternionic types $p - q \equiv 4, 6 \pmod 8$ the matrix Π has two different forms: $\Pi = \mathcal{E}_{\alpha_1}\mathcal{E}_{\alpha_2}\cdots\mathcal{E}_{\alpha_a}$ ($\dot{\mathcal{E}}_{\alpha_t} = -\mathcal{E}_{\alpha_t}$), $a \equiv 0 \pmod 2$; $\Pi = \mathcal{E}_{\beta_1}\mathcal{E}_{\beta_2}\cdots\mathcal{E}_{\beta_b}$ ($\dot{\mathcal{E}}_{\beta_r} = \mathcal{E}_{\beta_r}$), $b \equiv 1 \pmod 2$. In turn, for the quaternionic types the matrix C of the antiautomorphism $\mathcal{A} \rightarrow \widetilde{\mathcal{A}^\star}$ has the two forms (see Theorem 7): 1) $\mathsf{C} = \mathcal{E}_{i_1}\mathcal{E}_{i_2}\cdots\mathcal{E}_{i_{p+q-k}}$ is the product of all symmetric matrices of the spinbasis of $\mathcal{C}\!\ell_{p,q}$ at $p + q - k \equiv 0 \pmod 2$; 2) $\mathsf{C} = \mathcal{E}_{j_1}\mathcal{E}_{j_2}\cdots\mathcal{E}_{j_k}$ is the product of all skewsymmetric matrices of the spinbasis at $k \equiv 1 \pmod 2$. Thus, in accordance with definition $\mathsf{F} = \Pi\mathsf{C}$ we have four products: $\mathsf{F} = \mathcal{E}_{\alpha_1\alpha_2\cdots\alpha_a}\mathcal{E}_{i_1i_2\cdots i_{p+q-k}}$, $\mathsf{F} = \mathcal{E}_{\alpha_1\alpha_2\cdots\alpha_a}\mathcal{E}_{j_1j_2\cdots j_k}$, $\mathsf{F} = \mathcal{E}_{\beta_1\beta_2\cdots\beta_b}\mathcal{E}_{i_1i_2\cdots i_{p+q-k}}$, $\mathsf{F} = \mathcal{E}_{\beta_1\beta_2\cdots\beta_b}\mathcal{E}_{j_1j_2\cdots j_k}$.

Let us examine the first product $\mathsf{F} = \mathcal{E}_{\alpha_1\alpha_2\cdots\alpha_a}\mathcal{E}_{i_1i_2\cdots i_{p+q-k}}$. In this case Π contains all the complex matrices of the spinbasis, among which there are symmetric and skewsymmetric matrices. In turn, C contains all the symmetric matrices, among which there are both complex and real matrices. It is obvious that in this case $\Pi\mathsf{C}$ contains a quantity of identical complex symmetric matrices. Therefore, the product F consists of all the complex skewsymmetric matrices and all the real symmetric matrices of the spinbasis. The product F is even, since the original product $\Pi\mathsf{C}$ is even also. It is easy to see that F coincides with the product $\mathcal{E}_{d_1}\mathcal{E}_{d_2}\cdots\mathcal{E}_{d_g}$ at $g \equiv 0 \pmod 2$.

Let us find permutation conditions of the matrix $\mathsf{F} = \mathcal{E}_{d_1}\mathcal{E}_{d_2}\cdots\mathcal{E}_{d_g}$ with the units of the spinbasis of $\mathcal{C}\!\ell_{p,q}$, $p - q \equiv 4, 6 \pmod 8$. For the complex and real parts we obtain

$$\mathsf{F}\mathcal{E}_{\alpha_\gamma} = (-1)^g\mathcal{E}_{\alpha_\gamma}\mathsf{F}, \tag{58}$$

$$\begin{aligned}\mathsf{F}\mathcal{E}_{\alpha_\delta} &= (-1)^{g-\delta}\mathcal{E}_{d_1}\mathcal{E}_{d_2}\cdots\mathcal{E}_{d_{g-2}},\\ \mathcal{E}_{\alpha_\delta}\mathsf{F} &= (-1)^{\delta-1}\mathcal{E}_{d_1}\mathcal{E}_{d_2}\cdots\mathcal{E}_{d_{g-2}},\end{aligned} \tag{59}$$

$$\begin{aligned}\mathsf{F}\mathcal{E}_{\beta_\gamma} &= (-1)^{g-\gamma}\mathcal{E}_{d_1}\mathcal{E}_{d_2}\cdots\mathcal{E}_{d_{g-2}},\\ \mathcal{E}_{\beta_\gamma}\mathsf{F} &= (-1)^{\gamma-1}\mathcal{E}_{d_1}\mathcal{E}_{d_2}\cdots\mathcal{E}_{d_{g-2}},\end{aligned} \tag{60}$$

$$\mathsf{F}\mathcal{E}_{\beta_\delta} = (-1)^g\mathcal{E}_{\beta_\delta}\mathsf{F}. \tag{61}$$

Therefore, since $g \equiv 0 \pmod 2$ the matrix F always commutes with the complex symmetric and real skewsymmetric matrices and always anticommutes with the complex skewsymmetric and real symmetric matrices of the spinbasis. A comparison of the permutation conditions (58)–(61) with the conditions (56)–(57) shows that $\mathsf{F} = \mathcal{E}_{d_1}\mathcal{E}_{d_2}\cdots\mathcal{E}_{d_g}$ at $g \equiv 0 \pmod 2$ automatically satisfies the conditions which define the matrix of the pseudoantiautomorphism $\mathcal{A} \to \widetilde{\overline{\mathcal{A}^\star}}$.

Let examine the second product $\mathsf{F} = \mathcal{E}_{\alpha_1\alpha_2\cdots\alpha_a}\mathcal{E}_{j_1j_2\cdots j_k}$. This product contains all the complex part of the spinbasis and all the skewsymmetric matrices. Therefore, in the product $\Pi\mathsf{C}$ there is a quantity of identical complex skewsymmetric matrices. The product F is odd and consists of all the complex symmetric and real skewsymmetric matrices of the spinbasis. It is easy to see that in this case F coincides with the product $\mathcal{E}_{c_1}\mathcal{E}_{c_2}\cdots\mathcal{E}_{c_s}$ at $s \equiv 1 \pmod 2$. Permutation conditions of the matrix $\mathsf{F} = \mathcal{E}_{c_1}\mathcal{E}_{c_2}\cdots\mathcal{E}_{c_s}$ with the units of the spinbasis are

$$\begin{aligned}\mathsf{F}\mathcal{E}_{\alpha_\gamma} &= (-1)^{s-\gamma}\mathcal{E}_{c_1}\mathcal{E}_{c_2}\cdots\mathcal{E}_{c_{s-2}},\\ \mathcal{E}_{\alpha_\gamma}\mathsf{F} &= (-1)^{\gamma-1}\mathcal{E}_{c_1}\mathcal{E}_{c_2}\cdots\mathcal{E}_{c_{s-2}},\end{aligned} \tag{62}$$

$$\mathsf{F}\mathcal{E}_{\alpha_\delta} = (-1)^s\mathcal{E}_{\alpha_\delta}\mathsf{F}, \tag{63}$$

$$\mathsf{F}\mathcal{E}_{\beta_\gamma} = (-1)^s\mathcal{E}_{\beta_\gamma}\mathsf{F}, \tag{64}$$

$$\begin{aligned}\mathsf{F}\mathcal{E}_{\beta_\delta} &= (-1)^{s-\delta}\mathcal{E}_{c_1}\mathcal{E}_{c_2}\cdots\mathcal{E}_{c_{s-2}},\\ \mathcal{E}_{\beta_\delta}\mathsf{F} &= (-1)^{\delta-1}\mathcal{E}_{c_1}\mathcal{E}_{c_2}\cdots\mathcal{E}_{c_{s-2}}.\end{aligned} \tag{65}$$

Therefore, since $s \equiv 1 \pmod 2$ the matrix F always commutes with the complex symmetric and real skewsymmetric matrices and always anticommutes with the complex skewsymmetric and real symmetric matrices of the spinbasis. Comparing the conditions (62)–(65) with the conditions (56) and (57) we see that $\mathsf{F} = \mathcal{E}_{c_1}\mathcal{E}_{c_2}\cdots\mathcal{E}_{c_s}$ at $s \equiv 1 \pmod 2$ identically satisfies the conditions which define the matrix of the transformation $\mathcal{A} \longrightarrow \widetilde{\widetilde{\mathcal{A}^\star}}$.

The third product $\mathsf{F} = \Pi\mathsf{C} = \mathcal{E}_{\beta_1\beta_2\cdots\beta_b}\mathcal{E}_{i_1i_2\cdots i_{p+q-k}}$ contains all the real part and all the symmetric matrices of the spinbasis. Therefore, in the product $\Pi\mathsf{C}$ there is a quantity of identical real symmetric matrices. Thus, the product F is odd and consists of all the real skewsymmetric and complex symmetric matrices of the spinbasis. It is easy to see that we came again to the matrix $\mathsf{F} = \mathcal{E}_{c_1}\mathcal{E}_{c_2}\cdots\mathcal{E}_{c_s}$ ($s \equiv 1 \pmod 2$) with the permutation conditions (62)–(65).

Finally, the fourth product $\mathsf{F} = \mathcal{E}_{\beta_1\beta_2\cdots\beta_b}\mathcal{E}_{j_1j_2\cdots j_k}$ contains all the real part and all the skewsymmetric matrices of the spinbasis. Therefore, in the product $\Pi\mathsf{C}$ there is a quantity of identical real skewsymmetric matrices. This product is equivalent to the matrix $\mathsf{F} = \mathcal{E}_{d_1}\mathcal{E}_{d_2}\cdots\mathcal{E}_{d_g}$ ($g \equiv 0 \pmod 2$) with the permutation conditions (58)–(61).

As with the pseudoantiautomorphism $\mathcal{A} \longrightarrow \widetilde{\widetilde{\mathcal{A}}}$, from the four products we have only two non-equivalent products. Let us find squares of the non-equivalent matrices $\mathsf{F} = \mathcal{E}_{d_1}\mathcal{E}_{d_2}\cdots\mathcal{E}_{d_g}$ ($g \equiv 0 \pmod 2$) and $\mathsf{F} = \mathcal{E}_{c_1}\mathcal{E}_{c_2}\cdots\mathcal{E}_{c_s}$ ($s \equiv 1 \pmod 2$):

$$\mathsf{F}^2 = \left(\mathcal{E}_{d_1}\mathcal{E}_{d_2}\cdots\mathcal{E}_{d_g}\right)^2 = \begin{cases} +\mathsf{I}, & \text{if } m+v \equiv 0,4 \pmod 8, \\ -\mathsf{I}, & \text{if } m+v \equiv 2,6 \pmod 8; \end{cases} \tag{66}$$

$$\mathsf{F}^2 = \left(\mathcal{E}_{c_1}\mathcal{E}_{c_2}\cdots\mathcal{E}_{c_s}\right)^2 = \begin{cases} +\mathsf{I}, & \text{if } u+l \equiv 3,7 \pmod 8, \\ -\mathsf{I}, & \text{if } u+l \equiv 1,5 \pmod 8. \end{cases} \tag{67}$$

6 The structure of $\mathsf{Ext}(\mathbb{C}_n)$

As noted previously, the group $\mathsf{Ext}(\mathbb{C}_n)$ is a finite group of order eight. This group contains as a subgroup the automorphism group $\mathsf{Aut}_\pm(\mathbb{C}_n)$ (reflection group). Moreover, in the case of $\Pi \sim \mathsf{I}$ (the subalgebra $C\!\ell_{p,q}$ has the ring $\mathbb{K} \simeq \mathbb{R}$, $p-q \equiv 0,2 \pmod 8$) the group $\mathsf{Ext}(\mathbb{C}_n)$ is reduced to its subgroup $\mathsf{Aut}_\pm(\mathbb{C}_n)$. The structure of the groups $\mathsf{Aut}_\pm(\mathbb{C}_n)$, $\mathsf{Aut}_\pm(C\!\ell_{p,q})$ is studied in detail (see Theorems 5 and 7).

There are six finite groups of order eight (see Table 1). One is cyclic and two are direct group products of cyclic groups, hence these three are Abelian. The remaining three groups are the quaternion group Q_4 with elements $\{\pm 1, \pm\mathbf{i}, \pm\mathbf{j}, \pm\mathbf{k}\}$, the dihedral group D_4, and the group $\mathbb{Z}_4 \overset{*}{\otimes} \mathbb{Z}_2$. All these groups are non–Abelian. As known, an important property of each finite group is its order structure. The order of a particular element α in the group is the smallest integer p for which $\alpha^p = 1$. The following table lists the number of distinct elements in each group which have order 2, 4, or 8 (the identity 1 is the only element of order 1).

	Type	Order structure 2	4	8
1. $\mathbb{Z}_2 \otimes \mathbb{Z}_2 \otimes \mathbb{Z}_2$	Abelian	7		
2. $\mathbb{Z}_4 \otimes \mathbb{Z}_2$		3	4	
3. $\mathbb{Z}_8$		1	2	4
4. D_4	Non–Abelian	5	2	
5. Q_4		1	6	
6. $\overset{*}{\mathbb{Z}}_4 \otimes \mathbb{Z}_2$		3	4	

Table 1. Finite groups of order 8.

Of course, $\mathbb{Z}_8$ does not occur as a $G(p,q)$ (Salingaros group), since every element of $G(p,q)$ has order 1, 2, or 4. The groups $\mathbb{Z}_4 \otimes \mathbb{Z}_2$ and $\overset{*}{\mathbb{Z}}_4 \otimes \mathbb{Z}_2$ have the same order structure, but their signatures (a,b,c,d,e,f,g) are different. Moreover, the group $\overset{*}{\mathbb{Z}}_4 \otimes \mathbb{Z}_2$ presents a first example of the finite group of order 8 which has an important physical meaning.

Example 1. Let us consider a Dirac algebra $\mathbb{C}_4$. In the algebra $\mathbb{C}_4$ we can evolve four different real subalgebras $C\!\ell_{1,3}$, $C\!\ell_{3,1}$, $C\!\ell_{4,0}$, $C\!\ell_{0,4}$. Let us evolve the spacetime algebra $C\!\ell_{1,3}$. The algebra $C\!\ell_{1,3}$ has the quaternionic division ring $\mathbb{K} \simeq \mathbb{H}$ $(p-q \equiv 6 \pmod 8)$ and, therefore, admits the following spinor representation (the well known γ-basis):

$$\gamma_0 = \begin{pmatrix} 1 & 0 & 0 & 0 \\ 0 & 1 & 0 & 0 \\ 0 & 0 & -1 & 0 \\ 0 & 0 & 0 & -1 \end{pmatrix}, \quad \gamma_1 = \begin{pmatrix} 0 & 0 & 0 & 1 \\ 0 & 0 & 1 & 0 \\ 0 & -1 & 0 & 0 \\ -1 & 0 & 0 & 0 \end{pmatrix},$$
$$\gamma_2 = \begin{pmatrix} 0 & 0 & 0 & -i \\ 0 & 0 & i & 0 \\ 0 & i & 0 & 0 \\ -i & 0 & 0 & 0 \end{pmatrix}, \quad \gamma_3 = \begin{pmatrix} 0 & 0 & 1 & 0 \\ 0 & 0 & 0 & -1 \\ -1 & 0 & 0 & 0 \\ 0 & 1 & 0 & 0 \end{pmatrix}. \tag{68}$$

The famous Dirac equation in the γ–basis looks like

$$\left(i\gamma_0 \frac{\partial}{\partial x_0} - i\boldsymbol{\gamma}\frac{\partial}{\partial \mathbf{x}} - m\right)\psi(x_0, \mathbf{x}) = 0. \tag{69}$$

The invariance of the Dirac equation with respect to P–, T–, and C–transformations leads to the following representation (see, for example, [3] and also many other textbooks on quantum field theory):

$$P \sim \gamma_0, \quad T \sim \gamma_1\gamma_3, \quad C \sim \gamma_2\gamma_0.$$

Thus, we can form a finite group of order 8 (CPT–group)

$$\{1,\ P,\ T,\ PT,\ C,\ CP,\ CT,\ CPT\} \sim$$
$$\sim \{1,\ \gamma_0,\ \gamma_1\gamma_3,\ \gamma_0\gamma_1\gamma_3,\ \gamma_2\gamma_0,\ \gamma_2,\ \gamma_2\gamma_0\gamma_1\gamma_3,\ \gamma_2\gamma_1\gamma_3\}\,. \quad (70)$$

It is easy to verify that a Cayley tableau of this group has a form

	1	γ_{0}	γ_{13}	γ_{013}	γ_{20}	γ_{2}	γ_{2013}	γ_{213}
1	1	γ_{0}	γ_{13}	γ_{013}	γ_{2}	γ_{2}	γ_{2013}	γ_{213}
γ_{0}	γ_{0}	1	γ_{013}	γ_{13}	$-\gamma_{2}$	$-\gamma_{20}$	$-\gamma_{213}$	$-\gamma_{2013}$
γ_{13}	γ_{13}	γ_{013}	-1	$-\gamma_{0}$	γ_{2013}	γ_{213}	$-\gamma_{20}$	$-\gamma_{2}$
γ_{013}	γ_{013}	γ_{13}	$-\gamma_{0}$	-1	$-\gamma_{213}$	$-\gamma_{2013}$	γ_{2}	γ_{20}
γ_{20}	γ_{20}	γ_{2}	γ_{2013}	γ_{213}	1	γ_{0}	γ_{13}	γ_{013}
γ_{2}	γ_{2}	γ_{20}	γ_{213}	γ_{2013}	$-\gamma_{0}$	-1	$-\gamma_{013}$	$-\gamma_{13}$
γ_{2013}	γ_{2013}	γ_{213}	$-\gamma_{20}$	γ_{2}	γ_{13}	γ_{013}	-1	$-\gamma_{0}$
γ_{213}	γ_{213}	γ_{2013}	$-\gamma_{2}$	$-\gamma_{20}$	$-\gamma_{013}$	$-\gamma_{13}$	γ_{0}	1

$\sim$

	1	P	T	PT	C	CP	CT	CPT
1	1	P	T	PT	C	CP	CT	CPT
P	P	1	PT	T	$-CP$	$-C$	$-CPT$	$-CT$
T	T	PT	-1	$-P$	CT	CPT	$-C$	$-CP$
PT	PT	T	$-P$	-1	$-CPT$	$-CT$	CP	C
C	C	CP	CT	CPT	1	P	T	PT
CP	CP	C	CPT	CT	$-P$	-1	$-PT$	$-T$
CT	CT	CPT	$-C$	CP	T	PT	-1	$-P$
CPT	CPT	CT	$-CP$	$-C$	$-PT$	$-T$	P	1

Hence it follows that the CPT–group (70) is a non–Abelian finite group of the order structure (3,4). In more details, it is the group $\mathbb{Z}_4 \overset{*}{\otimes} \mathbb{Z}_2$ with the signature $(+,-,-,+,-,-,+)$.

Theorem 10. *Let* $\mathbb{C}_n$ *be the Clifford algebra over the field* $\mathbb{F} = \mathbb{C}$ *and let* $\mathsf{Ext}(\mathbb{C}_n) = \{\mathsf{I},\ \mathsf{W},\ \mathsf{E},\ \mathsf{C},\ \Pi,\ \mathsf{K},\ \mathsf{S},\ \mathsf{F}\}$ *be an extended automorphism group of the algebra* $\mathbb{C}_n$*, where* $\mathsf{W},\ \mathsf{E},\ \mathsf{C},\ \Pi,\ \mathsf{K},\ \mathsf{S},\ \mathsf{F}$ *are spinor representations of the transformations* $\mathcal{A} \rightarrow \mathcal{A}^\star$, $\mathcal{A} \rightarrow \widetilde{\mathcal{A}}$, $\mathcal{A} \rightarrow \widetilde{\mathcal{A}^\star}$, $\mathcal{A} \rightarrow \overline{\mathcal{A}}$, $\mathcal{A} \rightarrow \overline{\mathcal{A}^\star}$, $\mathcal{A} \rightarrow \overline{\widetilde{\mathcal{A}}}$, $\mathcal{A} \rightarrow \overline{\widetilde{\mathcal{A}^\star}}$. *Then over the field* $\mathbb{F} = \mathbb{C}$

in dependence on a division ring structure of the real subalgebras $\mathcal{C}\ell_{p,q} \subset \mathbb{C}_n$ *there exist following isomorphisms between finite groups and groups* $\mathsf{Ext}(\mathbb{C}_n)$*:*

1) $\mathbb{K} \simeq \mathbb{R}$*, types* $p - q \equiv 0, 2 \pmod 8$*.*
In this case the matrix Π *of the pseudoautomorphism* $\mathcal{A} \longrightarrow \overline{\mathcal{A}}$ *is proportional to the unit matrix (identical transformation) and the extended automorphism group* $\mathsf{Ext}(\mathbb{C}_n)$ *is reduced to the group of fundamental automorphisms* $\mathsf{Aut}_{\pm}(\mathbb{C}_n)$*.*

2) $\mathbb{K} \simeq \mathbb{H}$*, types* $p - q \equiv 4, 6 \pmod 8$*.*
In dependence on a spinbasis structure of the subalgebra $\mathcal{C}\ell_{p,q}$ *there exist the following group isomorphisms:* $\mathsf{Ext}_{-}(\mathbb{C}_n) \simeq \mathbb{Z}_2 \otimes \mathbb{Z}_2 \otimes \mathbb{Z}_2$ *with the signature* $(+,+,+,+,+,+,+)$ *and* $\mathsf{Ext}(\mathbb{C}_n) \simeq \mathbb{Z}_4 \otimes \mathbb{Z}_2$ *with* $(+,+,+,-,-,-,-)$ *for the type* $p - q \equiv 4 \pmod 8$ *if* $m, v, l, u \equiv 0 \pmod 2$*, where* m *and* l *are quantities of complex skewsymmetric and symmetric matrices, and* u *and* v *are quantities of real skewsymmetric and symmetric matrices of the spinbasis of* $\mathcal{C}\ell_{p,q}$*. Correspondingly, at* $m, v, l, u \equiv 0 \pmod 2$ *there exist Abelian groups* $\mathsf{Ext}_{-}(\mathbb{C}_n) \simeq \mathbb{Z}_4 \otimes \mathbb{Z}_2$ *with* $(+,-,-,d,e,f,g)$ *for the type* $p - q \equiv 4 \pmod 8$ *and* $\mathsf{Ext}_{-}(\mathbb{C}_n) \simeq \mathbb{Z}_4 \otimes \mathbb{Z}_2$ *with* $(-,+,-,d,e,f,g)$*,* $(-,-,+,d,e,f,g)$ *for the type* $p-q \equiv 6 \pmod 8$*, where among the symbols* d, e, f, g *there are two pluses and two minuses.*

If $m, v, l, u \equiv 1 \pmod 2$ *or if among* m, v, l, u *there are both even and odd numbers, then there exists the non–Abelian group* $\mathsf{Ext}_{+}(\mathbb{C}_n) \simeq Q_4$ *with the signatures* $(-,-,-,d,e,f,g)$ *for the type* $p-q \equiv 6 \pmod 8$*, where among* d, e, f, g *there are one plus and three minuses. And also there exist* $\mathsf{Ext}_{+}(\mathbb{C}_n) \simeq D_4$ *with* $(+,-,+,d,e,f,g)$*,* $(+,+,-,d,e,f,g)$ *for the type* $p - q \equiv 4 \pmod 8$ *and* $\mathsf{Ext}_{+}(\mathbb{C}_n) \simeq D_4$ *with* $(-,+,+,d,e,f,g)$ *for the type* $p - q \equiv 6 \pmod 8$*, where among the symbols* d, e, f, g *there are three pluses and one minus. Besides, there exist the groups* $\mathsf{Ext}_{+}(\mathbb{C}_n) \simeq Q_4$ *with the signatures* $(+,-,-,-,-,-,-)$ *for* $p - q \equiv 4 \pmod 8$ *and* $(-,+,-,-,-,-,-)$*,* $(-,-,+,-,-,-,-)$ *for* $p - q \equiv 6 \pmod 8$*. And also there exist the groups* $\mathsf{Ext}_{+}(\mathbb{C}_n) \simeq D_4$ *with* $(+,+,+,d,e,f,g)$*,* $(+,-,-,+,+,+,+)$ *for the type* $p - q \equiv 4 \pmod 8$ *and* $(a,b,c,+,+,+,+)$ *for the type* $p - q \equiv 6 \pmod 8$ *(among the symbols* a, b, c *there are one plus and two minuses, and among* d, e, f, g *there are two pluses and two minuses). There exists the non–Abelian group* $\mathsf{Ext}_{+}(\mathbb{C}_n) \simeq \overset{*}{\mathbb{Z}}_4 \otimes \mathbb{Z}_2$ *with the signatures* $(+,-,-,d,e,f,g)$ *for the type* $p - q \equiv 4 \pmod 8$ *and* $(-,+,-,d,e,f,g)$*,* $(-,-,+,d,e,f,g)$ *for the type* $p - q \equiv 6 \pmod 8$*, where among* d, e, f, g *there are two pluses and two minuses. And also there exist* $\mathsf{Ext}_{+}(\mathbb{C}_n) \simeq \overset{*}{\mathbb{Z}}_4 \otimes \mathbb{Z}_2$ *with* $(+,-,+,d,e,f,g)$*,* $(+,+,-,d,e,f,g)$ *for* $p - q \equiv 4 \pmod 8$ *and* $(-,+,+,d,e,f,g)$ *for* $p - q \equiv 6 \pmod 8$*, where among* d, e, f, g *there are one plus and three minuses. Finally, for the type* $p - q \equiv 6 \pmod 8$ *there exists* $\mathsf{Ext}_{+}(\mathbb{C}_n) \simeq \overset{*}{\mathbb{Z}}_4 \otimes \mathbb{Z}_2$ *with* $(-,-,-,d,e,f,g)$*, where among the symbols* d, e, f, g *there are three pluses and one minus. The full number of the different signatures* (a,b,c,d,e,f,g) *is equal to 64.*

Proof. First of all, it is necessary to define permutation relations between the elements of the group Ext. We start with the matrix of the pseudoautomorphism $\mathcal{A} \to \overline{\mathcal{A}}$ (permutation relations between the elements W, E and C are found in Theorem 7). As known, for the types $p-q \equiv 4,6 \pmod 8$ the matrix Π exists in the two different forms: 1) $\Pi = \mathcal{E}_{\alpha_1}\mathcal{E}_{\alpha_2}\cdots\mathcal{E}_{\alpha_a}$ is the product of all complex matrices of the spinbasis at $a \equiv 0 \pmod 2$; 2) $\Pi = \mathcal{E}_{\beta_1}\mathcal{E}_{\beta_2}\cdots\mathcal{E}_{\beta_b}$ is the product of all real matrices of the spinbasis at $b \equiv 1 \pmod 2$.

Let us consider permutation relations of Π with the matrix K of the pseudoautomorphism $\mathcal{A} \to \overline{\mathcal{A}^\star}$. The matrix K also exists in the two different forms: $\mathsf{K} = \mathcal{E}_{\alpha_1}\mathcal{E}_{\alpha_2}\cdots\mathcal{E}_{\alpha_a}$ at $a \equiv 1 \pmod 2$ and $\mathsf{K} = \mathcal{E}_{\beta_1}\mathcal{E}_{\beta_2}\cdots\mathcal{E}_{\beta_b}$ at $b \equiv 0 \pmod 2$. In virtue of the definition $\mathsf{K} = \Pi\mathsf{W}$, where $\mathsf{W} = \mathcal{E}_1\mathcal{E}_2\cdots\mathcal{E}_{p+q}$ is the spinor representation of the automorphism $\mathcal{A} \to \mathcal{A}^\star$, the matrix $\Pi = \mathcal{E}_{\alpha_1}\mathcal{E}_{\alpha_2}\cdots\mathcal{E}_{\alpha_a}$ corresponds to a matrix $\mathsf{K} = \mathcal{E}_{\beta_1}\mathcal{E}_{\beta_2}\cdots\mathcal{E}_{\beta_b}$, since $n = p+q$ is always even for the types $p-q \equiv 4,6 \pmod 8$. Correspondingly, for the matrix $\Pi = \mathcal{E}_{\beta_1}\mathcal{E}_{\beta_2}\cdots\mathcal{E}_{\beta_b}$ we obtain $\mathsf{K} = \mathcal{E}_{\alpha_1}\mathcal{E}_{\alpha_2}\cdots\mathcal{E}_{\alpha_a}$, where $a, b \equiv 1 \pmod 2$. It is easy to see that in both cases we have a relation

$$\Pi\mathsf{K} = (-1)^{ab}\mathsf{K}\Pi, \tag{71}$$

that is, at $a, b \equiv 0 \pmod 2$ the matrices Π and K always commute and at $a, b \equiv 1 \pmod 2$ always anticommute.

Let us find now permutation relations of Π with the matrix S of the pseudoantiautomorphism $\mathcal{A} \to \overline{\widetilde{\mathcal{A}}}$. As known, the matrix S exists in the two non-equivalent forms: 1) $\mathsf{S} = \mathcal{E}_{c_1}\mathcal{E}_{c_2}\cdots\mathcal{E}_{c_s}$ is the product of all complex symmetric and real skewsymmetric matrices at $s \equiv 0 \pmod 2$; 2) $\mathsf{S} = \mathcal{E}_{d_1}\mathcal{E}_{d_2}\cdots\mathcal{E}_{d_g}$ is the product of all complex skewsymmetric and real symmetric matrices at $g \equiv 1 \pmod 2$. From $\mathsf{S} = \Pi\mathsf{E}$ it follows that $\Pi = \mathcal{E}_{\alpha_1}\mathcal{E}_{\alpha_2}\cdots\mathcal{E}_{\alpha_a}$ corresponds to $\mathsf{S} = \mathcal{E}_{c_1}\mathcal{E}_{c_2}\cdots\mathcal{E}_{c_s}$ if $\mathsf{E} = \mathcal{E}_{j_1}\mathcal{E}_{j_2}\cdots\mathcal{E}_{j_k}$ and $\mathsf{S} = \mathcal{E}_{d_1}\mathcal{E}_{d_2}\cdots\mathcal{E}_{d_g}$ if $\mathsf{E} = \mathcal{E}_{i_1}\mathcal{E}_{i_2}\cdots\mathcal{E}_{i_{p+q-k}}$. In turn, the matrix $\Pi = \mathcal{E}_{\beta_1}\mathcal{E}_{\beta_2}\cdots\mathcal{E}_{\beta_b}$ corresponds to $\mathsf{S} = \mathcal{E}_{d_1}\mathcal{E}_{d_2}\cdots\mathcal{E}_{d_g}$ if $\mathsf{E} = \mathcal{E}_{j_1}\mathcal{E}_{j_2}\cdots\mathcal{E}_{j_k}$ and to $\mathsf{S} = \mathcal{E}_{c_1}\mathcal{E}_{c_2}\cdots\mathcal{E}_{c_s}$ if $\mathsf{E} = \mathcal{E}_{i_1}\mathcal{E}_{i_2}\cdots\mathcal{E}_{i_{p+q-k}}$. Thus, taking into account that $\mathsf{S} = \Pi\mathsf{E}$, we obtain

$$\begin{aligned} \Pi\mathsf{S} &= (-1)^{\frac{a(a-1)}{2}+\tau}\mathcal{E}_{j_1}\mathcal{E}_{j_2}\cdots\mathcal{E}_{j_k}, \\ \mathsf{S}\Pi &= (-1)^{\frac{a(a-1)}{2}+\tau-m+ak}\mathcal{E}_{j_1}\mathcal{E}_{j_2}\cdots\mathcal{E}_{j_k} \end{aligned} \tag{72}$$

for the matrices $\Pi = \mathcal{E}_{\alpha_1}\mathcal{E}_{\alpha_2}\cdots\mathcal{E}_{\alpha_a}$ and $\mathsf{S} = \mathcal{E}_{c_1}\mathcal{E}_{c_2}\cdots\mathcal{E}_{c_s}$, where m is the number of complex skewsymmetric matrices of the spinbasis of $\mathcal{C}\!\ell_{p,q}$, $p-q \equiv 4,6 \pmod 8$. Since a comparison $ak \equiv 0 \pmod 2$ holds always, then the matrices Π and S commute at $m \equiv 0 \pmod 2$ and anticommute at $m \equiv 1 \pmod 2$. Correspondingly,

$$\begin{aligned} \Pi\mathsf{S} &= (-1)^{\frac{a(a-1)}{2}+\tau}\mathcal{E}_{i_1}\mathcal{E}_{i_2}\cdots\mathcal{E}_{i_{p+q-k}}, \\ \mathsf{S}\Pi &= (-1)^{\frac{a(a-1)}{2}+\tau-l+a(p+q-k)}\mathcal{E}_{i_1}\mathcal{E}_{i_2}\cdots\mathcal{E}_{i_{p+q-k}} \end{aligned} \tag{73}$$

for the matrices $\Pi = \mathcal{E}_{\alpha_1}\mathcal{E}_{\alpha_2}\cdots\mathcal{E}_{\alpha_a}$ and $\mathsf{S} = \mathcal{E}_{d_1}\mathcal{E}_{d_2}\cdots\mathcal{E}_{d_g}$, where l is the number of complex symmetric matrices of the spinbasis. Since $a(p+q-k) \equiv 0 \pmod 2$ ($a \equiv 0$

(mod 2), $p+q-k \equiv 1 \pmod 2$), then in this case the matrices Π and S commute at $l \equiv 0 \pmod 2$ and anticommute at $l \equiv 1 \pmod 2$. Further, we have

$$\begin{aligned} \Pi\mathsf{S} &= (-1)^{\frac{b(b-1)}{2}+\tau}\mathcal{E}_{j_1}\mathcal{E}_{j_2}\cdots\mathcal{E}_{j_k}, \\ \mathsf{S}\Pi &= (-1)^{\frac{b(b-1)}{2}+\tau-u+bk}\mathcal{E}_{j_1}\mathcal{E}_{j_2}\cdots\mathcal{E}_{j_k} \end{aligned} \tag{74}$$

for the matrices $\Pi = \mathcal{E}_{\beta_1}\mathcal{E}_{\beta_2}\cdots\mathcal{E}_{\beta_b}$ and $\mathsf{S} = \mathcal{E}_{d_1}\mathcal{E}_{d_2}\cdots\mathcal{E}_{d_g}$, where u is the number of real skewsymmetric matrices of the spinbasis. Since $bk \equiv 0 \pmod 2$ ($b \equiv 1 \pmod 2$, $k \equiv 0 \pmod 2$), then Π and S commute at $u \equiv 0 \pmod 2$ and anticommute at $u \equiv 1 \pmod 2$. Finally,

$$\begin{aligned} \Pi\mathsf{S} &= (-1)^{\frac{b(b-1)}{2}+\tau}\mathcal{E}_{i_1}\mathcal{E}_{i_2}\cdots\mathcal{E}_{i_{p+q-k}}, \\ \mathsf{S}\Pi &= (-1)^{\frac{b(b-1)}{2}+\tau-v+b(p+q-k)}\mathcal{E}_{i_1}\mathcal{E}_{i_2}\cdots\mathcal{E}_{i_{p+q-k}} \end{aligned} \tag{75}$$

for the matrices $\Pi = \mathcal{E}_{\beta_1}\mathcal{E}_{\beta_2}\cdots\mathcal{E}_{\beta_b}$ and $\mathsf{S} = \mathcal{E}_{c_1}\mathcal{E}_{c_2}\cdots\mathcal{E}_{c_s}$, where v is the number of real symmetric matrices. Therefore, permutation conditions of the matrices Π and S in this case have the form $b(p+q-k) \equiv v \pmod 2$, that is, Π and S commute at $v \equiv 1 \pmod 2$ and anticommute at $v \equiv 0 \pmod 2$, since $b, p+q-k \equiv 1 \pmod 2$.

Now we find permutation conditions of Π with the matrix F of the pseudoantiautomorphism $\mathcal{A} \to \widetilde{\overline{\mathcal{A}^\star}}$. In turn, the matrix F exists also in the two non-equivalent forms: $\mathsf{F} = \mathcal{E}_{d_1}\mathcal{E}_{d_2}\cdots\mathcal{E}_{d_g}$ at $g \equiv 0 \pmod 2$ and $\mathsf{F} = \mathcal{E}_{c_1}\mathcal{E}_{c_2}\cdots\mathcal{E}_{c_s}$ at $s \equiv 1 \pmod 2$. From the definition $\mathsf{F} = \Pi\mathsf{C}$ it follows that $\Pi = \mathcal{E}_{\alpha_1}\mathcal{E}_{\alpha_2}\cdots\mathcal{E}_{\alpha_a}$ corresponds to $\mathsf{F} = \mathcal{E}_{d_1}\mathcal{E}_{d_2}\cdots\mathcal{E}_{d_g}$ if $\mathsf{C} = \mathcal{E}_{i_1}\mathcal{E}_{i_2}\cdots\mathcal{E}_{i_{p+q-k}}$ and to $\mathsf{F} = \mathcal{E}_{c_1}\mathcal{E}_{c_2}\cdots\mathcal{E}_{c_s}$ if $\mathsf{C} = \mathcal{E}_{j_1}\mathcal{E}_{j_2}\cdots\mathcal{E}_{j_k}$. The matrix $\Pi = \mathcal{E}_{\beta_1}\mathcal{E}_{\beta_2}\cdots\mathcal{E}_{\beta_b}$ corresponds to $\mathsf{F} = \mathcal{E}_{c_1}\mathcal{E}_{c_2}\cdots\mathcal{E}_{c_s}$ if $\mathsf{C} = \mathcal{E}_{i_1}\mathcal{E}_{i_2}\cdots\mathcal{E}_{i_{p+q-k}}$ and to $\mathsf{F} = \mathcal{E}_{d_1}\mathcal{E}_{d_2}\cdots\mathcal{E}_{d_g}$ if $\mathsf{C} = \mathcal{E}_{j_1}\mathcal{E}_{j_2}\cdots\mathcal{E}_{j_k}$. Thus, taking into account that $\mathsf{F} = \Pi\mathsf{C}$, we obtain

$$\begin{aligned} \Pi\mathsf{F} &= (-1)^{\frac{a(a-1)}{2}+\tau}\mathcal{E}_{i_1}\mathcal{E}_{i_2}\cdots\mathcal{E}_{i_{p+q-k}}, \\ \mathsf{F}\Pi &= (-1)^{\frac{a(a-1)}{2}+\tau-l+a(p+q-k)}\mathcal{E}_{i_1}\mathcal{E}_{i_2}\cdots\mathcal{E}_{i_{p+q-k}} \end{aligned} \tag{76}$$

for the matrices $\Pi = \mathcal{E}_{\alpha_1}\mathcal{E}_{\alpha_2}\cdots\mathcal{E}_{\alpha_a}$ and $\mathsf{F} = \mathcal{E}_{d_1}\mathcal{E}_{d_2}\cdots\mathcal{E}_{d_g}$. It is easy to see that Π and F commute at $l \equiv 0 \pmod 2$ and anticommute at $l \equiv 1 \pmod 2$, since $a, p+q-k \equiv 0 \pmod 2$. Analogously,

$$\begin{aligned} \Pi\mathsf{F} &= (-1)^{\frac{a(a-1)}{2}+\tau}\mathcal{E}_{j_1}\mathcal{E}_{j_2}\cdots\mathcal{E}_{j_k}, \\ \mathsf{F}\Pi &= (-1)^{\frac{a(a-1)}{2}+\tau-m+ak}\mathcal{E}_{j_1}\mathcal{E}_{j_2}\cdots\mathcal{E}_{j_k} \end{aligned} \tag{77}$$

for $\Pi = \mathcal{E}_{\alpha_1}\mathcal{E}_{\alpha_2}\cdots\mathcal{E}_{\alpha_a}$ and $\mathsf{F} = \mathcal{E}_{c_1}\mathcal{E}_{c_2}\cdots\mathcal{E}_{c_s}$. Therefore, Π and F commute at $m \equiv 0 \pmod 2$ and anticommute at $m \equiv 1 \pmod 2$, since $a \equiv 0 \pmod 2$, $k \equiv 1 \pmod 2$. Further, we have

$$\begin{aligned} \Pi\mathsf{F} &= (-1)^{\frac{b(b-1)}{2}+\tau}\mathcal{E}_{i_1}\mathcal{E}_{i_2}\cdots\mathcal{E}_{i_{p+q-k}}, \\ \mathsf{F}\Pi &= (-1)^{\frac{b(b-1)}{2}+\tau-v+b(p+q-k)}\mathcal{E}_{i_1}\mathcal{E}_{i_2}\cdots\mathcal{E}_{i_{p+q-k}} \end{aligned} \tag{78}$$

for the matrices $\Pi = \mathcal{E}_{\beta_1}\mathcal{E}_{\beta_1}\cdots\mathcal{E}_{\beta_b}$ and $\mathsf{F} = \mathcal{E}_{c_1}\mathcal{E}_{c_2}\cdots\mathcal{E}_{c_s}$. In this case, Π and F commute at $v \equiv 0 \pmod 2$ and anticommute at $v \equiv 1 \pmod 2$, since $b \equiv 1 \pmod 2$, $p+q-k \equiv 0 \pmod 2$. Finally,

$$\begin{aligned} \Pi\mathsf{F} &= (-1)^{\frac{b(b-1)}{2}+\tau}\mathcal{E}_{j_1}\mathcal{E}_{j_2}\cdots\mathcal{E}_{j_k}, \\ \mathsf{F}\Pi &= (-1)^{\frac{b(b-1)}{2}+\tau-u+bk}\mathcal{E}_{j_1}\mathcal{E}_{j_2}\cdots\mathcal{E}_{j_k} \end{aligned} \tag{79}$$

for $\Pi = \mathcal{E}_{\beta_1}\mathcal{E}_{\beta_2}\cdots\mathcal{E}_{\beta_b}$ and $\mathsf{F} = \mathcal{E}_{d_1}\mathcal{E}_{d_2}\cdots\mathcal{E}_{d_g}$. Therefore, in this case permutation conditions of the matrices Π and F have the form $bk \equiv u \pmod 2$, that is, Π and F commute at $u \equiv 1 \pmod 2$ and anticommute at $u \equiv 0 \pmod 2$, since $b, k \equiv 1 \pmod 2$.

Let us define now permutation conditions of Π with the matrices W, E and C of the transformations $\mathcal{A} \to \mathcal{A}^\star$, $\mathcal{A} \to \widetilde{\mathcal{A}}$ and $\mathcal{A} \to \widetilde{\mathcal{A}^\star}$, respectively. First of all, according to Theorem 9 in the case of subalgebras $\mathcal{C}\!\ell_{p,q}$ with the real ring $\mathbb{K} \simeq \mathbb{R}$ (types $p-q \equiv 0, 2 \pmod 8$) the matrix Π is proportional to the unit matrix and, therefore, Π commutes with W, E and C. In case of the ring $\mathbb{K} \simeq \mathbb{H}$ (types $p-q \equiv 4, 6 \pmod 8$) the matrix Π exists in the two forms: Π_a at $a \equiv 0 \pmod 2$ and Π_b at $b \equiv 1 \pmod 2$. Since $a+b = p+q$, then the matrix W can be represented by a product $\mathcal{E}_{\alpha_1}\mathcal{E}_{\alpha_2}\cdots\mathcal{E}_{\alpha_a}\mathcal{E}_{\beta_1}\mathcal{E}_{\beta_2}\cdots\mathcal{E}_{\beta_b}$ and for $\Pi = \mathcal{E}_{\alpha_1}\mathcal{E}_{\alpha_2}\cdots\mathcal{E}_{\alpha_a}$ we have

$$\begin{aligned} \Pi\mathsf{W} &= (-1)^{\frac{a(a-1)}{2}}\sigma(\alpha_1)\sigma(\alpha_2)\cdots\sigma(\alpha_a)\mathcal{E}_{\beta_1}\mathcal{E}_{\beta_2}\cdots\mathcal{E}_{\beta_b}, \\ \mathsf{W}\Pi &= (-1)^{\frac{a(a-1)}{2}+ba}\sigma(\alpha_1)\sigma(\alpha_2)\cdots\sigma(\alpha_a)\mathcal{E}_{\beta_1}\mathcal{E}_{\beta_2}\cdots\mathcal{E}_{\alpha_b}. \end{aligned} \tag{80}$$

Hence it follows that Π and W commute at $ab \equiv 0 \pmod 2$ and anticommute at $ab \equiv 1 \pmod 2$, but $a \equiv 0 \pmod 2$ and, therefore, the matrices Π and W always commute in this case. Taking $\Pi = \mathcal{E}_{\beta_1}\mathcal{E}_{\beta_2}\cdots\mathcal{E}_{\beta_b}$, we find the following conditions

$$\begin{aligned} \Pi\mathsf{W} &= (-1)^{\frac{b(b-1)}{2}+ab}\sigma(\beta_1)\sigma(\beta_2)\cdots\sigma(\beta_b)\mathcal{E}_{\alpha_1}\mathcal{E}_{\alpha_2}\cdots\mathcal{E}_{\alpha_a}, \\ \mathsf{W}\Pi &= (-1)^{\frac{b(b-1)}{2}}\sigma(\beta_1)\sigma(\beta_2)\cdots\sigma(\beta_b)\mathcal{E}_{\alpha_1}\mathcal{E}_{\alpha_2}\cdots\mathcal{E}_{\alpha_a}. \end{aligned} \tag{81}$$

Hence it follows that $ab \equiv 1 \pmod 2$, since in this case $a, b \equiv 1 \pmod 2$ ($p+q = a+b$ is an even number). Therefore, at $b \equiv 1 \pmod 2$ the matrices Π and W always anticommute.

Let us find now permutation conditions between Π and the matrix E of the antiautomorphism $\mathcal{A} \to \widetilde{\mathcal{A}}$. As known (see Theorem 7), the matrix E exists in the two non-equivalent forms. First of all, if $\Pi = \mathcal{E}_{\alpha_1}\mathcal{E}_{\alpha_2}\cdots\mathcal{E}_{\alpha_a}$ and $\mathsf{E} = \mathcal{E}_{j_1}\mathcal{E}_{j_2}\cdots\mathcal{E}_{j_k}$, then it is obvious that Π and E contain m identical complex skewsymmetric matrices. We can represent the matrices Π and E in the form of the following products: $\Pi = \mathcal{E}_{\alpha_1}\mathcal{E}_{\alpha_2}\cdots\mathcal{E}_{\alpha_l}\mathcal{E}_{i_1}\mathcal{E}_{i_2}\cdots\mathcal{E}_{i_m}$ and $\mathsf{E} = \mathcal{E}_{i_1}\mathcal{E}_{i_2}\cdots\mathcal{E}_{i_m}\mathcal{E}_{j_1}\mathcal{E}_{j_2}\cdots\mathcal{E}_{j_u}$, where l and u are the numbers of complex symmetric and real skewsymmetric matrices, respectively. Therefore,

$$\begin{aligned} \Pi\mathsf{E} &= (-1)^{\frac{m(m-1)}{2}}\sigma(i_1)\sigma(i_2)\cdots\sigma(i_m)\mathcal{E}_{\alpha_1}\mathcal{E}_{\alpha_2}\cdots\mathcal{E}_{\alpha_l}\mathcal{E}_{j_1}\mathcal{E}_{j_2}\cdots\mathcal{E}_{j_u}, \\ \mathsf{E}\Pi &= (-1)^{\frac{m(m-1)}{2}+m(u+l)}\sigma(i_1)\sigma(i_2)\cdots\sigma(i_m)\mathcal{E}_{\alpha_1}\mathcal{E}_{\alpha_2}\cdots\mathcal{E}_{\alpha_l}\mathcal{E}_{j_1}\mathcal{E}_{j_2}\cdots\mathcal{E}_{j_u}, \end{aligned} \tag{82}$$

that is, Π and E commute at $m(u+l) \equiv 0 \pmod 2$ and anticommute at $m(u+l) \equiv 1 \pmod 2$.

Analogously, if $\Pi = \mathcal{E}_{\alpha_1}\mathcal{E}_{\alpha_2}\cdots\mathcal{E}_{\alpha_a}$ and $\mathsf{E} = \mathcal{E}_{i_1}\mathcal{E}_{i_2}\cdots\mathcal{E}_{i_{p+q-k}}$, then it is easy to see that in this case Π and E contain l identical complex symmetric matrices. Then $\Pi = \mathcal{E}_{\alpha_1}\mathcal{E}_{\alpha_2}\cdots\mathcal{E}_{\alpha_m}\mathcal{E}_{i_1}\mathcal{E}_{i_2}\cdots\mathcal{E}_{i_l}$, $\mathsf{E} = \mathcal{E}_{i_1}\mathcal{E}_{i_2}\cdots\mathcal{E}_{i_l}\mathcal{E}_{i_1}\mathcal{E}_{i_2}\cdots\mathcal{E}_{i_v}$ (v is the number of all real symmetric matrices of the spinbasis) and

$$\begin{aligned}
\Pi\mathsf{E} &= (-1)^{\frac{l(l-1)}{2}}\sigma(i_1)\sigma(i_2)\cdots\sigma(i_l)\mathcal{E}_{\alpha_1}\mathcal{E}_{\alpha_2}\cdots\mathcal{E}_{\alpha_m}\mathcal{E}_{i_1}\mathcal{E}_{i_2}\cdots\mathcal{E}_{i_v},\\
\mathsf{E}\Pi &= (-1)^{\frac{l(l-1)}{2}+l(m+v)}\sigma(i_1)\sigma(i_2)\cdots\sigma(i_l)\mathcal{E}_{\alpha_1}\mathcal{E}_{\alpha_2}\cdots\mathcal{E}_{\alpha_m}\mathcal{E}_{i_1}\mathcal{E}_{i_2}\cdots\mathcal{E}_{i_v}. \quad (83)
\end{aligned}$$

Therefore, in this case Π and E commute at $l(m+v) \equiv 0 \pmod 2$ and anticommute at $l(m+v) \equiv 1 \pmod 2$.

In turn, the matrices $\Pi = \mathcal{E}_{\beta_1}\mathcal{E}_{\beta_2}\cdots\mathcal{E}_{\beta_b}$ and $\mathsf{E} = \mathcal{E}_{j_1}\mathcal{E}_{j_2}\cdots\mathcal{E}_{j_k}$ contain u identical real skewsymmetric matrices. Therefore, $\Pi = \mathcal{E}_{\beta_1}\mathcal{E}_{\beta_2}\cdots\mathcal{E}_{\beta_v}\mathcal{E}_{i_1}\mathcal{E}_{i_2}\cdots\mathcal{E}_{i_u}$, $\mathsf{E} = \mathcal{E}_{i_1}\mathcal{E}_{i_2}\cdots\mathcal{E}_{i_u}\mathcal{E}_{j_1}\mathcal{E}_{j_2}\cdots\mathcal{E}_{j_m}$ and

$$\begin{aligned}
\Pi\mathsf{E} &= (-1)^{\frac{u(u-1)}{2}}\sigma(i_1)\sigma(i_2)\cdots\sigma(i_u)\mathcal{E}_{\beta_1}\mathcal{E}_{\beta_2}\cdots\mathcal{E}_{\beta_v}\mathcal{E}_{j_1}\mathcal{E}_{j_2}\cdots\mathcal{E}_{j_m},\\
\mathsf{E}\Pi &= (-1)^{\frac{u(u-1)}{2}+u(m+v)}\sigma(i_1)\sigma(i_2)\cdots\sigma(i_u)\mathcal{E}_{\beta_1}\mathcal{E}_{\beta_2}\cdots\mathcal{E}_{\beta_v}\mathcal{E}_{j_1}\mathcal{E}_{j_2}\cdots\mathcal{E}_{j_m}. \quad (84)
\end{aligned}$$

Hence it follows that Π and E commute at $u(m+v) \equiv 0 \pmod 2$ and anticommute at $u(m+v) \equiv 1 \pmod 2$.

Finally, the matrices $\Pi = \mathcal{E}_{\beta_1}\mathcal{E}_{\beta_2}\cdots\mathcal{E}_{\beta_b}$ and $\mathsf{E} = \mathcal{E}_{i_1}\mathcal{E}_{i_2}\cdots\mathcal{E}_{i_{p+q-k}}$ contain v identical real symmetric matrices. Therefore, in this case $\Pi = \mathcal{E}_{\beta_1}\mathcal{E}_{\beta_2}\cdots\mathcal{E}_{\beta_u}\mathcal{E}_{i_1}\mathcal{E}_{i_2}\cdots\mathcal{E}_{i_v}$, $\mathsf{E} = \mathcal{E}_{i_1}\mathcal{E}_{i_2}\cdots\mathcal{E}_{i_v}\mathcal{E}_{i_1}\mathcal{E}_{i_2}\cdots\mathcal{E}_{i_l}$ and

$$\begin{aligned}
\Pi\mathsf{E} &= (-1)^{\frac{v(v-1)}{2}}\sigma(i_1)\sigma(i_2)\cdots\sigma(i_v)\mathcal{E}_{\beta_1}\mathcal{E}_{\beta_2}\cdots\mathcal{E}_{\beta_u}\mathcal{E}_{i_1}\mathcal{E}_{i_2}\cdots\mathcal{E}_{i_l},\\
\mathsf{E}\Pi &= (-1)^{\frac{v(v-1)}{2}+v(u+l)}\sigma(i_1)\sigma(i_2)\cdots\sigma(i_v)\mathcal{E}_{\beta_1}\mathcal{E}_{\beta_2}\cdots\mathcal{E}_{\beta_u}\mathcal{E}_{i_1}\mathcal{E}_{i_2}\cdots\mathcal{E}_{i_l}, \quad (85)
\end{aligned}$$

that is, in this case Π and E commute at $v(u+l) \equiv 0 \pmod 2$ and anticommute at $v(u+l) \equiv 1 \pmod 2$.

It is easy to see that permutation conditions of Π with the matrix C of the antiautomorphism $\mathcal{A} \to \widetilde{\mathcal{A}^\star}$ are analogous to the conditions (82)–(85). Indeed, at $\Pi = \mathcal{E}_{\alpha_1}\mathcal{E}_{\alpha_2}\cdots\mathcal{E}_{\alpha_a}$ and $\mathsf{C} = \mathcal{E}_{i_1}\mathcal{E}_{i_2}\cdots\mathcal{E}_{i_{p+q-k}}$ these conditions are analogous to (83), that is, $l(m+v) \equiv 0, 1 \pmod 2$. For the matrices $\Pi = \mathcal{E}_{\alpha_1}\mathcal{E}_{\alpha_2}\cdots\mathcal{E}_{\alpha_a}$ and $\mathsf{C} = \mathcal{E}_{j_1}\mathcal{E}_{j_2}\cdots\mathcal{E}_{j_k}$ we obtain the condition (82), that is, $m(u+l) \equiv 0, 1 \pmod 2$. In turn, for $\Pi = \mathcal{E}_{\beta_1}\mathcal{E}_{\beta_2}\cdots\mathcal{E}_{\beta_b}$ and $\mathsf{C} = \mathcal{E}_{i_1}\mathcal{E}_{i_2}\cdots\mathcal{E}_{i_{p+q-k}}$ we have the condition (85), that is, $v(u+l) \equiv 0, 1 \pmod 2$. Finally, the matrices $\Pi = \mathcal{E}_{\beta_1}\mathcal{E}_{\beta_2}\cdots\mathcal{E}_{\beta_b}$ and $\mathsf{C} = \mathcal{E}_{j_1}\mathcal{E}_{j_2}\cdots\mathcal{E}_{j_k}$ correspond to (84) with $u(m+v) \equiv 0, 1 \pmod 2$.

Let us consider now permutation conditions of the matrix K of $\mathcal{A} \to \overline{\mathcal{A}^\star}$ with other elements of the group $\mathsf{Ext}(\mathbb{C}_n)$. As it has been shown previously, the structure of K is analogous to the structure of Π, that is, $\mathsf{K} = \mathcal{E}_{\alpha_1}\mathcal{E}_{\alpha_2}\cdots\mathcal{E}_{\alpha_a}$ at $a \equiv 1 \pmod 2$

and $\mathsf{K} = \mathcal{E}_{\beta_1}\mathcal{E}_{\beta_2}\cdots\mathcal{E}_{\beta_b}$ at $b \equiv 0 \pmod 2$. Therefore, permutation conditions for K are similar to the conditions for Π. Permutation conditions between K and Π are defined by the relation (71). Coming to the matrix S of the pseudoantiautomorphism $\mathcal{A} \to \widetilde{\overline{\mathcal{A}}}$ we see that permutation conditions between K and S are analogous to (72)–(75). Namely, if $\mathsf{K} = \mathcal{E}_{\beta_1}\mathcal{E}_{\beta_2}\cdots\mathcal{E}_{\beta_b}$ and $\mathsf{S} = \mathcal{E}_{c_1}\mathcal{E}_{c_2}\cdots\mathcal{E}_{c_s}$, then from (75) it follows that K and S commute at $v \equiv 0 \pmod 2$ and anticommute at $v \equiv 1 \pmod 2$, since in this case $b \equiv 0 \pmod 2$ and $p+q-k \equiv 0 \pmod 2$. Analogously, if $\mathsf{K} = \mathcal{E}_{\alpha_1}\mathcal{E}_{\alpha_2}\cdots\mathcal{E}_{\alpha_b}$ and $\mathsf{S} = \mathcal{E}_{d_1}\mathcal{E}_{d_2}\cdots\mathcal{E}_{d_g}$, then from (73) we find that K and S commute at $l \equiv 0 \pmod 2$ and anticommute at $l \equiv 1 \pmod 2$, since $a \equiv 1 \pmod 2$, $p+q-k \equiv 0 \pmod 2$ for this case. Further, if $\mathsf{K} = \mathcal{E}_{\beta_1}\mathcal{E}_{\beta_2}\cdots\mathcal{E}_{\beta_b}$ and $\mathsf{S} = \mathcal{E}_{d_1}\mathcal{E}_{d_2}\cdots\mathcal{E}_{d_g}$, then form (74) we find that in this case K and S commute at $u \equiv 0 \pmod 2$ and anticommute at $u \equiv 1 \pmod 2$, since $b \equiv 0 \pmod 2$, $k \equiv 1 \pmod 2$. Finally, if $\mathsf{K} = \mathcal{E}_{\alpha_1}\mathcal{E}_{\alpha_2}\cdots\mathcal{E}_{\alpha_a}$ and $\mathsf{S} = \mathcal{E}_{c_1}\mathcal{E}_{c_2}\cdots\mathcal{E}_{c_s}$, then from (72) it follows that K and S commute at $m \equiv 1 \pmod 2$ and anticommute at $m \equiv 0 \pmod 2$, since in this case $a, k \equiv 1 \pmod 2$.

In like manner we can find permutation conditions of K with the matrix F of the pseudoantiautomorphism $\mathcal{A} \to \widetilde{\overline{\mathcal{A}^\star}}$. Indeed, for $\mathsf{K} = \mathcal{E}_{\beta_1}\mathcal{E}_{\beta_2}\cdots\mathcal{E}_{\beta_b}$ and $\mathsf{F} = \mathcal{E}_{d_1}\mathcal{E}_{d_2}\cdots\mathcal{E}_{d_g}$ from (79) it follows that K and F commute at $u \equiv 0 \pmod 2$ and anticommute at $u \equiv 1 \pmod 2$, since in this case $b, k \equiv 0 \pmod 2$. Further, if $\mathsf{K} = \mathcal{E}_{\alpha_1}\mathcal{E}_{\alpha_2}\cdots\mathcal{E}_{\alpha_a}$ and $\mathsf{F} = \mathcal{E}_{c_1}\mathcal{E}_{c_2}\cdots\mathcal{E}_{c_s}$, then from (77) we find that K and F commute at $m \equiv 0 \pmod 2$ and anticommute at $m \equiv 1 \pmod 2$, since $a \equiv 1 \pmod 2$, $k \equiv 0 \pmod 2$. In turn, for the matrices $\mathsf{K} = \mathcal{E}_{\beta_1}\mathcal{E}_{\beta_2}\cdots\mathcal{E}_{\beta_b}$ and $\mathsf{F} = \mathcal{E}_{c_1}\mathcal{E}_{c_2}\cdots\mathcal{E}_{c_s}$ from (78) we obtain that K and F commute at $v \equiv 0 \pmod 2$ and anticommute at $v \equiv 1 \pmod 2$, since $b \equiv 0 \pmod 2$, $p+q-k \equiv 1 \pmod 2$. Finally, if $\mathsf{K} = \mathcal{E}_{\alpha_1}\mathcal{E}_{\alpha_2}\cdots\mathcal{E}_{\alpha_a}$ and $\mathsf{F} = \mathcal{E}_{d_1}\mathcal{E}_{d_2}\cdots\mathcal{E}_{d_g}$, then from (76) it follows that K and F commute at $l \equiv 1 \pmod 2$ and anticommute at $l \equiv 0 \pmod 2$, since in this case $a, p+q-k \equiv 1 \pmod 2$.

It is easy to see that in virtue of similarity of the matrices K and Π, permutation conditions of K with the elements of $\mathsf{Aut}_\pm(C\!\ell_{p,q})$ are analogous to the conditions for Π. Indeed, if $\mathsf{K} = \mathcal{E}_{\beta_1}\mathcal{E}_{\beta_2}\cdots\mathcal{E}_{\beta_b}$, then from (81) it follows that K and W always commute, since in this case $a, b \equiv 0 \pmod 2$. In turn, if $\mathsf{K} = \mathcal{E}_{\alpha_1}\mathcal{E}_{\alpha_2}\cdots\mathcal{E}_{\alpha_a}$, then from (80) we see that K and W always anticommute, since $a, b \equiv 1 \pmod 2$. Further, if $\mathsf{K} = \mathcal{E}_{\beta_1}\mathcal{E}_{\beta_2}\cdots\mathcal{E}_{\beta_b}$ and $\mathsf{E} = \mathcal{E}_{j_1}\mathcal{E}_{j_2}\cdots\mathcal{E}_{j_k}$, then from (84) it follows that K and E commute at $u(m+v) \equiv 0 \pmod 2$ and anticommute at $u(m+v) \equiv 1 \pmod 2$. For the matrices $\mathsf{K} = \mathcal{E}_{\alpha_1}\mathcal{E}_{\alpha_2}\cdots\mathcal{E}_{\alpha_a}$ and $\mathsf{E} = \mathcal{E}_{j_1}\mathcal{E}_{j_2}\cdots\mathcal{E}_{j_k}$ from (82) it follows $m(u+l) \equiv 0, 1 \pmod 2$. Correspondingly, for the matrices $\mathsf{K} = \mathcal{E}_{\beta_1}\mathcal{E}_{\beta_2}\cdots\mathcal{E}_{\beta_b}$ and $\mathsf{E} = \mathcal{E}_{i_1}\mathcal{E}_{i_2}\cdots\mathcal{E}_{i_{p+q-k}}$ from (85) we obtain the condition $v(u+l) \equiv 0, 1 \pmod 2$. For $\mathsf{K} = \mathcal{E}_{\alpha_1}\mathcal{E}_{\alpha_2}\cdots\mathcal{E}_{\alpha_a}$ and $\mathsf{E} = \mathcal{E}_{i_1}\mathcal{E}_{i_2}\cdots\mathcal{E}_{i_{p+q-k}}$ from (83) we have $l(m+v) \equiv 0, 1 \pmod 2$. In turn, for $\mathsf{K} = \mathcal{E}_{\beta_1}\mathcal{E}_{\beta_2}\cdots\mathcal{E}_{\beta_b}$ and $\mathsf{C} = \mathcal{E}_{i_1}\mathcal{E}_{i_2}\cdots\mathcal{E}_{i_{p+q-k}}$ from (85) we obtain $v(u+l) \equiv 0, 1 \pmod 2$, for $\mathsf{K} = \mathcal{E}_{\alpha_1}\mathcal{E}_{\alpha_2}\cdots\mathcal{E}_{\alpha_a}$ and $\mathsf{C} = \mathcal{E}_{i_1}\mathcal{E}_{i_2}\cdots\mathcal{E}_{i_{p+q-k}}$ from (83) we obtain $l(m+v) \equiv 0, 1 \pmod 2$, for $\mathsf{K} = \mathcal{E}_{\beta_1}\mathcal{E}_{\beta_2}\cdots\mathcal{E}_{\beta_b}$ and $\mathsf{C} = \mathcal{E}_{j_1}\mathcal{E}_{j_2}\cdots\mathcal{E}_{j_k}$ from (84) it follows $u(m+v) \equiv 0, 1 \pmod 2$ and, finally, for $\mathsf{K} = \mathcal{E}_{\alpha_1}\mathcal{E}_{\alpha_2}\cdots\mathcal{E}_{\alpha_a}$ and

$\mathsf{C} = \mathcal{E}_{j_1}\mathcal{E}_{j_2}\cdots\mathcal{E}_{j_k}$ from (82) we have $m(u+l) \equiv 0, 1 \pmod 2$.

Let consider permutation conditions of the matrix S of the transformation $\mathcal{A} \longrightarrow \overline{\widetilde{\mathcal{A}}}$ with other elements of the group $\mathsf{Ext}(\mathbb{C}_n)$. Permutation conditions of S with the matrices Π and K have been defined previously (see (72)–(75)). Now we define permutation conditions of S with the matrix F of the pseudoantiautomorphism $\mathcal{A} \longrightarrow \overline{\widetilde{\mathcal{A}^\star}}$ and elements of the subgroup $\mathsf{Aut}_\pm(C\!\ell_{p,q})$. So, let $\mathsf{S} = \mathcal{E}_{c_1}\mathcal{E}_{c_2}\cdots\mathcal{E}_{c_s}$ and $\mathsf{F} = \mathcal{E}_{d_1}\mathcal{E}_{d_2}\cdots\mathcal{E}_{d_g}$, where $s \equiv 0 \pmod 2$ and $g \equiv 0 \pmod 2$. As known, in this case the product S contains all complex symmetric matrices and all real skewsymmetric matrices of the spinbasis. In turn, the product F contains all complex skewsymmetric and real symmetric matrices. Therefore, the product SF does not contain identical matrices. Then

$$\mathsf{SF} = (-1)^{sg}\mathsf{FS}, \tag{86}$$

that is, in this case S and F always commute, since $s, g \equiv 0 \pmod 2$. If $\mathsf{S} = \mathcal{E}_{d_1}\mathcal{E}_{d_2}\cdots\mathcal{E}_{d_g}$ and $\mathsf{F} = \mathcal{E}_{c_1}\mathcal{E}_{c_2}\cdots\mathcal{E}_{c_s}$, where $s, g \equiv 1 \pmod 2$, then from (86) it follows that S and F always anticommute.

Further, if $\mathsf{S} = \mathcal{E}_{c_1}\mathcal{E}_{c_2}\cdots\mathcal{E}_{c_s}$, then permutation conditions of S with the matrix W of the automorphism $\mathcal{A} \longrightarrow \mathcal{A}^\star$ have the form:

$$\begin{aligned}
\mathsf{SW} &= (-1)^{\frac{s(s-1)}{2}}\sigma(c_1)\sigma(c_2)\cdots\sigma(c_s)\mathcal{E}_{d_1}\mathcal{E}_{d_2}\cdots\mathcal{E}_{d_g},\\
\mathsf{WS} &= (-1)^{\frac{s(s-1)}{2}+sg}\sigma(c_1)\sigma(c_2)\cdots\sigma(c_s)\mathcal{E}_{d_1}\mathcal{E}_{d_2}\cdots\mathcal{E}_{d_g},
\end{aligned} \tag{87}$$

that is, in this case S always commutes with W, since $s, g \equiv 0 \pmod 2$. In turn, the matrix $\mathsf{S} = \mathcal{E}_{d_1}\mathcal{E}_{d_2}\cdots\mathcal{E}_{d_g}$ always anticommutes with W, since $s, g \equiv 1 \pmod 2$.

Let us define now permutation conditions between S and E. If $\mathsf{S} = \mathcal{E}_{c_1}\mathcal{E}_{c_2}\cdots\mathcal{E}_{c_s}$ and $\mathsf{E} = \mathcal{E}_{j_1}\mathcal{E}_{j_2}\cdots\mathcal{E}_{j_k}$, then the product SE contains u identical real skewsymmetric matrices. Hence it follows that $\mathsf{S} = \mathcal{E}_{c_1}\mathcal{E}_{c_2}\cdots\mathcal{E}_{c_l}\mathcal{E}_{i_1}\mathcal{E}_{i_2}\cdots\mathcal{E}_{i_u}$ and $\mathsf{E} = \mathcal{E}_{i_1}\mathcal{E}_{i_2}\cdots\mathcal{E}_{i_u}\mathcal{E}_{j_1}\mathcal{E}_{j_2}\cdots\mathcal{E}_{j_m}$. Then

$$\begin{aligned}
\mathsf{SE} &= (-1)^{\frac{u(u-1)}{2}}\sigma(i_1)\sigma(i_2)\cdots\sigma(i_u)\mathcal{E}_{c_1}\mathcal{E}_{c_2}\cdots\mathcal{E}_{c_l}\mathcal{E}_{j_1}\mathcal{E}_{j_2}\cdots\mathcal{E}_{j_m},\\
\mathsf{ES} &= (-1)^{\frac{u(u-1)}{2}+u(l+m)}\sigma(i_1)\sigma(i_2)\cdots\sigma(i_u)\mathcal{E}_{c_1}\mathcal{E}_{c_2}\cdots\mathcal{E}_{c_l}\mathcal{E}_{j_1}\mathcal{E}_{j_2}\cdots\mathcal{E}_{j_m},
\end{aligned} \tag{88}$$

that is, S and E commute at $u(l+m) \equiv 0 \pmod 2$ and anticommute at $u(l+m) \equiv 1 \pmod 2$.

In turn, the products $\mathsf{S} = \mathcal{E}_{d_1}\mathcal{E}_{d_2}\cdots\mathcal{E}_{d_g}$ and $\mathsf{E} = \mathcal{E}_{j_1}\mathcal{E}_{j_2}\cdots\mathcal{E}_{j_k}$ contain m identical complex skewsymmetric matrices. Therefore, $\mathsf{S} = \mathcal{E}_{d_1}\mathcal{E}_{d_2}\cdots\mathcal{E}_{d_v}\mathcal{E}_{i_1}\mathcal{E}_{i_2}\cdots\mathcal{E}_{i_m}$, $\mathsf{E} = \mathcal{E}_{i_1}\mathcal{E}_{i_2}\cdots\mathcal{E}_{i_m}\mathcal{E}_{j_1}\mathcal{E}_{j_2}\cdots\mathcal{E}_{j_u}$ and

$$\begin{aligned}
\mathsf{SE} &= (-1)^{\frac{m(m-1)}{2}}\sigma(i_1)\sigma(i_2)\cdots\sigma(i_m)\mathcal{E}_{d_1}\mathcal{E}_{d_2}\cdots\mathcal{E}_{d_v}\mathcal{E}_{j_1}\mathcal{E}_{j_2}\cdots\mathcal{E}_{j_u},\\
\mathsf{ES} &= (-1)^{\frac{m(m-1)}{2}+m(v+u)}\sigma(i_1)\sigma(i_2)\cdots\sigma(i_m)\mathcal{E}_{d_1}\mathcal{E}_{d_2}\cdots\mathcal{E}_{d_v}\mathcal{E}_{j_1}\mathcal{E}_{j_2}\cdots\mathcal{E}_{j_u},
\end{aligned} \tag{89}$$

that is, permutation conditions between S and E in this case have the form $m(v+u) \equiv 0,1 \pmod{2}$.

Further, the products $\mathsf{S} = \mathcal{E}_{d_1}\mathcal{E}_{d_2}\cdots\mathcal{E}_{d_g}$ and $\mathsf{E} = \mathcal{E}_{i_1}\mathcal{E}_{i_2}\cdots\mathcal{E}_{i_{p+q-k}}$ contain v identical real symmetric matrices. Then $\mathsf{S} = \mathcal{E}_{d_1}\mathcal{E}_{d_2}\cdots\mathcal{E}_{d_m}\mathcal{E}_{i_1}\mathcal{E}_{i_2}\cdots\mathcal{E}_{i_v}$, $\mathsf{E} = \mathcal{E}_{i_1}\mathcal{E}_{i_2}\cdots\mathcal{E}_{i_v}\mathcal{E}_{i_1}\mathcal{E}_{i_2}\cdots\mathcal{E}_{i_l}$ and

$$\begin{aligned}\mathsf{SE} &= (-1)^{\frac{v(v-1)}{2}}\sigma(i_1)\sigma(i_2)\cdots\sigma(i_v)\mathcal{E}_{d_1}\mathcal{E}_{d_2}\cdots\mathcal{E}_{d_m}\mathcal{E}_{i_1}\mathcal{E}_{i_2}\cdots\mathcal{E}_{i_l},\\ \mathsf{ES} &= (-1)^{\frac{v(v-1)}{2}+v(m+l)}\sigma(i_1)\sigma(i_2)\cdots\sigma(i_v)\mathcal{E}_{d_1}\mathcal{E}_{d_2}\cdots\mathcal{E}_{d_m}\mathcal{E}_{i_1}\mathcal{E}_{i_2}\cdots\mathcal{E}_{i_l},\end{aligned} \quad (90)$$

that is, permutation conditions between S and E are $v(m+l) \equiv 0,1 \pmod{2}$.

Finally, the products $\mathsf{S} = \mathcal{E}_{c_1}\mathcal{E}_{c_2}\cdots\mathcal{E}_{c_s}$ and $\mathsf{E} = \mathcal{E}_{i_1}\mathcal{E}_{i_2}\cdots\mathcal{E}_{i_{p+q-k}}$ contain l identical complex symmetric matrices and, therefore, $\mathsf{S} = \mathcal{E}_{c_1}\mathcal{E}_{c_2}\cdots\mathcal{E}_{c_u}\mathcal{E}_{i_1}\mathcal{E}_{i_2}\cdots\mathcal{E}_{i_l}$, $\mathsf{E} = \mathcal{E}_{i_1}\mathcal{E}_{i_2}\cdots\mathcal{E}_{i_l}\mathcal{E}_{i_1}\mathcal{E}_{i_2}\cdots\mathcal{E}_{i_v}$. Then

$$\begin{aligned}\mathsf{SE} &= (-1)^{\frac{l(l-1)}{2}}\sigma(i_1)\sigma(i_2)\cdots\sigma(i_l)\mathcal{E}_{c_1}\mathcal{E}_{c_2}\cdots\mathcal{E}_{c_u}\mathcal{E}_{i_1}\mathcal{E}_{i_2}\cdots\mathcal{E}_{i_v},\\ \mathsf{ES} &= (-1)^{\frac{l(l-1)}{2}+l(u+v)}\sigma(i_1)\sigma(i_2)\cdots\sigma(i_l)\mathcal{E}_{c_1}\mathcal{E}_{c_2}\cdots\mathcal{E}_{c_u}\mathcal{E}_{i_1}\mathcal{E}_{i_2}\cdots\mathcal{E}_{i_v}\end{aligned} \quad (91)$$

and permutation conditions for S and E in this case have the form $l(u+v) \equiv 0,1 \pmod{2}$.

It is easy to see that permutation conditions between S and C are analogous to (88)–(91). Indeed, if $\mathsf{S} = \mathcal{E}_{c_1}\mathcal{E}_{c_2}\cdots\mathcal{E}_{c_s}$ and $\mathsf{C} = \mathcal{E}_{i_1}\mathcal{E}_{i_2}\cdots\mathcal{E}_{i_{p+q-k}}$, then from (91) it follows the comparison $l(u+v) \equiv 0,1 \pmod{2}$. In turn, if $\mathsf{S} = \mathcal{E}_{d_1}\mathcal{E}_{d_2}\cdots\mathcal{E}_{d_g}$ and $\mathsf{C} = \mathcal{E}_{i_1}\mathcal{E}_{i_2}\cdots\mathcal{E}_{i_{p+q-k}}$, then from (90) we obtain $v(m+l) \equiv 0,1 \pmod{2}$. Further, for $\mathsf{S} = \mathcal{E}_{d_1}\mathcal{E}_{d_2}\cdots\mathcal{E}_{d_g}$ and $\mathsf{C} = \mathcal{E}_{j_1}\mathcal{E}_{j_2}\cdots\mathcal{E}_{j_k}$ from (89) it follows that $m(v+u) \equiv 0,1 \pmod{2}$. Analogously, for $\mathsf{S} = \mathcal{E}_{c_1}\mathcal{E}_{c_2}\cdots\mathcal{E}_{c_s}$ and $\mathsf{C} = \mathcal{E}_{j_1}\mathcal{E}_{j_2}\cdots\mathcal{E}_{j_k}$ from (88) we have $u(l+m) \equiv 0,1 \pmod{2}$.

Finally, let us consider permutation conditions of the matrix F of $\mathcal{A} \to \widetilde{\overline{\mathcal{A}^\star}}$ with other elements of the group $\mathsf{Ext}(\mathbb{C}_n)$. Permutation conditions of F with the matrices Π, K and S have been found previously (see (76)–(79), (86)). Now we define permutation conditions between F and the elements of the subgroups $\mathsf{Aut}_\pm(C\ell_{p,q})$. It is easy to see that permutation conditions between F and W are equivalent to (87), that is, $\mathsf{F} = \mathcal{E}_{d_1}\mathcal{E}_{d_2}\cdots\mathcal{E}_{d_g}$ always commute with W, since $s, g \equiv 0 \pmod{2}$, and $\mathsf{F} = \mathcal{E}_{c_1}\mathcal{E}_{c_2}\cdots\mathcal{E}_{c_s}$ always anticommute with W, since in this case $s, g \equiv 1 \pmod{2}$. In turn, permutation conditions between F and E are equivalent to (88)–(91). Indeed, if $\mathsf{F} = \mathcal{E}_{d_1}\mathcal{E}_{d_2}\cdots\mathcal{E}_{d_g}$ and $\mathsf{E} = \mathcal{E}_{j_1}\mathcal{E}_{j_2}\cdots\mathcal{E}_{j_k}$, then from (89) it follows the comparison $m(v+u) \equiv 0,1 \pmod{2}$. For $\mathsf{F} = \mathcal{E}_{c_1}\mathcal{E}_{c_2}\cdots\mathcal{E}_{c_s}$ and $\mathsf{E} = \mathcal{E}_{j_1}\mathcal{E}_{j_2}\cdots\mathcal{E}_{j_k}$ from (88) we have $u(l+m) \equiv 0,1 \pmod{2}$. Analogously, for $\mathsf{F} = \mathcal{E}_{c_1}\mathcal{E}_{c_2}\cdots\mathcal{E}_{c_s}$ and $\mathsf{E} = \mathcal{E}_{i_1}\mathcal{E}_{i_2}\cdots\mathcal{E}_{i_{p+q-k}}$ from (91) we obtain $l(u+v) \equiv 0,1 \pmod{2}$, and for $\mathsf{F} = \mathcal{E}_{d_1}\mathcal{E}_{d_2}\cdots\mathcal{E}_{d_g}$, $\mathsf{E} = \mathcal{E}_{i_1}\mathcal{E}_{i_2}\cdots\mathcal{E}_{i_{p+q-k}}$ from (90) it follows $v(m+l) \equiv 0,1 \pmod{2}$. It is easy to see that permutation conditions between F and C are equivalent to

(88)–(91). Namely, for $\mathsf{F}=\mathcal{E}_{d_1}\mathcal{E}_{d_2}\cdots\mathcal{E}_{d_g}$, $\mathsf{C}=\mathcal{E}_{i_1}\mathcal{E}_{i_2}\cdots\mathcal{E}_{i_{p+q-k}}$ from (90) we obtain $v(m+l)\equiv 0,1 \pmod 2$, for $\mathsf{F}=\mathcal{E}_{c_1}\mathcal{E}_{c_2}\cdots\mathcal{E}_{c_s}$, $\mathsf{C}=\mathcal{E}_{i_1}\mathcal{E}_{i_2}\cdots\mathcal{E}_{i_{p+q-k}}$ from (91) it follows $l(u+v)\equiv 0,1 \pmod 2$. Correspondingly, for $\mathsf{F}=\mathcal{E}_{c_1}\mathcal{E}_{c_2}\cdots\mathcal{E}_{c_s}$, $\mathsf{C}=\mathcal{E}_{j_1}\mathcal{E}_{j_2}\cdots\mathcal{E}_{j_k}$ from (88) we find $u(l+m)\equiv 0,1 \pmod 2$, and for $\mathsf{F}=\mathcal{E}_{d_1}\mathcal{E}_{d_2}\cdots\mathcal{E}_{d_g}$, $\mathsf{C}=\mathcal{E}_{j_1}\mathcal{E}_{j_2}\cdots\mathcal{E}_{j_k}$ from (89) we see that $m(v+u)\equiv 0,1 \pmod 2$.

Now, we are in a position to define a detailed classification for extended automorphism groups $\mathsf{Ext}(\mathbb{C}_n)$. First of all, since for the subalgebras $\mathcal{C}\!\ell_{p,q}$ over the ring $\mathbb{K}\simeq\mathbb{R}$ the group $\mathsf{Ext}(\mathbb{C}_n)$ is reduced to $\mathsf{Aut}_\pm(\mathbb{C}_n)$, then all essentially different groups $\mathsf{Ext}(\mathbb{C}_n)$ correspond to the subalgebras $\mathcal{C}\!\ell_{p,q}$ with the quaternionic ring $\mathbb{K}\simeq\mathbb{H}$, $p-q\equiv 4,6 \pmod 8$. Let us classify the groups $\mathsf{Ext}(\mathbb{C}_n)$ with respect to their subgroups $\mathsf{Aut}_\pm(\mathcal{C}\!\ell_{p,q})$. Taking into account the structure of $\mathsf{Aut}_\pm(\mathcal{C}\!\ell_{p,q})$ at $p-q\equiv 4,6$ (mod 8) (see Theorem 7) we obtain for the group $\mathsf{Ext}(\mathbb{C}_n)=\{\mathsf{I},\mathsf{W},\mathsf{E},\mathsf{C},\Pi,\mathsf{K},\mathsf{S},\mathsf{F}\}$ the following possible realizations:

$$\mathsf{Ext}^1(\mathbb{C}_n)=\left\{\mathsf{I},\mathcal{E}_{12\cdots p+q},\mathcal{E}_{j_1j_2\cdots j_k},\mathcal{E}_{i_1i_2\cdots i_{p+q-k}},\mathcal{E}_{\alpha_1\alpha_2\cdots\alpha_a},\mathcal{E}_{\beta_1\beta_2\cdots\beta_b},\mathcal{E}_{c_1c_2\cdots c_s},\mathcal{E}_{d_1d_2\cdots d_g}\right\},$$
$$\mathsf{Ext}^2(\mathbb{C}_n)=\left\{\mathsf{I},\mathcal{E}_{12\cdots p+q},\mathcal{E}_{j_1j_2\cdots j_k},\mathcal{E}_{i_1i_2\cdots i_{p+q-k}},\mathcal{E}_{\beta_1\beta_2\cdots\beta_b},\mathcal{E}_{\alpha_1\alpha_2\cdots\alpha_a},\mathcal{E}_{d_1d_2\cdots d_g},\mathcal{E}_{c_1c_2\cdots c_s}\right\},$$
$$\mathsf{Ext}^3(\mathbb{C}_n)=\left\{\mathsf{I},\mathcal{E}_{12\cdots p+q},\mathcal{E}_{i_1i_2\cdots i_{p+q-k}},\mathcal{E}_{j_1j_2\cdots j_k},\mathcal{E}_{\alpha_1\alpha_2\cdots\alpha_a},\mathcal{E}_{\beta_1\beta_2\cdots\beta_b},\mathcal{E}_{d_1d_2\cdots d_g},\mathcal{E}_{c_1c_2\cdots c_s}\right\},$$
$$\mathsf{Ext}^4(\mathbb{C}_n)=\left\{\mathsf{I},\mathcal{E}_{12\cdots p+q},\mathcal{E}_{i_1i_2\cdots i_{p+q-k}},\mathcal{E}_{j_1j_2\cdots j_k},\mathcal{E}_{\beta_1\beta_2\cdots\beta_b},\mathcal{E}_{\alpha_1\alpha_2\cdots\alpha_a},\mathcal{E}_{c_1c_2\cdots c_s},\mathcal{E}_{d_1d_2\cdots d_g}\right\}.$$

The groups $\mathsf{Ext}^1(\mathbb{C}_n)$ and $\mathsf{Ext}^2(\mathbb{C}_n)$ have Abelian subgroups $\mathsf{Aut}_-(\mathcal{C}\!\ell_{p,q})$ ($\mathbb{Z}_2\otimes\mathbb{Z}_2$ or $\mathbb{Z}_4$). In turn, the groups $\mathsf{Ext}^3(\mathbb{C}_n)$ and $\mathsf{Ext}^4(\mathbb{C}_n)$ have only non-Abelian subgroups $\mathsf{Aut}_+(\mathcal{C}\!\ell_{p,q})$ ($Q_4/\mathbb{Z}_2$ or $D_4/\mathbb{Z}_2$).

Let us start with the group $\mathsf{Ext}^1(\mathbb{C}_n)$. All the elements of $\mathsf{Ext}^1(\mathbb{C}_n)$ are even products, that is, $p+q\equiv 0 \pmod 2$, $k\equiv 0 \pmod 2$, $a\equiv 0 \pmod 2$, $b\equiv 0$ (mod 2), $s\equiv 0 \pmod 2$ and $g\equiv 0 \pmod 2$. At this point, the elements I, W, E, C form Abelian subgroups $\mathbb{Z}_2\otimes\mathbb{Z}_2$ or $\mathbb{Z}_4$ (see Theorem 7). In virtue of (71) the element Π commutes with K, and from (72) it follows that Π commutes with S at $m\equiv 0$ (mod 2). From (76) we see that Π commutes with F at $l\equiv 0 \pmod 2$, and from (80) it follows that Π commutes with W. The conditions (82) show that Π commutes with E at $m(u+l)\equiv 0 \pmod 2$ and commutes with C at $l(m+v)\equiv 0 \pmod 2$. Further, the element K commutes with S at $v\equiv 0 \pmod 2$ and commutes with F at $u\equiv 0 \pmod 2$. And also $\mathsf{K}\in\mathsf{Ext}^1$ always commutes with W and commutes correspondingly with E and C at $u(m+v)\equiv 0 \pmod 2$ and $v(u+l)\equiv 0 \pmod 2$. From (86) and (87) it follows that the element S always commutes with F and W. The conditions (88) and (91) show that S commutes with E and C correspondingly at $u(l+m)\equiv 0 \pmod 2$ and $l(u+v)\equiv 0 \pmod 2$. In virtue of (87) the element F always commutes with W. Finally, from (89) and (90) it follows that F commutes with E and C correspondingly at $m(v+u)\equiv 0 \pmod 2$ and $v(m+l)\equiv 0 \pmod 2$. Thus, the group $\mathsf{Ext}^1(\mathbb{C}_n)$ is Abelian at $m,l,u,v\equiv 0 \pmod 2$. In case of the subgroup $\mathsf{Aut}_-(\mathcal{C}\!\ell_{p,q})\simeq\mathbb{Z}_2\otimes\mathbb{Z}_2$ ($p-q\equiv 4 \pmod 8$) we obtain an Abelian group $\mathsf{Ext}^1_-(\mathbb{C}_n)\simeq\mathbb{Z}_2\otimes\mathbb{Z}_2\otimes\mathbb{Z}_2$ with the signature $(+,+,+,+,+,+,+)$ for the elements Π, K, S and F with positive squares ($m-l\equiv 0,4 \pmod 8$, $v-u\equiv 0,4 \pmod 8$),

$u+l\equiv 0,4 \pmod 8$ and $m+v\equiv 0,4 \pmod 8$). It is easy to see that for the type $p-q\equiv 4 \pmod 8$ there exists also $\mathsf{Ext}^1_-(\mathbb{C}_n)\simeq \mathbb{Z}_4\otimes\mathbb{Z}_2$ with the signature $(+,+,+,-,-,-,-)$ and the subgroup $\mathbb{Z}_2\otimes\mathbb{Z}_2$, where $m-l\equiv 2,6 \pmod 8$, $v-u\equiv 2,6 \pmod 8$, $u+l\equiv 2,6 \pmod 8$ and $m+v\equiv 2,6 \pmod 8$. Further, for the type $p-q\equiv 4 \pmod 8$ there exist Abelian groups $\mathsf{Ext}^1_-(\mathbb{C}_n)\simeq\mathbb{Z}_4\otimes\mathbb{Z}_2$ with the signatures $(+,-,-,d,e,f,g)$ and subgroups $\mathbb{Z}_4$, where among the symbols d, e, f, g there are two pluses and two minuses. Correspondingly, at $m,v,l,u\equiv 0 \pmod 2$ for the type $p-q\equiv 6 \pmod 8$ there exist Abelian groups $\mathsf{Ext}^1_-(\mathbb{C}_n)\simeq\mathbb{Z}_4\otimes\mathbb{Z}_2$ with the signatures $(-,+,-,d,e,f,g)$ and $(-,-,+,d,e,f,g)$ if $m-u\equiv 0,1,4,5 \pmod 8$, $v-l\equiv 2,3,6,7 \pmod 8$ and $m-u\equiv 2,3,6,7 \pmod 8$, $v-l\equiv 0,1,4,5 \pmod 8$.

It is easy to see that from the comparison $k,a,b,s,g\equiv 0 \pmod 2$ it follows that the numbers m, v, l, u are simultaneously even or odd. The case $m,v,l,u\equiv 0 \pmod 2$, considered previously, gives rise to the Abelian groups Ext^1_-. In contrast to this, the case $m,v,l,u\equiv 1 \pmod 2$ gives rise to non-Abelian groups Ext^1_+ with Abelian subgroups $\mathbb{Z}_4$ and $\mathbb{Z}_2\otimes\mathbb{Z}_2$ (it follows from (71)–(72)). Namely, in this case we have the group $\mathsf{Ext}^1_+\simeq \overset{*}{\mathbb{Z}_4}\otimes\mathbb{Z}_2$ with the subgroup $\mathbb{Z}_4$ for $p-q\equiv 4,6 \pmod 8$ (it should be noted that signatures of the groups $\mathbb{Z}_4\otimes\mathbb{Z}_2$ and $\overset{*}{\mathbb{Z}_4}\otimes\mathbb{Z}_2$ do not coincide), the group $\mathsf{Ext}^1_+\simeq Q_4$ with the subgroup $\mathbb{Z}_4$ for $p-q\equiv 4,6 \pmod 8$ and $\mathsf{Ext}^1_+\simeq D_4$ with $\mathbb{Z}_2\otimes\mathbb{Z}_2$ for the type $p-q\equiv 4 \pmod 8$.

Let us consider now the group $\mathsf{Ext}^2(\mathbb{C}_n)$. In this case among the elements of Ext^2 there are both even and odd elements: $k\equiv 0 \pmod 2$, $b\equiv 1 \pmod 2$, $a\equiv 1 \pmod 2$, $g\equiv 1 \pmod 2$ and $s\equiv 1 \pmod 2$. At this point, the elements I, W, E, C form Abelian subgroups $\mathbb{Z}_2\otimes\mathbb{Z}_2$ and $\mathbb{Z}_4$. In virtue of (71) the element Π always anticommutes with K, and from (86) it follows that the elements S and F always anticommute. Therefore, all the groups Ext^2 are non-Abelian. Among these groups there are the following isomorphisms: $\mathsf{Ext}^2_+\simeq\overset{*}{\mathbb{Z}_4}\otimes\mathbb{Z}_2$ with the signatures $(+,-,-,d,e,f,g)$ for the type $p-q\equiv 4 \pmod 8$ and $(-,+,-,d,e,f,g)$, $(-,-,+,d,e,f,g)$ for $p-q\equiv 6 \pmod 8$, where among the symbols d, e, f, g there are two pluses and two minuses; $\mathsf{Ext}^2_+\simeq Q_4$ with $(+,-,-,-,-,-,-)$ for $p-q\equiv 4 \pmod 8$ and $(-,+,-,-,-,-,-)$, $(-,-,+,-,-,-,-)$ for $p-q\equiv 6 \pmod 8$; $\mathsf{Ext}^2_+\simeq D_4$ with $(a,b,c,+,+,+,+)$ and $(+,+,+,d,e,f,g)$, where among a, b, c there are two minuses and one plus, and among d, e, f, g there are two pluses and two minuses. For all the groups Ext^2 among the numbers m, v, u, l there are both even and odd numbers.

Let consider the group $\mathsf{Ext}^3(\mathbb{C}_n)$. First of all, the groups Ext^3 contain non-Abelian subgroups $\mathsf{Aut}_+(C\!\ell_{p,q})$ (the elements E and C are odd). Therefore, all the groups Ext^3 are non-Abelian. Among these groups there are the following isomorphisms: $\mathsf{Ext}^3_+\simeq D_4$ with $(+,-,+,d,e,f,g)$ and $(+,+,-,d,e,f,g)$ for the type $p-q\equiv 4 \pmod 8$, where among d, e, f, g there are three pluses and one minus; $\mathsf{Ext}^3_+\simeq Q_4$ with $(-,-,-,d,e,f,g)$, where among d, e, f, g there are one plus and three minuses; $\mathsf{Ext}^3_+ \simeq D_4$ with $(-,+,+,d,e,f,g)$, where among d, e, f, g there are three pluses and one minus (the type $p-q\equiv 6 \pmod 8$). Besides, there exist the groups $\mathsf{Ext}^3_+ \simeq \overset{*}{\mathbb{Z}_4\otimes\mathbb{Z}_2}$ with the signatures $(+,-,+,d,e,f,g)$, $(+,+,-,d,e,f,g)$ for the type $p-q\equiv 4 \pmod 8$ and $(-,-,-,d,e,f,g)$, $(-,+,+,d,e,f,g)$ for $p-q\equiv 6$ (mod 8), where among d, e, f, g there are one plus and three minuses.

Finally, let us consider the group $\mathsf{Ext}^4(\mathbb{C}_n)$. These groups contain non–Abelian subgroups $\mathsf{Aut}_+(C\!\ell_{p,q})$ and, therefore, all Ext^4 are non–Abelian. The isomorphism structure of Ext^4 is similar to Ext^3.

It is easy to see that a full number of all possible signatures (a,b,c,d,e,f,g) is equal to $2^7=128$. At this point, we have eight signature types: (seven '+'), (one '−', six '+'), (two '−', five '+'), (three '−', four '+'), (four '−', three '+'), (five '−', two '+'), (six '−', one '+'), (seven '−'). However, only four types from enumerated above correspond to finite groups of order 8: (seven '+') $\to \mathbb{Z}_2\otimes\mathbb{Z}_2\otimes\mathbb{Z}_2$, (two '−', five '+') $\to D_4$, (four '−', three '+') $\to \mathbb{Z}_4\otimes\mathbb{Z}_2$ ($\overset{*}{\mathbb{Z}_4\otimes\mathbb{Z}_2}$) and (six '−', one '+') $\to Q_4$. Therefore, for the group Ext there exist 64 different realizations. □

Example 2. Let us study an extended automorphism group of the Dirac algebra $\mathbb{C}_4$. We evolve in $\mathbb{C}_4$ the real subalgebra with the quaternionic ring. Let it be the spacetime algebra $C\!\ell_{p,q}$ with a spinbasis defined by the matrices (68). We define now elements of the group $\mathsf{Ext}(\mathbb{C}_4)$. First of all, the matrix of the automorphism $\mathcal{A}\to\mathcal{A}^\star$ has a form: $\mathsf{W}=\gamma_0\gamma_1\gamma_2\gamma_3$. Further, since

$$\gamma_0^{\mathsf{T}}=\gamma_0,\quad \gamma_1^{\mathsf{T}}=-\gamma_1,\quad \gamma_2^{\mathsf{T}}=-\gamma_2,\quad \gamma_3^{\mathsf{T}}=-\gamma_3,$$

then in accordance with Theorem 7 the matrix E of the antiautomorphism $\mathcal{A}\to\widetilde{\mathcal{A}}$ is an even product of skewsymmetric matrices of the spinbasis (68), that is, $\mathsf{E}=\gamma_1\gamma_3$. From the definition $\mathsf{C}=\mathsf{E}\mathsf{W}$ we find that the matrix of the antiautomorphism $\mathcal{A}\to\widetilde{\mathcal{A}^\star}$ has a form $\mathsf{C}=\gamma_0\gamma_2$. γ–basis contains three real matrices γ_0, γ_1 and γ_3, therefore, for the matrix of the pseudoautomorphism $\mathcal{A}\to\overline{\mathcal{A}}$ we obtain $\Pi=\gamma_0\gamma_1\gamma_3$ (see Theorem 9). Further, in accordance with $\mathsf{K}=\Pi\mathsf{W}$ for the matrix of the pseudoautomorphism $\mathcal{A}\to\overline{\mathcal{A}^\star}$ we have $\mathsf{K}=\gamma_2$. Finally, for the pseudoantiautomorphisms $\mathcal{A}\to\overline{\widetilde{\mathcal{A}}}$, $\mathcal{A}\to\overline{\widetilde{\mathcal{A}^\star}}$ from the definitions $\mathsf{S}=\Pi\mathsf{E}$, $\mathsf{F}=\Pi\mathsf{C}$ it follows $\mathsf{S}=\gamma_0$, $\mathsf{F}=\gamma_1\gamma_2\gamma_3$. Thus, we come to the following extended automorphism group:

$$\mathsf{Ext}(\mathbb{C}_4)\simeq\{\mathsf{I},\ \mathsf{W},\ \mathsf{E},\ \mathsf{C},\ \Pi,\ \mathsf{K},\ \mathsf{S},\ \mathsf{F}\}\simeq \{\mathsf{I},\ \gamma_0\gamma_1\gamma_2\gamma_3,\ \gamma_1\gamma_3,\ \gamma_0\gamma_2,\ \gamma_0\gamma_1\gamma_3,\ \gamma_2,\ \gamma_0,\ \gamma_1\gamma_2\gamma_3\}. \quad (92)$$

The Cayley tableau of this group has a form:

	I	γ_{0123}	γ_{13}	γ_{02}	γ_{013}	γ_{2}	γ_{0}	γ_{123}
I	I	γ_{0123}	γ_{13}	γ_{02}	γ_{013}	γ_{2}	γ_{0}	γ_{123}
γ_{0123}	γ_{0123}	$-$I	γ_{02}	$-\gamma_{012}$	$-\gamma_{2}$	γ_{013}	$-\gamma_{123}$	γ_{0}
γ_{13}	γ_{13}	γ_{02}	$-$I	$-\gamma_{0123}$	$-\gamma_{0}$	$-\gamma_{123}$	γ_{013}	γ_{2}
γ_{02}	γ_{02}	$-\gamma_{13}$	$-\gamma_{0123}$	I	γ_{123}	$-\gamma_{0}$	$-\gamma_{2}$	γ_{013}
γ_{013}	γ_{013}	γ_{2}	$-\gamma_{0}$	$-\gamma_{123}$	$-$I	$-\gamma_{0123}$	γ_{13}	γ_{02}
γ_{2}	γ_{2}	$-\gamma_{013}$	$-\gamma_{123}$	γ_{0}	γ_{0123}	$-$I	$-\gamma_{02}$	γ_{13}
γ_{0}	γ_{0}	γ_{123}	γ_{013}	γ_{2}	γ_{13}	γ_{02}	I	γ_{0123}
γ_{123}	γ_{123}	$-\gamma_{0}$	γ_{2}	$-\gamma_{013}$	$-\gamma_{02}$	γ_{13}	$-\gamma_{0123}$	I

$\simeq$

	I	W	E	C	Π	K	S	F
I	I	W	E	C	Π	K	S	F
W	W	$-$I	C	$-\Pi$	$-$K	Π	$-$F	S
E	E	C	$-$I	$-$W	$-$S	$-$F	Π	K
C	C	$-$E	$-$W	I	F	$-$S	$-$K	Π
Π	Π	K	$-$S	$-$F	$-$I	$-$W	E	C
K	K	$-\Pi$	$-$F	S	W	$-$I	$-$C	E
S	S	F	Π	K	E	C	I	W
F	F	$-$S	K	$-\Pi$	$-$C	E	$-$W	I

As follows from this tableau, the group $\mathsf{Ext}(\mathbb{C}_4)$ is non-Abelian. $\mathsf{Ext}_+(\mathbb{C}_4)$ contains Abelian group of spacetime reflections $\mathsf{Aut}_-(C\ell_{1,3}) \simeq \mathbb{Z}_4$ as a subgroup. It is easy to see that the group (92) is a group of the form Ext^2_+ with order structure $(3, 4)$. More precisely, the group (92) is a finite group $\overset{*}{\mathbb{Z}}_4 \otimes \mathbb{Z}_2$ with the signature $(-,-,+,-,-,+,+)$.

Coming back to example 1, we see that the groups (70) and (92) are isomorphic:

$$\{1,\ P,\ T,\ PT,\ C,\ CP,\ CT,\ CPT\} \simeq \{\mathsf{I},\ \mathsf{W},\ \mathsf{E},\ \mathsf{C},\ \Pi,\ \mathsf{K},\ \mathsf{S},\ \mathsf{F}\} \simeq \overset{*}{\mathbb{Z}}_4 \otimes \mathbb{Z}_2.$$

Moreover, the subgroups of spacetime reflections of these groups are also isomorphic:

$$\{1,\ P,\ T,\ PT\} \simeq \{\mathsf{I}, \mathsf{W}, \mathsf{E}, \mathsf{C}\} \simeq \mathbb{Z}_4.$$

Thus, we come to the following result: the finite group (70), derived from the analysis of invariance properties of the Dirac equation with respect to discrete transformations C, P and T, is isomorphic to an extended automorphism group of the Dirac algebra $\mathbb{C}_4$. This result allows us to study discrete symmetries and their group structure for physical fields of any spin (without handling to analysis of relativistic wave equations).

7 CPT–structures

As it has been shown previously, there exist 64 different signatures (a, b, c, d, e, f, g) for the extended automorphism group $\mathsf{Ext}(\mathbb{C}_n)$ of the complex Clifford algebra $\mathbb{C}_n$. At this point, the group of fundamental automorphisms, $\mathsf{Aut}_{\pm}(C\!\ell_{p,q})$, which has 8 different signatures (a, b, c), is defined as a subgroup of $\mathsf{Ext}(\mathbb{C}_n)$. As known, the Clifford–Lipschitz group $\mathbf{Pin}(n, \mathbb{C})$ (an universal covering of the complex orthogonal group $O(n, \mathbb{C})$) is completely constructed within the algebra $\mathbb{C}_n$ (see definition (8)). If we take into account spacetime reflections, then according to [25, 26, 9] there exist 8 types of universal covering (PT–structures) described by the group $\mathbf{Pin}^{a,b,c}(n, \mathbb{C})$. As it shown in [28, 29], the group $\mathbf{Pin}^{a,b,c}(n, \mathbb{C})$ (correspondingly $\mathbf{Pin}^{a,b,c}(p, q)$ over the field $\mathbb{F} = \mathbb{R}$) is completely defined within the algebra $\mathbb{C}_n$ (correspondingly $C\!\ell_{p,q}$) by means of identification of the reflection subgroup $\{1, P, T, PT\}$ with the automorphism group $\{\mathrm{Id}, \star, \widetilde{\ }, \widetilde{\star}\}$ of $\mathbb{C}_n$ (correspondingly $C\!\ell_{p,q}$). In turn, the pseudoautomorphism $\mathcal{A} \to \overline{\mathcal{A}}$ of $\mathbb{C}_n$ and the extended automorphism group $\{\mathrm{Id}, \star, \widetilde{\ }, \widetilde{\star}, \overline{\ }, \overline{\star}, \overline{\widetilde{\ }}, \overline{\widetilde{\star}}\} \simeq \mathbb{Z}_2 \otimes \mathbb{Z}_2 \otimes \mathbb{Z}_2$ allows us to give a further generalization of the Clifford–Lipschitz group (8) (correspondingly (2)). We claim that there exist 64 types of the universal covering (CPT–structures) for the complex orthogonal group $O(n, \mathbb{C})$:

$$\mathbf{Pin}^{a,b,c,d,e,f,g}(n, \mathbb{C}) \simeq \frac{(\mathbf{Spin}_+(n, \mathbb{C}) \odot C^{a,b,c,d,e,f,g})}{\mathbb{Z}_2}, \tag{93}$$

where $C^{a,b,c,d,e,f,g}$ are five double coverings of the group $\mathbb{Z}_2 \otimes \mathbb{Z}_2 \otimes \mathbb{Z}_2$. All the possible double coverings $C^{a,b,c,d,e,f,g}$ are given in the following table:

$a\ b\ c\ d\ e\ f\ g$	$C^{a,b,c,d,e,f,g}$	Type
$+\ +\ +\ +\ +\ +\ +$	$\mathbb{Z}_2 \otimes \mathbb{Z}_2 \otimes \mathbb{Z}_2 \otimes \mathbb{Z}_2$	Abelian
three '+' and four '−'	$\mathbb{Z}_4 \otimes \mathbb{Z}_2 \otimes \mathbb{Z}_2$	
one '+' and six '−'	$Q_4 \otimes \mathbb{Z}_2$	Non–Abelian
five '+' and two '−'	$D_4 \otimes \mathbb{Z}_2$	
three '+' and four '−'	$\overset{*}{\mathbb{Z}}_4 \otimes \mathbb{Z}_2 \otimes \mathbb{Z}_2$	

The group (93) with non–Abelian $C^{a,b,c,d,e,f,g}$ we will call *Cliffordian* and respectively *non–Cliffordian* when $C^{a,b,c,d,e,f,g}$ is Abelian.

Analogously, over the field $\mathbb{F} = \mathbb{R}$ there exist 64 universal coverings of the real orthogonal group $O(p, q)$:

$$\rho^{a,b,c,d,e,f,g} : \mathbf{Pin}^{a,b,c,d,e,f,g} \longrightarrow O(p, q),$$

where

$$\mathbf{Pin}^{a,b,c,d,e,f,g}(p,q) \simeq \frac{(\mathbf{Spin}_+(p,q) \odot C^{a,b,c,d,e,f,g})}{\mathbb{Z}_2}. \tag{94}$$

It is easy to see that in case of the algebra $\mathcal{C}\ell_{p,q}$ (or subalgebra $\mathcal{C}\ell_{p,q} \subset \mathbb{C}_n$) with the real division ring $\mathbb{K} \simeq \mathbb{R}$, $p-q \equiv 0, 2 \pmod 8$, CPT–structures, defined by the groups (93) and (94), are reduced to the eight Shirokov–Dąbrowski PT–structures.

Further, using the well-known isomorphism (9) we obtain for the group $O(n,\mathbb{C})$ with odd dimensionality the following universal covering:

$$\mathbf{Pin}^{a,b,c,d,e,f,g}(n,\mathbb{C}) \simeq \mathbf{Pin}^{a,b,c,d,e,f,g}(n-1,\mathbb{C}) \bigcup \mathbf{e}_{12\cdots n}\, \mathbf{Pin}^{a,b,c,d,e,f,g}(n-1,\mathbb{C}).$$

Correspondingly, in virtue of $\mathcal{C}\ell_{p,q} \simeq \mathbb{C}_{n-1}$ ($p-q \equiv 3, 7 \pmod 8$, $n = p+q$) and (5) for the group $O(p,q)$ with odd dimensionality we have

$$\mathbf{Pin}^{a,b,c,d,e,f,g}(p,q) \simeq \mathbf{Pin}^{a,b,c,d,e,f,g}(n-1,\mathbb{C})$$

for $p-q \equiv 3, 7 \pmod 8$ and

$$\begin{aligned} \mathbf{Pin}^{a,b,c,d,e,f,g}(p,q) &\simeq \mathbf{Pin}^{a,b,c,d,e,f,g}(p,q-1) \bigcup \mathbf{e}_{12\cdots n}\, \mathbf{Pin}^{a,b,c,d,e,f,g}(p,q-1), \\ \mathbf{Pin}^{a,b,c,d,e,f,g}(p,q) &\simeq \mathbf{Pin}^{a,b,c,d,e,f,g}(q,p-1) \bigcup \mathbf{e}_{12\cdots n}\, \mathbf{Pin}^{a,b,c,d,e,f,g}(q,p-1) \end{aligned}$$

for the types $p-q \equiv 1, 5 \pmod 8$.

Theorem 11. *Let $\mathbf{Pin}^{a,b,c,d,e,f,g}(n,\mathbb{C})$ be an universal covering of the complex orthogonal group $O(n,\mathbb{C})$ of the space $\mathbb{C}^n$ associated with the complex algebra $\mathbb{C}_n$. Squares of the symbols $a, b, c, d, e, f, g \in \{-,+\}$ correspond to squares of the elements of the finite group $\mathsf{Ext} = \{\mathsf{I}, \mathsf{W}, \mathsf{E}, \mathsf{C}, \Pi, \mathsf{K}, \mathsf{S}, \mathsf{F}\}$: $a = \mathsf{W}^2$, $b = \mathsf{E}^2$, $c = \mathsf{C}^2$, $d = \Pi^2$, $e = \mathsf{K}^2$, $f = \mathsf{S}^2$, $g = \mathsf{F}^2$, where W, E, C, Π, K, S, F are matrices of the automorphisms $\mathcal{A} \to \mathcal{A}^\star$, $\mathcal{A} \to \widetilde{\mathcal{A}}$, $\mathcal{A} \to \widetilde{\mathcal{A}^\star}$, $\mathcal{A} \to \overline{\mathcal{A}}$, $\mathcal{A} \to \overline{\mathcal{A}^\star}$, $\mathcal{A} \to \overline{\widetilde{\mathcal{A}}}$, $\mathcal{A} \to \overline{\widetilde{\mathcal{A}^\star}}$. Then over the field $\mathbb{F} = \mathbb{C}$ in dependence on a division ring structure $\mathbb{K} = f\mathcal{C}\ell_{p,q}f$ of the real subalgebras $\mathcal{C}\ell_{p,q} \subset \mathbb{C}_n$, there exist the following universal coverings (CPT–structures) of the group $O(n,\mathbb{C})$:*

1) $\mathbb{K} \simeq \mathbb{R}$, $p-q \equiv 0, 2 \pmod 8$.
In this case CPT–structures are reduced to the eight Shirokov–Dąbrowski PT–structures

$$\mathbf{Pin}^{a,b,c}(n,\mathbb{C}) \simeq \frac{(\mathbf{Spin}_+(n,\mathbb{C}) \odot C^{a,b,c})}{\mathbb{Z}_2},$$

where $C^{a,b,c}$ are double coverings of the group $\{1, P, T, PT\} \simeq \{\mathsf{I}, \mathsf{W}, \mathsf{E}, \mathsf{C}\} \simeq \mathbb{Z}_2 \otimes \mathbb{Z}_2$.

2) $\mathbb{K} \simeq \mathbb{H}$, $p-q \equiv 4, 6 \pmod 8$.
In this case we have 64 universal coverings:
a) Non–Cliffordian group

$$\mathbf{Pin}^{+,+,+,+,+,+,+}(n,\mathbb{C}) \simeq \frac{(\mathbf{Spin}_+(n,\mathbb{C}) \odot \mathbb{Z}_2 \otimes \mathbb{Z}_2 \otimes \mathbb{Z}_2 \otimes \mathbb{Z}_2)}{\mathbb{Z}_2}$$

exists if the subalgebra $\mathcal{C}\!\ell_{p,q}$ *admits the type* $p-q\equiv 4 \pmod 8$. *Non–Cliffordian groups*

$$\mathbf{Pin}^{a,b,c,d,e,f,g}(n,\mathbb{C})\simeq\frac{(\mathbf{Spin}_+(n,\mathbb{C})\odot\mathbb{Z}_4\otimes\mathbb{Z}_2\otimes\mathbb{Z}_2)}{\mathbb{Z}_2}$$

exist with the signature $(+,+,+,-,-,-,-)$ *when* $\mathcal{C}\!\ell_{p,q}$ *has the type* $p-q\equiv 4 \pmod 8$, *and also these groups with the signatures* (a,b,c,d,e,f,g) *exist when* $p-q\equiv 6 \pmod 8$, *where among the symbols* a, b, c *there are two minuses and one plus, and among* d, e, f, g *– two pluses and two minuses.*
b) Cliffordian groups

$$\mathbf{Pin}^{a,b,c,d,e,f,g}(n,\mathbb{C})\simeq\frac{(\mathbf{Spin}_+(n,\mathbb{C})\odot Q_4\otimes\mathbb{Z}_2)}{\mathbb{Z}_2}$$

exist with the signature $(+,-,-,-,-,-,-)$ *when* $p-q\equiv 4 \pmod 8$ *and with the signatures* $(-,+,-,-,-,-,-)$, $(-,-,+,-,-,-,-)$ *when* $p-q\equiv 6 \pmod 8$. *And also these groups exist with the signature* $(-,-,-,d,e,f,g)$ *if* $p-q\equiv 6 \pmod 8$, *where among the symbols* d, e, f, g *there are one plus and three minuses. Cliffordian groups*

$$\mathbf{Pin}^{a,b,c,d,e,f,g}(n,\mathbb{C})\simeq\frac{(\mathbf{Spin}_+(n,\mathbb{C})\odot D_4\otimes\mathbb{Z}_2)}{\mathbb{Z}_2}$$

exist with the signatures $(+,-,-,+,+,+,+)$ *and* $(+,+,+,d,e,f,g)$ *when* $\mathcal{C}\!\ell_{p,q}$ *has the type* $p-q\equiv 4 \pmod 8$ *and among* d, e, f, g *there are two minuses and two pluses, and also these groups exist with* $(+,-,+,d,e,f,g)$ *and* $(+,+,-,d,e,f,g)$, *where among* d, e, f, g *there are three pluses and one minus. Cliffordian groups of this type exist also with the signatures* $(a,b,c,+,+,+,+)$ *and* $(-,+,+,d,e,f,g)$ *when* $p-q\equiv 6 \pmod 8$, *where among* a, b, c *there are two minuses and one plus, and among* d, e, f, g *there are three pluses and one minus. Cliffordian groups*

$$\mathbf{Pin}^{a,b,c,d,e,f,g}(n,\mathbb{C})\simeq\frac{(\mathbf{Spin}_+(n,\mathbb{C})\odot\overset{*}{\mathbb{Z}}_4\otimes\mathbb{Z}_2\otimes\mathbb{Z}_2)}{\mathbb{Z}_2}$$

exist with the signatures $(+,-,-,d,e,f,g)$ *when* $p-q\equiv 4 \pmod 8$ *and among the symbols* d, e, f, g *there are two pluses and two minuses, and also these groups exist with* $(+,-,+,d,e,f,g)$ *and* $(+,+,-,d,e,f,g)$, *where* $p-q\equiv 4 \pmod 8$ *and among* d, e, f, g *there are one plus and three minuses. Cliffordian groups of this type exist also with* $(-,+,-,d,e,f,g)$ *and* $(-,-,+,d,e,f,g)$ *if* $p-q\equiv 6 \pmod 8$, *where among* d, e, f, g *there are two pluses and two minuses. And also these groups exist with* $(-,-,-,d,e,f,g)$ *if* $p-q\equiv 6 \pmod 8$, *where among* d, e, f, g *there are three pluses and one minus.*

References

[1] V. Bargmann, E. P. Wigner, Group theoretical discussion of relativistic wave equations, *Proc. Nat. Acad.* USA **34**, 211–223 (1948).

[2] V. Bargmann, *J. Math. Phys.* **5**, 862 (1964).

[3] V. B. Berestetskii, E. M. Lifshitz, L.P. Pitaevskii, Quantum Electrodynamics, *Course of Theoretical Physics* Vol. 4, 2nd Edition (Pergamon Press, Oxford, 1982).

[4] M. Blau, L. Dabrowski, Pin structures on manifolds quotiented by discrete groups, *J. Geometry and Physics* **6**, 143-157, (1989).

[5] I. L. Buchbinder, D. M. Gitman, A. L. Shelepin, Discrete symmetries as automorphisms of proper Poincaré group, *Int. J. Theor. Phys.* **41**, 753–790 (2002).

[6] A. Chamblin, On the Obstructions to Non-Cliffordian Pin Structures, *Commun. Math. Phys.* **164**, 67-87, (1994).

[7] C. Chevalley, The construction and study of certain important algebras, *Publications of Mathematical Society of Japan* No 1 (Herald Printing, Tokyo, 1955).

[8] J. F. Cornwell, Group Theory in Physics (Academic Press, San Diego, 1984).

[9] L. Dąbrowski, Group Actions on Spinors (Bibliopolis, Naples, 1988).

[10] I. M. Gel'fand, A. M. Yaglom, General relativistic–invariant equations and infinite–dimensional representations of the Lorentz group, *Zh. Ehksp. Teor. Fiz.* **18**, 703–733 (1948).

[11] I. M. Gel'fand, R. A. Minlos, Z. Ya. Shapiro, *Representations of the Rotation and Lorentz Groups and their Applications* (Pergamon Press, Oxford, 1963).

[12] D. M. Gitman, A. L. Shelepin, Fields on the Poincaré Group: Arbitrary Spin Description and Relativistic Wave Equations, *Int. J. Theor. Phys.* **40**(3), 603–684 (2001).

[13] A. Hurwitz, Uber die Komposition der quadratischen Formen, *Math. Ann.* **88**, 1–25 (1923).

[14] H. Joos, Zur darstellungstheorie der inhomogenen Lorentzgrouppe als grundlade quantenmechanische kinematick, *Fortschr. Phys.* **10**, 65 (1962).

[15] T. K. Kuo, Internal-symmetry groups and their automorphisms, *Phys. Rev.* D**4**, 3620–3637 (1971).

[16] R. Lipschitz, Untersuchungen über die Summen von Quadraten (Max Cohen und Sohn, Bonn, 1886).

[17] L. Michel, Invariance in quantum mechanics and group extension, in *Group Theoretical Concepts and Methods in Elementary Particle Physics*, pages 135–200 (Gordon & Breach, New York, 1964).

[18] H. Minkowski, Raum and Zeit, *Phys. Zs.* **10**, 104 (1909).

[19] J. Radon, Lineare Scharen orthogonaler Matrizen, *Abh. Math. Seminar Hamburg* **1**, 1–24 (1922).

[20] W. Rarita, J. Schwinger, On a theory of particles with half-integral spin, *Phys. Rev.* **60**, 61 (1941).

[21] P. K. Rashevskii, The Theory of Spinors, (in Russian) *Uspekhi Mat. Nauk* **10**, 3–110 (1955); English translation in *Amer. Math. Soc. Transl.* (Ser. 2) **6**, 1 (1957).

[22] P. K. Rashevskii, About Mathematical Foundations of Quantum Electrodynamics, (in Russian) *Uspekhi Mat. Nauk* **13**, 3–110 (1958).

[23] N. Salingaros, Realization, extension, and classification of certain physically important groups and algebras, *J. Math. Phys.* **22**, 226-232, (1981).

[24] N. Salingaros, The relationship between finite groups and Clifford algebras, *J. Math. Phys.* **25**, 738-742, (1984).

[25] Yu. M. Shirokov, Group theoretical analysis of the foundations of relativistic quantum mechanics. IV, V , *Zh. Ehksp. Teor. Fiz.* **34**, 717–724 (1958); **36**, 879–888 (1959).

[26] Yu. M. Shirokov, Spacial and time reflections in the relativistic theory, *Zh. Ehksp. Teor. Fiz.* **38**, 140–150 (1960).

[27] Z. K. Silagadze, On the internal parity of antiparticles, *Sov. J. Nucl. Phys.* **55**, 392–396 (1992).

[28] V. V. Varlamov, Fundamental Automorphisms of Clifford Algebras and an Extension of Dąbrowski Pin Groups, *Hadronic Journal* **22**, 497–535 (1999).

[29] V. V. Varlamov, Discrete Symmetries and Clifford Algebras, *Int. J. Theor. Phys.* **40**, No. 4, 769–805 (2001).

[30] V. V. Varlamov, Clifford Algebras and Discrete Transformations of Spacetime, *Proceedings of Third Siberian Conference on Mathematical Problems of Spacetime Physics of Complex Systems*, Novosibirsk, June 20–22 2000. Publishing House of the Institute of Mathematics, Novosibirsk, pp. 97–135, 2001.

[31] S. Weinberg, Feinman rules for any spin I & II & III, *Phys. Rev.* **133B**, 1318–1332 & **134B**, 882–896 (1964) & **181B**, 1893–1899 (1969).

[32] H. Weyl, Classical Groups (Princeton University Press, New York, 1946).

[33] E. P. Wigner, *Group Theory* (Academic Press, New York, 1956).

In: Mathematical Physics Research at the Cutting Edge
Editor: C.V. Benton, pp. 101-139
ISBN 1-59033-939-8

Cross Recurrence Plots and Their Applications

Norbert Marwan* and Jürgen Kurths
*Nonlinear Dynamics Group, Institute of Physics,
University of Potsdam, 14415 Potsdam, Germany,
marwan@agnld.uni-potsdam.de

Abstract

Cross recurrence plots are a new tool for nonlinear data analysis. They exhibit characteristic structures which can be used for the study of differences between two processes or for the alignment and search for matching sequences of two data series, even in the case when cross-correlation techniques fails or when the data are nonstationary. Selected applications of the introduced techniques to various kind of data demonstrate their potential.

1 Introduction

A major task in bi- or multivariate data analysis is to compare or to find interrelations between different time series. Often, these data are gained from natural systems, which show generally nonstationary and complex behaviour. Furthermore, these systems are often observed by rather few measurements providing short data series. Linear approaches of time series analysis are often not sufficient to analyse this kind of data. In the last two decades a great variety of nonlinear techniques has been developed to analyse data of complex systems (cf. Abarbanel et al., 1993; Kantz and Schreiber, 1997). Most popular are methods for estimation of fractal dimensions, Lyapunov exponents or mutual information (Kantz and Schreiber, 1997; Kurths and Herzel, 1987; Mandelbrot, 1982; Wolf et al., 1985). However, most of these methods need rather long data series. The uncritical application of these methods especially to natural data often leads to pitfalls.

In the last decade a new method based on nonlinear data analysis has become popular: recurrence plots (Eckmann et al., 1987). Recurrence is a fundamental property of dissipative dynamical systems. Even though small disturbations of such a system cause exponential divergence of its state, after some time the system will reach a state that is arbitrary close to the former state and pass through a similar evolution. Recurrence plots visualize such recurrent behaviour of dynamical systems. Although they are not completely theoretically understood, practitioners of this method claim its relevance for short and nonstationary data. These features are indeed the crucial advantage of recurrence plots. Zbilut and Webber Jr. (1992) have made an important further step by introducing a quantification analysis based on recurrence plots, which became well known in the analysis especially of physiological data. Hundreds of works and publications using this quantification analysis can be found in literature. It seems that the reason for this amazing growth in the popularity of recurrence plots is not only the technical aspect. Recurrence plots can be very decorative and attract attention.

An extension of the method of recurrence plots to *cross recurrence plots* (CRPs) enables investigating the time dependent behaviour of two processes which are both recorded in a single time series (Zbilut et al., 1998; Marwan and Kurths, 2002; Marwan et al., 2002a). The basic idea of this approach is to compare the phase space trajectories of two processes in the same phase space. CRPs can be used in order to study the similarity of two different phase space trajectories.

In order to understand the methods based on CRPs, we will first review the concepts of phase space trajectories and recurrence plots. In the following sections we will expand these concepts to CRPs and develop further measures of complexity, which are based on CRPs and evaluate the similarity of the considered systems. This nonlinear approach enables us to identify epochs when there are linear and even nonlinear interrelations between both systems. In the last section we will apply the methods of CRPs to data from geology.

2 Review on Recurrence Plots

2.1 Phase Space

The analysis of phase space trajectories is a basic concept of nonlinear data analysis. In this subsection a brief introduction of this concept is given. For further reading see for example Eckmann and Ruelle (1985), Abarbanel et al. (1993) or Ott (1993).

The states of systems in nature or engineering typically change in time. The state of a system can be described by its d state variables

$$x_1(t), x_2(t), \ldots, x_d(t), \tag{1}$$

which form a vector $\vec{x}(t)$ in a d-dimensional space which is called phase space. This vector moves in time and in the direction that is specified by its velocity vector

$$\dot{\vec{x}}(t) = \partial_t \vec{x}(t) = \vec{F}(x). \tag{2}$$

The temporary succession of the phase space vectors forms a trajectory (phase space trajectory, orbit). The velocity field $\vec{F}(x)$ is tangent to this trajectory. For autonomous systems the trajectory must not cross itself. The time evolution of the trajectory explains the dynamics of the system, i. e. the attractor of the system. If $\vec{F}(x)$ is known, the state at a given time can be determined by integrating the equation system (2). However, a graphical visualization of the trajectory enables the determination of a state without integrating the equations. The shape of the trajectory gives hints about the system; periodic respective chaotic systems have characteristic phase space portraits.

The observation of a real process usually does not yield all possible state variables. Either not all state variables are known or not all of them can be measured. Most often only one observation $u(t)$ is available. Since measurements result in discrete time series, the observations will be written in the following as u_i, where $t = i\,\Delta t$ and Δt is the sampling rate of the measurement. Couplings between the system's components imply that each single component contains essential information about the dynamics of the whole system. Therefore, an equivalent phase space trajectory, which preserves the topological structures of the original phase space trajectory, can be reconstructed by using only one observation or time series, respectively (Packard et al., 1980; Takens, 1981). A method frequently used for reconstructing such a trajectory $\hat{\vec{x}}(t)$ is the time delay method: $\hat{\vec{x}}_i = (u_i, u_{i+\tau}, \ldots, u_{i+(m-1)\tau})^T$, where m is the embedding dimension and τ is the time delay (index based; the real time delay is $\tau\,\Delta t$). The preservation of the topological structures of the original trajectory is guaranteed if $m \geq 2d+1$, where d is the dimension of the attractor (Takens, 1981).

Both embedding parameters, the dimension m and the delay τ, have to be chosen appropriately. Different approaches are possible for the determination of these embedding parameters (cf. Cao, 1997; Kantz and Schreiber, 1997). A rather common method for the estimation of the embedding dimension is the investigation of the changes in the neighbourhood of phase space points under changes of the embedding dimension. Such a dimension has to be taken where the neighbourhood of phase space points (e.g. the amount of false nearest neighbours) does not change. Possible means of determining the delay are the *autocovariance function* or the *mutual information*.

A phase space trajectory or its reconstruction can be used in order to estimate characteristic properties of the dynamical system, like Lyapunov exponents, various types of dimensions etc. (cf. Eckmann and Ruelle, 1985; Abarbanel et al., 1993; Ott, 1993). Besides, the phase space reconstruction is the starting point for the construction of a recurrence plot.

2.2 Recurrence Plots

The recurrence plot (RP) is a tool for visualizing the dynamics of phase space trajectories. Usually, a phase space does not have a dimension (two or three) which allows it to be pictured. Higher dimensional phase spaces can only be visualized by projection into the two or three dimensional sub-spaces. However, an RP enables us to visualize the m-dimensional phase space trajectory through a two-dimensional representation of its recurrences (Fig. 1).

The recurrence plot is defined as

$$\mathbf{R}(t_1, t_2) = \Theta\left(\varepsilon(t_1) - \|\vec{x}(t_1) - \vec{x}(t_2)\|\right), \tag{3}$$

or for time-discrete variables ($t = i\Delta t$)

$$\mathbf{R}_{i,j} = \Theta\left(\varepsilon_i - \|\vec{x}_i - \vec{x}_j\|\right), \tag{4}$$

where $\varepsilon(t)$ or ε_i is a predefined cut-off distance, $\|\cdot\|$ is the norm (e. g. the Euclidean norm) and $\Theta(x)$ is the Heaviside function. The values *one* and *zero* in this matrix can be simply visualized by the colours black and white. Depending on the kind of the application, ε_i can be a fixed value or it can be changed for each i in such a way that in the ball with the radius ε_i a predefined amount of nearest neighbours occurs. The choice of a fixed amount of nearest neighbours will provide a constant density of recurrence points in each column of the RP. The radius ε_i of such a neighbourhood changes for each $\vec{x}_i$ ($i = 1 \ldots N$) and $\mathbf{R}_{i,j} \neq \mathbf{R}_{j,i}$ because the vicinity of $\vec{x}_i$ does not have to be the same as that of $\vec{x}_j$. This property leads to an asymmetric RP, but all columns of the RP have the same recurrence density. For the use of this neighbourhood criterion, we make the following statement: ε is the parameter for

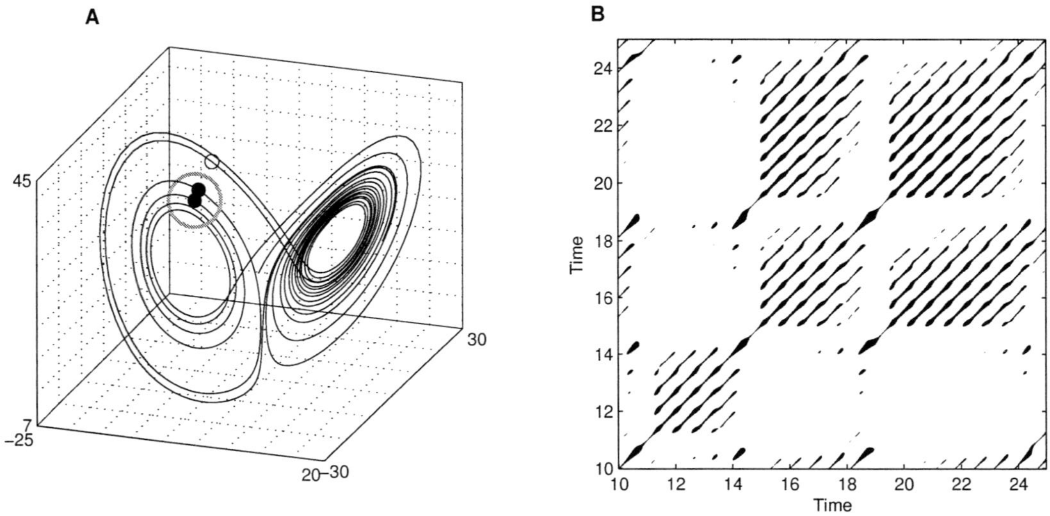

Figure 1: (A) Segment of the phase space trajectory of the Lorenz system (for standard parameters $r = 28$, $\sigma = 10$, $b = \frac{8}{3}$; Lorenz, 1963) computed by using its three components and (B) its corresponding recurrence plot. A point of the trajectory at j which falls into the neighbourhood (gray circle in (A)) of a given point at i is considered as a recurrence point (black point on the trajectory in (A)). This is marked with a black point in the RP at the location (i, j). A point outside the neighbourhood (small circle in (A)) causes a white point in the RP. The radius of the neighbourhood for the RP is $\varepsilon = 5$.

the predefinition of the recurrence density, but does not mean the radius of the vicinity. This means that with a given $\varepsilon = 0.15$ the real, locally chosen ε_i is adjusted in such a way that the neighbourhood covers 15% of all phase space vectors, and thus the recurrence density is 0.15. We denote this neighbourhood as *fixed amount of nearest neighbours (FAN)*.

Since $\mathbf{R}_{i,i} = 1$ $(i = 1 \ldots N)$ by definition, the RP has a black main diagonal line, the *line of identity (LOI)*, with an angle of $\pi/4$. It has to be noted that a single recurrence point at (i, j) does not contain any information about the current states at the times i and j. However, it is possible to reconstruct the properties of the data from the totality of all recurrence points. McGuire et al. (1997) have shown the preservation of main dynamical properties for the distance matrix $\mathbf{D}^m_{i,j} = \|\vec{x}_i - \vec{x}_j\|$. Nevertheless, the phase space trajectory can also be reconstructed from the binary RP, where the information about the absolute length of the phase space vectors is lost. The RP provides information for reordering the indices of the phase space vectors, such that the vectors are sorted by their norm. If the cumulative distribution of the lengths of the phase space vectors is known, the restored phase space trajectory will recover its amplitude by equating the sorted indices with this distribution.

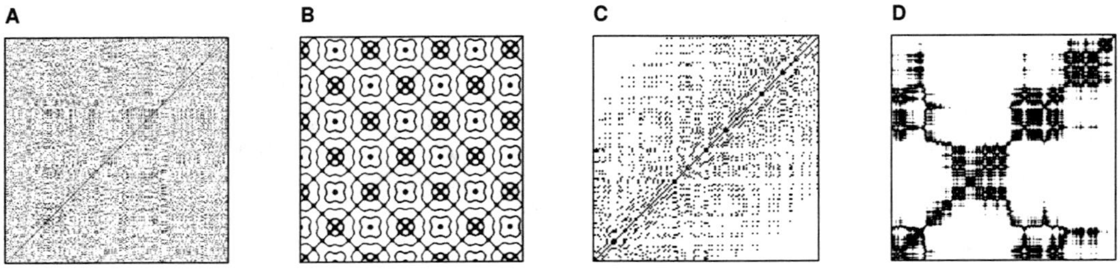

Figure 2: Characteristic typology of recurrence plots: (A) homogeneous (uniformly distributed noise), (B) periodic (super-positioned harmonic oscillations), (C) drift (logistic map $x_{i+1} = 4x_i(1 - x_i)$ corrupted with a linearly increasing term) and (D) disrupted (Brownian motion). These examples illustrate how different RPs can be. The used data have the length 400 (A, B, D) and 150 (C), respectively; no embeddings are used; the thresholds are $\varepsilon = 0.2$ (A, C, D) and $\varepsilon = 0.4$ (B).

An RP exhibits characteristic large-scale and small-scale patterns which are caused by typical dynamical behavior (Eckmann et al., 1987; Marwan et al., 2002b; Webber Jr. and Zbilut, 1994), e. g. diagonals or horizontal and vertical black lines. The large-scale patterns were denoted by Eckmann et al. (1987) as *typology* and the small-scale patterns as *texture*. The typology offers a global impression which can be characterized as *homogeneous*, *periodic*, *drift* and *disrupted* (Fig. 2).

Single, isolated recurrence points occur if states are rare, if they do not persist for any time or if they fluctuate heavily. However, they are not a unique sign of chance or noise (for example in maps). A single recurrence point contains no information about the state itself.

A *diagonal line* $\mathbf{R}_{i+k,j+k} = 1$ (for $k = 1 \ldots l$, where l is the length of the diagonal line) occurs when the trajectory visits the same region of the phase space at different times and a segment of the trajectory runs parallel to another segment. The length of this diagonal line is determined by the duration of such similar local evolution of the trajectory segments. The direction of these diagonal structures can differ. Diagonal lines parallel to the LOI (angle $\pi/4$) represent the parallel running of trajectories for the same time evolution. The diagonal structures perpendicular to the LOI represent the parallel running with contrary times (mirrored segments; this is often a hint for an inappropriate embedding). Since the definition of the maximal Lyapunov exponent uses the time of the parallel running of trajectories, the relationship between the diagonal lines in an RP and the maximal Lyapunov exponent is obvious. There exist different attempts to relate the diagonal lines with the maximal Lyapunov exponent (Trulla et al., 1996; Choi et al., 1999; Gao and Cai, 2000).

A *vertical (horizontal) line* $\mathbf{R}_{i,j+k} = 1$ (for $k = 1 \ldots v$, with v the length of the vertical line) marks a time length in which a state does not change or changes very slowly. It seems that the state is trapped for some time. This is a typical behaviour of laminar states (intermittency).

In a more general sense the line structures in an RP exhibit locally the time relationship between the current trajectory segments. A line structure in an RP of length l corresponds to the closeness of the segment $f(T_1(t))$ to another segment $f(T_2(t))$, where $T_1(t)$ and $T_2(t)$ are the local time scales which preserve that $f(T_1(t)) \approx f(T_2(t))$ for some time $t = 1 \ldots l\Delta t$. The local slope $\mathfrak{m}(t)$ of a line in an RP represents the ratio between the local time derivatives of these time transformations $T_i(t)$

$$\mathfrak{m}(t) = \frac{\partial_t T_1(t)}{\partial_t T_2(t)}. \tag{5}$$

We will consider here an illustrative example. A further explanation of the relationship between the slope of the lines and the trajectories is given in Subsec. 3.3. Let us consider a function $f(T) = T(t)$ with a section of a monotonical, linear increase $T_{lin} = t$ and another (hyperbolic) section which follows $T_{hyp} = -\sqrt{r^2 - t^2}$ (Fig. 3A). Since the ratio between the derivatives of the functions T_i of the linear and the hyperbolic sections

$$\mathfrak{m} = \frac{\partial_t T_{lin}(t)}{\partial_t T_{hyp}(t)} = \frac{t}{\sqrt{r^2 - t^2}} \tag{6}$$

corresponds to the derivative of a circle line with a radius r, a bowed line structure with the form of a circle occurs in the RP (Fig. 3C).

The small scale structures, diagonal and vertical lines, are the base of a quantitative analysis of the RPs, which is known as *recurrence quantification analysis (RQA)*. This analysis has been developed to assess the RPs and to detect transitions (e. g. bifurcation points) in complex systems (Trulla et al., 1996; Webber Jr. and Zbilut, 1994; Zbilut and Webber Jr., 1992; Marwan et al., 2002b). The quantification tech-

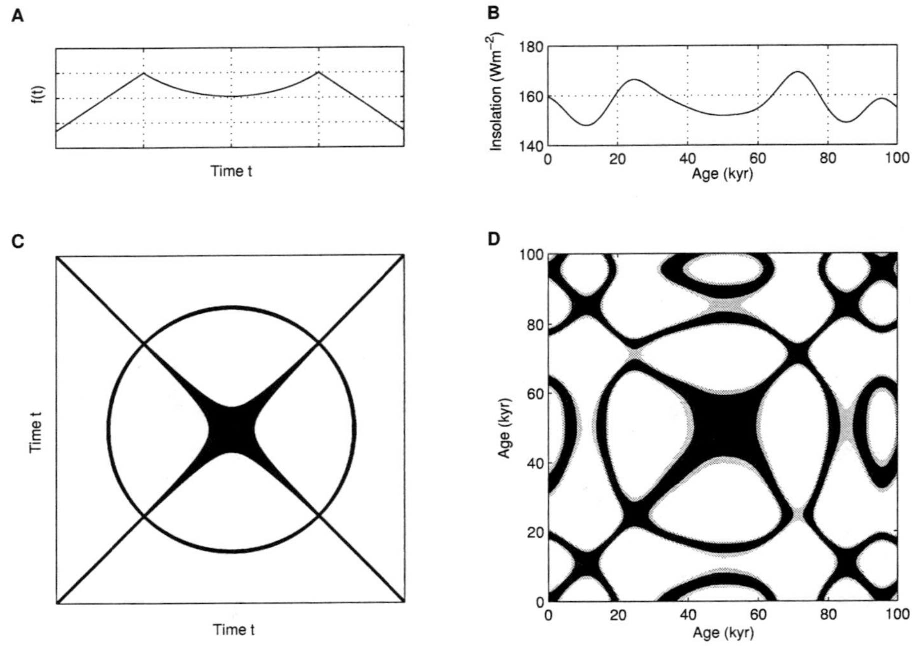

Figure 3: (A, C) Illustrative example of the relationship between the slope of lines in an RP and the local derivatives of the involved trajectory segments. Since the ratio between the local derivative of the linear and the hyperbolic sections corresponds to the derivative of a circle line, a circle occurs in the RP. (B, D) A corresponding structure found in nature: the solar insolation on the latitude 44°N for the last 100 kyr (data from Berger and Loutre, 1991). RPs created without embedding; in (D) an RP for a larger threshold is additionally shown in gray.

nique contains numerous measures of complexity as *recurrence rate, determinism, laminarity, trapping time* etc.

The RPs test the distance between all points of the same phase space trajectory. However, why should it not be possible to test each point of one trajectory with each point of another trajectory in the same phase space? This leads us to the concept of *cross recurrence plots (CRP)*, which we will focus on in the next section.

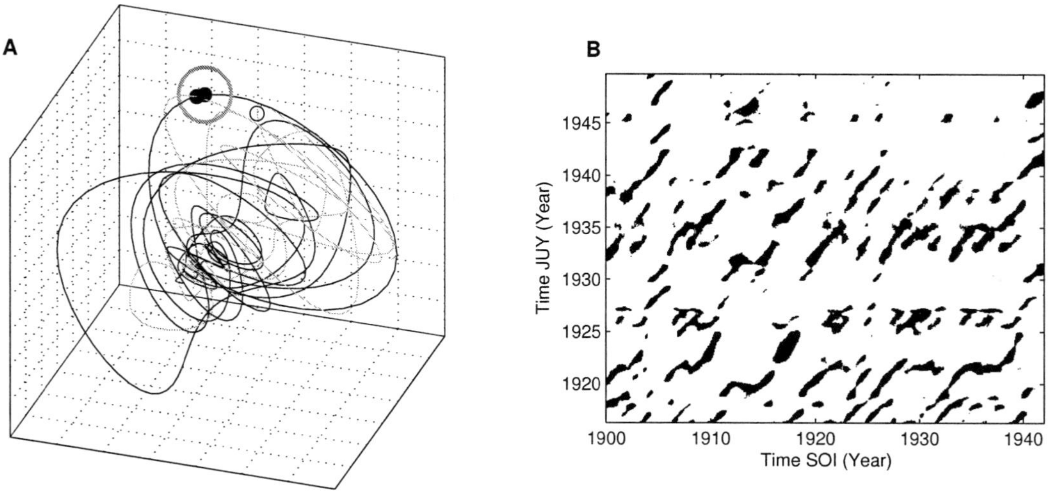

Figure 4: (A) Segments of the phase space trajectories of the El Niño Southern Oscillation Index (SOI, black line; data from the Climate Server of NOAA http://ferret.wrc.noaa.gov) and a precipitation time series of San Salvador de Jujuy (Argentina, gray line; data from Bianchi and Yañez (1992)) by using time delay embedding (smoothed, monthly data; $\tau = 7$ months). In (B) the corresponding cross recurrence plot is shown. If a point of the precipitation trajectory at j (black point on the gray line in (A)) falls into the neighbourhood (gray circle in (A)) of a point of the SOI trajectory at i, in the CRP at the location (i, j), a black point will be marked. A point outside the neighbourhood (small circle in (A)) is marked as a white point in the CRP. For creating this CRP the FAN criterion with $\varepsilon = 0.15$ is used.

3 Cross Recurrence Plots

3.1 Definition of Cross Recurrence Plots

Starting with the concept of RPs we regard a phase space with one trajectory $\vec{x}_i$ of length N_x. Now we add a second trajectory $\vec{y}_j$ with the length N_y into the same phase space (Fig. 4). The test between all points of the first trajectory with all points of the second trajectory leads to the *cross recurrence plot (CRP)*

$$\mathbf{CR}_{i,j}^{m,\varepsilon_i} = \Theta\left(\varepsilon_i - \left\|\vec{x}_i - \vec{y}_j\right\|\right), \quad \vec{x}_i, \vec{y}_j \in \mathrm{R}^m, \quad i = 1 \dots N_x,\ j = 1 \dots N_y. \tag{7}$$

The notation is analogous to the definition of RPs (Eq. 4). If in the second trajectory a state at time j is close to a state on the first trajectory at time i, a black dot will be assigned to the matrix **CR** at location (i, j). This occurrence of neighbours in both trajectories is not a "recurrence" of states, hence, the matrix (Eq. 7) does not represent recurrences but the conjunctures of states of both systems. Therefore, this representation is not really a "cross *recurrence* plot". Nevertheless we call it "cross recurrence plot" in order to follow the way of a generalization of RPs and because of the occurrence of the term "cross recurrence quantification" in the literature for the parallel concept of the generalization of the RQA (Zbilut et al., 1998). The vectors $\vec{x}$ and $\vec{y}$ do not need to have the same length, hence the matrix **CR** is not necessarily square. This extension of RPs was firstly used by Zbilut et al. (1998) for the *cross recurrence quantification*. Independently of their work, the concept of cross recurrence plots also surfaces in Marwan (1999). If the second vector $\vec{y}_j$ is the same as the vector $\vec{x}_j$, the CRP will correspond to the RP of $\vec{x}_j$.

Both trajectories for the creation of a CRP have to represent the same dynamical system with equal state variables because they are in the same phase space. This must be taken into account if time series of different measurements (e. g. temperature and pressure) are involved. For the embedding and the following CRP analysis the time series can be taken from different measurements if they are components or state variables of the same system. The time series can also be from different subsystems, which belong to the same system (e. g. the sub-systems El Niño Southern Oscillation and North Atlantic Oscillation within system of the global atmospheric oscillation). A precedent data normalization may solve the problems of different units and amplitude scaling. However, the application of CRPs to measurements of completely different systems, which cannot be regarded as observations of the same dynamical system (e. g. a stocks index and the precession of the Earth's rotation), makes no sense. For such different kinds of data the presently developed concept of intersected RPs can be used (Romano et al., 2003).

Assuming that both trajectories come from the same process but have different absolute values, the CRP will not yield the expected RP if a fixed threshold ε is chosen. Therefore, it is necessary to adapt both trajectories to the same range of values, e. g. by using a normalization to the standard deviation. However, the application of a fixed amount of nearest neighbours (FAN), i. e. ε_i changes for each state x_i, solves this problem automatically, and a modification of the amplitudes is not necessary. This choice of a neighbourhood has the additional advantage of working well for slowly changing trajectories (e. g. drift).

Since the values of $\mathbf{CR}_{i,i}$ $(i = 1 \dots N)$ are not necessarily one, the black main diagonal usually vanishes. As we will discuss in Subsec. 3.3, the line of identity (LOI) can be replaced by the *line of synchronization (LOS)*, may be bowed and may ultimately not have the angle $\pi/4$. However, the lines which are more or less diagonally oriented are also of interest. They represent segments of both trajectories, which run nearly parallel for some time. The frequency and lengths of these lines are obviously related to a certain similarity between the dynamics of both subsystems.

A time dilatation or time compression of one of the trajectories causes a distortion of the main diagonal line. This case will be discussed in subsection 3.3. In the following subsection we presume the situation that both systems have the same time scale (equal length N and sample time Δt), hence, the CRP is an $N \times N$ array.

3.2 Measures for Similarities Between Two Observed Processes

The long diagonal structures in the CRP reveal similar time evolution of the trajectories of both processes. It is obvious that a progressively increased similarity between both processes causes an increase of the recurrence point density along the main diagonal $\mathbf{CR}_{i,i}$ $(i = 1 \dots N)$ until a black straight main diagonal line occurs (which would be in fact the LOI) and the CRP becomes an RP. Thus, the occurrence of diagonal lines in a CRP can be used in order to benchmark the similarity between the considered processes.

In order to quantify this similarity, some quantitative measures have to be defined. Since we are interested in the occurrence of the more or less discontinuous diagonal lines, these measures should be diagonalwise applied (Marwan and Kurths, 2002).

Let us consider a diagonal $\mathbf{CR}_{i,j}$ $(j - i = k = \text{const.})$ which is parallel to the main diagonal and has a time distance $t = k\,\Delta t$ from the main diagonal. The recurrence points in this diagonal correspond with tests between the time delayed trajectories (delay t). In the following, some RQA measures will be redefined for these diagonals. Hence, these measures will be functions of the distance k from the main diagonal. Using this approach it is possible to assess the similarity in the dynamics depending on a certain time delay.

Following this procedure, we need to define the frequency distributions of the diagonal line lengths $P_k^{\varepsilon}(l) = \{l_i;\ i = 1 \dots N_l\}$ (N_l is the absolute number of diagonal lines) for each diagonal parallel to the main diagonal $\mathbf{CR}_{i,j}^{m,\varepsilon}$ $(j - i = k)$. For $k = 0$ this line is the LOI, $k > 0$ diagonals above and $k < 0$ diagonals below the LOI, which represent positive and negative time delays, respectively.

The recurrence rate RR is now modified to

$$RR_k = RR_*(t) = \frac{1}{N-k} \sum_{j-i=k} \mathbf{CR}_{i,j}^{m,\varepsilon} = \frac{1}{N-k} \sum_{l=1}^{N-k} l\, P_k^{\varepsilon}(l) \tag{8}$$

and reveals the probability of the occurrence of similar states in both systems with a certain delay $t = k\,\Delta t$. A high density of recurrence points in a diagonal results in a high value of RR_*. This is the case for systems whose trajectories often visit the same phase space regions.

Analogous to the RQA the determinism

$$DET_k = \frac{\sum_{l=l_{min}}^{N-k} l\, P_k^{\varepsilon}(l)}{\sum_{l=1}^{N-k} l\, P_k^{\varepsilon}(l)} \tag{9}$$

is the proportion of recurrence points forming long diagonal structures to all recurrence points, but here it is constrained to the considered diagonal. Smooth trajectories with long autocorrelation times will result in a CRP with long diagonal structures, even if the trajectories are not linked to each other (this effect corresponds to the tangential motion of one trajectory). In order to avoid the counting of such "false" diagonals, the lower limit for the diagonal line length l_{min} should be of the order of the autocorrelation time.

Stochastic as well as heavily fluctuating processes cause none or only short diagonals, whereas deterministic processes cause longer diagonals. As mentioned above, if two deterministic processes have the same or similar time evolution, i. e. parts of the phase space trajectories meet the same phase space regions for certain times, the amount of longer diagonals will increase and the amount of shorter diagonals will decrease. The average diagonal line length

$$L_k = \frac{\sum_{l=l_{min}}^{N-k} l\, P_k^{\varepsilon}(l)}{\sum_{l=l_{min}}^{N-k} P_k^{\varepsilon}(l)} \tag{10}$$

quantifies the duration of such a similarity in the dynamics. A high coincidence of both trajectories increases the length of these diagonals. Besides, the entropy of the probability $P_k^{\varepsilon}(l)$ can also be defined. Still, we focus here on the first three measures.

High values of RR_* represent high probabilities of the occurrence of the same state in both processes, high values of DET_* and L_* represent a long time span of the occurrence of a similar dynamics in both processes. Whereas DET_* and L_* are sensitive to fast and highly fluctuating data, RR_* measures the probabilities of the occurrence of the same states in spite of these high fluctuations (noisy data). It is important to emphasize that these parameters are statistical measures and that their validity increases with the size of the CRP, i. e. with the observation length.

An additional CRP

$$\mathbf{CR}^{-}_{i,j} = \Theta\left(\varepsilon_i - \left\|\vec{x}_i + \vec{y}_j\right\|\right) \tag{11}$$

with opposite signed second trajectory $-\vec{y}_j$ allows to distinguish positive and negative relations between the considered trajectories (Marwan and Kurths, 2002). In order to recognize the measures for both possible CRPs, we add the superscript index + to the measures for the positive linkage and the superscript index − for the negative linkage, e. g. RR^+_k and RR^-_k.

Another approach used to study the positive and negative relations between the considered trajectories involves the composited measures for the recurrence rate

$$RR^c_k = \frac{1}{N-k} \sum_{j-i=k} \left(\mathbf{CR}^{+}_{i,j} - \mathbf{CR}^{-}_{i,j}\right), \tag{12}$$

the determinism

$$DET^c_k = DET^+_k - DET^-_k, \tag{13}$$

and the average diagonal length

$$L^c_k = L^+_k - L^-_k, \tag{14}$$

where $P^{\pm}_k(l)$ is the histogram of the diagonal line lengths in $\mathbf{CR}^{\pm}_{i,j}$ $(j - i = k)$, as it is used in Marwan et al. (2003). This representation is similar to those of the cross correlation function and is more intuitive than the separate representation of RR^+_*, RR^-_* etc. However, for the investigation of interrelations based on even functions, these composited measures are not suitable.

A substantial advantage of this method is its capability of finding nonlinear similarities in short and nonstationary time series with high noise levels as they typically occur, e. g., in biology or earth sciences.

However, the shortness and nonstationarity of data limit this method as well. As mentioned above, one way to reduce problems accompanying nonstationary data is the alternative choice of a neighbourhood with a fixed amount of neighbours.

3.3 Time Scale Alignment of Time Series

In data analysis one is often faced with time series measured on varying time scales. These could be, for example, sets from borehole or core data in geophysics or tree rings in dendrochronology. Sediment cores might have undergone a number of coring disturbances such as compression or stretching. Moreover, cores from different sites with differing sedimentation rates would have different temporal resolutions. All these factors require a method of synchronizing or aligning the time scales.

Regarding the conventional RP (Eq. 4), a black main diagonal line (LOI) can always be found in the plot because of the identity of the (i, i) states. The RP can be considered as a special case of the CRP which usually does not have a main diagonal because the (i, i) states are not identical.

Assuming two identical trajectories, the CRP is the same as the RP of one trajectory and contains an LOI. If we slightly modify the values of the second trajectory, the LOI will become somewhat disrupted. This leads to the situation discussed in Subsec. 3.2. However, if we do not modify the amplitudes but stretch or compress slightly the second trajectory, the LOI will be kept continuous but not as a straight line with an angle of $\pi/4$. Rather this line can be bowed (Fig. 5). The local slope of lines in an RP as well as CRP corresponds to the transformation of the time axes of the two considered trajectories (Marwan et al., 2002a). A time shift between the trajectories causes a dislocation of the LOS. Hence, the LOS may lie rather far from the main diagonal of the CRP.

For illustration let us consider two sine functions where we rescale the time axis of the second sine function in the following way

$$\sin(\varphi t) \longrightarrow \sin\big(\varphi t + a \sin(\psi t)\big). \tag{15}$$

The terms rescaling and synchronization are used here in the meaning of the rescaling of the time scale. The rescaling of the second sine function with different parameters a results in a deformation of the main diagonal (Fig. 5). The distorted line contains the information on the rescaling, which we constructively use in order to re-synchronize the two functions. Therefore, this distorted diagonal is called *line of synchronization (LOS)*.

In the following, we present a toy model in order to explain the relation between the time series $f(t_1), g(t_2)$ and the LOS $t_2 = \phi(t_1)$. In a one dimensional situation, the CRP is simply

$$\mathbf{CR}(t_1, t_2) = \Theta\big(\varepsilon - \|f(t_1) - g(t_2)\|\big). \tag{16}$$

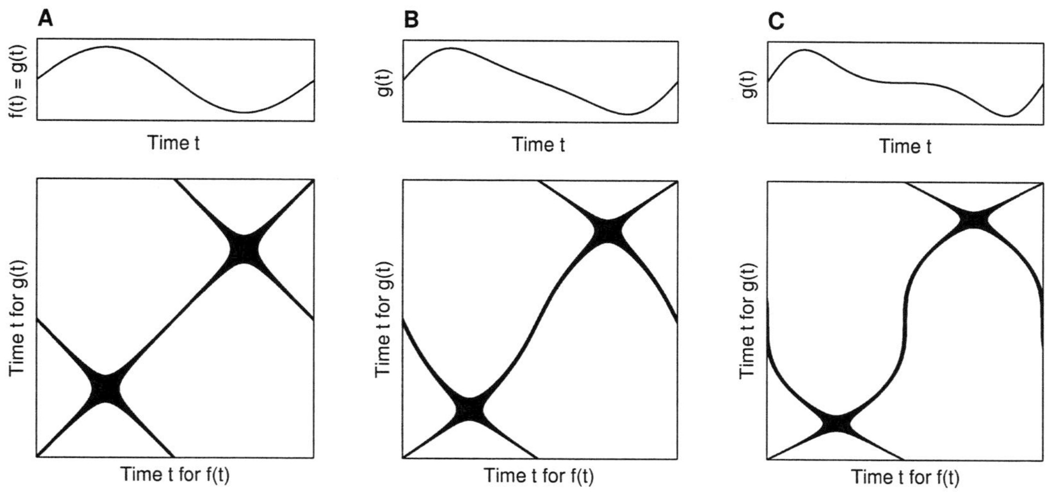

Figure 5: Cross recurrence plots of sine functions $f(t) = \sin(\varphi t)$ and $g(t) = \sin(\varphi t + a\sin(\psi t))$, whereas (A) $a = 0$, (B) $a = 0.5$ and (C) $a = 1$. The variation in the time domain leads to a deforming of the synchronization line. The CRPs are computed without embedding.

Provided that we set $\varepsilon = 0$ to simplify the condition, (Eq. 16) will deliver a recurrence point if

$$f(t_1) \equiv g(t_2). \tag{17}$$

In general, this is an implicit condition that links the variable t_1 to t_2. Considering the physical examples above, it can be assumed that the time series are essentially the same; i. e. $f \equiv g$ up to a rescaling function of time. So we can state

$$f(t_1) \equiv f(\phi(t_1)). \tag{18}$$

In some special cases (18) can be resolved with respect to t_1. An example of such a special case is a system of two sine functions with different frequencies

$$f(t) = \sin(\varphi \cdot t + \alpha), \quad g(t) = \sin(\psi \cdot t + \beta) \tag{19}$$

Using (17) and (18) we find

$$\sin(\varphi\, t_1 + \alpha) - \sin(\psi\, t_2 + \beta) = 0, \tag{20}$$

and one explicit solution of this equation is

$$\Rightarrow \quad t_2 = \phi(t_1) = \left(\frac{\varphi}{\psi} t_1 + \gamma\right) \tag{21}$$

with $\gamma = \frac{\alpha-\beta}{\psi}$. In this special case the slope $\mathfrak{m}$ of the main line in the corresponding cross recurrence plot represents the frequency ratio, and the distance between the origin of the axes and the intersection of the LOS with the ordinate reveals the phase difference. Considering the time transformation functions $T_1 = \varphi \cdot t + \alpha$ and $T_2 = \psi \cdot t + \beta$ whithin the (Eqs. 19), we get the same result for the slope of the LOS by the ratio of the derivatives (cf. Eq. 5)

$$\mathfrak{m} = \frac{\partial_t T_1(t)}{\partial_t T_2(t)} = \frac{\varphi}{\psi}. \tag{22}$$

The function $t_2 = \phi(t_1)$ is the transfer or rescaling function which allows to rescale the second system to the first system. If the rescaling function is not linear, the LOS will also be curved.

If the functions $f(\cdot)$ and $g(\cdot)$ are not identical, our method will in general not be capable of deciding whether the difference in the time series is due to different dynamics or to simple rescaling. So the assumption that the dynamics remain equal up to a rescaling in time (the underlying systems must be the same) is essential. Nevertheless, for some cases where $f \neq g$, the method can be applied in the same way. If we consider the functions $f(\cdot) = a \cdot \bar{f}(\cdot) + b$ and $g(\cdot) = \bar{g}(\cdot)$, whereby $f(\cdot) \neq g(\cdot)$ are the observations and $\bar{f}(\cdot) = \bar{g}(\cdot)$ are the states, normalization, with respect to the mean and the standard deviation, will allow to use our method,

$$f(\cdot) = a \cdot \bar{f}(\cdot) + b \longrightarrow \tilde{f}(\cdot) = \frac{f(\cdot) - \langle f(\cdot) \rangle}{\sigma\left(f(\cdot)\right)} \tag{23}$$

$$\tilde{g}(\cdot) = \frac{g(\cdot) - \langle g(\cdot) \rangle}{\sigma\left(g(\cdot)\right)}. \tag{24}$$

With $\bar{g}(\cdot) = \bar{f}(\cdot)$ the functions $\tilde{f}(\cdot)$ and $\tilde{g}(\cdot)$ are the same after the normalization, hence, our method can be applied without any further modification.

For application one has to determine the LOS – usually non-parametrically – and then rescale one of the time series by using this transfer function. This connection between the local slope of the LOS and the relation between the segments of the trajectories also applies to other line structures in CRPs as well as RPs.

This technique can also be used in order to find the closest matching segments in two data series. For example, in the geological framework there could be a long reference data series which has a time scale and a second but short profile with the same physical measurement. The task lies in finding the section in the reference data which matches to the second profile in order to yield the corresponding time scale for the profile. This section can be found by looking for a more or less continuous black line in the CRP (the dislocated LOS).

The CRP based alignment of time series has conspicuous similarities with the method of sequence slotting described by Thompson and Clark (1989). The first step in their method is the calculation of a distance matrix ($\mathbf{D}^{m}_{i,j} = \|\vec{x}_i - \vec{x}_j\|$), which allows the use of multivariate data sets. Thompson and Clark (1989) referred to the distance measure as dissimilarity. It is used to determine the alignment function in such a way that the sum of the dissimilarities along a path in the distance matrix is minimized. This approach is based on dynamic programming methods which were mainly developed for speech pattern recognition in the 1970's (e. g. Sakoe and Chiba, 1978). In contrast, RPs were developed to visualize the phase space behaviour of dynamical systems. Therefore, a threshold was introduced to make recurrent states visible. The involvement of a FAN in the phase space and the possibility of increasing the embedding dimensions, which enhance the quality of the transfer function, distinguishes the CRP approach from the sequence slotting method.

4 Current Developments of Recurrence Plots

During the last five years a rather promising development of recurrence plots has been in progress. These new findings work toward a better understanding of the structures found in RPs. An RP can be used in order to obtain some properties of dynamical systems, such as the Rényi entropy, the correlation dimension or the information dimension (Faure and Korn, 1998; Gao, 1999; Thiel et al., 2003). The most recent development proposes intersections of RPs and time shifted RPs

$$\mathbf{R}^{m,\hat{\varepsilon}}_{i,j} \cdot \mathbf{R}^{m,\tilde{\varepsilon}}_{i+\tau,j+\tau} \tag{25}$$

which can be used for the estimation of the generalized mutual information (Thiel et al., 2003). Furthermore, this approach can also be applied to different phase space trajectories, which leads to a completely new concept of cross recurrence plots (Romano et al., 2003, this kind of cross recurrence plot is denoted as XRP). Based on this new approach, the cross mutual information and Rényi entropy can be estimated. In addition, the XRP can be used to study phase synchronization in complex systems (Rosenblum et al., 1996). The XRP can be applied to measurements of different systems whose observations cannot be considered as state variables of the same system. XRPs are not restricted to only two systems; it is a multivariate analysis tool. In contrast to CRPs, XRPs can only be applied to time series of equal time scale, length and sample resolution.

The development of RP based methods is not yet concluded. The very last years in particular have shown that large potential lies in the analysis of RPs.

5 Applications

The high potential for the analysis based on recurrence or cross recurrence plots arises with their applicability. Hundreds of applications of recurrence plots and recurrence quantification analysis, especially to physiological data, represent the increasing importance of these methods. In this section selected applications of the newest strategies based on cross recurrence plots to geological data are presented. Methods of linear and nonlinear data analysis mostly fail in these applications because of the rather short length of the time series and their nonstationarity.

5.1 Similarities Found within Present and Past Climatic Data Series

Cross recurrence plots can be used for studying a similar time evolution of phase space trajectories and hence to assess the similarity or interrelation between the underlying processes. The following example illustrates the functioning of this technique on natural data from geology.

Data from geology are often characterized as short and nonstationary. The unique character of outcrops or drilling cores does not usually allow to repeat or refine a measurement. Therefore, data analysis of geological data is often confronted with problems regarding the length, nonstationarity or gaps in the data. In the previous application of CRPs we have seen that this method can be used for this kind of data. Therefore, in this subsection the application of CRPs will be used for the analysis of palaeo-climatology data that are of short length and nonstationarity (Marwan et al., 2003; Trauth et al., 2003).

Higher variability in rainfall and river discharge could be of major importance in landslide generation in the northwestern Argentine Andes. A potential cause of such variability is the El Niño/ Southern Oscillation (ENSO). Annual layered deposits of a landslide-dammed lake in the Santa Maria Basin (site El Paso, Province Salta, NW Argentina) with an age of 30 000 ^{14}C years provide an archive of precipitation variability during this time (Fig. 6). The annual cycle of wet summers

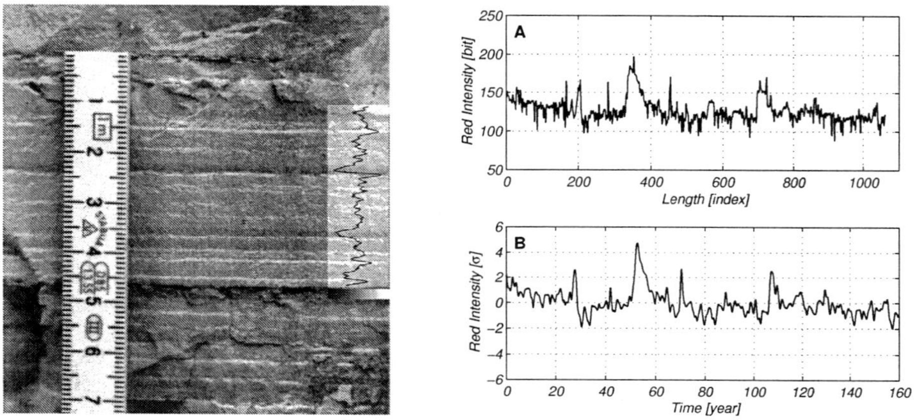

Figure 6: Left: Photograph of varved lake sediments from the El Paso site in the Santa Maria Basin with cyclic occurrence of dark red colourations recording more precipitation and sediment flux with ENSO-like periodicities (Trauth and Strecker, 1999). The overlayed curve shows a representative red colour intensity transect of the deposits. Right: Red intensity values of the lake sediments of site EP160 on (A) a length scale and on (B) a time scale and after smoothing and normalization; the unit of raw data is one bit, the unit of transformed and smoothed data is the standard deviation σ.

and dry winters caused significant changes in the lake's sedimentation. During the rainy season mainly ocher coloured silty sediments were deposited; during the subsequent dry season a thin white layer consisting of the skeletons of silica algae (diatoms) was deposited. Due to its white colour, the diatomaceous layer can be used to identify single years in these sediments. Recurring intense red colouration of the silty part of the annual layers comes from reworked older sediments which are eroded and deposited only during extreme rainfall events. Therefore, the intensity of red colour in the varved deposits can be interpreted as a proxy for precipitation variation in the Santa Maria Basin (Trauth and Strecker, 1999; Trauth et al., 2000). The more intense red colouration is evidence of more precipitation during the rainy season. The estimate of the power spectrum of the red colour intensity reveals significant peaks within the ENSO frequency band of two to four years, suggesting an ENSO-like influence (Trauth et al., 2000). Because of the nonstationarity of these data (the sedimentation process in a lake is not stationary, which results in nonstationary proxy variables for the in-lake processes) linear correlation analysis is unsuitable. Therefore, the CRP analysis is applied to these data.

Our research includes the quantification analysis of CRPs of an index data series of the ENSO (Southern Oscillation Index, SOI) and the modern as well as palaeo-precipitation data in order to compare the magnitude and causes of rainfall variability in the NW Argentine Andes today and during the time of enhanced landsliding around 30 000 ^{14}C years ago (Marwan et al., 2003; Trauth et al., 2003). For the assessment of the modern ENSO influence on local rainfall in NW Argentina, the monthly precipitation data from the three stations San Salvador de Jujuy (JUY), Salta (SAL) and San Miguel de Tucuman (TUC) are analyzed (Figs. 7, 8). These locations are influenced by different local winds (Fig. 7); Jujuy and Salta mainly receive northeasterly and easterly moisture-bearing winds during the summer rainy season, whereas Tucuman is characterized by southerly and south-westerly winds (Prohaska, 1976).

An appended surrogate test provides an evaluation of the results of the CRP analysis. The assumption for the surrogate data is that the considered processes are linearly independent and do not have any similar dynamics. These surrogates should reveal some features like in our original data but also features caused by the randomness of a possible correlation (stochastic processes). Linear correlated noise is a paradigmatic example for such processes (Kantz and Schreiber, 1997). We calculate a surrogate time series based on this class of processes with the following

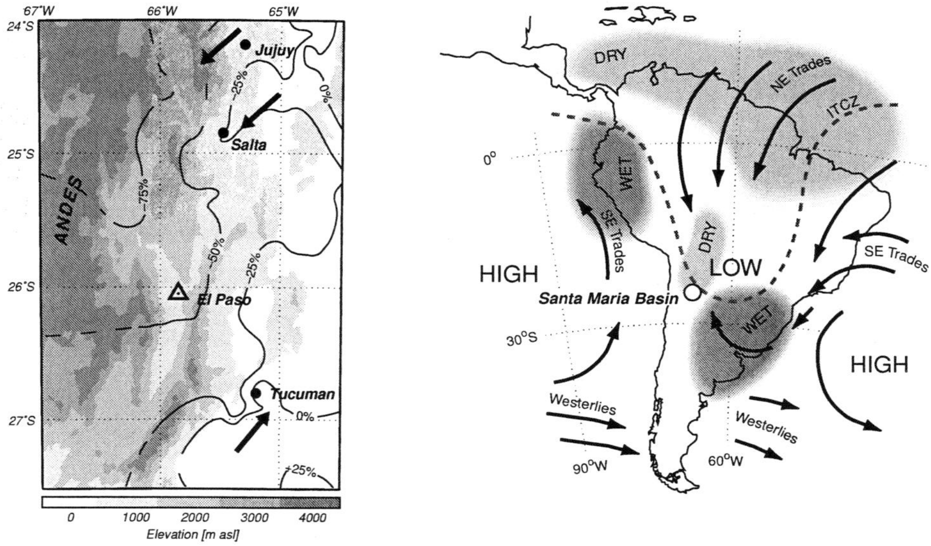

Figure 7: Left: Study area in the Santa Maria Basin with the locality of annual layered lake deposits from the El Paso site, the relative precipitation anomaly during the El Niño 1965/66 compared to mean annual precipitation (annual precipitation as a mean from July to June; data from Bianchi and Yañez, 1992) and the prevailing wind directions during January (black arrows; wind directions from Prohaska, 1976). Right: Present-day airflow pattern during the summer rainy season and principal areas of rainfall anomalies during El Niño events in South America (modified after Trauth et al., 2000).

recursive function, an autoregressive process of order p,

$$x_n = \sum_{i=1}^{p} a_p \, x_{n-p} + b \, \xi_n,$$

where ξ is white noise and a_i are coefficients which determine the auto-correlation of the system and allow to adapt this stochastic system to our natural processes. We fit the model to the precipitation series of the station Tucuman. Then we perform the CRP analysis using the SOI data and the ensemble of, e. g. 10,000 realizations of precipitation series produced by the AR model. Using the distributions of the RR and L measures obtained from these CRPs, we estimate their empirical confidence bounds (we will use the 2σ-bounds which approximately correspond with the 95% confidence level).

With these confidence bounds we evaluate the obtained measures of CRP and the relations of the natural processes. Since the surrogates are from a stationary

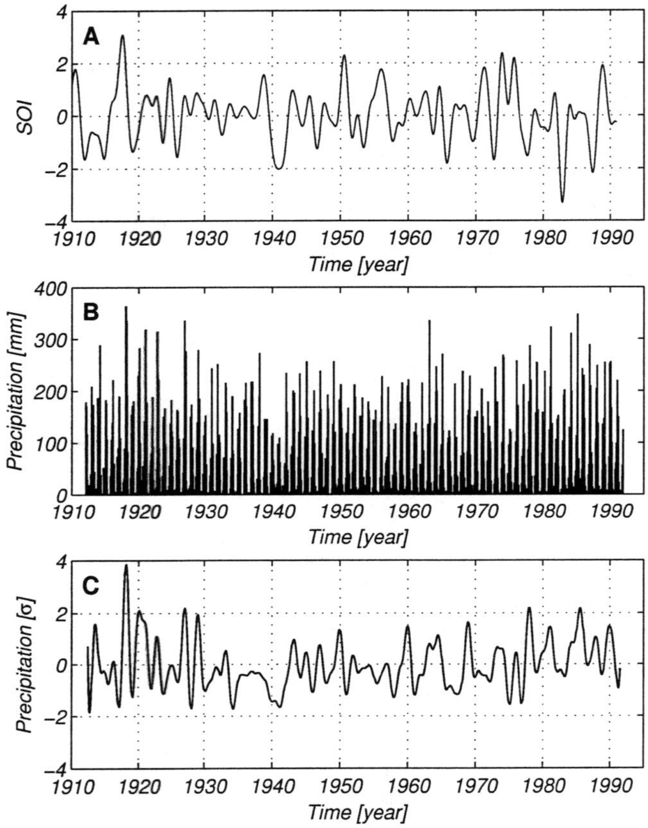

Figure 8: Smoothed and σ-normalized time series of the Southern Oscillation Index (A), monthly precipitation data of Salta (B) and its smoothed and σ-normalized time series (C). SOI based on COADS data from the NOAA Live Access Server (http://ferret.wrc.noaa.gov).

system and the natural data are nonstationary, we have further applied this kind of evaluation to more stationary segments in the natural data and got the same results. This kind of surrogates is a special realization, which is prototypical for linear stochastic processes. There are, of course, a lot of other possibilities to construct surrogates (cf. Kantz and Schreiber, 1997).

The CRPs of pairs of SOI and present-day precipitation as well as SOI and palaeo-precipitation show similar features (Fig. 9). These significant similarities indicate that the red colour intensity records from the varved lake sediment do reflect rainfall in NW Argentina. First, we discuss the CRP of Salta precipitation (data series SAL) vs. the Southern Oscillation Index (SOI) and the CRP of red colour intensity of varves (data series EP160) vs. SOI. The x-axis represents time along the phase space trajectory of the SOI, whereas the y-axis represents the time along the phase space trajectory of SAL or EP160, respectively. The CRP of SAL vs. SOI exhibits longer diagonal lines in two to four year intervals, which matches the same frequency band obtained by the power spectral analysis (Fig. 9). This indicates that some parts of the phase space trajectory of the SOI recur in epochs of the phase space trajectory of SAL after relocating by the time of two to four years. Vertical white bands in the CRP represent less frequent states in SOI, whereas horizontal white bands represent less frequent states in SAL. The latter occurs with intervals of more than ten years. The CRP between EP160 and SOI shows similar characteristics as the CRP described above (Fig. 9). Longer diagonal lines have spacings of about two to four years. White bands occur at time scales of more than ten years. Some linkages in both CRPs are obvious through visual inspection. Next, a quantitative analysis of the CRPs is performed in order to study statistically these relations and to allocate the predefined causality patterns to certain localities.

We find that the parameter RR_*^c of the CRPs between TUC and SOI has small negative values which do not exceed the 2σ-bounds and do not show preferences for a distinct lag. The parameter L_*^c also has small values, but it has rather small maxima and minima at delays of -1, 4 and 8 months. These results indicate that the precipitation in Tucuman is not strongly influenced by ENSO. If there is a weak influence, the rainfall will increase during El Niño (Fig. 10 A, E). However, the analysis of JUY and SOI reveals clear positive values around a lag of zero and negative values after 8 – 12 months, which suggests a significant link between Jujuy rainfall and ENSO (Fig. 10 C, G). The measures for the analysis of SAL versus SOI show smaller maxima for a delay of about zero and minima after a lag of 8

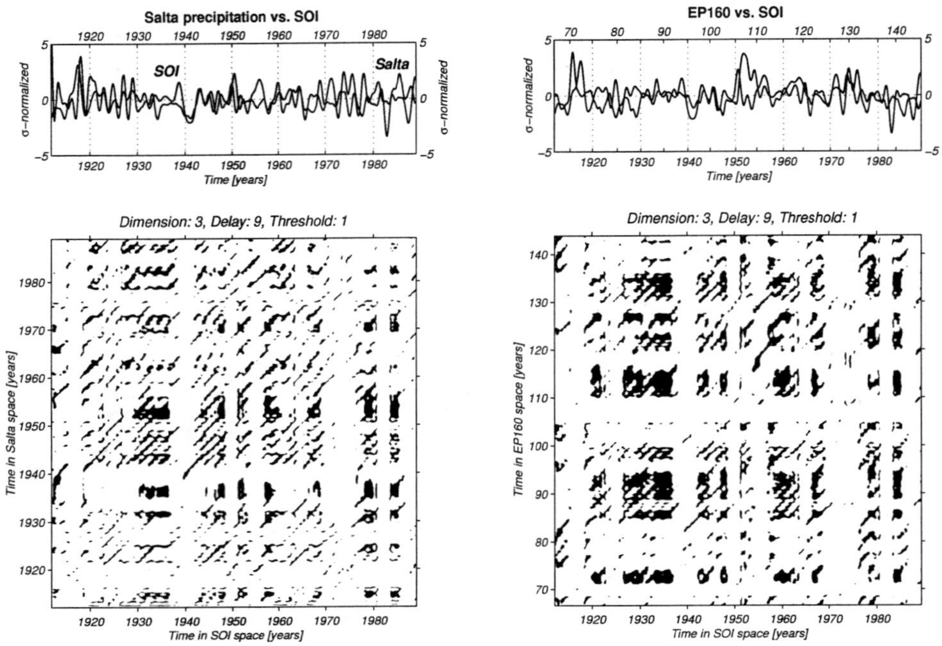

Figure 9: Left: Cross recurrence plot of SOI vs. precipitation data from the city of Salta (data shown at top). Black points represent the occurrence of similar states in both processes. Diagonal lines correspond with epochs of similar dynamics in both processes. The amount and length of these lines can be used as measures of the similarity of both processes. Right: Cross recurrence plot of SOI vs. the best matching section of palaeo-precipitation (EP160, data shown at top). The x-axis shows the time along the phase space trajectory of the SOI and the y-axis that of SAL and EP160, respectively.

– 12 months. Therefore, we infer a weaker link between Salta rainfall and ENSO (Fig. 10 B, F; the disrupted minima in the L_*^c parameter at around ten months is due to the short data length and a resulting nonstationarity in the CRP). The measures for both SAL and JUY exceed the 2σ-bounds.

The 30 000 ^{14}C year old precipitation data are not simply comparable with present-day data, because there is no information available about how to synchronize the rainfall records with modern climate indices. Therefore, we seek the time window in these data showing the highest coincidence in the dynamics using maximum values for RR_*^c and L_*^c as the key criterion. The linear correlation coefficients could be used to find such a sequence, but this results in numerous ambiguous possibilities.

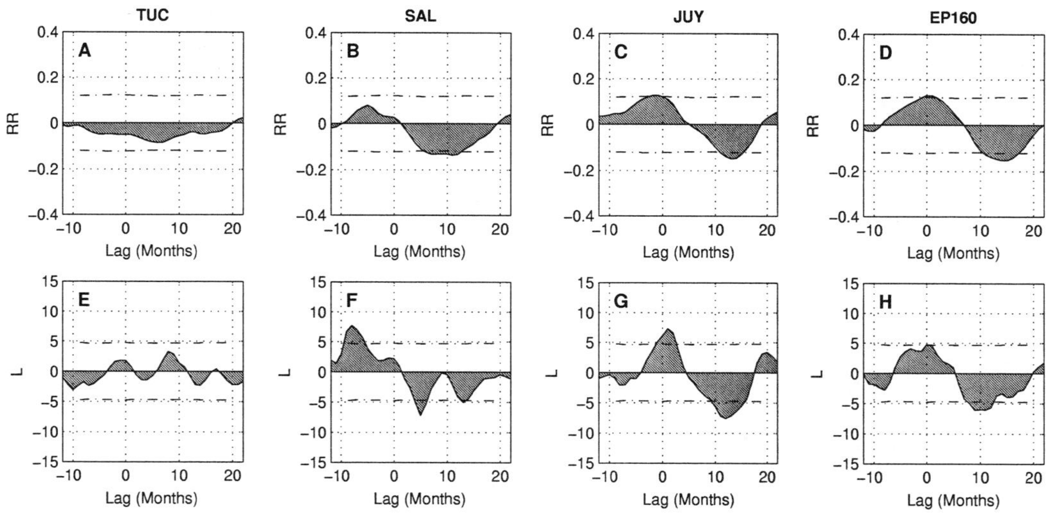

Figure 10: RR_*^c and L_*^c measures of the cross recurrence plots between SOI and precipitation in Tucuman (A, E), Salta (B, F), Jujuy (C, G) and palaeo-precipitation (D, H). Extreme values reveal high similarity between the dynamics of the rainfall and the ENSO. The dash-dotted lines are the empirical 2σ-bounds from the distributions of an ensemble of data based on a 5th-order AR-model.

The complexity measures based on CRP provide a differentiated search that also considers time based features of the signal. This method reveals indeed a clearer result. The measures presented herein are not the only measures used. For maintaining clarity, the further measures are not presented in this application, although they are used to find the sequence in the sediment data. Even though the observed coincidence is not very high, it yields the time section in the palaeo-precipitation record EP160 which can be in best accordance with modern data. In our palaeoclimate data EP160 we find such a section represented by maximum and minima values for RR_*^c and L_*^c for delays of about zero and ten months, similar to those found for JUY and SAL (Fig. 10D, H). The RR_*^c and L_*^c measures also exceed the 2σ-bounds.

The similarities between the time series of the present-day rainfall data and the palaeo-precipitation record from the lake sediments suggest that an ENSO-like oscillation was active around 30 000 ^{14}C years ago (roughly corresponding to 34 000 cal. years BP), which corresponds with the results of the investigation of Coccolithophores production (Beaufort et al., 2001). In the semiarid basins of the NW Argentine Andes, the ENSO-like variation could have caused significant fluctuations in local rainfall around 30 000 ^{14}C years ago similar to modern conditions. Together with generally higher moisture levels, as indicated by lake balance modeling results (Bookhagen et al., 2001), this mechanism could help to explain more frequent landsliding approximately 34 000 years ago in the semiarid basins of the Central Andes. For the comparison of the past and modern climate conditions, the CRP analysis has been used because a linear correlation analysis would reveal ambiguous results.

5.2 Time Scale Alignment of Borehole Data

The CRP contains information about the time synchronization of data series (in the following the terms synchronization and rescaling refers to the alignment of the time scales). This is revealed by the distorted main diagonal, the LOS. A non-parametric rescaling function is provided by isolating this LOS from the CRP and can be used for the re-alignment of the time scales of the considered time series. We expect that this approach will open a wide range of applications, such as scale alignment and pattern recognition, e. g. in geology, molecular biology or ecology.

In this application we consider geophysical measurements of two sediment cores from the Makarov Basin, in the central Arctic Ocean, PS 2178-3 and PS 2180-2 (Marwan et al., 2002a) and compare the method of cross recurrence plot matching with the conventional method of visual wiggle matching (interactive adjustment). The task is to align the data of the PS 2178-3 core (data length $N = 436$) with the scale of the PS 2180-2 (data length $N = 251$) in order to get a depth-depth-function which that to synchronize both data sets (Fig. 11).

The phase space trajectories are formed by the following normalized six measures: low field magnetic susceptibility (κ_{LF}), anhysteretic remanent magnetization (ARM), ratio of anhysteretic susceptibility to κ_{LF} (κ_{ARM}/κ_{LF}), relative palaeointensity (PJA), median destructive field of ARM (MDF_{ARM}) and inclination (INC). Each measure is used as one component of the phase space vector. However, this embedding can be combined with the time delay method according to Takens (1981) in order to further increase the dimension of the phase-space.

Using an embedding of $m = 3$ (absolute dimension is $3 \times 6 = 18$), $\tau = 1$ and a recurrence criterion of FAN with $\varepsilon = 0.05$, the resulting CRP shows a clear LOS and some clustering of black patches (Fig. 12). Black patches arise whenever the variation in the data is smaller than the used vicinity threshold ε for a given time (plateau). The next step is to fit a nonparametric function (the desired depth-depth-

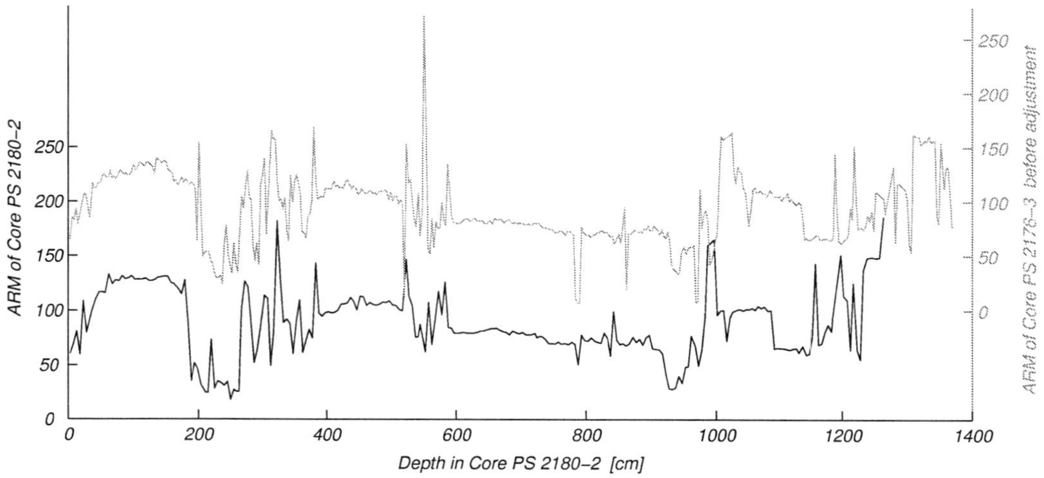

Figure 11: ARM data of the boreholes PS 2178-3 GPC and PS 2180-2 GPC in the Central Arctic Ocean before adjustment.

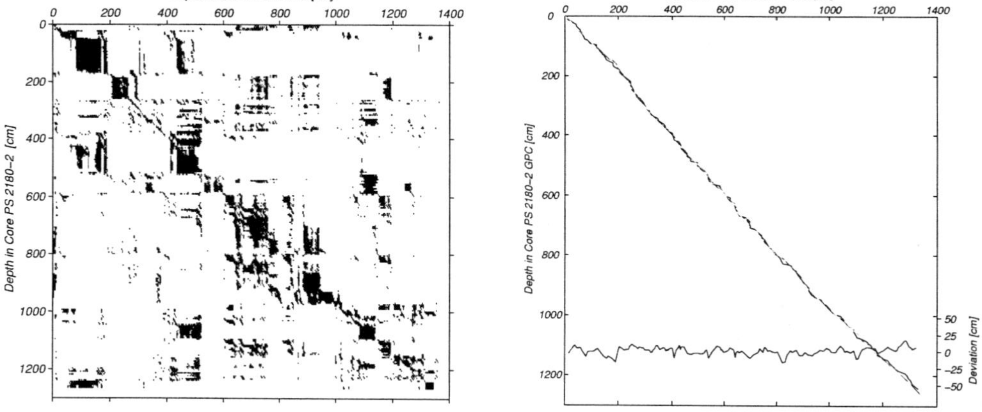

Figure 12: Left: Cross recurrence plot based on six normalized sediment parameters and an additional embedding dimension of $m = 3$ ($\tau = 1$, $\varepsilon = 0.05$) Right: Depth-depth-curves. In black the curve gained with the CRP, in gray the manually matching result. The horizontal curve shows the deviation between both results.

curve) to the LOS in this CRP (Fig. 12). Different approaches can be considered for this procedure. However, they could have to be chosen appropriately because they have a large effect on the quality of the found LOS. In our example a two step algorithm is chosen that is able to tend locally towards the direction of the centre of gravity of clustered black points. A detailed explanation is given in Marwan et al. (2002a). With so determined LOS we are able to align the scale of the PS 2178-3 core to that of PS 2180-2 (Fig. 13).

The determination of the depth-depth-function with the conventional method of visual wiggle matching is based on the interactive and parallel searching for the same structures in the different parameters of both data sets. If the adjustment does not work in a section of the one parameter, one can use another parameter for this section, which allows the multivariate adjustment of the data sets. The recognition of the same structures in the data sets requires a degree of experience. However, human eyes are usually better in the visual assessment of complex structures than a computational algorithm.

Our depth-depth-curve differs slightly from the curve which was gained by the visual wiggle matching (Fig. 12). However, despite our rather simple algorithm used to fit the non-parametric adjustment function to the LOS, we obtained a good result of adjusted data series. If they are well adjusted, the correlation coefficient between the parameters of the adjusted data and the reference data should not vary so much. The correlation coefficients between the reference and adjusted data series is about 0.70 – 0.80, where the correlation coefficients of the interactive rescaled data varies from 0.71 – 0.87 (Tab. 1). The χ^2 measure of the correlation coefficients emphasizes more variation for the wiggle matching than for the CRP rescaling. The results obtained with the CRP rescaling can be further improved by a more suitable algorithm for the search of the LOS.

The comparison of the CRP aligned geophysical measurements with the conventional visual matching (wiggle matching) shows an acceptable reliability level of the new method (Marwan et al., 2002a). The advantage is the automatic, objective and multivariate alignment. Moreover, further attempts exist to align geological data automatically. They either use parametrical approaches (minimal cost functions, Fourier series estimation of the mapping function and others; Martinson et al., 1982; Brüggemann, 1992) or they have to fit a large number of parameters and apply trial-and-error algorithms (sequence slotting; Thompson and Clark, 1989).

Table 1: Correlation coefficients ρ_1 (wiggle matching) and ρ_2 (CRP matching) between adjusted data and reference data and their χ^2 deviation. The correlation of the interactive adjusted data varies more than the automatic adjusted data. The data length is $N = 170$ (wiggle matching) and $N = 250$ (CRP matching). The difference between the both correlation coefficients ρ_1 and ρ_2 is significant at a 99 % significance level, when the test measure $\hat{z}$ is greater than $z_{0.01} = 2.576$.

Parameter	ρ_1	ρ_2	$\hat{z}$
ARM	0.8667	0.7846	6.032
MDF_{ARM}	0.8566	0.7902	4.791
κ_{LF}	0.7335	0.7826	2.661
κ_{ARM}/κ_{LF}	0.8141	0.8049	0.614
PJA	0.7142	0.6995	0.675
INC	0.7627	0.7966	1.990
χ^2	141.4	49.1	

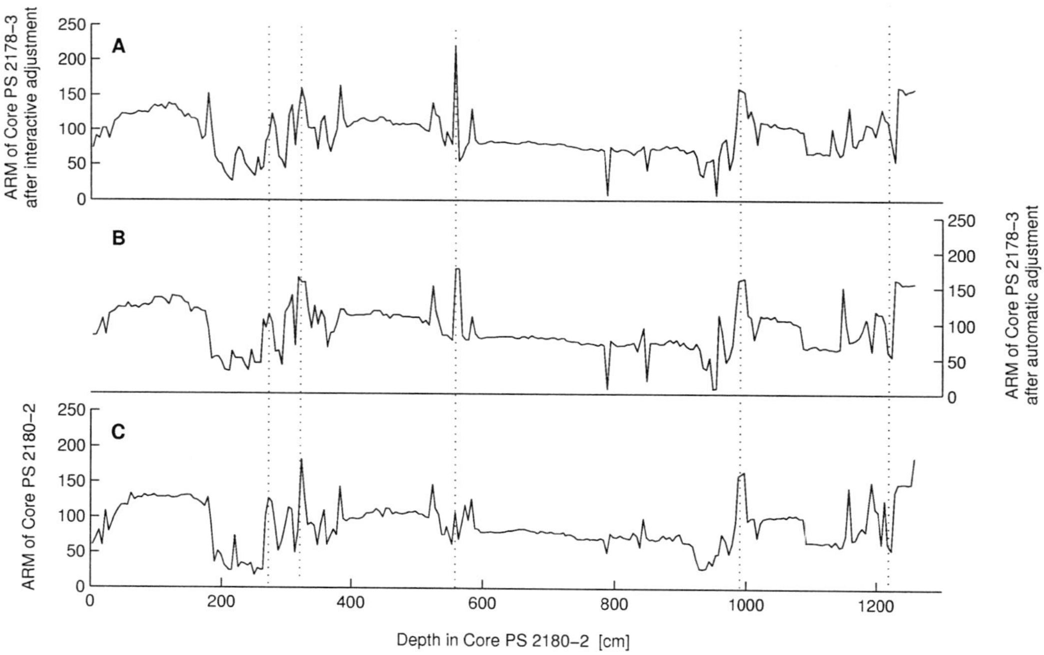

Figure 13: The ARM data are exemplary shown after alignment by wiggle matching (A) and by automatic alignment (B) using the LOS from Fig. 12. Plot (C) shows the reference data.

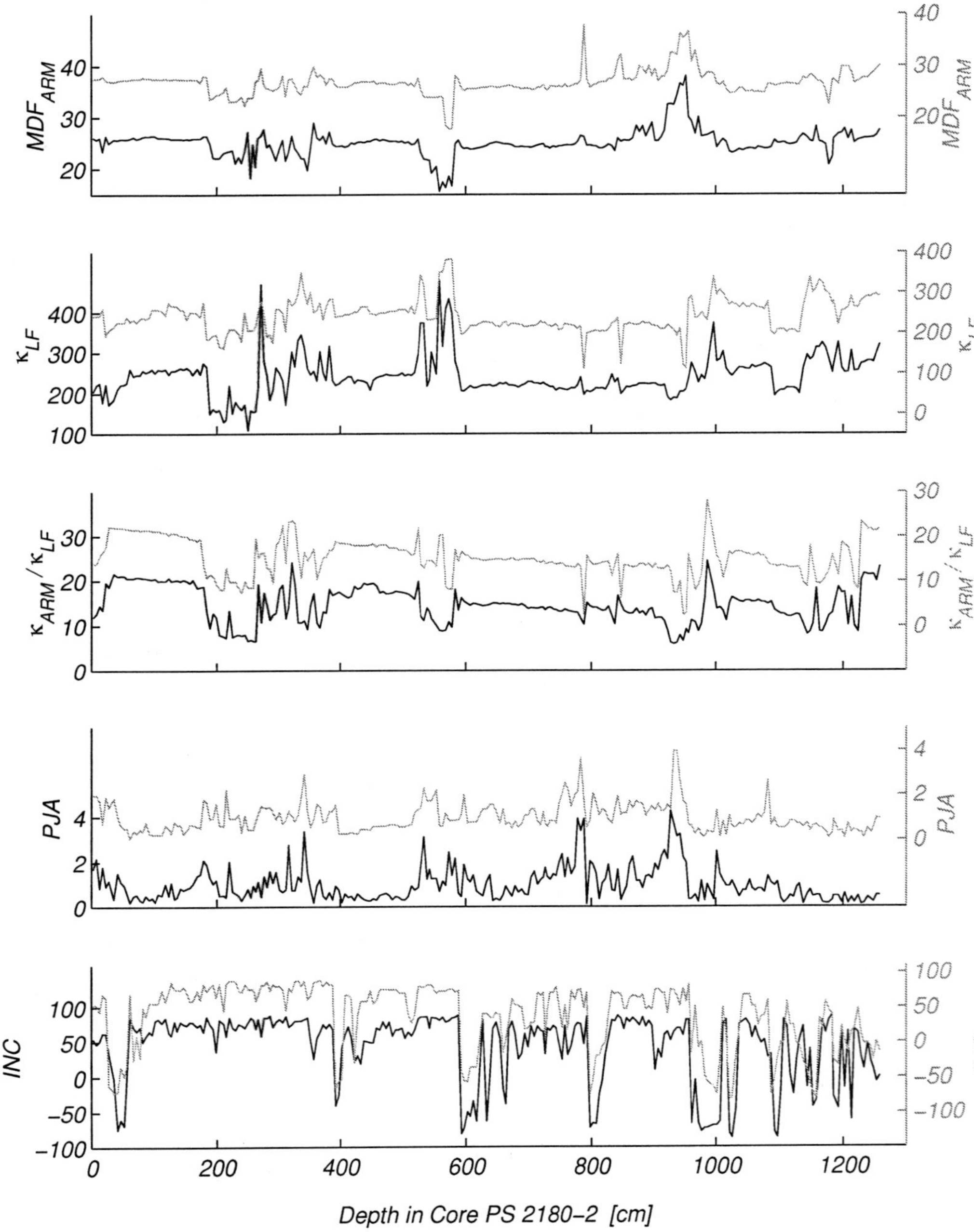

Figure 14: The adjusted marine sediment parameters. The construction of the CRP was done with the normalized parameters. In this plots we show the parameters, which are not normalized.

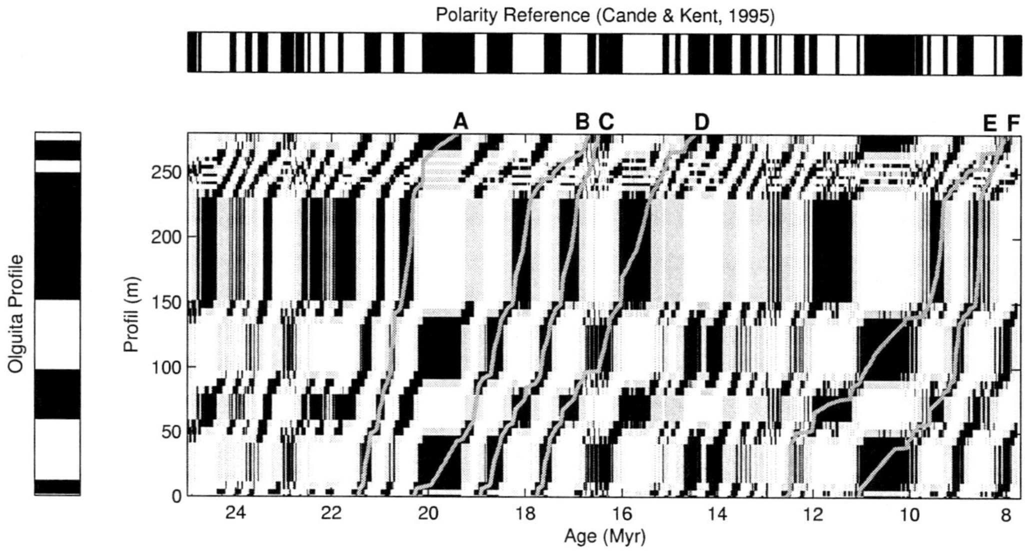

Figure 15: CRP between the polarity data of the Olguita profile and the reference data according to Cande and Kent (1995). In the polarity data the white colour marks a polarity of the Earth's magnetic field in the present, whereas the black colour marks a reversal. Six potential LOS are marked with gray lines (A–F, corresponding to the potential LOS given in Fig. 16).

5.3 Search for an Appropriate Sequence in a Geological Profile (Magnetostratigraphy)

In the following application of CRP the possibility of finding an appropriate sequence in a given data series relating to a reference series (and vice versa, respectively) is presented. For this task the LOS in the CRP must be found. Although we present only applications in geology here, the methods based on CRPs can also be applied to data from other scientific field. The search of sequences in reference data based on CRPs has been also successfully applied in gene sequencing and speech recognition (Marwan, 2003).

From a sediment profile (Olguita profile, Patagonia, Argentina; Warkus, 2002) a measurement of the palaeo-polarity of the Earth's magnetic field (along with other measurements) is available. The starting point for any geological investigation of such a profile is determining the time at which these sediments were deposited. By applying the magnetostratigraphic approach and a geomagnetic polarity reference with known time scale, the polarity measurements can be used to determine a possible time scale for the profile. Cande and Kent (1995) provide such a geomagnetic polarity reference, which covers the last 83 Myr. The Olguita profile contains seven reversals. The polarity data consist of the values one, for the polarity direction as today, and the values zero, for the inverse polarity. Unfortunately, this data series is too short (only 16 measurements) for a credible analysis. Nevertheless, for our purpose of demonstration we will enlarge this data by interpolation. The Olguita profile is transformed to an equidistant scale of 300 data points and the reference data is transformed to an equidistant scale of 1 200 data points.

A CRP is created from these two data series by using an embedding dimension $m = 4$, a delay of $\tau = 6$ and a neighbourhood criterion of FAN (30% recurrence rate). Varying degrees of continuous lines between 21 and 16 Myr BP and between 12 and 8 Myr BP occur in the CRP, which can be interpreted as the desired LOS (Fig. 15). We will analyse six of these possibilities to estimate the LOS. The search for the potential LOS is conducted using the same algorithm described in Marwan et al. (2002a). Moreover, we can evaluate the quality of these potential LOS by introducing a quality factor that takes into consideration the amount of gaps $N_\circ$ and black dots $N_\bullet$ on this line

$$Q = \frac{N_\bullet}{N_\bullet + N_\circ} \, 100\%. \tag{26}$$

A larger Q is a better LOS; $Q = 100\%$ stands for an absolute continuous line. Moreover, the obtained LOS can be interpreted as the sedimentation rate (Fig. 16). Abrupt changes in the sedimentation rate are not expected, thus, the potential LOS should not change abruptly. As an evaluator for this criterion we can use the averaged second derivative with respect to the time $\langle \partial_t^2 \rangle$.

The potential LOS differs slightly in the Q factor, but more in the occurrence of abrupt changes in their slope (Fig. 16 and Tab. 2). The LOS in Fig. 16C has the smallest $\langle \partial_t^2 \rangle$ and could be, therefore, a good LOS for the dating of the Olguita profile. Regarding this result, the Olguita profile would have an age between 16.5 and 18.9 Myr and an age-depth-relation as it is represented by the possibility of a LOS in Fig. 16C. Warkus' investigation reveals the same result (Warkus, 2002), although he also mentioned that the dating based on the polarity data is ambiguous.

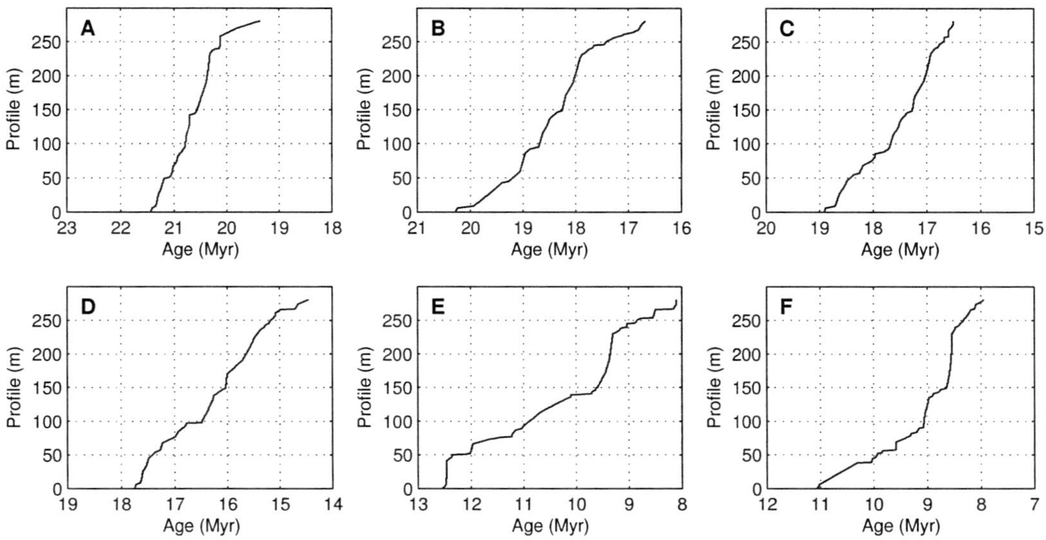

Figure 16: Potential LOS of the CRP presented in Fig. 15. They correspond to the potential sedimentation rates of the Olguita profile and mark sequences in the polarity reference, which match with the Olguita profile. Due to this matching, the Olguita profile can be dated.

Table 2: Possible ages of the Olguita profile, which are based on the found potential LOS (Fig. 16) and characteristics of these potential LOS.

Plot	Age (Myr)	$N_\bullet$	$N_\circ$	Q (%)	$\langle \partial_t^2 \rangle$
A	19.4–21.4	345	23	93.8	5.5
B	16.7–20.3	407	43	90.4	12.5
C	16.5–18.9	351	15	95.9	5.0
D	14.4–17.8	392	16	96.1	20
E	8.1–12.6	482	16	96.8	23
F	7.9–11.1	399	13	96.8	18

6 Conclusion

The extension of the concept of recurrence plots to a test for interrelations between two different phase space trajectories leads to cross recurrence plots (CRPs). From the point of view of a CRP, an RP can be considered as a special case of a CRP for two identical processes. However, if these two processes become progressively different, typical structures of the RP, like the main diagonal (*line of identity, LOI*), will dissolve. A quantification of these structures has been used in order to assess the variation or similarity between the dynamics of both processes.

The CRP analysis provides another useful application. The orientation of the line structures in the CRP is related to the time relation between the corresponding segments of the phase space trajectories. In the case of two sufficiently similar processes with different time dilatations, the CRP shows a bowed line of identity which is called *line of synchronization (LOS)*. This line corresponds to the transfer function between the time scales of the considered time series. A nonparametrical function fitted to LOS can be used in order to align the two processes to the same time scale.

Considering two processes, where epochs of the second are partly contained in the first, the CRP facilitates finding the location of these epochs in the first process.

Applications to real data from geology have revealed the applicability of the methods based on CRPs. Applying CRPs we were able to investigate palaeoclimate conditions, to align geophysical data from different boreholes to the same time/ depth scale and to find possible time-scales of a geological profile by using a reference data set.

A Matlab® toolbox for the application of recurrence plots as well as cross recurrence plots is available through the WorldWideWeb. An online and printable manual with illustrative examples as well as an extensive bibliography of applications of RPs and CRPs can also be found there. The current address is `http://www.agnld.uni-potsdam.de/~marwan/toolbox`.

Acknowledgment

We are grateful to Marco Thiel, Carmen M. Romano and Udo Schwarz for new ideas, fruitful discussions and suggestions. We also acknowledge Martin Trauth

(Institute of Geosciences, University of Potsdam), Norbert Nowaczyk (GeoForschungsZentrum Potsdam) and Frank Warkus (Institute of Geosciences, University of Potsdam) for cooperation and providing data. Some part of this research was supported by the Priority Programme 1097, *Geomagnetic Variations, Spatio-temporal structure, processes and effects on system Earth* of the Deutsche Forschungsgemeinschaft as well by the ESA-Project MAP AO-99-030, *2D and 3D Quantification of Bone Structure and its Changes in Microgravity Condition by Measures of Complexity*.

References

ABARBANEL, H. D. I., BROWN, R., SIDOROWICH, J. J., TSIMRING, L. S., The analysis of observed chaotic data in physical systems. Review of Modern Physics 65 (4), 1993, 1331–1392.
DOI: 10.1103/RevModPhys.65.1331

BEAUFORT, L., DE GARIDEL-THORON, T., MIX, A. C., PISIAS, N. G., ENSO-like Forcing on Oceanic Primary Production During the Late Pleistocene. Science 293, 2001, 2440–2444.

BERGER, A., LOUTRE, M., Insolation values for the climate of the last 10 million years. Quaternary Science Reviews 10, 1991, 297–317.

BIANCHI, A. R., YAÑEZ, C. E., Las precipitaciones en el noroeste Argentino. Instituto Nacional de Tecnologia Agropecuaria, Estacion Experimental Agropecuaria Salta, 1992.

BOOKHAGEN, B., HASELTON, K., TRAUTH, M. H., Hydrological modelling of a Pleistocene landslide-dammed lake in the Santa Maria Basin, NW Argentina. Palaeogeography, Palaeoclimatology, Palaeoecology 169, 2001, 113–127.
DOI: 10.1016/S0031-0182(01)00221-8

BRÜGGEMANN, W., A Minimal Cost Function Method For Optimizing the Age-Depth Relation of Deep-Sea Sediment Cores. Paleoceanography 7 (4), 1992, 467–487.

CANDE, S. C., KENT, D. V., Revised calibration of the geomagnetic polarity timescale for the late Cretaceous and Cenozoic. Journal of Geophysical Research 100, 1995, 6093–6095.

CAO, L., Practical method for determining the minimum embedding dimension of a scalar time series. Physica D 110 (1–2), 1997, 43–50.
DOI: 10.1016/S0167-2789(97)00118-8

CHOI, J. M., BAE, B. H., KIM, S. Y., Divergence in perpendicular recurrence plot; quantification of dynamical divergence from short chaotic time series. Physics Letters A 263 (4–6), 1999, 299–306.
DOI: 10.1016/S0375-9601(99)00751-3

ECKMANN, J.-P., KAMPHORST, S. O., RUELLE, D., Recurrence Plots of Dynamical Systems. Europhysics Letters 5, 1987, 973–977.

ECKMANN, J.-P., RUELLE, D., Ergodic theory of chaos and strange attractors. Review of Modern Physics 57 (3), 1985, 617–656.
DOI: 10.1103/RevModPhys.57.617

FAURE, P., KORN, H., A new method to estimate the Kolmogorov entropy from recurrence plots: its application to neuronal signals. Physica D 122 (1–4), 1998, 265–279.
DOI: 10.1016/S0167-2789(98)00177-8

GAO, J. B., Recurrence Time Statistics for Chaotic Systems and Their Applications. Physical Review Letters 83 (16), 1999, 3178–3181.
DOI: 10.1103/PhysRevLett.83.3178

GAO, J. B., CAI, H. Q., On the structures and quantification of recurrence plots. Physics Letters A 270 (1–2), 2000, 75–87.
DOI: 10.1016/S0375-9601(00)00304-2

KANTZ, H., SCHREIBER, T., Nonlinear Time Series Analysis. University Press, Cambridge, 1997.

KURTHS, J., HERZEL, H., An attractor in a solar time series. Physica D 25, 1987, 165–172.
DOI: 10.1016/0167-2789(87)90099-6

LORENZ, E. N., Deterministic Nonperiodic Flow. Journal of the Atmospheric Sciences 20, 1963, 120–141.

MANDELBROT, B. B., The fractal geometry of nature. Freeman, San Francisco, 1982.

MARTINSON, D. G., MENKE, W., STOFFA, P., An Inverse Approach to Signal Correlation. Journal of Geophysical Research 87, 1982, 4807–4818.

MARWAN, N., Untersuchung der Klimavariabilität in NW Argentinien mit Hilfe der quantitativen Analyse von Recurrence Plots. Master's thesis, Dresden University of Technology, Dresden University of Technology, October 1999.

MARWAN, N., Encounters With Neighbours – Current Developments Of Concepts Based On Recurrence Plots And Their Applications. Ph.D. thesis, University of Potsdam, 2003.

MARWAN, N., KURTHS, J., Nonlinear analysis of bivariate data with cross recurrence plots. Physics Letters A 302 (5–6), 2002, 299–307.
DOI: `10.1016/S0375-9601(02)01170-2`

MARWAN, N., THIEL, M., NOWACZYK, N. R., Cross Recurrence Plot Based Synchronization of Time Series. Nonlinear Processes in Geophysics 9 (3/4), 2002a, 325–331.

MARWAN, N., TRAUTH, M. H., VUILLE, M., KURTHS, J., Comparing modern and Pleistocene ENSO-like influences in NW Argentina using nonlinear time series analysis methods. Climate Dynamics (in press), 2003.
DOI: `10.1007/s00382-003-0335-3`

MARWAN, N., WESSEL, N., KURTHS, J., Recurrence Plot Based Measures of Complexity and its Application to Heart Rate Variability Data. Physical Review E 66 (2), 2002b, 026702.
DOI: `10.1103/PhysRevE.66.026702`

MCGUIRE, G., AZAR, N. B., SHELHAMER, M., Recurrence matrices and the preservation of dynamical properties. Physics Letters A 237 (1–2), 1997, 43–47.
DOI: `10.1016/S0375-9601(97)00697-X`

OTT, E., Chaos in Dynamical Systems. University Press, Cambridge, 1993.

PACKARD, N. H., CRUTCHFIELD, J. P., FARMER, J. D., SHAW, R. S., Geometry from a Time Series. Physical Review Letters 45 (9), 1980, 712–716.
DOI: `10.1103/PhysRevLett.45.712`

PROHASKA, F. J., The climate of Argentina, Paraguay and Urugay. Vol. 12 of World Survey of Climatlogy. Elsevier, Amsterdam, Oxford, New York, 1976. pp. 13–73.

ROMANO, M., THIEL, M., KURTHS, J., A new definition of Cross Recurrence Plots. Physics Letters A (subm.), 2003.

ROSENBLUM, M. G., PIKOVSKY, A. S., KURTHS, J., Phase Synchronization of Chaotic Oscillators. Physical Review Letters 76, 1996, 1804.
DOI: 10.1103/PhysRevLett.76.1804

SAKOE, H., CHIBA, S., Dynamic programming algorithm optimization for spoken word recognition. IEEE Trans. Acoustics, Speech and Signal Proc. 26, 1978, 43–49.

TAKENS, F., Detecting Strange Attractors in Turbulence. Vol. 898 of Lecture Notes in Mathematics. Springer, Berlin, 1981. pp. 366–381.

THIEL, M., ROMANO, M. C., KURTHS, J., Analytical description of Recurrence Plots of white noise and chaotic processes. Chaos (subm.), 2003.

THOMPSON, R., CLARK, R. M., Sequence slotting for stratigraphic correlation between cores: theory and practice. Journal of Paleolimnology 2, 1989, 173–184.

TRAUTH, M. H., ALONSO, R. A., HASELTON, K., HERMANNS, R., STRECKER, M. R., Climate change and mass movements in the northwest Argentine Andes. Earth and Planetary Science Letters 179 (2), 2000, 243–256.
DOI: 10.1016/S0012-821X(00)00127-8

TRAUTH, M. H., BOOKHAGEN, B., MARWAN, N., STRECKER, M. R., Multiple landslide clusters record Quaternary climate changes in the northwestern Argentine Andes. Palaeogeography Palaeoclimatology Palaeoecology 194 (1–3), 2003, 109–121.
DOI: 10.1016/S0031-0182(03)00273-6

TRAUTH, M. H., STRECKER, M. R., Formation of landslide-dammed lakes during a wet period between 40,000 and 25,000 yr B. P. in northwestern Argentina. Palaeogeography, Palaeoclimatology, Palaeoecology 153 (1–4), 1999, 277–287.
DOI: 10.1016/S0031-0182(99)00078-4

TRULLA, L. L., GIULIANI, A., ZBILUT, J. P., WEBBER JR., C. L., Recurrence quantification analysis of the logistic equation with transients. Physics Letters A 223 (4), 1996, 255–260.
DOI: 10.1016/S0375-9601(96)00741-4

WARKUS, F., Die neogene Hebungsgeschichte der Patagonischen Anden im Kontext der Subduktion eines aktiven Spreizungszentrums. Ph.D. thesis, University of Potsdam, Institute of Earth Sciences, 2002.
URL: `urn:nbn:de:kobv:517-0000555`

WEBBER JR., C. L., ZBILUT, J. P., Dynamical assessment of physiological systems and states using recurrence plot strategies. Journal of Applied Physiology 76 (2), 1994, 965–973.

WOLF, A., SWIFT, J. B., SWINNEY, H. L., VASTANO, J. A., Determining Lyapunov Exponents from a Time Series. Physica D 16 (3), 1985, 285–317.
DOI: `10.1016/0167-2789(85)90011-9`

ZBILUT, J. P., GIULIANI, A., WEBBER JR., C. L., Detecting deterministic signals in exceptionally noisy environments using cross-recurrence quantification. Physics Letters A 246 (1–2), 1998, 122–128.
DOI: `10.1016/S0375-9601(98)00457-5`

ZBILUT, J. P., WEBBER JR., C. L., Embeddings and delays as derived from quantification of recurrence plots. Physics Letters A 171 (3–4), 1992, 199–203.
DOI: `10.1016/0375-9601(92)90426-M`

In: Mathematical Physics Research at the Cutting Edge
Editor: C.V. Benton, pp. 141-188
ISBN 1-59033-939-8

Analytical Solutions of the Radiative Transfer Equation in One-Dimensional Spherical Geometry with Central Symmetry

Charles H Aboughantous*

Votan, 4548 Tigerland Avenue, Baton Rouge, Louisiana 70820, USA

Abstract. Analytical solutions of the transfer equation in spherical geometry with central symmetry are obtained on the spatial domain, in finite spheres and in infinite homogeneous and heterogeneous pure absorbing media, in LTE and for monochromatic unpolarized radiation. One set of solutions is obtained using a revised version of the discrete ordinates method and another set of solutions is obtained from the symmetrized transfer equation.

The discrete ordinates method is applied to the angular derivative using a revised structure of the set of discrete ordinates weaved from un-normalized circular functions. Gauss-Legendre quadrature of even order is used but the method is equally suitable for other quadratures with symmetric set of abscissas and weights of user's choice. The set of discrete ordinates equations is conservative and closed; a starter intensity is not needed. The angular derivative of the transfer equation is represented by a set of angular parameters that are calculated directly and without recursion from the abscissas and weights of the quadrature and without the constraint of asymptotic conditions. In order for the solution to be finite everywhere in the sphere and to satisfy the physical requirements of reciprocity of path, inverse square law and conservation of energy, proper symmetry requirements are applied to the intensity vectors. A comparison of the solutions obtained using the proposed method and the solutions of the integral equation demonstrates the validity of the method in the point source configuration and in the interior of spheres.

An alternative approach to solving the discrete ordinates equations is to solve the reduced transfer equation. By the process of symmetrizing the transfer equation, the angular derivative cancels out being an odd function on the angular domain and a reduced equation is obtained. The reduced transfer equation obtained in this manner is as rigorous as the transfer equation for all the moments of the specific intensity. This is demonstrated by a rigorous analytical proof and numerically. The numerical verification is accomplished by comparing the moments computed from the symmetrized solutions of the discrete ordinates equations with the moments computed from the solution of the reduced transfer equation. The agreement is perfect if not for the round-off.

1. Introduction

A diversity of numerical methods were devoted to the solution the transfer equation in spherical geometry. The most popular method, however, is the discrete ordinates method because of the simplicity of the boundary condition of the specific intensity. While efforts were successful in coupling the discrete ordinates method with analytical solution in slab geometry [1] [2], fewer efforts were devoted to produce analytical solutions in dis-

* Email address: votan@sprintmail.com

crete ordinates formalism in spherical geometry. Chandrasekhar [1] proposed an analytic approach based on the P_n approximation in discrete directions. In order to obtain the solution for the transfer equation, he expanded the specific intensity in P_4 and applied a sequence of transformations to the moments of the specific intensity in specific directions defined by the abscissas of Gauss-Legendre (GL) quadrature. These transformations yielded a Lommel equation for an accessory function. The solution was then converted to the total intensity, the first and the second moments. This approach is tedious and unyielding to expansions for $n > 4$. Chandrasekhar [1], as well as other authors [3], viewed the method wholly equivalent to the spherical harmonic method.

Further developments in the discrete ordinates formalism in spherical geometry were made in the realm of numerical methods. These efforts led to a set of discrete ordinates structured from *angular parameters* that approximate the angular derivative. The angular parameters are computed recursively from the abscissas and weights of GL quadrature constrained to a constant asymptotic specific intensity [4]; we refer to this method as the *recursive discrete ordinates* (RDO) method. While the underlying idea of the angular parameter is admittedly valid, its implementation with the asymptotic conditions yields solutions that are not quite satisfactory. These deficiencies were recognized by other users and some remedies were proposed [5] [6].

The shortcoming of the RDO method is the asymptotic condition on the angular parameters. It implies a flat spatial derivative or at least slowly varying intensity in space. Such a condition prevails in the deep interior of stars, it is not valid near the surface of stars, in relatively small spheres, around the interface between two thermodynamically different media and in the micropellet of laser induced fusion. On the other hand, the angular parameters of the RDO derived from abscissas of even order GL quadrature couple intensities directly from $[-1, 0]$ angular domain with intensities from $[0, +1]$ angular domain. That is, the angular derivative in the discrete space of ordinates straddles $\mu = 0$. This may not be objectionable in plane geometry where little consideration is given to symmetry, particularly for unpolarized radiation. In spherical geometry, the coupling of ψ^+ with ψ^- is permissible only at $\mu = 0$; indeed, the angular derivative of differential calculus couples intensities directly only at $\mu = 0$. The structural inconsistency of the RDO method destroys the closure of the discrete ordinates equations. The closure is accomplished by importing a *starter intensity* solution of the transfer equation of slab geometry without consideration to symmetry.

The practice in the RDO method is to use the starter intensity in the direction $\mu = -1$. This choice would be legitimate, in principle, with Radau quadrature where $\mu = -1$ is an abscissa. It is inconsistent with GL quadrature where $\mu = -1$ is not an abscissa. That is, the domain of definition of the starter intensity is outside the domain of definition of the discrete ordinates equations. To this effect, the solution with GL quadrature is conditioned by a boundary condition on the angular domain not belonging to the discrete space of ordinates. The inconsistency of the solution with RDO is compounded with the choice of the starter intensity of plane geometry. In spherical geometry, the intensity in the direction $\mu = -1$ is radial, that is, it obeys the inverse square law. The solution in plane geometry does not exhibit this inverse square behavior. The import of these approximations to the solution is a *dip* at the center of the sphere. This behavior of the intensity was believed nonphysical and attempts were made to cure the dip.

One approach to cure the dip evolved around applying Radau quadrature in the first angular cell and GL quadrature in the interior angular cells using the same structure of RDO. The dip was almost cured with micrometric spatial cells [5]. An alternative approach was proposed where the starter direction cosine has to be found by numerical experimentation. It was found that this starter direction cosine depends on the radius of the sphere, on the spatial grid and its magnitude can be larger than 1 in some spheres. Instead, hybrid heuristic recipes were proposed and appeared to have almost resolved the problem at least by graphical demonstrations [6].

A recent approach complemented the condition of zero spatial derivative of the specific intensity at the center by requiring an isotropic intensity at $r = 0$. For the most part the GL quadrature is replaced by an angular difference $\Delta\mu$. The RDO structure is retained unchanged but now it is associated with a set of interpolating functions representing the specific intensity in the angular cells. This discrete ordinates boundary value problem is designed to compare well with the solution of the integral equation in the interior of a sphere. The dip at the center appeared to be cured but the starter intensity of plane geometry is still needed for the closure of the discrete ordinates equations [7].

We understand the apparent success of this approach in that the solution is consistent with the underlying hypothesis. Its structural consistency is still not convincing, specifically, the RDO with its consequential starter intensity and the finiteness of the spatial derivative at the center; the flaw of the starter intensity as a boundary condition is discussed in great details in Part IV of this chapter. The finite derivative at the center can be made to satisfy symmetry boundary condition. However, symmetry at the center does not necessarily imply finite derivative nor does it require finiteness of the derivative at that point. Considering that symmetry at the center is natural boundary condition, *a priori* condition of finite derivative at that point becomes a redundant boundary condition. Redundant boundary conditions lead to inconsistency [8]. These considerations led us to believe that the discrete ordinates boundary value problem presented in [7] is not representative of the natural boundary value problem of energy flow in spheres in general.

Another recent approach transformed the angular derivative of the transfer equation in conservation form with a skilful application of the finite Legendre transform (FLT). The angular derivative was transformed into an expression in terms of moments of the specific intensity in Legendre polynomials [9]; these are the spherical harmonic moments [10] but they were never used before to approximate the angular derivative as in FLT method. The resulting transfer equation becomes integrodifferential equation, differential in r, integral in μ. The integrals cannot be evaluated in closed form, a gaussian quadrature was used for that purpose. The FLT transfer equations differ from the traditional discrete ordinates equations in that the latter are expressed in terms of discrete difference of the angular derivative, the former are continuous functions in μ. The method was tested with a sample problem consisting of a spherical cavity with a reflecting concentric sphere, the pellet in this chapter, of radius half the radius of the host cavity. It is not clear whether symmetry has given any consideration at the surface of the pellet.

We revisited the structure of the set of discrete ordinates in one-dimensional spherical geometry with central symmetry and proposed an alternative approach. The new set is based on even order GL quadrature merely as a matter of convenience. The method can be easily adapted to GL quadrature of odd order, or to other gaussian quadratures. The angular derivative is discretized with a finite set of angular parameters derived directly without recursion from the abscissas and weights of the quadrature, and they are not constrained to an asymptotic condition. Consequently, the set of discrete ordinates equations is closed and there is no need for starter intensity.

In order to validate the structure of the proposed set of discrete ordinates, we carried out the general analytic solution in a homogeneous infinite medium in LTE, both, continuous-in-r and in end-points forms. The latter solution is in fact a numerical algorithm free of spatial truncation errors. Considering that the approximation introduced by discrete ordinates is indeed an approximation of the divergence term of the transfer equation, the validity of the proposed discrete ordinates set is demonstrated in vacuum. The import of the approximation to the solution in pure absorbing media is also examined quantitatively; the solutions are symmetrized before validation.

The discrete ordinates solutions have numerical limitations on the order of discrete ordinates. This is demonstrated numerically in Part II and in Part III. We looked at the problem from a different vantage and proposed an alternative simple approach which is to symmetrize the transfer equation before carrying out the solution. By this process the angular derivative cancels out being an odd function on the angular domain. The resulting reduced transfer equation is as rigorous as the original equation with respect to the moments of the specific intensity. The validity and the limitations of the solutions of the reduced equation are discussed in Part V.

2. Definition of the problem

Consider a sphere of radius R embedding a concentric *pellet* of small radius $\varepsilon < R$. The pellet and the sphere may or may not be thermodynamically identical. Whichever is the case we treat them as two distinct media. Considering that the transfer equation object of this paper is the linearized form of the transport equation, this equation is not valid in the proximity of and at the center. This is understood in light of the omission of the pressure tensor from the equation. Therefore, the solution in the interior of the pellet is not addressed in this chapter. We will assume throughout that ε is large enough so that the linearized equation is valid on the domain $[\varepsilon, R]$.

The sphere is assumed homogeneous and isothermal, characterized by its blackbody constant B, an absorption coefficient κ and emission density κB; it will be stratified to simulate a heterogeneous medium in a later section. The transfer equation may be written in conservation form as:

$$\frac{\mu}{r^2}\,\partial_r\left(r^2\psi_r\right) + \frac{1}{r}\,\partial_\mu\left(\eta^2\,\psi_r\right) + \kappa\psi_r \;=\; \kappa B + Q \tag{2.1}$$

where ∂_r is the tensor notation for the derivative with respect to $r \in [\varepsilon, R]$, ψ is the specific intensity, μ the direction cosine on $[-1, +1]$ and $\eta^2 = (1 - \mu^2)$ and Q is a scattering emission term. The subscript in ψ_r is for the spatial variable; the angular variable is omitted, it is implied by the mere use of the letter ψ; we used the symbol ψ for the specific intensity to avoid confusion with the traditional symbol I reserved for the identity matrix. The boundary condition to (2.1) is a uniform intensity designated by ψ_R^-.

We introduce one simplification to (2.1) by seeking a solution for $\tilde{\psi}_r = r^2\psi_r$. Then we would have $\tilde{B} = r^2 B$ and $\tilde{Q} = r^2 Q$ and (2.1) would read:

$$\mu\,\partial_r\tilde{\psi}_r \;+\; \frac{1}{r}\,\partial_\mu\left(\eta^2\,\tilde{\psi}_r\right) + \kappa\tilde{\psi}_r \;=\; \kappa\tilde{B} + \tilde{Q} \tag{2.2}$$

The natural boundary conditions for this problem are $\tilde{\psi}_R^- = R^2\psi_R^-$ and symmetry at the center; the spatial domain of definition remains the same: $r \in [\varepsilon, R]$.

It is noticeable that (2.2) is formally comparable with the transfer equation in slab geometry except for the additive term in ∂_μ. Therefore, if a simple representation of the angular derivative can be found, then the formal mathematical solution of (2.2) can be carried out analytically using the method of [2]. In that case, the scattering term makes the task of carrying out the solution significantly more tedious but it adds little to the generality of the method we propose in this chapter. For this reason, and in order to be concise yet without affecting the rigor of the developments, we find it convenient to drop the scattering term from the subsequent equations and we seek the solution in a gray medium without scattering. That's amply sufficient to demonstrate the validity of our method.

The search for the solution of (2.2) is greatly simplified using Schuster's technique of two opposing streams [11] now extended to all directions defined by $\mu \in [0, 1]$ and $r \in [\varepsilon, R]$:

Centripetal equation:
$$\mu\,\partial_r\psi_r^- \;+\; \frac{1}{r}\,\partial_\mu\left(\eta^2\,\tilde{\psi}_r^-\right) - \kappa\tilde{\psi}_r^- \;=\; -\kappa\tilde{B} \tag{2.3}$$

Centrifugal equation:
$$\mu\,\partial_r\psi_r^+ \;+\; \frac{1}{r}\,\partial_\mu\left(\eta^2\,\tilde{\psi}_r^+\right) + \kappa\tilde{\psi}_r^+ \;=\; \kappa\tilde{B} \tag{2.4}$$

The mathematical boundary conditions for the problem defined by these equations are $\tilde{\psi}_\varepsilon^-$ and $\tilde{\psi}_\varepsilon^+$ at the surface of the pellet. They will be used to initiate the solutions which subsequently will be resolved in terms of the natural boundary condition ψ_R^- by appropriate inversion of the solution of the centripetal equation. This approach was very successful in plane geometry [2].

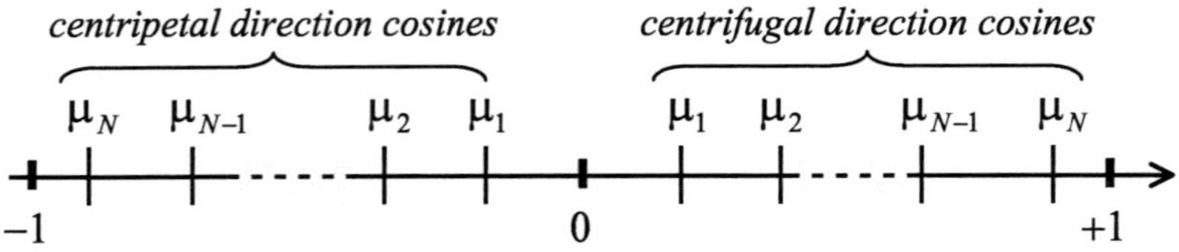

Figure 3.1. Layout of the angular grid for the centripetal and the centrifugal direction cosines. The boundary values ±1 are references to the actual boundary limits for the direction cosines. None of the direction cosines should be construed as a negative quantity.

PART I. THE DISCRETE ORDINATES EQUATIONS

3. The set of discrete ordinates

We define our set of discrete ordinates using the traditional set of weights and abscissas of GL quadrature of even order:

$$S_{2N} \equiv \{w_n, \mu_n : w_n \in (0, 1), \mu_n \in (0, 1), n = 1, 2, \ldots, N\} \tag{3.1}$$

We label the ordinates so that $\mu_1 < \ldots < \mu_N < 1.0$ and we order them in the sequence shown in figure 3.1. By this arrangement, larger n implies larger direction cosine and $\mu_n > \mu_{n-1}$ is always true in either stream. All direction cosines are positive as specified by the set S_{2N} and the weights are normalized so that: $\Sigma_1^N w_n = 1$. This set of discrete ordinates was previously used by Feautrier in slab geometry [12].

We define a *discrete ordinates derivative* the operator $\delta/\delta\mu_n$ where $\delta\mu_n$ is a *differential entity* in S_{2N} about the direction cosine μ_n, conceptually different from the traditional finite difference $\Delta\mu = \mu_n - \mu_{n-1}$. We find the worth of $\delta\mu_n$ from the very definition of Gauss quadrature: if $f(\mu)$ is a polynomial of degree no greater than $4N-1$, then at some point $\mu_n \in [a, b] \subset (-1, +1)$ such that $\mu_k \notin [a, b]\ \forall k \neq n$, we must have exactly:

$$w_n f(\mu_n) \equiv w_n f_n = \int_a^b f(\mu)\,\mathrm{d}\mu \tag{3.2}$$

It follows that if we wish to integrate the discrete ordinates derivative of our function $f(\mu)$ on the same domain $[a, b]$, we must have:

$$w_n \left.\frac{\mathrm{d}f}{\mathrm{d}\mu}\right|_{\mu_n} = w_n \frac{\delta f_n}{\delta\mu_n} = \int_a^b \mathrm{d}f = f_b - f_a \tag{3.3}$$

It is apparent from (3.3) that if we assign the value $f_b - f_a$ to δf_n, then it is imperative to assign the weight w_n to $\delta\mu_n$. Therefore, for gaussian discrete ordinates that satisfy identity (3.3) we must have:

$$\delta\mu_n = w_n \quad \Leftrightarrow \quad \delta f_n = f_n - f_{n-1} \tag{3.4}$$

It follows that the angular derivative of f transforms into a discrete ordinates derivative by the representation:

$$\left.\frac{\partial f}{\partial \mu}\right|_{\mu_n} \rightarrow \frac{f_n - f_{n-1}}{w_n} \tag{3.5}$$

If we choose the function *f* of identity (3.2) to be the operand of the angular derivative of (2.1), then (3.3) yields:

$$w_n \frac{\delta\left[\eta^2 \psi\right]_n}{\delta\mu_n} = \delta\left[\eta^2 \psi\right]_n = \eta_n^2 \psi_n - \eta_{n-1}^2 \psi_{n-1} \tag{3.6}$$

which is the proper quadrature of the angular derivative on the specified domain. The omission of the tilde from the intensity is merely a notational convenience in this section. The procedure applies earnestly to both ψ and $\tilde{\psi}$.

There is still one bump in the way of the quadrature of the angular derivative, the closure under quadrature: the quadrature of the angular derivative of (2.1) must match the integral of the same:

$$\sum_{n=1}^{2N}\left(w_n \frac{\delta\left[\eta^2 \psi\right]_n}{\delta\mu_n}\right) = \int_{-1}^{1} \partial_\mu\left[\eta^2 \psi\right] \mathrm{d}\mu \tag{3.7}$$

It is readily apparent that the integral of the right side of (3.7) vanishes and, therefore, the sum of the left side must vanish as well. Expand the summation of (3.7) following the indices pattern shown in figure 3.1 and make use of identity (3.6), all the terms cancel out except those affected by the index *N*. Equating this result with the vanishing integral of (3.7) yields:

$$\eta_N^2\left(\psi_N^+ + \psi_N^-\right) = 0 \tag{3.8}$$

We recognize that in the asymptotic limits as $N \rightarrow \infty$ the identity (3.8) vanishes by reason of asymptotic direction cosine $\mu_\infty = 1 \Rightarrow \eta_\infty = 0$. It follows that for any finite *N* the nullity of identity (3.8) must be postulated because η_N is never equal to zero. To this end, the value $\mu_N = 1$ must be excluded simply because this value of direction cosine is not an abscissa of GL quadrature and hence it is not contained in the set S_{2N} defined by (3.1). A direct approach to resolve this paradox is to work with unnormalized circular functions (UCF): the circular functions on the unit circle map onto circular functions on the UCF circle. To accomplish this we choose the radius of our circle equal to μ_N and then discretize the circular functions on the new circle. Therefore, the following transformation of the sine function applies:

$$\left.\begin{matrix} \textit{Unit circle} \\ \eta^2 = 1 - \mu^2 \end{matrix}\right\} \rightarrow \left\{\begin{matrix} \textit{UCF circle} \\ \eta_n^2 = \mu_N^2 - \mu_n^2 \end{matrix}\right. \Rightarrow \eta_N = 0 \tag{3.9}$$

The set of discrete ordinates defined by (3.1) along with identities (3.2) and transformation (3.9) is complete. It is apparent from (3.9) that μ_N is the *nominal* normal direction cosine for the radial direction of radiation and μ_1 is the nominal tangential direction in S_{2N}.

Another thing we took care of when we expanded the summation (3.7): the discrete ordinates derivative about μ_1. In accordance with (3.6) we would have to write:

$$\delta\left(\eta^2\psi\right)\Big|_1 = \eta_1^2\psi_1 - \eta_0^2\psi_0 \tag{3.10}$$

Considering that η_n maps onto the set S_{2N} by the circular relation (3.9), this mapping does not exist for $n = 0$. This is because the index $n = 0$ does not belong to the set S_{2N} defined by (3.1). Therefore, if $\delta(\eta^2\psi)|_1$ is to be defined on S_{2N}, the term in η_0 of identity (3.10) must be dropped out notwithstanding any other considerations. With that, we will be left with only one significant term: $\delta\left(\eta^2\psi\right)\Big|_1 = \eta_1^2\psi_1$.

It is readily apparent that by removing $\eta_0^2\psi_0$ from the equations, we destroyed the coupling of the intensities at $\mu = 0$; this coupling is achieved by the derivative of differential calculus. The legitimacy of this decoupling should be understood from the fact that none of the boundary values of $[0, 1] \supset \{\mu_n\}$ is accounted for in GL quadrature of even order. We note, however, that the symmetry preserves the coupling of the intensities of all directions at the point where we apply the boundary condition at the center of a sphere, or at the surface of the pellet as it will be discussed later. We note that the coupling by the angular derivative is a different process from the coupling by scattering. Therefore, however we manipulate the coupling with the angular derivative, that has no bearing on scattering, which we conveniently dropped it out from the equation.

Finally, the specific intensities are summed by quadrature from the set S_{2N}:

$$f_\alpha = \frac{1}{2}\sum_{n=1}^{N} w_n\mu_n^\alpha\left(\psi_{r,n}^+ + (-1)^\alpha\psi_{r,n}^-\right) \tag{3.11}$$

where $\alpha = 0$ is for the total intensity, $\alpha = 1$ for the flux, $\alpha = 2$ for the second moment, etc.

We have illustrated the method of discretizing the angular derivative using GL quadrature of even order. One can use GL quadrature with odd order. In that case, $\mu_0 = 0$ is abscissa of the quadrature and the second term of (3.10) should be retained and the centrifugal and centripetal intensities are coupled at $\mu = 0$; the values of $\psi_0^\pm$ can be obtained directly from (2.2). We note, however, that the proposed method is not exclusive to GL quadrature. Any quadrature of user choice could be used. A comparison between the efficiency of various quadratures is presented in [1].

4. The discrete ordinates transfer equations

The two-streams equations (2.3) and (2.4) in the nth direction on S_{2N} and for $r \in [\varepsilon, R]$ may be written as:

$$\mu_n\,\partial_r\widetilde{\psi}_n^- + \frac{1}{r}\frac{\delta\left[\eta^2\widetilde{\psi}^-\right]_n}{w_n} - \kappa\widetilde{\psi}_n^- = -\kappa\widetilde{B} \tag{4.1}$$

$$\mu_n\,\partial_r\widetilde{\psi}_n^+ + \frac{1}{r}\frac{\delta\left[\eta^2\widetilde{\psi}^+\right]_n}{w_n} + \kappa\widetilde{\psi}_n^+ = \kappa\widetilde{B} \tag{4.2}$$

Define the parameters:

$$\beta_n^n = \frac{\eta_n^2}{w_n \mu_n}; \quad \beta_n^{n-1} = \frac{\eta_{n-1}^2}{w_n \mu_n}; \quad \lambda_n = \frac{\kappa}{\mu_n} \tag{4.3}$$

These parameters have the following properties:

$$\beta_n^k > 0, \ \forall n, k \neq N; \qquad \beta_n^{n-1} > \beta_n^n, \ \forall n > 1$$

$$\beta_N^N = 0, \ \forall N; \ N \to \infty \Rightarrow \beta_1^1 \to \infty, \ \beta_N^{N-1} \to 0$$

β_1^0 not defined, fill its place by a zero

smaller n $\Rightarrow$ larger β

Make use of identities (4.3) and rearrange (4.1) and (4.2) to read:

$$\partial_r \tilde{\psi}_n^- + \left[\frac{\beta_n^n}{r} - \lambda_n\right]\tilde{\psi}_n^- - \frac{1}{r}\beta_n^{n-1}\tilde{\psi}_{n-1}^- = -\lambda_n \tilde{B} \tag{4.4}$$

$$\partial_r \tilde{\psi}_n^+ + \left[\frac{\beta_n^n}{r} + \lambda_n\right]\tilde{\psi}_n^+ - \frac{1}{r}\beta_n^{n-1}\tilde{\psi}_{n-1}^+ = \lambda_n \tilde{B} \tag{4.5}$$

4.1. Matrix representation of the transfer equations

Define the matrix elements:

$$\mathrm{B}_n^n = \beta_n^n; \quad \mathrm{B}_n^{n-1} = -\beta_n^{n-1}; \quad \Lambda_n^n = \lambda_n \tag{4.6}$$

There should be no confusion between the beta matrix element B_n^k and the blackbody constant B. The latter is italic type font and not indexed. Make use of (4.6) and rewrite (4.5) in matrix form:

$$\partial_r \tilde{\Psi}^+ = \left(-\frac{1}{r}\mathbf{B} - \Lambda\right)\tilde{\Psi}^+ + \tilde{B}\lambda = \mathbf{H}\tilde{\Psi}^+ + \tilde{B}\lambda \tag{4.7}$$

This is the S_{2N} matrix equation on $[\varepsilon, R]$ for the centrifugal intensity. The mathematical boundary condition at the lower end of the domain of definition is $\tilde{\Psi}_\varepsilon^+$. In general, this boundary condition is not known *a priori*, it will be resolved from the solution of the centripetal equation.

Make use of identities (4.6) and rewrite (4.4) in matrix form:

$$\partial_r \tilde{\Psi}^- = \left(-\frac{1}{r}\mathbf{B} + \Lambda\right)\tilde{\Psi}^- - \tilde{B}\lambda = \mathbf{H}^*\tilde{\Psi}^- - \tilde{B}\lambda \tag{4.8}$$

This is the S_{2N} matrix equation on $[\varepsilon, R]$ for the centripetal intensity. Its boundary condition is $\tilde{\Psi}_\varepsilon^-$ which is to be resolved in terms of the natural boundary condition $\tilde{\Psi}_R^-$ by appropriate inversion of the solution.

The two equations (4.7) and (4.8) merged together yield the matrix equation of the radiative transfer equation defined on [ε, R]:

$$\partial_r \begin{bmatrix} \widetilde{\Psi}^- \\ \widetilde{\Psi}^+ \end{bmatrix} = \begin{bmatrix} \mathrm{H}^* & \mathbf{0} \\ \mathbf{0} & \mathrm{H} \end{bmatrix} \begin{bmatrix} \widetilde{\Psi}^- \\ \widetilde{\Psi}^+ \end{bmatrix} + \widetilde{B} \begin{bmatrix} -\lambda \\ +\lambda \end{bmatrix} \tag{4.9}$$

or, in compact form:

$$\partial_r \widetilde{\Psi} = \mathbf{G}\widetilde{\Psi} + \widetilde{B}\lambda \tag{4.10}$$

and the boundary condition is the vector:

$$\widetilde{\Psi}_b = \left[\widetilde{\Psi}_\varepsilon^- \ \widetilde{\Psi}_\varepsilon^+ \right]^T \tag{4.11}$$

The formal solution for (4.10) may be written in the form:

$$\widetilde{\Psi}_r = \mathrm{H}(r)\widetilde{\Psi}_b + \int_\varepsilon^r \widetilde{B}_x \mathrm{H}(r-x)\lambda \, \mathrm{d}x \tag{4.12}$$

where $\mathcal{G}(r)$ is the fundamental matrix of (4.10). It follows that the solution for the transfer equation in this representation reduces to determining the fundamental matrix $\mathcal{G}$. However, it is less cumbersome and more instructive to solve the centripetal and the centrifugal equations individually in terms of their mathematical boundary conditions then resolve the solutions in terms of the natural boundary condition. This approach is particularly useful in the present case in a medium without scattering. In what follows, we first carry out the solution of the centrifugal equation alone and we apply it to the point source configuration in PART II. The complete solution of the two equations in the interior of a sphere hosting a concentric reflective pellet is presented in PART III. A discussion on the validity of the method and a comparative analysis with the RDO method is presented in PART IV.

PART II. THE POINT SOURCE CONFIGURATION

5. Solutions of the centrifugal equation

5.1. Formal representation of the solution

Let Γ be the integral of matrix H of (4.7) on [ε, R]. Then the elements of Γ are:

$$\Gamma_n^n = \beta_n^n \ln\zeta - \lambda_n(r-\varepsilon) \qquad \zeta = \varepsilon / r \tag{5.1}$$

$$\Gamma_n^{n-1} = -\beta_n^{n-1} \ln\zeta$$

It can be shown that the eigenvalues of matrix Γ are its diagonal elements and the corresponding eigenvectors are obtained from the recursion relation:

$$\mathrm{V}_n^n = 1 \qquad \forall n$$

$$\mathrm{V}_n^k = 0 \qquad \text{for } k > n$$

$$\mathrm{V}_n^k = \frac{\Gamma_n^{n-1}}{\Gamma_k^k - \Gamma_n^n} \mathrm{V}_{n-1}^k \qquad \text{for } k < n = 2, 3, \ldots, N \tag{5.2}$$

It follows that the eigentable $\mathbf{V}_{\varepsilon:r}$ is a lower triangular matrix all its elements are dimensionless. Hence, the solution for the centripetal equation may be cast in the form:

$$\Psi_r^+ = \zeta^2 \mathbf{S}_{\varepsilon:r} \Psi_\varepsilon^+ + \mathbf{Q}_{r:\varepsilon}^+ \lambda \tag{5.3}$$

$$\mathbf{S}_{\varepsilon:r} = \mathbf{V}_{\varepsilon:r} \left[\zeta^{\beta_n^n} e^{-\lambda_n (r-\varepsilon)} \right] \mathbf{V}_{\varepsilon:r}^{-1} \tag{5.4}$$

$$\mathbf{Q}_{r:\varepsilon}^+ = B \int_\varepsilon^r (x/r)^2 \mathbf{S}_{x:r}\, \mathrm{d}x$$

The disposition of the double indices mirrors the disposition of the same parameters of the ratio $\zeta = \varepsilon/r$ in the spherical operator **S** and the limits of integration of the integral of the emission term **Q**. For the problem at hand, we assume that the radiance Ψ_ε^+ is prescribed. Using the ART properties [2], then the solution (5.3) reads:

$$\Psi_r^+ = \mathbf{T}_r^\varepsilon \Psi_\varepsilon^+ + \mathbf{P}_r^\varepsilon \tag{5.5}$$

$$\mathbf{T}_r^\varepsilon = \zeta^2 \mathbf{S}_{\varepsilon:r}\,, \qquad \mathbf{P}_r^\varepsilon = \mathbf{Q}_{r:\varepsilon} \lambda$$

The expression (5.5) is the complete solution for the centrifugal equation (2.3) in a spherical shell of thickness $r - \varepsilon : r \in [\varepsilon, R]$ and R can be arbitrarily large. The ART properties $\mathbf{T}_r^\varepsilon$ and $\mathbf{P}_r^\varepsilon$ are the centrifugal transmittance and the centrifugal radiance of the shell, respectively; the transport is from ε to r.

5.2. The point source problem

A particular case of the centrifugal intensity is that of a sphere of radius ε with isotropic and uniform radiance ψ_ε embedded in an infinite cold pure absorber, or simply placed in vacuum. The specific intensity for this problem is given by (5.3) without the emission term:

$$\Psi_r^+ = \zeta^2 \mathbf{S}_{\varepsilon:r} \Psi_\varepsilon^+ \qquad r \geq \varepsilon \tag{5.6}$$

More often, the sphere is defined as a source of strength $q = 4\pi\varepsilon^2 \psi_\varepsilon$. Then (5.6) reduces to:

$$\Psi_r^+ = \frac{q}{4\pi} \frac{1}{r^2} \mathbf{S}_{\varepsilon:r} \mathbf{1} \qquad r \geq \varepsilon \tag{5.7}$$

where **1** is an isotropic column vector. Consider the asymptotic case for $r >> \varepsilon$. For large N, all the β's are positive except $\beta_N^N = 0$. In this asymptotic limit, $\mathbf{S}_{\varepsilon:r} \to e^{-\kappa r}$, since all the exponentials in κ/μ vanish, or do not contribute to the quadrature for the total intensity. Then the expression (5.7) reduces to:

$$\psi_r = \frac{q}{4\pi} \frac{e^{-\kappa r}}{r^2} \qquad r >> \varepsilon \tag{5.8}$$

This expression for the point source problem is reported as a particular case of the flux

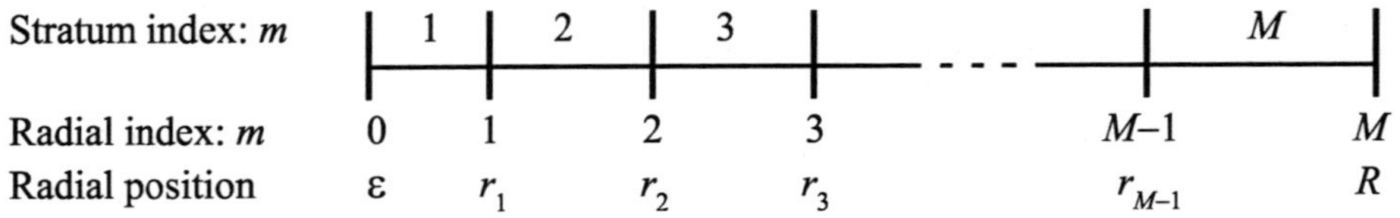

Figure 6.1. Labeling of the strata and their boundaries.

limited diffusion theory without restriction to the lower bound for r [13]. In the proximity of the surface of the pellet, however small or large ε may be, either equation (5.6) or (5.7) should be used, whichever applies.

6. The stratified medium problem

The continuous-in-r solution of the previous sections is complete in a homogeneous medium. If the medium is not homogeneous but stratified with homogeneous shells, a continuous-in-r solution can be sought for each shell individually. The ensemble of these solutions becomes the solution in the entire sphere if the boundary values for each shell are known. To obtain this global solution we first solve for the intensities at the interfaces between strata.

Consider a sphere made of M homogeneous shells and a pellet. We label the shell contiguous to the pellet with index $m = 1$, and the last shell with $m = M$ as illustrated in figure 6.1. Each shell is characterized by its opacity κ_m and a blackbody constant B_m. In this configuration, the mth stratum is bounded by r_{m-1} and r_m. The subscript r_m for the radial position of the mth interface will be designated by the index m such as $\Psi_m \equiv \Psi(r_m)$. Hence, the *end-points* solution transcribed from (5.5) becomes:

$$\Psi^+_m = \mathbf{T}^{m-1}_m \Psi^+_{m-1} + \mathbf{P}^{m-1}_m \qquad m = 1, 2, \dots, M \tag{6.1}$$

This is indeed a numerical algorithm free of spatial truncation errors. It is valid for homogeneous and heterogeneous media. The heterogeneous medium is assumed stratified into M homogeneous shells. Opacities in r^{-n} are more appropriate in astrophysical problems although not in the simplistic case of a pure absorber. In that case, the factor of λ_n of (5.1) becomes the integral of r^{-n}. We did not implement such opacities in our derivations. Homogeneous strata are sufficient to validate the proposed structure of the set S_{2N}.

The specific intensities calculated with the end-points algorithm can be used as boundary values for the continuous-in-r solutions of §5 now defined on the domain $r \in [r_{m-1}, r_m]$. Then (5.3) restricted to the mth shell transcribes into:

$$\Psi^+_r = \zeta^2_{m-1}\mathbf{S}^{m-1}_r \Psi^+_{m-1} + \mathbf{Q}^r_{m-1}\lambda_m \tag{6.2}$$

$$\zeta_{m-1} = r_{m-1}/r$$

7. Validation of the set of discrete ordinates

The solution we derived in the previous sections is an approximation on the angular domain. The manmade approximation is in the divergence term of the transfer equation, trailing behind it the consequential approximate specific intensity and its moments. The material and the emission components of the solution are not affected by this approximation. For this reason, we demonstrate the validity of the solution for the divergence term alone without emission and interaction with the medium. This condition is met in vacuum. In what follows, we examine the solution in vacuum as well as the import of the approximation to the transfer process in representative absorbing homogeneous media.

Consider a spherical surface of radius ε characterized by its isotropic radiance ψ_ε^+ and embedded in a medium of opacity κ, or eventually vacuum. The specific intensity at point $r \geq \varepsilon$ in a direction defined by μ is given as:

$$\psi_r^+ = \psi_\varepsilon^+ e^{-\kappa s(\mu)} \tag{7.1}$$

where:

$$s(\mu) = r[\mu - (\zeta^2 - \eta^2)^{1/2}]$$

$$\mu \geq \mu_0 = (1 - \zeta^2)^{1/2}$$

Hence the α-moment at r:

in an absorber:

$$f_\alpha = \frac{\psi_\varepsilon^+}{2}\int_{\mu_0}^{1} \mu^\alpha e^{-\kappa s(\mu)} d\mu \tag{7.2}$$

in vacuum:

$$f_\alpha = \frac{\psi_\varepsilon^+}{2(\alpha+1)}\left(1 - \mu_0^{\alpha+1}\right) \tag{7.3}$$

It is noticeable that the $1/r^2$ behavior of the specific intensities in the present configuration is not explicit in the expression of the total intensity (7.1), it is explicit in the lower limit of (7.2). It can be made explicit in the expression of the specific intensity by applying the linear transformation $\mu = (1 - \mu_0)\lambda + \mu_0$, where $\lambda \in [0, +1]$. The transformed expression of (7.1) reads:

$$\psi_r^+ = \psi_\varepsilon^+ (1 - \mu_0)\, e^{-\kappa s(\lambda)} \tag{7.4}$$

Integration of this expression on [0, 1] yields exactly the same moments of (7.2). The benefit from this λ-transformation is merely to explicit the $1/r^2$ behavior of the specific intensity. Indeed, for small ζ we would have:

$$\mu_0 = 1 - (\varepsilon^2/r^2)/2$$

which explicits the asymptotic inverse square law in (7.4), as well as in (7.3).

Total intensities calculated using the discrete ordinates solution (6.1) are compared graphically with the total intensities calculated with (7.2) and (7.3). The two sets of data are graphically congruent for as little N as 16 in vacuum and $N = 10$ in pure absorber. The graphs for the total intensity, the flux and the second moment in vacuum are shown in figures 7.1, 7.2 and 7.3, respectively. The label *exact* in these figures refers to the quantities expressed by (7.3). The graphs for the total intensity, the flux and the second moment in an absorber are shown in figures 7.4, 7.5 and 7.6, respectively. The label *exact* in these figures refers to the quantities expressed by (7.2) which was integrated numerically. The extent of the graphs to $\zeta = 1/3$ is deliberate for the interest of showing details of the discrepancies particularly near the surface of the sphere. Other values of ζ were tested. The

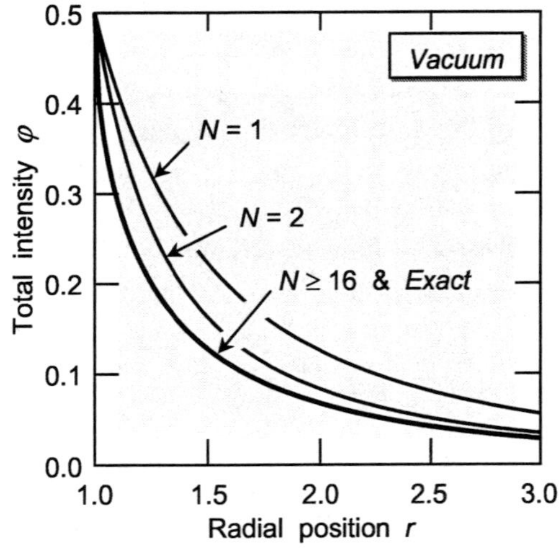

Figure 7.1. Graphs of total intensities generated in vacuum with normalized radiance of a sphere of radius ε = 1.0.

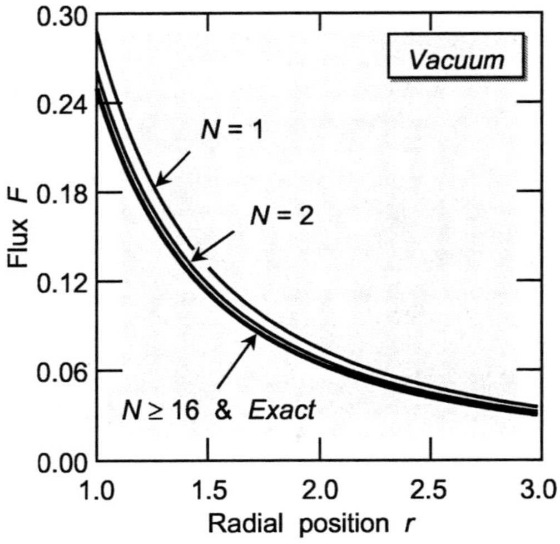

Figure 7.2. Graphs of fluxes generated in vacuum with normalized radiance of a sphere of radius ε = 1.0.

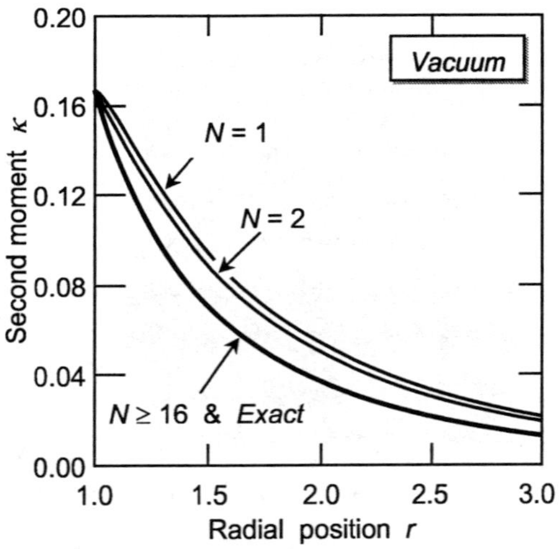

Figure 7.3. Graphs of second moments of the specific intensities generated in vacuum with normalized radiance of a sphere of radius ε = 1.0.

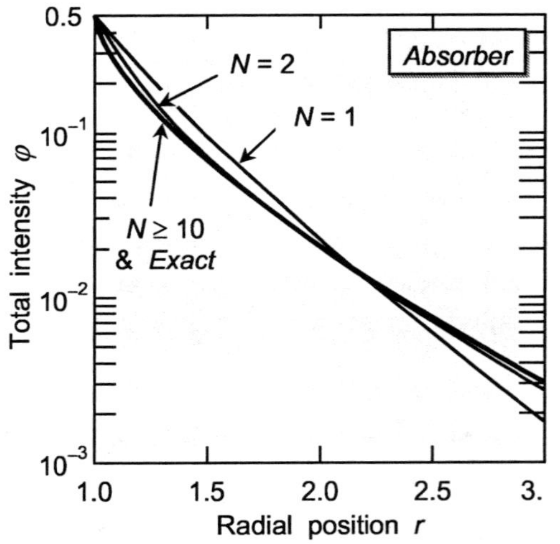

Figure 7.4. Graphs of total intensities generated in a cold homogeneous medium of opacity κ = 1 with normalized radiance of a sphere of radius ε = 1.0.

graphical congruence was achieved with values of $N = 10$.

The graphs of the total intensities in these figures are smooth monotonically decreasing quite as expected. Their degenerate specific intensities are not so. Figure 7.7 shows the graphs of specific intensities generated in vacuum in different directions defined by μ_n extracted from the set of $N = 40$ discrete ordinates; the graph of the total intensity is shown in the same figure. The intensity $\psi_{N=40}$, which corresponds to μ_N, is nominally emitted normally to the surface of the radiant pellet, yet this intensity peaks to

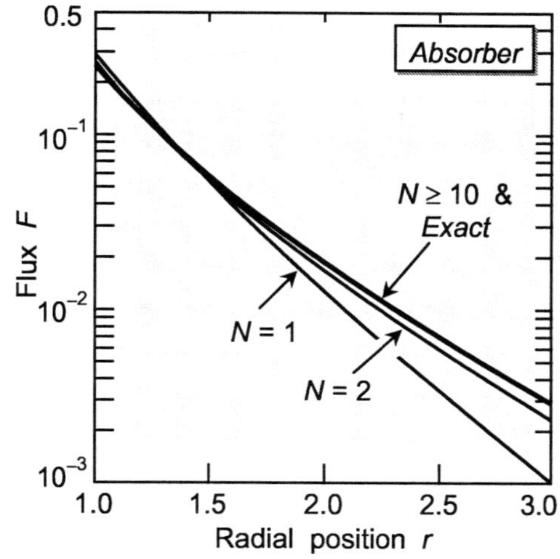

Figure 7.5. Graphs of fluxes generated in a cold homogeneous medium of opacity $\kappa = 1$ with normalized radiance of a sphere of radius $\varepsilon = 1.0$.

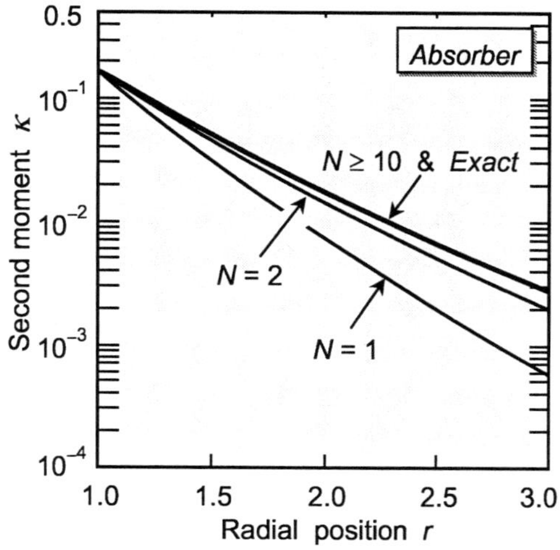

Figure 7.6. Graphs of the second moments generated in a cold homogeneous medium of opacity $\kappa = 1$ with normalized radiance of a sphere of radius $\varepsilon = 1.0$.

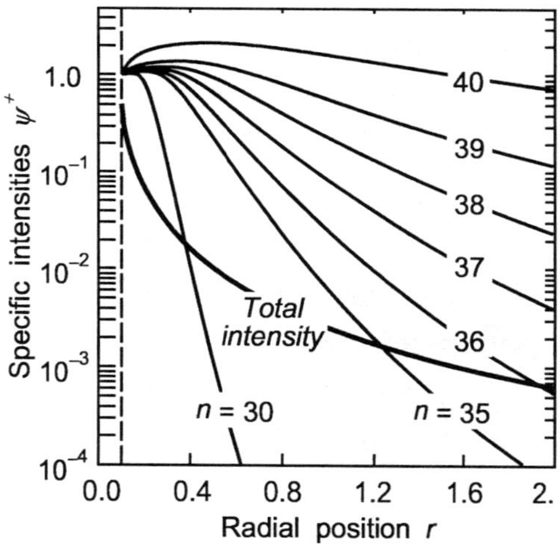

Figure 7.7. Graphs of the total intensity and some of its angular degenerates specific intensities in $N = 40$ discrete ordinates in vacuum. They are generated from a pellet of radius $\varepsilon = 0.1$.

a little more than twice its surface value before it starts to decrease monotonically. The peak gets smaller and closer to the surface of the pellet with decreasing n. This behavior is attributable to the coupling of the intensities by the angular derivative: specific intensities in slant directions contribute to the intensity in the radial direction.

The pattern of these graphs is generic. It was observed with all radiating pellets and for all orders of discrete ordinates we experimented with; the magnitudes of the intensities are smaller in absorbing media by reason of attenuation.

The reading of figure 7.7 suggests a way, however simplistic it may be, to visualize graphically the variation of the radiation field in the interior of a spherical cavity. Let $R = 2$ be the surface of a cavity with a concentric reflective pellet and let ψ_R^- be the intensity of the external radiation field. If we preserve the integrity of the principle of reciprocity of path and we choose ψ_R^- such that the intensity at the surface of the pellet is isotropic, as illustrated in figure 7.7, then the

Table 7.1. Computed differences for the total intensities $\Delta\varphi$, fluxes ΔF and second moments ΔK obtained from the exact values and the discrete ordinates values; the conservation of energy E is computed in discrete ordinates. Various orders of discrete ordinates N are considered at different radial positions. The source is a macropellet of radius $\varepsilon = 1.0$ its radiance is normalized to 1.

	Radial position $r = 1$ to 10^7 in vacuum media						
N	1	2	4	10	10^2	10^4	10^7
				Total intensity $\Delta\varphi$			
10	5.5×10^{-17}	1.3×10^{-3}	2.5×10^{-4}	2.9×10^{-5}	2.2×10^{-7}	2.2×10^{-11}	2.4×10^{-17}
20	1.1×10^{-16}	5.6×10^{-4}	9.8×10^{-5}	1.0×10^{-5}	5.9×10^{-8}	5.6×10^{-12}	7.6×10^{-18}
30	1.6×10^{-16}	3.9×10^{-4}	5.9×10^{-5}	5.7×10^{-6}	2.7×10^{-8}	2.5×10^{-12}	4.5×10^{-18}
40	1.1×10^{-16}	2.5×10^{-4}	4.1×10^{-5}	3.9×10^{-6}	1.6×10^{-8}	1.4×10^{-12}	3.4×10^{-18}
50	1.1×10^{-16}	2.1×10^{-4}	3.9×10^{-5}	3.3×10^{-6}	1.4×10^{-8}	1.2×10^{-12}	3.2×10^{-18}
				Flux ΔF			
10	4.9×10^{-4}	1.2×10^{-4}	3.0×10^{-5}	4.9×10^{-6}	4.9×10^{-8}	4.9×10^{-12}	6.9×10^{-18}
20	1.2×10^{-4}	3.1×10^{-5}	7.8×10^{-6}	1.2×10^{-6}	1.2×10^{-8}	1.2×10^{-12}	3.2×10^{-18}
30	5.6×10^{-5}	1.4×10^{-5}	3.5×10^{-5}	5.6×10^{-7}	5.6×10^{-9}	5.6×10^{-13}	2.5×10^{-18}
40	3.1×10^{-5}	7.8×10^{-6}	1.9×10^{-6}	3.1×10^{-7}	3.1×10^{-9}	3.1×10^{-13}	2.3×10^{-18}
50	2.0×10^{-5}	2.3×10^{-5}	4.0×10^{-6}	5.4×10^{-7}	5.4×10^{-9}	5.4×10^{-13}	2.5×10^{-18}
				Second moment ΔK			
10	2.7×10^{-17}	6.4×10^{-4}	1.6×10^{-4}	1.8×10^{-5}	1.2×10^{-7}	1.2×10^{-11}	1.0×10^{-17}
20	5.5×10^{-17}	2.8×10^{-4}	7.2×10^{-5}	7.3×10^{-6}	3.4×10^{-8}	3.1×10^{-12}	1.1×10^{-18}
30	1.9×10^{-16}	1.8×10^{-4}	4.5×10^{-5}	4.5×10^{-6}	1.6×10^{-8}	1.4×10^{-12}	5.8×10^{-19}
40	8.3×10^{-17}	1.3×10^{-4}	3.3×10^{-5}	3.2×10^{-6}	9.8×10^{-9}	7.9×10^{-13}	1.2×10^{-18}
50	8.3×10^{-17}	8.5×10^{-5}	2.3×10^{-5}	2.6×10^{-7}	3.3×10^{-9}	1.7×10^{-13}	1.8×10^{-18}
				Energy balance E			
10	0.0	1.7×10^{-15}	1.1×10^{-16}	2.5×10^{-16}	4.9×10^{-16}	1.6×10^{-16}	4.2×10^{-16}
20	0.0	7.9×10^{-13}	3.9×10^{-13}	1.5×10^{-13}	1.8×10^{-13}	1.8×10^{-13}	1.8×10^{-13}
30	0.0	3.8×10^{-10}	2.4×10^{-11}	1.0×10^{-10}	1.5×10^{-10}	1.5×10^{-10}	1.5×10^{-10}
40	0.0	2.0×10^{-7}	1.0×10^{-7}	4.8×10^{-8}	3.3×10^{-8}	3.3×10^{-8}	3.3×10^{-8}
50	0.0	7.3×10^{-5}	4.3×10^{-5}	3.4×10^{-5}	3.4×10^{-5}	3.4×10^{-5}	3.4×10^{-5}

external radiation field becomes physically unacceptable. On the other hand, if ψ_R^- is isotropic, then the radiation field becomes nonphysical most everywhere in the cavity.

This naïve attempt to construct the solution in the spherical cavity lacks the effect of the superposition of the contributions from the angular derivatives of the opposing streams of intensities. The culprit is the unfiltered implementation of the angular derivative in the opposing streams of the radiation field. The proper implementation of the angular derivative in the interior of spheres requires symmetry considerations that are not

Table 7.2. Computed differences for the total intensities $\Delta\varphi$, fluxes ΔF and second moments ΔK obtained from the exact values and the discrete ordinates values; the conservation of energy E is computed in discrete ordinates. Various orders of discrete ordinates N are considered at different radial positions. The source is a micropellet of radius $\varepsilon = 10^{-7}$ its radiance is normalized to 1.

	Radial position $r = 10^{-7}$ to 1 in vacuum media						
N	10^{-7}	10^{-6}	10^{-4}	10^{-2}	10^{-1}	0.5	1.0
	Total intensity $\Delta\varphi$						
10	5.5×10^{-17}	2.9×10^{-5}	2.2×10^{-9}	2.2×10^{-13}	2.2×10^{-15}	9.6×10^{-17}	2.4×10^{-17}
20	1.1×10^{-16}	1.0×10^{-5}	5.6×10^{-10}	5.6×10^{-14}	5.4×10^{-16}	3.0×10^{-17}	7.7×10^{-18}
30	1.6×10^{-16}	5.7×10^{-6}	2.5×10^{-10}	2.5×10^{-14}	2.3×10^{-16}	1.8×10^{-17}	5.5×10^{-18}
40	1.1×10^{-16}	3.9×10^{-6}	1.4×10^{-10}	1.4×10^{-14}	1.2×10^{-16}	1.3×10^{-17}	3.4×10^{-18}
50	1.1×10^{-16}	3.3×10^{-6}	1.2×10^{-10}	1.2×10^{-14}	1.0×10^{-16}	1.3×10^{-17}	3.2×10^{-18}
	Flux ΔF						
10	4.9×10^{-4}	4.9×10^{-6}	4.9×10^{-10}	4.9×10^{-14}	4.6×10^{-16}	2.7×10^{-17}	6.9×10^{-18}
20	1.2×10^{-4}	1.2×10^{-6}	1.2×10^{-10}	1.2×10^{-14}	1.0×10^{-16}	1.3×10^{-17}	3.2×10^{-18}
30	5.6×10^{-5}	5.6×10^{-7}	5.6×10^{-11}	5.6×10^{-15}	3.4×10^{-17}	1.0×10^{-17}	2.5×10^{-18}
40	3.1×10^{-5}	3.1×10^{-7}	3.1×10^{-11}	3.1×10^{-15}	9.4×10^{-18}	9.6×10^{-18}	2.3×10^{-18}
50	2.0×10^{-5}	5.5×10^{-7}	5.4×10^{-11}	5.4×10^{-15}	3.2×10^{-17}	1.0×10^{-17}	2.5×10^{-18}
	Second moment ΔK						
10	2.7×10^{-17}	1.8×10^{-5}	1.2×10^{-9}	1.2×10^{-13}	1.2×10^{-15}	5.2×10^{-17}	1.0×10^{-17}
20	5.5×10^{-17}	7.3×10^{-6}	3.1×10^{-10}	3.1×10^{-14}	3.3×10^{-16}	4.6×10^{-18}	1.1×10^{-18}
30	1.9×10^{-16}	4.5×10^{-6}	1.4×10^{-10}	1.4×10^{-14}	1.6×10^{-16}	2.3×10^{-18}	5.8×10^{-19}
40	8.3×10^{-17}	3.2×10^{-6}	8.0×10^{-11}	7.9×10^{-15}	1.0×10^{-16}	4.8×10^{-18}	1.2×10^{-18}
50	8.3×10^{-17}	2.1×10^{-6}	1.7×10^{-11}	1.7×10^{-15}	3.9×10^{-17}	7.3×10^{-18}	1.8×10^{-18}
	Energy balance E						
10	0.0	1.2×10^{-30}	3.4×10^{-30}	9.7×10^{-30}	6.1×10^{-31}	1.1×10^{-29}	5.2×10^{-30}
20	0.0	1.6×10^{-27}	1.8×10^{-27}	1.8×10^{-27}	1.8×10^{-27}	1.8×10^{-27}	1.8×10^{-27}
30	0.0	1.0×10^{-24}	1.5×10^{-24}	1.5×10^{-24}	1.5×10^{-24}	1.5×10^{-24}	1.5×10^{-24}
40	0.0	4.7×10^{-22}	3.3×10^{-22}	3.3×10^{-22}	3.3×10^{-22}	3.3×10^{-22}	3.3×10^{-22}
50	0.0	3.4×10^{-19}	3.4×10^{-19}	3.4×10^{-19}	3.4×10^{-19}	3.4×10^{-19}	3.4×10^{-19}

transparent in the analysis of this section. They are discussed in PART III.

Tabulated data were also generated in vacuum for macrometric and micrometric pellets and for different orders of discrete ordinates N. Samples of these data are shown in Table 7.1 for a spherical region bounded by $\varepsilon = 1.0$ and $r = 10^7$, and in Table 7.2 for a spherical region bounded by $\varepsilon = 10^{-7}$ and $r = 1.0$. The data in these tables are generated with 200 spatial intervals. Larger and smaller number of spatial intervals reproduced the same values. This is expected since the solutions are exact in r.

Table 7.3. Tabulated data for the total intensity φ, the flux F, and the second moment K, at the surface of a radiating pellet of radius $\varepsilon = 1$ and at radial positions r_3 and r_5, and the energy balance E in the volume of the shell of thickness $r_5 - \varepsilon$. The data are computed in N discrete ordinates and using the exact expression in sphere of coefficients of absorption $\kappa = 1$ and 4.

	$\varepsilon = 1.0$, $r_3 = 3.0$, $r_5 = 5.0$, $\kappa = 1.0$									
N	φ_1	$\varphi_3\times10^3$	$\varphi_5\times10^4$	F_1	$F_3\times10^3$	$F_5\times10^4$	K_1	$K_3\times10^3$	$K_5\times10^4$	$E\times10^7$
10	0.5	3.003	1.363	0.2504	2.894	1.338	1.6	2.793	1.315	6.7
20	0.5	3.034	1.396	0.2501	2.943	1.378	1.6	2.857	1.361	6.9
30	0.5	3.043	1.405	0.2500	2.957	1.390	1.6	2.875	1.374	7.0
40	0.5	3.048	1.410	0.2500	2.964	1.395	1.6	2.884	1.380	6.3
50	0.5	3.051	1.412	0.2500	2.968	1.398	1.6	2.889	1.384	22.0
Ext.	0.5	3.060	1.421	0.2500	2.981	1.408	1.6	2.906	1.396	-
	$\varepsilon = 1.0$, $r_3 = 3.0$, $r_5 = 5.0$, $\kappa = 4.0$									
N	φ_1	$\varphi_3\times10^6$	$\varphi_5\times10^{10}$	F_1	$F_3\times10^6$	$F_5\times10^{10}$	K_1	$K_3\times10^6$	$K_5\times10^{10}$	$E\times10^9$
10	0.5	4.221	4.384	0.2504	4.117	4.328	1.6	4.019	4.275	4.8
20	0.5	4.355	4.676	0.2501	4.264	4.636	1.6	4.178	4.598	2.8
30	0.5	4.387	4.746	0.2500	4.300	4.710	1.6	4.216	4.675	9.7
40	0.5	4.400	4.774	0.2500	4.314	4.740	1.6	4.232	4.707	52.0
50	0.5	4.407	4.789	0.2500	4.322	4.756	1.6	4.239	4.723	-
Ext.	0.5	4.426	4.829	0.2500	4.342	4.798	1.6	4.261	4.768	-

The quantity $\Delta\varphi = |\varphi_{discr} - \varphi_{exact}|$ represents the absolute value of the difference between the total intensity computed in discrete ordinates with (6.1) and the total intensity computed with (7.3). Similarly, ΔF is the absolute value of the difference between the discrete ordinates and the exact fluxes, and ΔK the absolute value of the difference between the discrete ordinates and the exact second moments. All quantities, φ, F and K of the tables are computed from a radiance ψ_ε^+ normalized to 1.0 using 16 significant digits arithmetics (16-SDA). Considering that in vacuum the **S**-operator is function of ζ only, one should expect the columns of the tables that correspond to the same ζ to be identically the same in both of the tables. We maintained $N \le 50$ in vacuum to avoid non-negligible round-off errors.

The quantity E in the tables represents the energy balance. It is obtained by integrating (2.1) over all directions and over the volume of interest. It is given as: $E = r^2F_r - \varepsilon^2F_\varepsilon + \kappa\varphi_{int}$, where $\varepsilon^2F_\varepsilon$ represents the total energy radiating out of the pellet, r^2F_r the total energy radiating out of the surface of radius r, and $\kappa\varphi_{int}$ the total energy absorbed in the volume of the shell, which is zero in vacuum; φ_{int} is the integral of the total intensity obtained numerically. Ideally, $E = 0$.

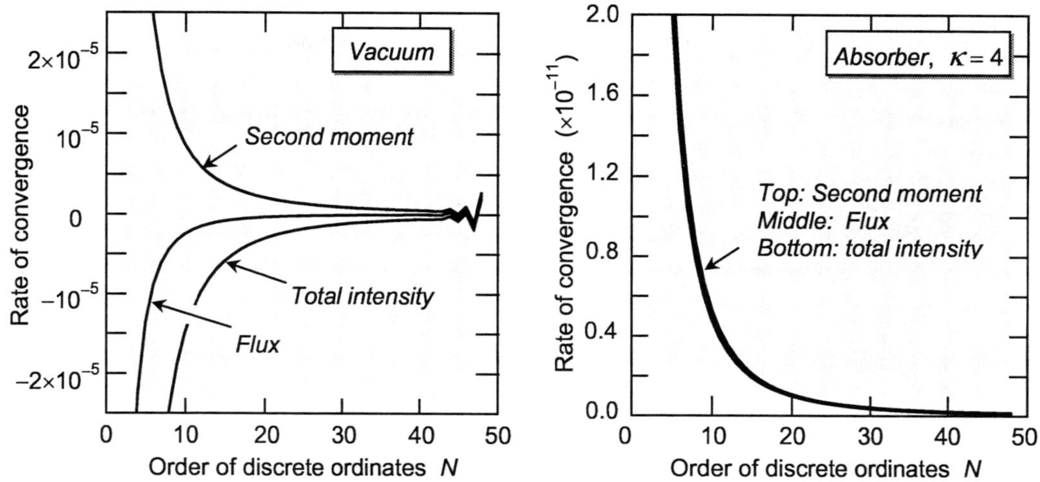

Figure 7.8. Graphs of the rate of convergence with respect to the order of discrete ordinates N of the computed total intensity, flux and second moment at $r = 5$ for a radiant pellet of radius $\varepsilon = 1$ and for two different media.

The information we obtain from the analysis of the data of the tables is perhaps most instructive in the block ΔF. The flux in this geometry varies rigorously as $1/r^2$ from the surface of the pellet forward. Therefore, one would expect that ΔF varies as $1/r^2$ within round-off errors. This appears to be truly the case in the two tables. On the other hand, the values of ΔF are different from zero but they get closer to zero in the asymptotic region. This is primarily because at the surface of the pellet, which is located in the first column of the tables, the exact flux is 0.25 exactly. Then, $\Delta F_\varepsilon = 0.25 - 0.5\times\Sigma w_i\mu_I$ can never be zero except in the limit as $N \to \infty$. Indeed, for the particular case of $N = 50$ of the tables, $\Sigma w_i\mu_i = 0.5000407$ computed in 16-SDA.

Unlike the case of the flux, $\Delta\varphi$ at the surface of the pellet is practically zero. This is because of the way the weights of the quadrature are calculated: $\Sigma w_i = 1.0 - 2\times10^{-16}$ in 16-SDA. However, a look at the data of the second column in the tables reveals that the total intensity computed in discrete ordinates is noticeably different from the one computed with the exact expression (7.3). This difference is attributable to the terms that represent the coupling of the intensities by the angular derivative. Finer angular grid reduces the value of $\Delta\varphi$ slowly with increasing N. The rate of convergence appears to be slow in this case.

The fluxes and total intensities needed to calculate E are all computed in discrete ordinates. The values of E appear to be uniform with increasing r and for the same value of N, but the magnitudes of the data of Table 7.1 are closely 14 orders of magnitude larger than the ones of Table 7.2. This is understood from the fact that F_ε is multiplied by $\varepsilon^2 = 10^{-14}$ at the surface of the micropellet (Tab. 7.2) and by 1.0 at the surface of the macropellet (Tab. 7.1), and F_r is multiplied by $r^2 = 1.0$ in the case of micropellet and by 10^{14} in the case of macropellet. It appears, however, that the value of E increases with increasing N in both micropellets and macropellets.

The increase in E, noticeable in both of the tables, is directly attributable to round-off errors in matrix operations: larger N generates larger matrices resulting in larger round-off errors. This can be visualized by this sample of data computed with $N = 50$ in the macropellet configuration (Tab. 7.1): $\varepsilon^2 F_\varepsilon = 0.25002$ and $r^2 F_r = 0.25005$. Keeping in mind that ε and r are exact, the difference 0.00003 is the result from round-off errors. By contrast, with $N = 10$, these numbers differ in the 13th significant digit: $\varepsilon^2 F_\varepsilon =$ 0.2504...018, $r^2 F_r = 0.2504...017$. These figures explain the increase in E as N increases from 10 to 50. Notwithstanding, the computed physical quantities get closer to the exact values with increasing N up to $N = 50$. Past this limit, the round-off error becomes overwhelming in vacuum media.

We collected data in absorptive media 5 and 20 mfp thick These data are shown in Table 7.3. They are computed with N discrete ordinates and with the exact expression (7.2) at different radial positions: at $\varepsilon = 1$, $r_5 = 5$ and at a surface halfway between ε and r_5, which corresponds to $r_3 = 3$. It appears that the values of φ, F, K and E increase with increasing N following a pattern similar to the one observed in the case of vacuum media, suggesting a convergence toward the exact values. The tabulated data in the rows labeled *exact* are obtained with 8,192 evaluations of the integrand of (7.2) using Romberg algorithm. No attempts were made to interpolate data at this stage. The raw data is intended to reveal the performance of the method in its native form.

The rate of convergence $\Delta f_\alpha / \Delta N$ computed in discrete ordinates for $\Delta N = 1$ is depicted graphically by figure 7.8 as a function of N and at the surface $r = 5$, in vacuum and in a pure absorber. It is apparent that the function Δf is smooth and monotonically decreasing but slowly converging to zero in both of the media, vacuum and absorber. However, wriggles in the graphs in vacuum start to develop as N increases past 40. These fluctuations are symptoms of round-off errors. They are small for $N \leq 50$ but they render the data useless for $N > 52$ in vacuum. The absorber medium flattens out these wriggles and the convergence is smooth but very slow all the way through $N = 50$; we have not experimented with $N > 52$. The flux appears to converge the fastest, followed by the second moment then by the total intensity in vacuum. In the absorber medium, the total intensity appears to converge the fastest, followed by the flux then by the second moment. However, the rate of convergence in this medium appears to be closely the same for all the three quantities and for all N.

It is apparent from the foregoing that the structure of the proposed set of discrete ordinates model in one dimensional geometry with central symmetry is sound. It leads to a solution that is in excellent agreement with the asymptotic empirical inverse square law, with the analytical solution of the integral equation and with flux limited diffusion theory.

PART III. THE TWO-STREAMS PROBLEM

The two-streams problem arises in media with either source or scattering emission, or both, or in a pure absorbing non-emitting sphere, or a cavity, immersed in a uniform radiation field. At first sight, (4.4) and (4.5) are not coupled and hence each equation can be solved independently from the other. This is always true for the solution with the mathematical boundary conditions $\psi_\varepsilon^\pm$. In reality the two equations are coupled but the coupling is not obvious until we resolve the mathematical solution in terms of the natural boundary condition. The coupling by the boundary condition is unrelated to the coupling by scattering which, as we indicated earlier, is not considered in this chapter.

The first thing we notice about (4.4) and (4.5) is that they differ only in the sign of λ. It follows that in vacuum, the solutions of the two equations are identical: $\psi_{n,vac}^- = \psi_{n,vac}^+$, $\forall r$. This identity expresses the reciprocity of path that will be used to validate the proposed solution. On the other hand, the bracketed term of (4.4) is always positive. It was shown that in the case of one-stream of centrifugal radiation field the intensity function ψ_n^+ is not monotonic on $[\varepsilon, r]$ but exhibits a maximum close to the ε-surface (sec. 7). This may not necessarily be true in the interior of a sphere considering the effect of the superposition of two opposing streams of radiation flow. By contrast, the bracketed term of (4.5) vanishes at some r_n associated with a subset $\{\lambda_n\}$, suggesting that the spatial derivative could vanish at r_n. When this happens the spatial position r_n corresponds to an extremum of the intensity. In that case, the function ψ_n^- is not monotonic. Consequently, the total intensity would become non-monotonic as well whether or not there is blackbody emission.

8. The formal solution of the transfer equation

The solution for the centrifugal equation was carried out in sec. 5 for the intensity vector Ψ_r^+ in terms of the mathematical boundary condition Ψ_ε^+. The expression for the solution given as (5.3) is valid for the present problem except that we have to resolve the boundary condition Ψ_ε^+ in terms of the natural boundary condition Ψ_R^-. This requires that we obtain the complete solution for the centripetal equation first. Considering that (4.7) and (4.8) differ only in the sign of λ_n, the mathematical solution for the centripetal equation can be obtained directly from (5.3) by changing the sign of λ_n:

$$\Psi_r^- = \zeta^2 \mathbf{Z}_{\varepsilon:r} \Psi_\varepsilon^- - \mathbf{Q}_{r:\varepsilon}^- \lambda \tag{8.1}$$

$$\mathbf{Z}_{\varepsilon:r} = \mathbf{U}_{\varepsilon:r} \left[\zeta^{\beta_n^n} e^{\lambda_n (r-\varepsilon)} \right] \mathbf{U}_{\varepsilon:r}^{-1} \tag{8.2}$$

$$\mathbf{Q}_{r:\varepsilon}^- = B \int_\varepsilon^r (x/r)^2 \mathbf{Z}_{x:r} \, \mathrm{d}x \tag{8.3}$$

The eigentable $\mathbf{U}_{\varepsilon:r}$ is constructed with the recursion relation (5.2) simply by changing the sign of λ in Γ_n^n. A useful property of the eigentables in vacuum and at the center of the sphere is that they are independent of r and ε, $\forall\{\varepsilon, r\}$:

$$\mathbf{U}_{\varepsilon:r}^{vac} = \mathbf{V}_{\varepsilon:r}^{vac} = \lim_{\varepsilon\to 0} \mathbf{U}_{\varepsilon:r} = \lim_{\varepsilon\to 0} \mathbf{V}_{\varepsilon:r} = \mathbf{V} \tag{8.4}$$

Consequently, $\mathbf{S}^{vac} = \mathbf{Z}^{vac}$ as expected. This is another way to express the reciprocity of path.

8.1. The centripetal intensity with natural boundary condition

In order to complete the solution for the centripetal intensity (8.1), an expression for the boundary intensity at ε-surface is needed. One might think that we could evaluate (8.1) at R, solve for Ψ_ε^- in terms of Ψ_R^-, then feed the value of Ψ_ε^- back into (8.1) to obtain an expression for Ψ_r^- in terms of Ψ_R^-. We previously used this technique in slab geometry [2]. It is particularly useful for unpolarized light in plane geometry, it is not responsive to the symmetry requirements in spherical geometry even with unpolarized radiation: the intensity at r is seen in a concave surface from the center vantage point, it is seen in a convex surface from the surface of the sphere. That is, the symmetry in spherical geometry is *distorted* relative to the symmetry in slab geometry. Therefore, direct inversion of (8.1) is not a valid approach. The solution obtained that way diverges most everywhere in the sphere.

A variation to the direct inversion is to integrate (4.8) directly from R to r with Ψ_R^- as boundary condition. The expression for the solution becomes the same one obtained by direct inversion. That is the symmetry is not properly accounted for in the direct integration from R to r. For that approach to work correctly (4.8) must be symmetrized before integration. Considering that (4.7) and (4.8) are coupled at the center, or at ε-surface with specular reflection boundary condition, the two equations must be symmetrized before integrating (4.8) from R to r. This problem is addressed in Part V of this chapter. Instead, we seek and expression for Ψ_ε^- assuming Ψ_r^- is known. We accomplish this by taking the *reciprocal* of the **Z**-matrix of (8.2).

Historically, reciprocal of a matrix and inverse of a matrix meant the same thing [14]. Modern literature rarely uses the terminology reciprocal of a matrix, if at all. In this chapter, we designate a *reciprocal* of a matrix to be the inverse of the matrix associated with symmetry application on the coupling parameter; the coupling parameter in the present case is the angular derivative imprinted as β-parameters in the **Z**-operator. This is understood if we realize that the coupling of the intensities at r relative to ε is symmetric to the coupling of the intensities at ε relative to r. It is difficult to determine explicitly how such a coupling is achieved in the structure of **Z**-matrix now that the derivative sprawls all over the matrix as β-parameters. One way around is to make a legitimate assumption and build from it the desired symmetry representation.

Define an operator **G** such that $(\mathbf{Z})_{reciprocal} \equiv \mathbf{G}\mathbf{Z}^{-1}$ and **G** is yet to be determined. Hence, evaluate (8.1) at *R*, solve the resulting expression for Ψ_ε^- then insert this boundary intensity into (8.1) and rearrange to obtain:

$$\Psi_r^- = \rho^2 \widetilde{\mathbf{Z}}_{\varepsilon:r} \mathbf{Z}_{\varepsilon:R}^{-1} \Psi_R^- + \rho^{-2} \widetilde{\mathbf{Z}}_{\varepsilon:r} \mathbf{Z}_{\varepsilon:R}^{-1} \mathbf{Q}_{R:\varepsilon}^- \boldsymbol{\lambda} - \mathbf{Q}_{r:\varepsilon}^- \boldsymbol{\lambda} \tag{8.5}$$

where $\rho = R/r$ and $\widetilde{\mathbf{Z}}_{\varepsilon:r} = \mathbf{Z}_{\varepsilon:r}\mathbf{G}$. We resolve $\widetilde{\mathbf{Z}}_{\varepsilon:r}$ to satisfy the following conditions: (i) boundary condition at $r = R$, (ii) reciprocity of path, and (iii) finiteness of the solution at *r* $\forall N$. When these conditions are satisfied, the solution is necessarily conservative. There is no need to impose the conservation of energy a condition on the solution, it is already embedded into the structure of the discrete set of ordinates. The boundary condition is satisfied if:

$$\widetilde{\mathbf{Z}}_{\varepsilon:R} \mathbf{Z}_{\varepsilon:R}^{-1} = \mathbf{I} \;\Rightarrow\; \widetilde{\mathbf{Z}}_{\varepsilon:r} = \widetilde{\mathbf{U}}_{\varepsilon:r} \left[\alpha^{\beta_n^n} \, e^{\lambda_n (r-\varepsilon)} \right] \widetilde{\mathbf{U}}_{\varepsilon:r}^{-1} \tag{8.6}$$

We find α of (8.6) by forcing (8.5) to satisfy the reciprocity of path, i.e., vacuum condition, and simultaneously the boundary condition at the surface of the sphere; clearly, the right side of (8.6) implies $\mathbf{G}(R) = \mathbf{I}$. Keeping in mind that $\alpha^{\beta_n^n} = e^{\beta_n^n \ln\alpha}$, then $\widetilde{\mathbf{U}}_{\varepsilon:r}$ differs from $\mathbf{U}_{\varepsilon\,:r}$ only in $\ln\alpha$ expressed as $\ln\zeta$ in Γ of (5.7). It follows that $\widetilde{\mathbf{U}}_{\varepsilon:r}^{vac} = \widetilde{\mathbf{U}}_{\varepsilon:\varepsilon} = \mathbf{V}$, a property we will use shortly to obtain the expression for the albedo of the pellet. Then (8.5) yields:

$$\Psi_r^- = \rho^2 \mathbf{V} \left[\alpha^{\beta_n^n} \right] \left[\zeta_R^{-\beta_n^n} \right] \mathbf{V}^{-1} \Psi_R^- \tag{8.7}$$

Finiteness of the intensity $\forall r$ and $\forall N$, and application of the surface boundary condition to this expression yield the value $\alpha = \zeta_R$. Hence:

$$\widetilde{\mathbf{Z}}_{\varepsilon:r} \mathbf{Z}_{\varepsilon:R}^{-1} = \widetilde{\mathbf{U}}_{\varepsilon:r} \left[\zeta_R^{\beta_n^n} \, e^{\lambda_n (r-\varepsilon)} \right] \widetilde{\mathbf{U}}_{\varepsilon:r}^{-1} \mathbf{U}_{\varepsilon:R} \left[\zeta_R^{-\beta_n^n} \, e^{-\lambda_n (R-\varepsilon)} \right] \mathbf{U}_{\varepsilon:R}^{-1} \tag{8.8}$$

and with that the solution of the transfer equation for the centripetal intensity is complete.

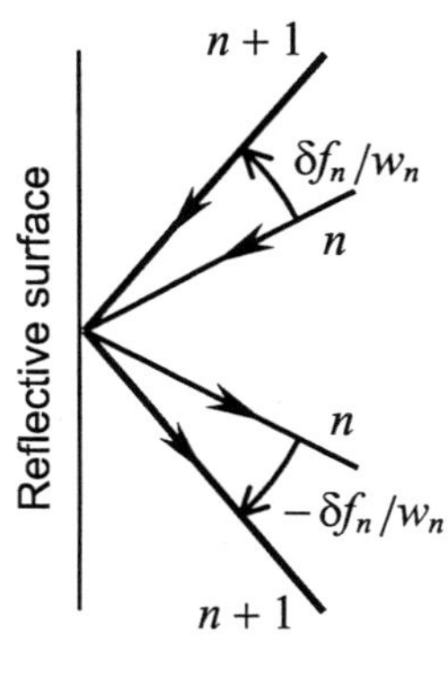

Figure 8.1. Symmetry effect on the angular derivative upon specular reflection.

8.2. The centrifugal intensity with natural boundary condition

We recognize that the angular derivative changes sign upon specular reflection (fig. 8.1). Such a change in sign is tantamount to application of symmetry on Ψ_ε^-. Therefore, we cannot simply equate Ψ_ε^+ with Ψ_ε^-. Instead, we seek an expression for Ψ_ε^+ in terms of Ψ_ε^-. Let **H** be the needed symmetry operator, yet to be determined, such that $\Psi_{\varepsilon}^{+} = \mathbf{H}\Psi_{\varepsilon}^{-}$. We first obtain the centripetal intensity at the surface of the pellet by evaluating (8.5) at $r = \varepsilon$:

$$\Psi_{\varepsilon}^{-} = \zeta_{R}^{-2}\,\widetilde{\mathbf{Z}}_{\varepsilon:\varepsilon}\,\mathbf{Z}_{\varepsilon:R}^{-1}\,\Psi_{R}^{-} + \zeta_{R}^{-2}\,\widetilde{\mathbf{Z}}_{\varepsilon:\varepsilon}\,\mathbf{Z}_{\varepsilon:R}^{-1}\,\mathbf{Q}_{R:\varepsilon}^{-}\,\lambda \tag{8.9}$$

Operate $\mathbf{H}$ on (8.9), insert the resulting expression into (8.1), define $\widetilde{\mathbf{S}}_{\varepsilon:r} = \mathbf{S}_{\varepsilon:r}\mathbf{H}\widetilde{\mathbf{Z}}_{\varepsilon:\varepsilon}$ and constrain the resulting expression to the reciprocity of path to obtain the complete solution for the centrifugal intensity in terms of the natural boundary condition:

$$\Psi_{r}^{+} = \rho^{2}\,\widetilde{\mathbf{S}}_{\varepsilon:r}\,\mathbf{Z}_{\varepsilon:R}^{-1}\,\Psi_{R}^{-} + \rho^{2}\,\widetilde{\mathbf{S}}_{\varepsilon:r}\,\mathbf{Z}_{\varepsilon:R}^{-1}\,\mathbf{Q}_{R:\varepsilon}^{-}\,\lambda + \mathbf{Q}_{r:\varepsilon}^{+}\,\lambda \tag{8.10}$$

$$\widetilde{\mathbf{S}}_{\varepsilon:r} = \widetilde{\mathbf{V}}_{\varepsilon:r}\left[\,\zeta_{R}^{\beta_{n}^{n}}\,e^{-\lambda_{n}(r-\varepsilon)}\right]\widetilde{\mathbf{V}}_{\varepsilon:r}^{-1}$$

where $\widetilde{\mathbf{V}}_{\varepsilon:r}$ is obtained from $\mathbf{V}_{\varepsilon:r}$ by replacing $\ln\zeta$ of (5.1) by $\ln\alpha$. One can verify that in vacuum, i.e., for $\lambda = 0$, the equations (8.5) and (8.10) become identically the same satisfying rigorously the inverse square law:

$$\Psi_{r}^{+} = \Psi_{r}^{-} = \frac{1}{r^{2}}\left(R^{2}\,\Psi_{R}^{-}\right) \tag{8.11}$$

This result is expected since (4.7) and (4.8) become identically the same Euler first order equation in matrix form. We note that (8.11) does not satisfy (4.4) or (4.5) in vacuum. This is because (8.11) is the symmetrized solution, (4.4) and (4.5) are not symmetrized at this point.

Another mathematical property of (8.5) and (8.10) is that they allow only the normal intensity to propagate deep into the sphere all the way through the center. All the intensities from all other directions vanish at the center; the normal intensity in S_{2N} is nominally represented by the *N*th direction for which $\beta_{N}^{N} = 0$.

8.3 Albedo of a sphere.

Evaluate (8.10) at *R* and rearrange to obtain:

$$\Psi_{R}^{+} = \mathbf{A}_{\varepsilon:R}\,\Psi_{R}^{-} + \mathbf{A}_{\varepsilon:R}\,\mathbf{Q}_{R:\varepsilon}^{-}\,\lambda + \mathbf{Q}_{R:\varepsilon}^{+}\,\lambda \tag{8.12}$$

$$\mathbf{A}_{\varepsilon:R} = \widetilde{\mathbf{S}}_{\varepsilon:R}\,\mathbf{Z}_{\varepsilon:R}^{-1}$$

It is apparent that the nature of the operation of $\mathbf{A}_{\varepsilon:R}$ on its operand adheres the significance of *albedo* to this operator. This albedo has little in common with the traditional albedo defined as the ratio of the incident to returned radiation resulting from scattering in the medium. The albedo in the present case is simply a manifestation of symmetry, a geometric property of the volume, whether or not there is scattering.

One application to (8.12) is to maintain *R* fix and treat ε as an independent variable. That way, one can evaluated the emergent intensity at the surface of the sphere emanating from a depth ε below the surface. If the sphere is not too opaque, the energy radiating from the whole sphere can be evaluated using the albedo of a solid sphere which can be obtained by evaluating the albedo $\mathbf{A}_{\varepsilon:R}$ at the limit as $\varepsilon \to 0$:

$$\lim_{\varepsilon \to 0} \mathbf{A}_{\varepsilon:R} = \mathbf{A}_R = \mathbf{V}\left[e^{-2\lambda R}\right]\mathbf{V}^{-1} \tag{8.13}$$

where $\mathbf{A}_R$ is the albedo of a solid homogeneous sphere of radius R.

8.4. The heterogeneous sphere

The solutions developed in the previous sections are valid for a homogeneous medium. If the sphere is not homogeneous, then the diagonal elements of the Γ-matrix become:

$$\Gamma_n^n = \left(2 + \beta_n^n\right)\ln\zeta - L_n(\varepsilon, r) \tag{8.14}$$

$$L_n(\varepsilon, r) = \int_\varepsilon^r \lambda_n \mathrm{d}r \tag{8.15}$$

where $L_n(\varepsilon, r)$ is the optical thickness of the spherical shell, to be used in $\mathbf{S}_{\varepsilon:r}$; the minus sign of (8.14) is used for the solution of the centrifugal intensity, it should be reversed to a plus sign for the solution of the centripetal intensity. It follows that the solutions of the previous sections apply to non-homogeneous spheres by simply making the substitutions: $\lambda_n(r - \varepsilon) \leftarrow L_n(\varepsilon, r)$.

If the sphere is stratified into M homogeneous strata, and each mth stratum is characterized by a uniform opacity κ_m and geometric thickness Δr_m, then the optical thickness of a sphere defined by its outer radius $r_k : k \le M$, is obtained by the summation:

$$L_{n,k} = \sum_{m=1}^{m=k} \lambda_{n,m}\Delta r_m \tag{8.16}$$

9. Quantitative analysis

We considered graphical and numerical data to demonstrate the native characteristics of the solutions using the proposed set of discrete ordinates. We experimented with pure absorbers homogeneous spheres of radius $R = 1$ and a pellet of radius $\varepsilon = 0.1$ with reflective surface. The expressions (8.5) and (8.10) are used in all calculations using 16-SDA. The spheres are exposed to a uniform and isotropic radiation field of normalized intensity $\psi_R^- = 1$. Total intensities and fluxes are computed using Gauss-Legendre quadrature (3.11).

Graphs of total intensities are shown in figure 9.1. They are generated with $N = 10$. The graph of the intensity in vacuum, designated by the opacity $\kappa = 0$, obeys rigorously the inverse square law (8.11), although it is generated with (8.5) and (8.10). This result validates numerically the reciprocity of path for all orders of discrete ordinates. The graphs show a minimum of intensity at some point in the interior of the absorbing spheres as predicted from the centripetal equation (4.4). The complexity of the analytical expressions, however, makes it impossible to determine the value of the radial point where the minimum occurs. The graphs of figure 9.2 illustrate visually the sensitivity of the total intensity to the order N of discrete ordinates. Increasing N above 10 makes no visual dif-

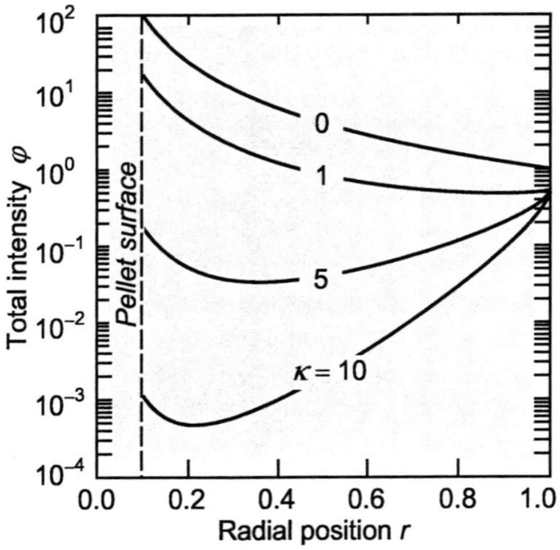

Figure 9.1. Graphs of total intensities in spherical media of different opacities. All the spheres embed a pellet of reflective surface: $R = 1$, $\varepsilon = 0.1$ and the external radiation field is isotropic normalized to 1.

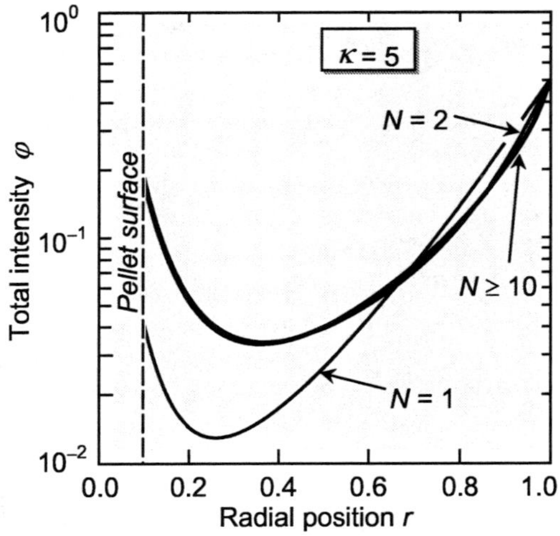

Figure 9.2. Graphs of the total intensity in a sphere for various orders N of discrete ordinates. The sphere embeds a pellet of reflective surface: $R = 1$, $\varepsilon = 0.1$ and the external radiation field is isotropic normalized to 1.

ference on the graph, understandably in pure absorber.

We generated graphs of fluxes in absorbing spheres. They are shown in figure 9.3. It is apparent that the fluxes spike in weak absorbing spheres before they vanish at the surface of the pellet; the flux vanishes at the surface of the pellet by reason of specular reflection boundary condition. Some fluxes in figure 9.3 do not spike in this sphere but they do spike in other spheres. For a given sphere, the tip of the spike varies with the magnitude of the absorption coefficient. Figure 9.4 shows the variations of the flux at that extremum point as a function of the absorption coefficient κ.

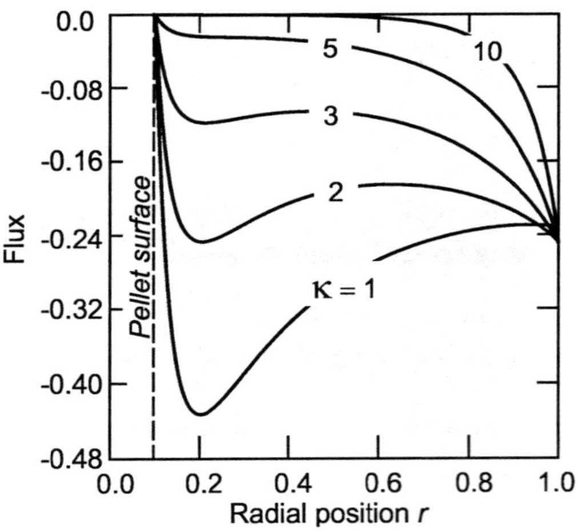

Figure 9.3. Graphs of fluxes in spheres of different opacities. All the spheres embed a pellet of reflective surface: $R = 1$, $\varepsilon = 0.1$ and the external radiation field is isotropic normalized to 1.

The spike is not a numerical aberration it is real. Figure 9.5 shows graphically where the spike comes from. For a given sphere, there is a range of opacities for which the difference between the centrifugal component F^+ and the magnitude of the centripetal component F^- of the flux has a maximum at some point, B in figure 9.5. The occurrence of this maximum and its radial position depend on R, ε and κ. It was not pos-

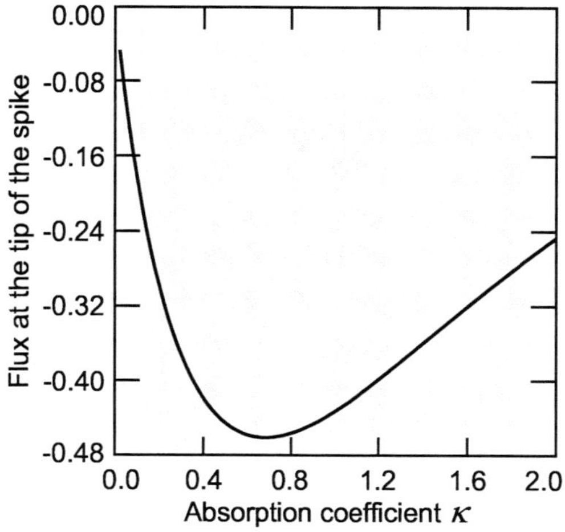

Figure 9.4. Variations of the magnitude of the flux at the tip of its spike with the opacity of a sphere embedding a pellet with reflective surface: $R = 1$, $\varepsilon = 0.1$ and the external radiation field is isotropic normalized to 1.

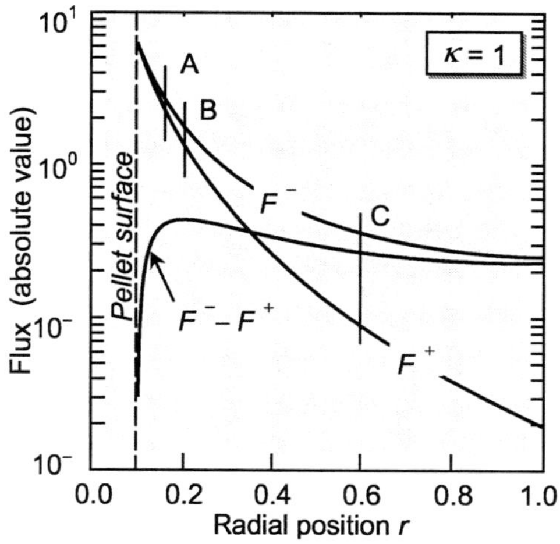

Figure 9.5. Graphs of centripetal flux F^- and centrifugal flux F^+, and their difference, in a sphere embedding a reflective pellet: $R = 1$, $\varepsilon = 0.1$. The difference between the partial fluxes is larger at B than than it is at A or at C.

sible to derive an analytical expression for that radial position, nor was it possible to determine for what opacity it occurs. The location of the spikes of figure 9.3 suggests as if they occur at 2ε. We determined by numerical experimentation that this is not true in general.

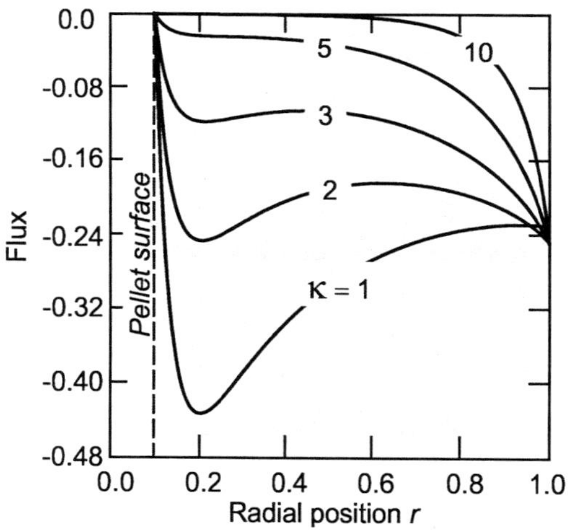

Figure 9.3. Graphs of fluxes in spheres of different opacities. All the spheres embed a pellet of reflective surface: $R = 1$, $\varepsilon = 0.1$ and the external radiation field is isotropic normalized to 1.

Numerical irregularities of the flux were observed particularly in spheres with very small opacities, $\kappa < 10^{-13}$, and in vacuum. These irregularities are attributable to numerical round-off. Figure 9.6 shows the threshold opacity in 16-SDA for which the effect of the round off becomes mostly noticeable at the spike location. The effect of the round off with $\kappa = 10^{-16}$ and in vacuum, $\kappa = 0.0$, are shown in figure 9.7; the data point at $R = 1.0$ in vacuum is exactly $F_R = 0.0$.

Numerical data were also analyzed in order to determine the convergence of the total intensity and the flux with increasing order of discrete ordinates. A sample of these data is shown in Table 9.1 for two spheres of different opacities. The total intensity at the sur-

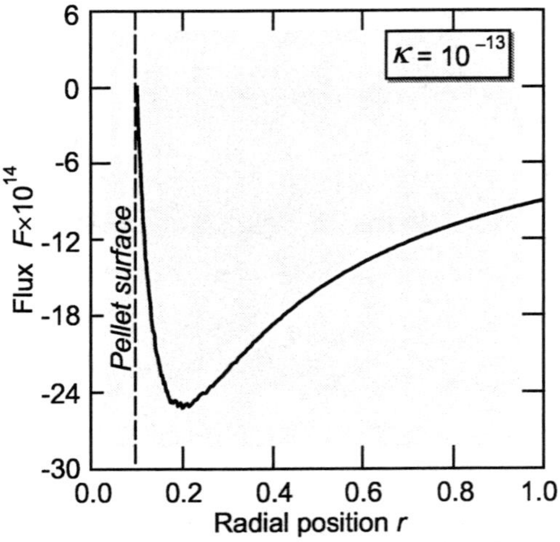

Figure 9.6. Graph of the flux in a sphere of negligible opacity embedding a pellet: $R = 1$, $\varepsilon = 0.1$ and the external radiation field is isotropic normalized to 1.

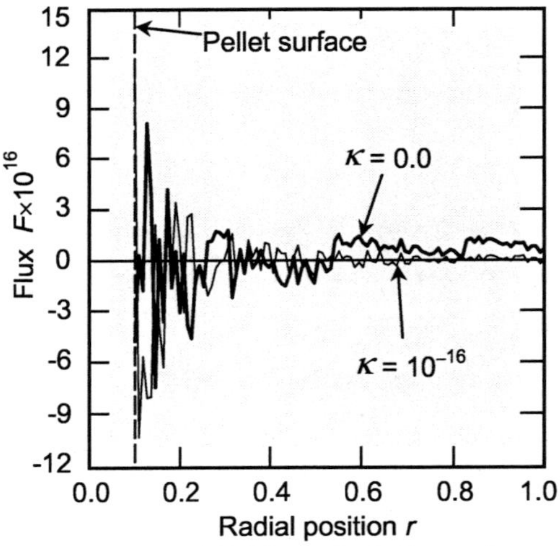

Figure 9.7. Numerical fluctuations of the flux in vacuum and in a medium that is practically a vacuum.

face of the sphere, designated by φ_R, appears to converge faster than the intensity at the surface of the pellet designated by φ_0. This is expected in a pure absorbing medium. The principal component of the intensity at the surface of the sphere comes from the boundary condition. Not much of centrifugal intensity contributes to the total intensity at the surface of the sphere, particularly in strongly absorbing media.

The flux at the surface of the pellet is not reported in Table 9.1. It is $F_0 = 0.0$ by reason of specular reflection. The flux at the surface of the sphere is reported as F_R. It converges very smoothly. Ideally, the conservation of energy, designated by $E = R^2F_R - \varepsilon^2F_0 + \kappa\varphi_{int}$, is zero. It is apparent from Table 9.1 that E is not quite zero, but very small. The discrepancy is attributable to round-off: as N increases the matrices become larger generating larger round off errors. Data in spherical cavity are not shown in the table. They are rigorously conform to the inverse square law: $\varphi_0 = 100$, $\varphi_R = 1$ for all N values we experimented with.

The highest order of the discrete ordinates in Table 9.1 is conspicuously no greater than $N = 32$. Larger values of N returned overflow from the evaluation of the diagonal matrices. This is true in the cases of small absorption coefficients. In the case of $\kappa = 5$, $N = 40$ could be tolerated with noticeable round-off particularly in E; stronger opacities tolerate greater values N without overflow but round-off become noticeable.

PART IV. COMPARATIVE ANALYSIS AND CONCLUSION

10. Flow versus streaming in central symmetry

We compared the moments of the specific intensities computed from the solution of the

Table 9.1. Numerical values for the total intensities φ_0 at the surface of the pellet, φ_R at the surface of the sphere, the flux F_R at the surface of the sphere, and the conservation of energy E. These data are generated with different orders N of discrete ordinates in spheres having the same radii $R = 1$ and $\varepsilon = 0.1$ but different opacities.

	$\kappa = 0.1$				$\kappa = 5.0$			
N	φ_0	φ_R	F_R	$E\times10^{16}$	φ_0	φ_R	F_R	$E\times10^{11}$
1	85.56	0.8660	−0.07732	1.1	0.0412	0.5000	−0.2886	0.5
2	81.38	0.8331	−0.07382	5.0	0.1871	0.5000	−0.2606	1.1
4	77.71	0.8100	−0.07092	4.5	0.1776	0.5000	−0.2528	2.3
8	75.21	0.8002	−0.06910	6.2	0.1778	0.5000	−0.2507	4.7
16	74.17	0.7993	−0.06837	12.1	0.1778	0.5000	−0.2501	9.4
32	74.08	0.7997	−0.06820	19.2	0.1778	0.5000	−0.2500	18.9

discrete ordinates equations with the moments computed from the solution of the integral equation. That comparison was carried out in the point source configuration in an infinite medium without scattering, that is, only the centrifugal equation (5.3) was considered in the comparison. The numerical agreement is near perfect (sec. 7). The significance of this demonstration is that the energy flow model depicted by the differential equation (DE) and the streaming model depicted by the integral equation (IE) are in perfect agreement in the one-stream representation of the intensities. In this section we expand the comparison to include moments computed from two-streams intensities.

The solution of IE in the interior of a homogeneous non-emissive sphere exposed to an isotropic and uniformly distributed radiation field is given as:

$$\psi_r = e^{-\kappa\left(\mu r + \sqrt{R^2 - r^2\eta^2}\right)}\psi_R^- \tag{10.1}$$

where $\mu \in [-1, +1]$. It is noticeable that neither (10.1) nor its moments exhibit the $1/r^2$ behavior. This is quite a contrast with the solution of DE in the interior of the sphere illustrated in figure 9.1, noticeably in the cavity. This illustration demonstrates that the total intensities, and eventually the higher moments, in the DE and the IE models are not reconcilable in the interior of spheres albeit the two solutions satisfy the same transfer equation (2.1) stripped from the scattering term. That leads us to conclude that the DE and the IE describe two different boundary value problems defined by different boundary conditions in the interior of spheres.

The surface boundary condition ψ_R^- is the same for both of the solutions. Fiddling with the spatial derivative of (10.1) we find $\partial_r \psi\,|_{r=0} = -\mu$, which implies symmetry at the center. The natural boundary condition at the center of the sphere is symmetry, but symmetry does not necessarily imply finite derivative at the center. Indeed, the solution of the discrete ordinates equations of this chapter satisfies the symmetry condition at the center but the spatial derivative at the center is not finite. Hence, the symmetry condition makes the DE and the IE boundary value problems irreconcilable.

The finite derivative at the center stems from the hypothesis of streaming: a differential pencil of radiation that enters the sphere at one point streams its way out of the sphere unimpeded. This hypothesis does not seem to be valid in central symmetry. Indeed, radiations that enter the sphere in directions normal to the surface, i.e., $\mu = -1$, end up accumulating their energy at the center of the sphere. This accumulation is not accounted for in (10.1), or its angular integral.

We indicated in the introduction that other efforts resolved the discrepancy between the moments computed from the solution of IE and the moments computed from the solution of DE using RDO in the interior of spheres. This is clearly a conflict between the RDO method, which is consistent with the streaming model, and the UCF method of this chapter, which is not consistent with the streaming model. A close look at the structure of the RDO reveals a fundamental flaw, which is the approximation of the angular derivative with recursive angular parameters and the consequential starter intensity. In that discrete representation, the angular derivative couples ψ^+ with ψ^- from both sides of $\mu = 0$, that is, $\Delta\mu$ straddles zero [7].

One consequence of coupling the intensities in that manner is the obvious ill behavior of the intensity in S_2 discrete ordinates. This can be demonstrated by defining the discrete angular derivative such that $\partial_\mu\psi = (\psi^+ - \psi^-)/\Delta\mu$, where $\mu = 1/3^{1/2}$, $\Delta\mu = 2/3^{1/2}$ and the weight $w = 1$. Then adding and subtracting the centripetal and centrifugal equations and making the appropriate eliminations lead to Helmholtz diffusion equation its solution varies as $1/r$ [15]. This is not a valid description nor is it an approximation for the radiation field in the point source configuration which carries the signature of the asymptotic $1/r^2$ behavior. We note that the S_2 solutions depicted by figures 7.1, 7.4 and 9.2 for $N = 1$ are not good approximations for the intensity either but the $1/r^2$ signature persists. The solution in $1/r$ is not a valid description of the radiation field in the interior of the sphere either. For one thing, it is not reconcilable with the IE model depicted by (10.1), and, on the other hand, it is not reconcilable with the empirical inverse square law, with the method proposed in this chapter and with the limited flux diffusion theory [13].

Another way of coupling the intensities by the angular derivative from both sides of $\mu = 0$ is the very structure of the RDO method. The S_2 discrete ordinates yield a second order equation its solution is plagued by a dip at the center of the sphere but it rejoins the solution of Helmholtz equation at the surface of the sphere [6].

These two illustrations highlight our objection to model the discrete angular derivative by coupling the intensities from both sides of $\mu = 0$. The angular derivative of differential calculus couples intensities ψ^+ in the domain $\mu > 0$ and intensities ψ^- in the domain of $\mu < 0$. It does not couple ψ^+ and ψ^- from either sides of $\mu = 0$. If that is the case in differential calculus, one could not justify straddling zero in the discrete representation of the derivative. Such a coupling would be valid for unpolarized radiation in plane geometry where symmetry is simple, it is not so in curved geometry (sec. 8).

Another consequence of coupling ψ^+ with ψ^- from both sides of $\mu = 0$ is an open set of discrete ordinates equations. The closure of the set is achieved with a starter intensity obtained by setting $\mu = -1$ in the transfer equation in standard form:

$$\mu \partial_r \psi + \frac{1}{r}\left(\eta^2 \partial_\mu \psi\right) + \kappa \psi = \kappa B \tag{10.2}$$

then, with a slight of hand the term $(\eta^2 \partial_\mu \psi)$ is set to zero. Consequently, the starter intensity is the solution of the equation of slab geometry.

11. The validity of the starter intensity

The radiative transfer in spherical geometry with central symmetry is a boundary value problem completely defined by two boundary conditions, namely, the surface intensity and the symmetry at the center. The starter intensity is an additional boundary condition on the angular domain. Therefore, the solution of the discrete ordinates equations using the RDO is conditioned by a redundant boundary condition of slab geometry. The first sign that reveals that such a boundary condition is not valid is that it violates the principle of conservation of energy.

Without loss of generality, consider the case of vacuum, it is equally informative as any other medium. The radial intensity must satisfy the conservation of energy which is expressed in its simplest form as $R^2 \psi_R^- = r^2 \psi_r^-$, which expresses the inverse square law. The starter intensity of slab geometry does not obey this inverse square law and therefore, it does not satisfy the conservation of energy in spheres.

Other investigators examined this problem and denied on themselves the correct solution [5]. They determined, rightfully, that we could not use $\mu = +1$ in (10.2) because the intensity does not fall off as $1/r^2$, but they legitimized $\mu = -1$ to generate a valid solution for (10.2). The legitimacy of such a solution is scuttled by inconsistency in vacuum: if ψ^+ in the normal direction falls off as $1/r^2$, reciprocity of path demands that ψ^- in the normal direction too falls off as $1/r^2$ and, consequently, the starter intensity of slab geometry is not valid.

These observations lead us to conclude that the solution of (10.2) in the direction of $\mu = -1$ is not a slab geometry intensity. It must have the signature of $1/r^2$. For that to be, we cannot simply set $\eta^2 = 0$ in (10.2), but rather we should search for the limit of $(\eta^2 \partial_\mu \psi)$ as $\mu \to -1$. To validate our contention we first need to prove the following theorem:

$$\lim_{\mu \to \pm 1}\left(\eta^2 \partial_\mu \psi\right) = \pm 2\psi \tag{11.1}$$

We note that (2.1) is obtained from (10.2) by adding and subtracting $2\mu\psi/r$ to the left side of the latter. Hence, equating the limits of (2.1) and (10.2) as $\mu \to 1$, we obtain:

$$\lim_{\mu \to 1}\left[\frac{\mu}{r^2}\partial_r\left(r^2 \psi\right) + \frac{1}{r}\partial_\mu\left(\eta^2 \psi\right)\right] = \lim_{\mu \to 1}\left[\mu \partial_r \psi + \frac{\eta^2}{r}\partial_\mu \psi\right] \tag{11.2}$$

Expand the limits and simplify to obtain:

$$2\psi + \partial_\mu\left(\eta^2 \psi\right)\Big|_{\mu=1} = \lim_{\mu \to 1}\left(\eta^2 \partial_\mu \psi\right) \tag{11.3}$$

Making use of the definition of a derivative, the left side derivative term reads:

$$\partial_\mu\left(\eta^2\psi\right)\Big|_{\mu=1} = \lim_{\delta\mu\to 0}\left.\frac{\left(1-\mu^2\right)\psi_\mu-\left(1-(\mu+\delta\mu)^2\right)\psi_{\mu+\delta\mu}}{\delta\mu}\right|_{\mu=1} \tag{11.4}$$

Considering that $\delta\mu$ is arbitrarily small, rewrite the binomial in $\delta\mu$ of the numerator of (11.4) as $\mu^2(1 + 2\delta\mu/\mu) \sim \mu^2$. This holds true for μ arbitrarily larger than $\delta\mu$. Then (11.4) reduces to:

$$\partial_\mu\left(\eta^2\psi\right)\Big|_{\mu=1} = \left(\eta^2\,\partial_\mu\psi\right)\Big|_{\mu=1} \tag{11.5}$$

The two sides of (11.5) are equal only when both sides are zero. Combine this result with (11.3) to complete the proof for $\mu = 1$. The same steps apply to $\mu = -1$ and that completes the proof of the theorem (11.1).

It is apparent from this analysis that $(\eta^2\partial_\mu\psi)_{\mu=\pm1}$ has a different value from $(\eta^2\partial_\mu\psi)_{\mu\to\pm1}$. It follows that (10.2) offers two possible solutions for the normal intensity depending on whether we set $\mu = -1$ or we take the limit as $\mu \to -1$. The proper choice should be such that the starter intensity must be consistent with the empirical inverse square law. For this condition to be satisfied unequivocally the choice has to be the limit as $\mu \to -1$.

The theorem (11.1) can also be proved in the discrete space of ordinates of this chapter:

$$\partial_\mu\left(\eta^2\psi\right)\Big|_{\mu=1} = \mu_N\left(\beta_N^N\psi_N-\beta_N^{N-1}\psi_{N-1}\right)_{N\to\infty} \tag{11.6}$$

By definition: $\beta_N^N = 0$, $\forall N$, $\mu_{N\to\infty} = 1$, and as $N \to \infty$, $\beta_N^{N-1} \to \beta_N^N = 0$ which states that (11.6) is identically zero. This result combined with (11.3) completes the proof of (11.1). We note that no proof to this theorem can be developed in the traditional discrete ordinates method.

Now we apply theorem (11.1) to the transfer equation (10.2) evaluated at $\mu \to -1$. The equation simplifies to read:

$$-\partial_r\psi - \frac{2}{r}\psi + \kappa\psi = \kappa B \tag{11.7}$$

Clearly, the solution of this equation has the signature of $1/r^2$, which is not a solution in slab geometry; in fact, (11.7) without the source term yields exactly the solution (5.8), and in vacuum the solution (8.11). Therefore, if a starter intensity is ever needed it has to be the solution of (11.7). Such a starter intensity conditions the solution of the traditional discrete ordinates equations to behave as $1/r^2$, which is fundamentally different from the solution initiated with the starter intensity of slab geometry. If $1/r^2$ starter intensity is used in the traditional discrete ordinates solution, the reported agreement in [7] between the IE and the DE will be destroyed. We note, however, that the implementation of such a starter intensity in the RDO method does not cure the problem arising from the angular derivative straddling $\mu = 0$.

Now we invoke syllogism: if the solution of the traditional discrete ordinates equations of the transfer problem in the interior of a sphere is flawed, and if that solution agrees well with the solution of the integral equation, then, we conclude, the IE model is not descriptive of the radiative transfer boundary value problem in the interior of spheres.

Therefore, we conclude, the discrepancy between the solution of IE and the solution obtained with the proposed discrete ordinates method should be resolved in favor of the solution of DE of this chapter.

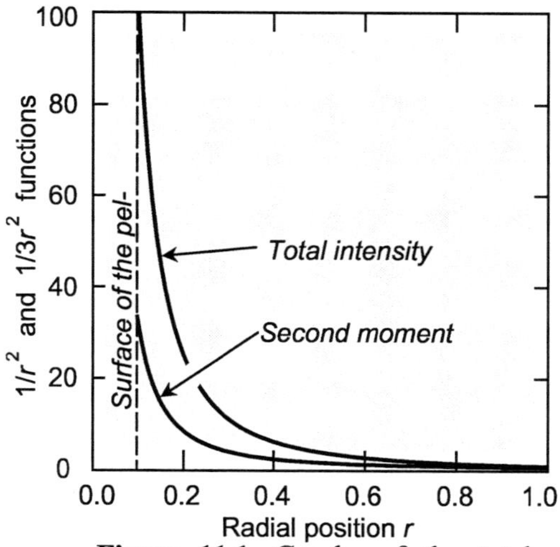

Figure 11.1. Graphs of the total intensity and the second moment in a cavity surrounded by an isotropic and uniformly distributed radiation field.

We observe that the $1/r^2$ intensity is counterintuitive at the limit as $r \to 0$. Nevertheless, this is the exact solution for (2.1). This paradox can be understood by realizing that (2.1) is the linear form of the transport equation; the pressure tensor is dropped out of the equation in the linearization process. Considering that the radiation pressure is proportional to the second moment of ψ [16], the solution of the transfer equation coupled with the radiation pressure is expected to produce a solution that deviates from $1/r^2$ increasingly as we get closer to the center. This inference can be extracted qualitatively from the graphs of figure 11.1.

It is apparent that the gradient of the function $1/(3r^2)$ of figure 11.1, which is the second moment of $1/r^2$ intensity, is vanishingly small near the surface of large spheres and it is unbound at the center. That is, the effect of the pressure on the $1/r^2$ intensity, one would expect, is negligible in the asymptotic region. As the pressure gradient increases with decreasing r, its effect on the intensity is to slow down its spatial rate of growth thus causing the intensity to deviate substantially from the $1/r^2$ behavior and eventually to level up to a finite value. That, however, does not necessarily lead to a flat intensity in vacuum as predicted by IE. One should differentiate between radiation flow field of this chapter and stagnant radiation field. The latter is well known in thermal radiative transfer where radiative energy is injected into an insulated cavity through a tiny orifice. When the injection is interrupted, an equilibrium state reigns in the hohlraum and the intensity is flat.

PART V. THE REDUCED TRANSFER EQUATION

12. The reduced transfer equation

It is apparent from the previous sections that the solution of the transfer equation has limitations on the discrete directions. We investigated an alternative approach that makes working with the transfer equation with central symmetry a great deal simpler than working with the discrete ordinates method.

Consider the standard form of the transfer equation (10.2) with emission from scattering:

$$\mu \partial_r \psi + \frac{\eta^2}{r} \partial_\mu \psi + \kappa \psi = \kappa B + Q \tag{12.1}$$

subject to the natural boundary conditions defined by a uniformly distributed intensity ψ_R^- at the surface of the sphere and symmetry at the center and $Q \equiv Q(r, \mu)$ is a scattering emission term. Adding and subtracting $2\mu\psi/r$ to the left side of (12.1) yields:

$$\frac{\mu}{r^2} \partial_r \left(r^2 \psi\right) + \frac{1}{r} \partial_\mu \left(\eta^2 \psi\right) + \kappa \psi = \kappa B + Q \tag{12.2}$$

which is (2.1) reproduced here for convenience. Integration of (12.2) on $\mu \in [-1, 1]$ yields the first moment equation:

$$\frac{1}{r^2} \partial_r \left(r^2 f_1\right) + \kappa f_0 = \kappa B + Q_0 \tag{12.3}$$

Higher moments equations can also be obtained. For instance, multiplying (12.1) by μ then adding and subtracting $(2\mu^2\psi/r + \eta^2\psi/r)$ to the left side yields:

$$\frac{\mu^2}{r^2} \partial_r \left(r^2 \psi\right) - \frac{\eta^2}{r} \psi + \frac{1}{r} \partial_\mu \left(\mu \eta^2 \psi\right) + \kappa \mu \psi = \kappa \mu B + \mu Q \tag{12.4}$$

Integration of (12.4) on $\mu \in [-1, 1]$ yields the second moment equation:

$$\partial_r f_2 + \frac{3}{r} f_2 + \kappa f_1 - \frac{1}{r} f_0 = Q_1 \tag{12.5}$$

One may continue this procedure to higher moments where the α-moment is defined as:

$$f_\alpha = \frac{1}{2} \int_{-1}^{+1} \mu^\alpha \psi \, \mathrm{d}\mu \tag{12.6}$$

which is the integral form of (3.11).

It is apparent from (12.3) and (12.5) that any set of moments equations is coupled and it is open. Therefore, a rigorous solution of the moments equations may not be possible but a solution accurate to a preselected threshold can be obtained [17]. An alternative approach is to work with the first moment equation (12.3). Instead of solving for the moments directly, we solve for the *degenerate intensity* ψ, which is solution for the *angular degenerate* of (12.3):

$$\frac{\mu}{r^2} \partial_r \left(r^2 \psi\right) + \kappa \psi + \mathrm{f}(r, \mu) = \kappa B + Q \tag{12.7}$$

where ψ is some function of r and μ, not necessarily a specific intensity, and $\mathrm{f}(r,\mu)$ is an odd function in $\mu \in [-1, +1]$ but otherwise arbitrary. In the particular case where $\mathrm{f}(r,\mu) =$

$r^{-1}\partial_\mu(\eta^2\psi)$, then (12.7) is identically the same as (12.2) and ψ is the specific intensity of (12.2). It follows from (12.7) that the degeneracy of (12.3) on the angular domain is not unique, this is understood in light of the arbitrariness of $f(r,\mu)$.

Theorem: If $f(r,\mu)$ is any real valued odd function in $\mu \in [-1, +1]$ but otherwise arbitrary function, then the moments of ψ solution of (12.7) are invariably the same moments of ψ solution of (12.2) if and only if (12.7) is constrained to the same boundary conditions of (12.2).

Proof. Consider the case of the two equations (12.2) and (12.3). They both satisfy the same boundary conditions $\mathcal{B}$ and the moments of ψ are $\{f_0, f_1\}$, where f_0 is the total intensity and f_1 is the flux. Let (12.7) be subject to an arbitrary set of boundary conditions $\mathcal{B}' \neq \mathcal{B}$. Then, its angular integral is an equation formally the same as (12.3) but now it satisfies the boundary conditions $\mathcal{B}'$. Therefore, the moments of ψ are f_0' and f_1' of (12.3). Obviously, neither is intensity or flux, in general. Considering that $\mathcal{B}'$ is arbitrary, we may choose $\mathcal{B}' \equiv \mathcal{B}$. With this choice of boundary conditions, the angular integral of (12.7) is the same moment equation (12.3) that is obtained from (12.2), that is, now f_0' and f_1' have the physical meanings of intensity and flux. Therefore, if $\{f_0, f_1\}$ are the moments of ψ solution of (12.2), they are also the moments of ψ if and only if (12.7) is subject to the same boundary condition of (12.2).

Consider the second moment equation (12.5). If f_0' and f_1' are moments of ψ satisfying the boundary conditions $\mathcal{B}'$, then f_2' is also a moment of ψ satisfying $\mathcal{B}'$. Therefore, if $\{f_0', f_1', f_2'\}$ are the moments of ψ, then they are invariably the same moments of ψ if and only if ψ satisfies the boundary condition $\mathcal{B}' \equiv \mathcal{B}$.

The proof of the theorem may be completed by recursion for all moments $\{f_\alpha : \alpha = 0, 1, \ldots\}$.

The validity of the theorem is exclusive to the moments of the specific intensity. It is obvious for that matter that $\psi \neq \psi\ \forall\mu$. Consequently if for any reasons the specific intensity is needed, or the half-range moments $f_\alpha^{\pm}$ are needed for their own sake, (12.7) offers little help except for the particular case of $f(r,\mu) = r^{-1}\partial_\mu(\eta^2\psi)$, which means in effect we are working with (12.2).

Our motive to work with the degenerate transfer equation is to bypass working with the angular derivative which introduces numerical round-off of its own. This problem can be resolved by choosing a simple odd function $f(r,\mu)$. The simplest of all functions is $f(r,\mu) = 0$, a choice that leads to the simplest degenerate equation:

$$\frac{\mu}{r^2}\partial_r\left(r^2\psi\right) + \kappa\psi = \kappa B + Q \tag{12.8}$$

We dub (12.8) the *reduced transfer equation* and ψ is the *reduced intensity*. We notice that (12.8) can be obtained by simply dropping the angular derivative from (12.2). It is apparent that the advantage in working with the reduced transfer equation is compelling. What follows is the solution of (12.8) with samples of applicable boundary conditions and pertinent analysis.

Further formal simplification of (12.8) may be obtained by defining the function $\tilde{\psi}_r = r^2\psi_r$. Additionally, since the scattering term is the same in either the transfer equation or the reduced equation, its retention in the equation is not compelling for the purpose of this chapter. Our objective is to validate the theorem, which is tantamount to removing the angular derivative from the transfer equation in the central symmetry problem. We meet our objective satisfactorily by considering the transformed reduced equation in a gray medium without scattering:

$$\partial_r\tilde{\psi} + \lambda\tilde{\psi} = \lambda r^2 B \tag{12.9}$$

where $\lambda = \kappa/\mu$, that is, λ is constant on the spatial domain; the case of a heterogeneous sphere will be examined in a later section.

We note that (12.9) is a partial differential equation. This is understood considering that $\tilde{\psi}$ is function of r and μ. Therefore, a set of two boundary conditions is needed in order to obtain the complete solution for (12.9). The first boundary condition will be designated by $\tilde{\psi}_R^- = R^2\psi_R^-$ where ψ_R^- is *natural boundary condition*. The second boundary condition is problem dependent, as illustrated in later sections, but it always boils down to a required symmetry at the center of the sphere consistently with the definition of the problem at hand.

The equation (12.9) is formally similar to the transfer equation in slab geometry. It follows that the symmetry requirements of sec. 8 are not needed for the solution of this equation. Simple planar symmetry is sufficient. We consider (12.9) as the *symmetrized* form of (12.2).

13. The two-streams reduced equations

The solution of (12.9) is straightforward and the natural boundary condition can be applied directly at the surface of the sphere for $\mu < 0$. The application of the second boundary condition requires splitting the solution into two-streams solution, one for $\mu < 0$ and one for $\mu > 0$. Instead, we find it convenient to use Schuster's two-streams technique [11]. Then have:

Centripetal equation:
$$\partial_r\tilde{\psi}^- = \lambda\tilde{\psi}^- - \lambda r^2 B \tag{13.1}$$

Centrifugal equation:
$$\partial_r\tilde{\psi}^+ = -\lambda\tilde{\psi}^+ + \lambda r^2 B \tag{13.2}$$

Considering that $r > 0$, the spatial domain of definition of these two equations is $[\varepsilon > 0, R]$ where ε is a radius of a concentric spherical surface and $\mu \in [0, 1]$. The ε-surface defines a *pellet* that is thermodynamically different from the sphere and it will be characterized by its absorption coefficient κ_p and its Plank function B_p; the case of $\varepsilon = 0$ will be discussed in due course. Consequently, the two equations (13.1) and (13.2) can be solved with the mathematical boundary conditions ψ_ε^- and ψ_ε^+, yet to be determined in terms of the natural boundary condition ψ_R^-.

We observe that (13.1) and (13.2) are symmetric. Therefore, one should expect that their solutions generate the same moments of the symmetrized intensities solutions of the non-symmetrized discrete ordinates equations of Part III. The first confirmation to such an expectation is that both, (13.1) and (13.2) have one common solution with the symmetrized solutions of the discrete ordinates equations. In vacuum, we would have: $\psi_r^\pm = \psi_r^\pm = (R/r)^2 \psi_R^-$, which expresses the reciprocity of path.

Once the solutions $\psi^\pm$ are obtained, their moments are computed using (3.11) with the substitution ψ for ψ. The choice of this quadrature is particularly instructive because it is also used in the discrete ordinates method. Therefore, the round-off error from the quadrature does not make part of any discrepancies between the moments computed from the reduced transfer equation and those computed using the discrete ordinates equations.

13.1. Solution of the centripetal equation

The solution of (13.1) on the domain [ε, R] can be obtained directly in terms of the mathematical boundary condition. Evaluate the solution at R and rewrite it to read:

$$\psi_\varepsilon^- = \frac{R^2}{\varepsilon^2} e^{-\lambda(R-\varepsilon)} \psi_R^- + \frac{B}{\varepsilon^2}\left[Q_\varepsilon^- - Q_R^- e^{-\lambda(R-\varepsilon)}\right] \tag{13.4}$$

$$Q_x^- = x^2 + \frac{2x}{\lambda} + \frac{2}{\lambda^2} \tag{13.5}$$

where ψ_R^- is the natural boundary condition. It is apparent from (13.4) that ε can be treated as an independent parameter and eventually an independent variable r. The complete expression for the centripetal intensity for $r \in [\varepsilon, R]$ becomes:

$$\psi_r^- = \frac{R^2}{r^2} e^{-\lambda(R-r)} \psi_R^- + \frac{B}{r^2}\left[Q_r^- - Q_R^- e^{-\lambda(R-r)}\right] \tag{13.6}$$

13.2. Solutions of the centrifugal equation

Direct integration of (13.2) using the mathematical boundary condition yields:

$$\psi_r^+ = \frac{\varepsilon^2}{r^2} e^{-\lambda(r-\varepsilon)} \psi_\varepsilon^+ + \frac{B}{r^2}\left[Q_r^+ - Q_\varepsilon^+ e^{-\lambda(r-\varepsilon)}\right] \tag{13.7}$$

$$Q_x^+ = x^2 - \frac{2x}{\lambda} + \frac{2}{\lambda^2} \tag{13.8}$$

The search for the boundary value ψ_ε^+ in terms of the natural boundary condition ψ_R^- depends on the optical processes that take place at ε-surface. We consider a few examples.

(a) Specular reflection. In this case, the reflection is perfect at ε-surface and it obeys Snell's law: $\psi_\varepsilon^+ = \psi_\varepsilon^-$ where ψ_ε^- is obtained from (13.4). Then (13.7) reads:

$$\psi_r^+ = \frac{R^2}{r^2} e^{-\lambda(R+r-2\varepsilon)} \psi_R^- + \frac{B}{r^2}\left[\frac{4\varepsilon}{\lambda} e^{-\lambda(r-\varepsilon)} - Q_R^- e^{-\lambda(R+r-2\varepsilon)} + Q_r^+\right] \tag{13.9}$$

This solution is valid if ε-surface is a spherical mirror, or the pellet is merely a cavity. In the latter case, the reflection is assumed at the center and $\psi_{r\le\varepsilon}^+ = \psi_{r\le\varepsilon}^-$ because of the principle of reciprocity of path within the cavity. It is noticeable that the reflective boundary condition is applied by setting $\psi^+ = \psi^-$ at the surface of the pellet without applying symmetry as we did in sec.8 to the specific intensity. This is because in sec. 8 the specific intensity is the solution of a non-symmetrized equation, in the present case ψ is the solution of a symmetrized equation.

(b) Albedo boundary condition. Evaluate (13.9) at R:

$$\psi_R^+ = e^{-2\lambda(R-\varepsilon)} \psi_R^- + \frac{B}{R^2}\left[\frac{4\varepsilon}{\lambda} e^{-\lambda(R-\varepsilon)} - Q_R^- e^{-2\lambda(R-\varepsilon)} + Q_R^+\right] \tag{13.10}$$

It is apparent from this expression that the operation of the coefficient of ψ_R^- on its operand bears the significance of *albedo* of a spherical shell of thickness $(R - \varepsilon)$. This albedo has little in common with the traditional definition of albedo as the ratio of the entering to the exiting radiation at a surface driven by scattering within the sphere. We do not have scattering in the present case. That is, the albedo $A_{R,\varepsilon} = e^{-2\lambda(R-\varepsilon)}$ is merely a manifestation of symmetry.

We obtain the albedo of a solid sphere of radius R by setting $\varepsilon = 0$ in (13.10): $A_R = e^{-2\lambda R}$. Hence, (13.10) can be resolved to express the centrifugal intensity at the surface of the pellet:

$$\hat{\psi}_\varepsilon^+ = e^{-2\lambda_p\varepsilon} \psi_\varepsilon^- + \frac{B_p}{\varepsilon^2}\left[Q_\varepsilon^+ - Q_\varepsilon^- e^{-2\lambda\varepsilon}\right]_p \tag{13.11}$$

where the quantities with subscript p pertain to the pellet and ψ_ε^- is given by (13.4). The intensity $\hat{\psi}_\varepsilon^+$ of (13.11) can now be used for the boundary value ψ_ε^+ of (13.7) to obtain the solution for the centrifugal equation with albedo boundary condition.

At the limit as $\varepsilon \to 0$ we should expect $\hat{\psi}_{\varepsilon\to 0}^+ \to \psi_0^+ = \psi_0^-$, but (13.11) yields:

$$\psi_0^+ = \psi_0^- - \left.\frac{4B_p}{\lambda_p\varepsilon}\right|_{\varepsilon\to 0} \tag{13.12}$$

This is manifestly contrary to the expectations: symmetry is expected at the center but (13.12) suggests otherwise. The missing information from (13.12) is that the limit term is undetermined: as $\varepsilon \to 0$ the pellet vanishes and drags B_p and κ_p with it to naught; one has to keep in mind that both B_p and κ_p are meaningful only in a statistical sense in the interior of a non-vanishing material volume. The apparent inconsistency of (13.12) illustrates the fact that the linearized transfer equation (12.1) is not valid at and in close proximity to the center.

(c) Mixed boundary condition. A number of physical situations may be described by this type of boundary condition, the imploded pellet of inertial fusion is one example. We illustrate the case of a partially reflective ε-surface. Let α be the fraction of the incident radiation that is reflected at the surface, then the reflected intensity is $\alpha\psi_\varepsilon^-$ and the albedo intensity at the surface of the pellet becomes:

$$\widehat{\psi}_\varepsilon^{\alpha+} = (1-\alpha)\, e^{-2\lambda_p \varepsilon}\psi_\varepsilon^- + \frac{B_p}{\varepsilon^2}\left[Q_\varepsilon^+ - Q_\varepsilon^- e^{-2\lambda\varepsilon}\right]_p \tag{13.13}$$

The mixed boundary intensity becomes:

$$\ddot{\psi}_\varepsilon^+ = \widehat{\psi}_\varepsilon^{\alpha+} + \alpha\psi_\varepsilon^- \tag{13.14}$$

where ψ_ε^- of (13.13) and (13.14) is obtained from (13.4) and the mixed boundary intensity $\ddot{\psi}_\varepsilon^+$ of (13.14) takes the place for ψ_ε^+ of (13.7) to complete the solution for the centrifugal intensity with this type of boundary condition.

13.3. Analytical properties of the solutions

First, we look at the intensity in the asymptotic region. Whichever boundary condition is applied at the surface of the pellet we obtain the diffusion regime: $r = R \to \infty \Rightarrow \psi^+ = \psi^- = \psi^+ = \psi^- = B$.

Define $\phi = (\psi^+ + \psi^-)/2$ and its real conjugate $\phi^* = (\psi^+ - \psi^-)/2$, these are commonly known as Feautrier parameters [12]. Historically, Schuster [11] seems to be the first to define ϕ as the mean intensity. Kozirev [18] defined ϕ as the total intensity in the direction corresponding to the root-mean-square of direction cosine $\mu = 3^{-1/2}$ and credited this to Eddington. Vladimirov [19] defined ϕ and ϕ^* as even and odd parity functions in 4π-steradians in his treaties on theory of particle transport and he credited them to Kuznetzov [20].

It is obvious from the expressions for the reduced intensities that the total intensity is singular at the center of the sphere. The property of the flux may be examined by analyzing the property of ϕ^* in the case of reflective boundary condition, and $\phi^{*\alpha}$ in the case of albedo boundary condition. Without loss of generality, we consider the case of a solid homogeneous sphere with a concentric surface of radius ε so that the interior of the pellet and the medium of the sphere have the same properties B and κ. We seek reflective and albedo boundary conditions at ε. Hence:

$$\phi_r^* = -\frac{R^2}{r^2}\psi_R^- e^{-\lambda(R-\varepsilon)}\sinh\lambda(r-\varepsilon) + \frac{B}{r^2}\left[\frac{2\varepsilon}{\lambda}e^{-\lambda(r-\varepsilon)} - \frac{2r}{\lambda} + Q_R^- e^{-\lambda(R-\varepsilon)}\sinh\lambda(r-\varepsilon)\right]$$

(13.15)

$$\phi_r^{*\alpha} = -\frac{R^2}{r^2}\psi_R^- e^{-\lambda R}\sinh\lambda r + \frac{B}{r^2}\left[-\frac{2r}{\lambda} + Q_R^- e^{-\lambda R}\sinh\lambda r\right] \tag{13.16}$$

It is apparent from (13.15) that the flux vanishes at $r = \varepsilon$. However, the flux of the discrete ordinates method spikes before it vanishes at $r = \varepsilon$. The justification of the spike is demonstrated graphically in the case of a sphere without emission (fig. 9.5). The expressions of the discrete ordinates solution of Part III are overly complex to carry out an analytic demonstration of the existence and the location of the spike. In contrast, the expression (13.15) is simple and manageable to determine the position r_{sp} of the spike. Set $\partial_r\phi^* = B = 0$ and rearrange to obtain the z-function:

$$z(r) = \int_0^1 \left[\mu r - (2\mu/\lambda)\tanh\lambda(r-\varepsilon)\right] \mathrm{d}\mu \tag{13.17}$$

The zero of this z-function corresponds to the location of the spike. We note that an equivalent expression to (13.17) can be obtained with $B > 0$. However, for the purpose of explaining the spike behavior of the flux, (13.17) suffices. Set $\partial_r z(r) = 0$ and rearrange to obtain:

$$\int_0^1 \tanh^2(\ell/\mu)\,\mathrm{d}\mu = \frac{1}{4} \tag{13.18}$$

where the optical length $\ell = \kappa(r - \varepsilon)$. Numerical integration of (13.18) reveals that there exist only one value $\ell = 0.5493069$ for which the flux in a non-emissive sphere has a point of inflection. Therefore, the flux can have two extrema, or it is monotonic with one point of inflection, or monotonic with no point of inflection; there is a point of inflection if $\kappa \geq 0.55/(R - \varepsilon)$. Numerical integration of (13.17) should yield the locations of the extrema points for a given sphere. Clearly, this result is valid for a uniform κ throughout a non-emissive sphere.

If we set $\varepsilon = 0$ in (13.15), we recover (13.16), which indicates that the flux is singular at the center of the sphere, except in vacuum. This is paradoxical since we must have $\psi_0^+ - \psi_0^- = 0$, which implies $F_0 = 0$ by reason of symmetry. The paradox is understood considering that ψ_0^+ and ψ_0^- are undetermined and hence $\psi_0^+ = \psi_0^-$ cannot be justified. This result is consistent with the invalidity of the linearized transfer equation at and in the close proximity of the center. However, we note that both (13.15) and (13.16) yield $r^2\phi_r^*\big|_{r=\varepsilon} = 0$ as $\varepsilon \to 0$. That is, although the flux is manifestly singular at the center, no flow of energy occurs through that point, which implies total reflection at the center of the sphere.

Another observation worth noting is the negative $2r/\lambda$ term inside the square brackets of (13.15) and (13.16). It suggests that the flux in the interior of emissive spheres immersed in vacuum could vanish at a point other than the center in the interior of the sphere. This null flux point defines an adiabatic surface its radius is independent of B but it depends on R, ε and κ.

14. The micropellet problem

The transfer equation is used as a diagnostic tool in inertial fusion of imploded micropellets. The energy density computed from the specific intensity, which is proportional to the zeroth moment of ψ, is then used as a source term for the hydrodynamics calculations of the imploded pellet. Considering that the pellet has a radius of 25 to 50 μ m, if the specific intensity is sought too close to the center, assuming the validity of the linearized transfer equation at that proximity to the center, the terms QB/r^2 of the solutions are bound to return an overflow message. One way to bypass this problem is to define a spherical shell of outer radius equal to the diameter of the pellet and inner radius equal to the radius of the pellet.

The exact specific intensity in the shell can be obtained from the solutions discussed in the previous section for $r \in [R, 2R]$ by making the substitutions $\varepsilon \leftarrow R$ and $R \leftarrow 2R$ in the expressions for the solutions of the reduced equation. The boundary condition at the outer surface of the shell is the same ψ_R^- of the micropellet. The inner surface of the shell coincides with the center of the micropellet, which is a reflective boundary. Once the specific intensity ψ_s is computed in the shell, the total energy E_s stored in the volume of the shell is computed from the integral of $\kappa_s\ \varphi_s$ on the volume of the shell. Then the energy in the micropellet is computed from $E_p = \alpha E_s$ where α is the ratio of the volume of the pellet to the volume of the shell. The same procedure applies to a stratum of the micropellet relative to a stratum of the shell. Detailed discussion on this subject can be found in [21].

15. The heterogeneous sphere

We considered the case of λ constant on the spatial domain. If $\lambda(r)$ is completely prescribed and if it is integrable, then the integration of (13.1) and (13.2) is straightforward using standard methods. Most often, the medium is stratified into homogeneous strata. In that case, the solutions of the previous section apply to each stratum individually.

Consider a sphere stratified into M strata not including the pellet and each stratum is designated by its index $m = 1, 2, ..., M$ so that the stratum adjacent to the pellet is designated by $m = 1$ and the outermost stratum by M. In this arrangement, the mth stratum is characterized by λ_m and B_m and it is bounded by $r_m > r_{m-1}$ (fig. 6.1). Consequently, the boundary conditions for each stratum are ψ_m and ψ_{m-1}. In order to determine the boundary conditions we use the solutions of the previous section with the following substitutions: $r_m \leftarrow R$ and $r_{m-1} \leftarrow \varepsilon$, $\psi_m^- \leftarrow \psi_R^-$ and $\psi_0^\pm \leftarrow \psi_\varepsilon^\pm$. Then, using the ART properties (Albedo, Radiance, Transmittance) [2], the solutions on the continuous variable r transcribe into the end-points solutions:

$$\psi_{m-1}^- = T_{m-1}^m \psi_m^- + P_{m-1}^m \tag{15.1}$$

$$\psi_m^+ = T_m^{m-1} \psi_{m-1}^+ + P_m^{m-1} \tag{15.2}$$

Table 16.1. Comparison of the moments computed using the discrete ordinates method and the reduced transfer method of this chapter. The differences are absolute values at different radial positions in spheres of radius $R = 1.0$ hosting a reflective pellet of radius $\varepsilon = 0.1$; κ is the opacity and N is the order of the quadrature/discrete ordinates. The external radiation field is uniform and isotropic of normalized intensity.

	$\kappa = 0.1$			$\kappa = 5.0$		
N	$r = 0.1$	$r = 0.55$	$r = 1.0$	$r = 0.1$	$r = 0.55$	$r = 1.0$
			Total intensities: $\Delta\varphi$			
1	0.0	8.9×10^{-16}	1.1×10^{-16}	1.4×10^{-17}	2.1×10^{-17}	4.4×10^{-16}
2	2.8×10^{-14}	8.9×10^{-16}	2.2×10^{-16}	0.0	2.1×10^{-17}	4.4×10^{-16}
4	1.4×10^{-14}	8.9×10^{-16}	1.1×10^{-16}	1.1×10^{-16}	2.1×10^{-17}	5.6×10^{-16}
8	1.4×10^{-14}	1.3×10^{-15}	1.1×10^{-16}	0.0	2.1×10^{-17}	7.8×10^{-16}
16	1.4×10^{-14}	8.9×10^{-16}	1.1×10^{-16}	1.1×10^{-16}	1.4×10^{-17}	1.1×10^{-15}
			Fluxes: ΔF			
1	1.5×10^{-15}	1.1×10^{-16}	5.6×10^{-17}	1.5×10^{-19}	1.0×10^{-17}	1.7×10^{-16}
2	4.2×10^{-16}	0.0	4.2×10^{-17}	2.7×10^{-18}	2.1×10^{-17}	1.7×10^{-16}
4	1.7×10^{-15}	0.0	4.2×10^{-17}	2.7×10^{-18}	0.0	3.3×10^{-16}
8	9.2×10^{-16}	9.7×10^{-17}	5.6×10^{-17}	2.8×10^{-18}	6.9×10^{-18}	2.8×10^{-16}
16	1.1×10^{-15}	0.0	0.0	5.9×10^{-21}	1.4×10^{-17}	1.7×10^{-16}
			Second moments: ΔK			
1	6.5×10^{-13}	2.0×10^{-14}	5.3×10^{-15}	2.7×10^{-16}	1.2×10^{-16}	0.0
2	3.5×10^{-13}	1.0×10^{-14}	2.8×10^{-15}	1.2×10^{-15}	2.1×10^{-16}	0.0
4	2.3×10^{-13}	7.3×10^{-15}	2.0×10^{-15}	7.8×10^{-16}	1.2×10^{-16}	0.0
8	5.0×10^{-14}	1.6×10^{-15}	5.0×10^{-16}	8.0×10^{-16}	1.0×10^{-16}	0.0
16	7.8×10^{-14}	2.7×10^{-15}	6.1×10^{-16}	8.3×10^{-17}	2.8×10^{-17}	0.0
			Third moments: ΔL			
1	1.2×10^{-15}	5.1×10^{-15}	3.1×10^{-15}	1.7×10^{-19}	6.4×10^{-17}	0.0
2	1.5×10^{-17}	3.5×10^{-15}	2.1×10^{-15}	2.8×10^{-18}	1.8×10^{-16}	0.0
4	1.3×10^{-15}	3.8×10^{-15}	2.2×10^{-15}	1.8×10^{-18}	9.7×10^{-17}	9.7×10^{-16}
8	9.4×10^{-16}	1.2×10^{-15}	5.5×10^{-16}	1.8×10^{-19}	9.0×10^{-17}	0.0
16	1.1×10^{-16}	8.3×10^{-16}	6.1×10^{-16}	4.8×10^{-18}	1.7×10^{-17}	0.0
			Fourth moment: ΔM			
1	2.1×10^{-13}	6.6×10^{-15}	1.8×10^{-15}	9.0×10^{-17}	3.7×10^{-17}	0.0
2	2.2×10^{-13}	6.6×10^{-15}	1.7×10^{-15}	9.0×10^{-16}	1.6×10^{-16}	0.0
4	2.5×10^{-13}	8.1×10^{-15}	2.3×10^{-15}	5.0×10^{-16}	8.0×10^{-17}	0.0
8	5.0×10^{-14}	1.7×10^{-17}	6.1×10^{-16}	6.0×10^{-16}	6.9×10^{-17}	0.0
16	3.9×10^{-14}	1.9×10^{-15}	5.0×10^{-16}	9.7×10^{-17}	1.7×10^{-17}	0.0

where T_x^y is the transmittance and P_x^y the radiance of a stratum; the transport is from y to x. The solutions of (15.1) start with $m = M$ for each μ-direction and continue with decreasing m. At $m = 1$, set $\psi_0^+ = \psi_0^-$ and proceed sweeping (15.2) with increasing m.

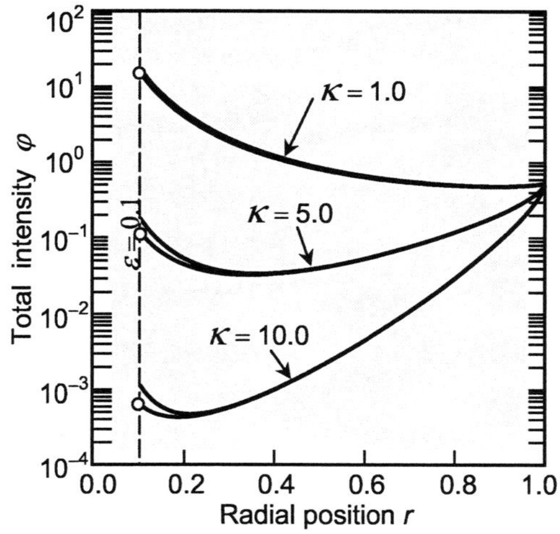

Figure 16.1. Graphs of intensities in solid homogeneous spheres of different opacities; B = 0. The graphs marked with a ball are generated with albedo boundary condition at $\varepsilon = 0.1$, the other graphs are generated with specular reflection boundary condition.

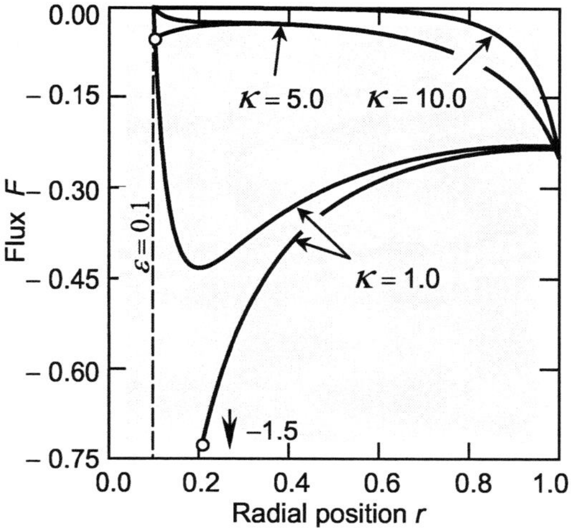

Figure 16.2. Graphs of fluxes in solid homogeneous spheres of different opacities; B=0. The graphs marked with a ball are generated with albedo boundary condition at $\varepsilon = 0.1$, the other graphs are generated with specular reflection boundary condition.

16. Quantitative analysis

We generated graphs for the moments of the specific intensities using the solution of the discrete ordinates equations of Part III and the solution of the reduced transfer equation of this Part V. The solution ψ using the discrete ordinates method contains the contribution of the angular derivative to the specific intensity, the solution ψ of the reduced equation does not. The computed specific intensities from the two solutions do not agree, as expected. In contrast, the moments of ψ and the moments of ψ are in perfect agreement if it wasn't round-off errors. The graphical comparison of the moments is perfect, pixel for pixel. For the sake of avoiding redundancy, we do not reproduce the graphs here. They are the same graphs of figures 7.1 through 7.6.

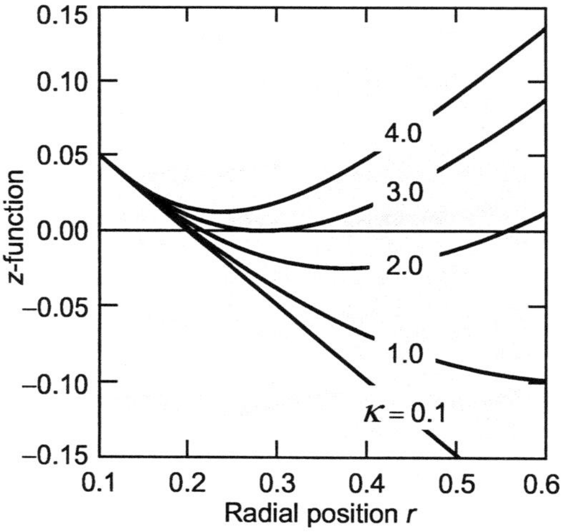

Figure 16.3. Variations of the z-function in spheres of different opacities κ. The radius of the spheres is R = 1.0 and the radius of the pellet $\varepsilon = 0.1$.

Numerical data for the moments, zeroth to fourth, using the discrete ordinates solution and the solution of the reduced equation were generated in two homogeneous spheres characterized by $B = 0$, $\kappa = 0.1$ and $\kappa = 5.0$. All computations were done with 16 significant digits arithmetics using equation (15.1) and (15.2) and their counterparts of the discrete ordinates method with reflective boundary condition at the surface of the pellet. We compared the data at the surface of the pellet, at mid-point in the shell bounded by $\varepsilon = 0.1$ and $R = 1.0$, and at the surface of the sphere.

We computed the absolute value of the difference between the moments of ψ designated with subscript *red*, and the moments of ψ designated with subscript *disc*. The data are shown in Table 16.1 as $\Delta\varphi = | \varphi_{disc} - \varphi_{red} |$ for the zeroth moment, ΔF for the first moment, ΔK the second moment, ΔL third moment and ΔM the forth moment. Ideally, the differences as predicted by the theorem of sec. 12 must be zero. The tabulated data show non-zero values but small enough to be treated as zeros within round-off error in the finite arithmetics of the computations. These results confirm the validity of the theorem. The CPU time ratio of the discrete ordinates computations to the reduced transfer computations increases with the order of discrete ordinates. The largest ratio measured with the data of Table 16.1 was about 140 to 1.

We generated three pairs of graphs for the total intensities and three pairs for the fluxes using the reduced transfer model in three solid homogeneous spheres of different opacities and without emission. A surface of radius $\varepsilon = 0.1$ is selected to simulate a pellet for the purpose of applying reflective and albedo boundary conditions at that location. Figure 16.1 shows the graphs of the total intensities and figure 16.2 shows the fluxes. The graphs that were generated with albedo boundary conditions terminate with a ball at $r = \varepsilon$, the other graphs were generated with reflective boundary condition. In all cases $\psi_R^- = 1.0$.

In the first sphere, $\kappa = 1.0$, the graphs for the intensity are nearly coinciding (fig. 16.1). This is expected since the radius of the pellet is only 0.1 mfp, the pellet behaves almost like a cavity: the reflected intensity is nearly the same as the transmitted intensity through pellet. The discrepancy between the graphs of each pair near the surface of the pellet increases with increasing κ. This is expected, all the energy that reaches the surface of the pellet is reflected at the surface, but only a fraction of it emerges from the pellet with albedo boundary condition, the other fraction is lost by absorption within the pellet. It is noticeable that the graphs in each pair coincide a short distance from the surface of the pellet. This is because most of the contribution to the total intensity in the region away from the surface of the pellet comes from the centripetal intensity; the centrifugal intensity faints out quickly relative to the centripetal intensity.

The graphs of the fluxes shown in figure 16.2 reveal the expected behavior: the fluxes computed with reflective boundary condition vanish at the surface of the pellet, the fluxes computed with albedo boundary condition do not. All fluxes are negative because there is no blackbody emission in these spheres. We experimented with $B_p > 0$ while maintaining $B_{sphere} = 0$. In those cases, the flux at the surface of the pellet becomes positive, then within a short distance in mfp units from ε-surface it becomes negative. That is, the incident flux is larger than the exiting flux at the surface of the sphere.

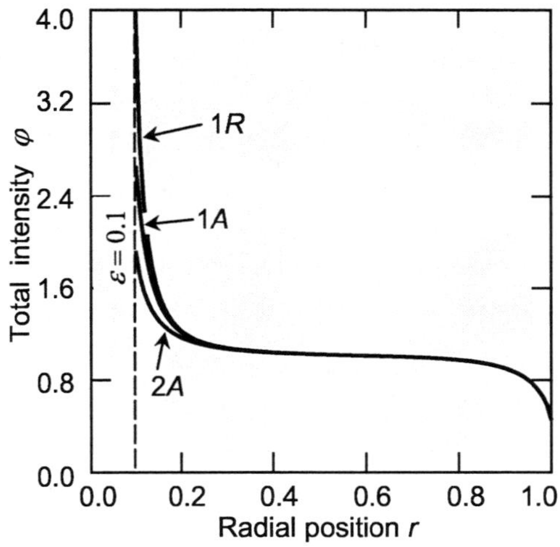

Figure 16.4. Graphs of total intensities in two spheres of different but uniform B and variable κ. Different boundary conditions, R for reflection, A for albedo, are applied at the surface of the pellet and vacuum boundary condition at the surface of the spheres.

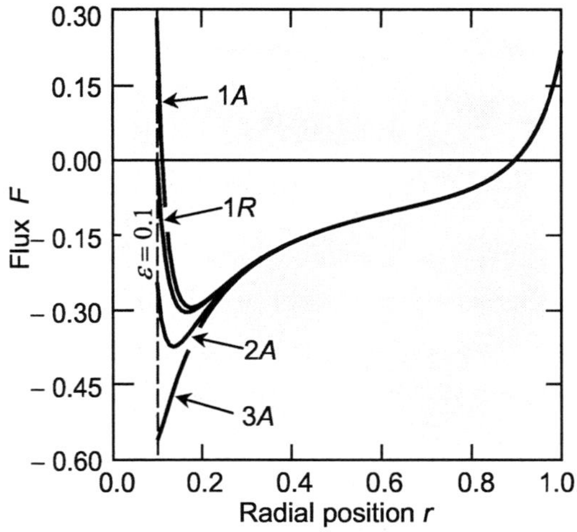

Figure 16.5. Graphs of fluxes in three spheres of different but uniform B and variable κ. Different boundary conditions, R for reflection, A for albedo, are applied at the surface of the pellet and vacuum boundary condition at the surface of the spheres.

In all the cases of figures 16.1 and 16.2, if we change ε the same graph is obtained with albedo boundary condition but only truncated at ε, it is a new graph with reflective boundary condition. In the latter case, changing ε is indeed changing the thickness of the shell bounded by ε and R, which is a different sphere. In the former case, changing ε is merely moving ε-surface around in the interior of the same solid sphere.

We note that the graph corresponding to $\kappa = 1.0$ of figure 16.2 spikes very closely at $r_c = 0.2$ which is a zero of the z-function of (13.17). There is only one spike corresponding to this opacity as predicted from the solution of (13.18). The variations of the z-function are shown in figure 16.3 for different opacities. The graphs show the existence and the locations of the zeros in a sphere of normalized radius $R = 1$; the location of the point of inflection is determined at the minimum of the graphs.

We experimented with heterogeneous spheres made of homogeneous strata. The absorption coefficient of the pellet is fixed at $\kappa = 10$ and $\kappa_m = 0.1/r_m^2$ in the mth stratum in the sphere. Total intensities and fluxes were calculated in three spheres characterized with different blackbody constants: $B = 10$ in the first sphere, $B = 5$ in the second sphere and $B = 2$ in the third sphere; the surface boundary condition is $\psi_R^- = 0$ in all cases. The graphs shown in figure 16.4 and in figure 16.5 are labeled with a number, which is the ordinal of the sphere, and a letter: A designates albedo boundary condition and R designates a reflective boundary condition at the surface of the pellet. The graphs of figure 16.5 show that the spike of the flux persists for some values of κ, ε, R, B of the sphere and B of the pellet.

It is noticeable that the flux in figure 16.5 vanishes at the adiabatic surface near the surface of the sphere, as predicted in Sec. 13. In some cases, the flux vanishes at another surface close to the surface of the pellet, graph 1*A*, or at the surface of the pellet with reflective boundary condition, graph 1*R*. The instructive information from this pattern of the flux is that an observer outside the sphere would not obtain radiative information from the region of the sphere interior to the adiabatic surface. The energy that radiates out of the sphere appears to be originating from a shell no deeper than the adiabatic surface.

It was shown that the medium hosting a radiation field sustains a mechanical radiative pressure proportional to the flux [16]. Consequently, the graphs of the flux of figure 16.5 are representative of the radiative forces on the sphere. It is apparent that the radiative energy tends to sputter the outer shell of the sphere while the inner shell is compressed with a maximum pressure at the spike location.

We experimented with stratified spheres characterized by inverse square opacities and inverse square emission law. The pattern of the graphs of figures 16.4 and 16.5 are representative of the total intensities and fluxes in all of these cases.

SUMMARY AND CONCLUSION

We developed a discrete ordinates method for radiative transfer in spherical geometry with central symmetry. The set of discrete ordinates is weaved with un-normalized circular functions. Consequently, the set of discrete ordinates is non-recursive and that led to a closed set of conservative discrete ordinates equations. We also proposed a reduced transfer equation an alternative to the traditional radiative transfer equation in spherical geometry with central symmetry. We carried out the analytic solutions in r of the discrete ordinates equations and the reduced transfer equation and we compared the numerical computations of the two solutions.

The formal analytical solutions of the discrete ordinates equations are straightforward with mathematical boundary conditions. The conversion of the solutions in terms of the mathematical boundary condition into solutions in terms of the natural boundary condition is accomplished by properly applying symmetry to both the centripetal and the centrifugal solutions. These solutions satisfy all the necessary conditions descriptive of the flow of energy in spheres, specifically, the natural boundary condition at the surface of the sphere, the symmetry condition at the center, the reciprocity of path, the inverse square law and the conservation of energy; a starter intensity is not needed, a contrast with the traditional discrete ordinates method.

The analysis of the solutions led us to conclude that the streaming model, represented by the integral equation, and the flow problem, represented by the differential equation, are equivalent in a one-directional centrifugal radiation field. Our analytical and numerical analyses has shown that this is not the case in central symmetry where the radiation field is defined by opposing streams of radiative energy. This finding is alien to the traditional belief that the integral equation and the differential equation are equivalent prescriptions for the radiative transfer in spheres.

We investigated the problem of symmetrizing the transfer equation before carrying out the solution. That led us to a reduced transfer equation its analytical solution is straightforward. The main trait of the reduced equation is that its solution is a reduced intensity which is not a specific intensity. The moments of the reduced intensity, however, are rigorously the moments of the specific intensity. The comparison of the moments computed from the solution of the reduced transfer equation and the moments computed from the solution of the discrete ordinates equations match perfectly as predicted. The simplicity of the reduced equation and its solutions are compelling to pursue further analysis beyond the LTE transfer problems.

We limited this chapter to the simple radiative transfer problem of monochromatic and unpolarized radiation without scattering under LTE conditions. We aimed to be brief and to the point. The proposed methods, however, are general. They apply to higher hierarchy of problems with scattering and for polarized radiation in spherical geometry with central symmetry. The scattering problem is a direct application of the method of [2]. The application of the method to large spheres, such as stars, is another problem that needs special attention. For one thing, the boundary shell looses focus on the origin but the curvature effect on the radiation field on the outer shell needs to be reckoned with.

Acknowledgments.

This work was funded by the Department of Navy under a grant N00173-001-G010 and was solicited under a protocol with the Department of Physics and Astronomy at Louisiana State University.

References

[1] S Chandrasekhar, 1950, *Radiative transfer*, Oxford University Press

[2] C H Aboughantous, 1996, A closed form analytic solution of the P_L-S_N equations of neutron transport in slab geometry, *J. Phys.* A, Math. Gen. **29**, 7137-7155

[3] B Davison, 1958, *Neutron transport theory*, Oxford University Press

[4] K Lathrop and B Carlson, 1967, Numerical solution of the Boltzmann transport equation, *J. Comp. Phys*. **2**, 173-197

[5] W F Walters and J E Morel, April 1991, Investigation of linear-discontinuous angular differencing for the 1-D spherical geometry S_N equations, Proc., *Intl Top Meet Math Comp React Phys*, **3**, Am Nuc Soc

[6] J E Morel and G R Montry, 1984, Analysis and elimination of the discrete ordinates flux dip, *Transp. Theo. Statis. Phys*. **13-5**, 615-633

[7] K D Lathrop, 2000, A comparison of angular difference schemes for one-dimensional spherical geometry S_N equations, *Nuc. Sci. Eng*. **134**, 239-264

[8] G Arfken, 1970, *Mathematical Methods for physicists*, 2nd ed., Academic Press, New York

[9] T Sghaier, M S Sifaoui and A Soufianai, 2000, Study of radiation in spherical media using discrete ordinates method associated with the finite Legendre transform, *JQSRT*, **64**, 329-351

[10] M M R Williams, 1971, *Mathematical methods in particle transport theory*, Wiley, New York

[11] A Schuster, 1905, Radiation through a foggy atmosphere, *ApJ*, **21**, 1-22

[12] P Feautrier, 1964, *Sur la résolution numérique de l'équation de transfert*, C. R. Acad. Sci., Paris **258**, 3189-3191

[13] C D Levermore and G C Pomraning, 1981, A flux limited diffusion theory, *ApJ.* **248**, 321-334

[14] R A Frazer, W J Duncan and A R Collar, 1938, *Elementary Matrices*, Cambridge University press, London

[15] S Glasstone and M C Edlund, 1966, *The elements of nuclear reactor theory*, Van Nostrand, New York

[16] D Mihalas and B W Mihalas, 1999, *Foundations of radiation hydrodynamics*, Dover, Mineola

[17] P G Martin, C Rogers and G B Rybicki, 1984, *Half-range moment methods for radiative transfer in spherical geometry. II. Implementation of the method*, ApJ, **284**, 317-326

[18] N A Kosirev, 1934, *Radiative equilibrium of extended atmospheres*, MNRAS, **34**, 430-442

[19] V S Vladimirov, 1961, *Mathematical problems of one-speed theory of particle transport*, Proc. V A Stekhov Math. Inst., **61**, Acad. Sc. USSR, Moscow

[20] E S Kuznetzov, 1951, *Radiative equilibrium of a gaseous sphere surrounding an absolutely black sphere*, Izv. An. USSR Ser. Geophys., 69-93

[21] C H Aboughantous, *Radiative transfer in spheres: I. Analytical solutions*, Report **NRL PA010**, Aug. 2001, ePrint astro-ph/0112237

In: Mathematical Physics Research at the Cutting Edge
Editor: C.V. Benton, pp. 189-246
ISBN 1-59033-939-8

Hyperspherical Functions and Harmonic Analysis on the Lorentz Group

V. V. Varlamov
Department of Mathematics, Siberia State University,
Kirova 42, Novokuznetsk 654007, Russia.

Abstract

Matrix elements of spinor and principal series representations of the Lorentz group are studied on the basis of complex angular momentum (helicity basis). It is shown that matrix elements are expressed via hyperspherical functions (relativistic spherical functions). In essence, the hyperspherical functions present themselves as a four-dimensional (with respect to a pseudo-euclidean metrics of Minkowski spacetime) generalization of the usual three-dimensional spherical functions. An explicit form of the hyperspherical functions is given. The hyperspherical functions of the spinor representations are represented by a product of generalized spherical functions and Jacobi functions. It is shown that zonal hyperspherical functions are expressed via the Appell functions. The associated hyperspherical functions are defined as the functions on a two-dimensional complex sphere. Integral representations, addition theorems, symmetry and recurrence relations for hyperspherical functions are given. In the case of the principal and supplementary series representations of the Lorentz group, the matrix elements are expressed via the functions represented by a product of spherical and conical functions. The hyperspherical functions of the principal series representations allow one to apply methods of harmonic analysis on the Lorentz group. Different forms of expansions of square integrable functions on the Lorentz group are studied. By way of example, an expansion of the wave function, representing the Dirac field $(1/2, 0) \oplus (0, 1/2)$, is given.

1 Introduction

Numerous applications of three-dimensional spherical functions in different areas of mathematical and theoretical physics are well known. In the XX century, under the influence of relativity theory, which represents the world as a four-dimensional pseudo-euclidean manifold, it is appeared a necessity to generalize Laplace three-dimensional spherical functions on the four-dimensional case. Four-dimensional spherical functions of an euclidean space was first studied by Fock [21] for the solution of the hydrogen atom problem in momentum representation. They have the form

$$\psi_{nlm}(\alpha,\theta,\varphi)=\frac{i^l\sin^l\alpha}{\sqrt{n^2(n^2-1^2)\cdots(n^2-l^2)}}\frac{d^{l+1}\cos n\alpha}{d(\cos\alpha)^{l+1}}Y_{lm}(\theta,\varphi), \tag{1}$$

where α, θ, φ are angles of the four-dimensional radius-vector in the euclidean space, $n=0,1,2,\ldots$. These functions are eigenfunctions of a square of the four-dimensional angular momentum operator L^2 (L^2 is an angular part, in the sense of α, θ, φ, of the Laplace operator).

In 1956, Dolginov [14] (see also [15, 16, 18]) considered an analytic continuation of the Fock four-dimensional spherical functions (1):

$$\psi_{Nlm}(\alpha,\theta,\varphi)=\frac{\sinh^l\alpha}{\sqrt{N^2(N^2-1^2)\cdots(N^2-l^2)}}\frac{d^{l+1}\cosh N\alpha}{d\cosh^{l+1}\alpha}Y_{lm}(\theta,\varphi), \tag{2}$$

where $0\le\alpha\le\infty$, $N=0,1,2,\ldots$. In turn, the functions (2), called in the works [14, 15, 16] as *relativistic spherical functions*, depend on angles of the radius-vector in the four-dimensional spacetime. At this point, if we replace in (2) N by in, where n is a real number and $0\le n\le\infty$, then we obtain basis functions of an irreducible unitary infinite-dimensional representation of the Lorentz group.

In 1952, Gel'fand and Z. Shapiro [22] (see also [25]) showed that matrix elements of three-dimensional rotation group are expressed via spherical functions (a relationship between special functions and group representations was first discovered by E. Cartan in 1929 [11]). The group theoretical interpretation of the theory of special functions was intensively studied by Vilenkin and Klimyk [76, 77]. At present, it is widely accepted that the theory of special functions is a 'functional aspect' of the group representation theory.

The relationship between matrix elements of the three-dimensional rotation group and spherical functions prompted a new way to definition of the four-dimensional analog of the spherical functions. Namely, these functions should be defined in terms of matrix elements of the Lorentz group. In sixties it is appeared series of the works devoted to this topics [19, 27, 61, 62, 57, 71, 38]. The works of Ström [61, 62] have been obtained the most influence. Ström used the fact, previously established by Naimark [47], that any Lorentz matrix can be represented in the form

$$\mathfrak{g}=u_1(\eta,\psi,0)\mathfrak{g}(a)u_2(\varphi_1,\theta,\varphi_2), \tag{3}$$

where $0\le\eta<4\pi$, $0\le\varphi_1,\varphi_2<2\pi$, $0\le\psi,\theta\le\pi$, $0\le a<\infty$, and u_1, u_2 belong to the group $SU(2)$ (an universal covering of the three-dimensional rotation group), $\mathfrak{g}(a)$ is an element of the one-parameter noncompact subgroup of $SL(2,\mathbb{C})$. The decomposition (3) induces a following form for the matrix elements of the Lorentz group:

$$D^{\nu\rho}_{JM,J'M'}(\mathfrak{g})=\sum_{\lambda=-\min(J,J')}^{\min(J,J')}D^J_{M\lambda}(\eta,\psi,0)D^{\nu\rho}_{JJ'\lambda}(a)D^{J'}_{\lambda M'}(\varphi_1,\theta,\varphi_2),$$

where $D^J_{M\lambda}(\eta,\psi,0)$, $D^{J'}_{\lambda M'}(\varphi_1,\theta,\varphi_2)$ are matrix elements of $SU(2)$, and the functions $D^{\nu\rho}_{JJ'\lambda}(a)$ of the principal series, calculated by Ström in the Gel'fand-Naimark basis, have the form

$$D^{\nu\rho}_{JJ'\lambda}(a)=\sum_{d=\max(0,-\nu-\lambda)}^{\min(J-\nu,J-\lambda)}\;\sum_{d'=\max(0,-\nu-\lambda)}^{\min(J'-\nu,J'-\lambda)}B^{\nu\rho}_{JJ'\lambda dd'}e^{-a(2d'+\lambda+\nu+1-\frac{1}{2}i\rho)}\times$$
$$\times\;{}_2F_1\left(\begin{matrix}1+J'-\frac{1}{2}i\rho,\nu+\lambda+d+d'+1\\ J+J'+2\end{matrix}\middle|\,1-e^{-2a}\right),$$

where

$$B^{\nu\rho}_{JJ'\lambda dd'}=\alpha^{\nu\rho^*}_J\alpha^{\nu\rho}_{J'}(-1)^{J+J'-2\lambda+d+d'}\frac{1}{(J+J'+1)!}\times$$
$$[(2J+1)(J-\nu)!(J+\nu)!(J-\lambda)!(J+\lambda)!(2J'+1)(J'-\nu)!(J'+\nu)!(J'-\lambda)!(J'+\lambda)!]^{\frac{1}{2}}\times$$
$$\frac{(\nu+\lambda+d+d')!(J+J'-\nu-\lambda-d-d')!}{d!(J-\lambda-d)!(J-\nu-d)!(\lambda+\nu+d)!d'!(J'-\lambda-d')!(J'-\nu-d')!(\lambda+\nu+d')!}$$

and

$$\alpha^{\nu\rho}_J=\prod_{s=|\nu|}^{J}\frac{-2s+i\rho}{(4s^2+\rho^2)^{\frac{1}{2}}}=\frac{\Gamma(-|\nu|+\frac{1}{2}i\rho+1)\Gamma(-J+\frac{1}{2}i\rho)}{\Gamma(-|\nu|+\frac{1}{2}i\rho+1)\Gamma(-J+\frac{1}{2}i\rho)}.$$

Matrix elements in the form of Ström and also in other forms [57, 71], which used the decomposition (3), are very complicate. An expansion problem of relativistic amplitudes requires the most simple form of the matrix elements for irreducible representations of the Lorentz group. Moreover, for the matrix elements in the Ström form or in the Sciarrino-Toller form and etc., the question about four-dimensional generalization of the Laplace spherical functions remains unclear. It should be noted that Dolginov-Toptygin relativistic spherical functions present the most degenerate form of the matrix elements of the Lorentz group. Smorodinsky and Huszar [33, 34, 60, 35, 36] found more simple method for definition (except the decomposition (3)) of the matrix elements of the Lorentz group by means of a complexification of the three-dimensional rotation group and solution of the equation on eigenvalues of the Casimir operators (see also [2]). In general case, obtained functions (later on called by Huszar [35, 36] as *spherical functions of the Lorentz group*) are products of the two hypergeometric functions. Matrix elements of spinor representations of the Lorentz group have been obtained by the author [67] via the complexification of a fundamental representation of the group $SU(2)$. The main advantage of such a definition is the most simple form of matrix elements expressed via a *hyperspherical functions*, which is a product of the generalized spherical functions P^l_{mn} and the Jacobi function $\mathfrak{P}^l_{mn}$. As known [22], the matrix elements of $SU(2)$ are defined by the functions P^l_{mn}, and matrix elements of the group $QU(2)$ of quasiunitary matrices of the second order, which is isomorphic to the group $SL(2,\mathbb{R})$[1], are expressed via the functions $\mathfrak{P}^l_{mn}$. The hyperspherical functions present the four-dimensional analog of the three-dimensional spherical functions[2]. In essence, these functions present itself a new class of special functions related to the class of hypergeometric functions.

2 Helicity Basis

Let $\mathfrak{g} \to T_\mathfrak{g}$ be an arbitrary linear representation of the proper orthochronous Lorentz group $\mathfrak{G}_+$ and let $\mathsf{A}_i(t) = T_{a_i(t)}$ be an infinitesimal operator corresponding the rotation $a_i(t) \in \mathfrak{G}_+$. Analogously, we have $\mathsf{B}_i(t) = T_{b_i(t)}$, where $b_i(t) \in \mathfrak{G}_+$ is a hyperbolic rotation. The operators A_i and B_i satisfy the following commutation relations:

$$\left.\begin{array}{lll}
[\mathsf{A}_1,\mathsf{A}_2]=\mathsf{A}_3, & [\mathsf{A}_2,\mathsf{A}_3]=\mathsf{A}_1, & [\mathsf{A}_3,\mathsf{A}_1]=\mathsf{A}_2,\\
[\mathsf{B}_1,\mathsf{B}_2]=-\mathsf{A}_3, & [\mathsf{B}_2,\mathsf{B}_3]=-\mathsf{A}_1, & [\mathsf{B}_3,\mathsf{B}_1]=-\mathsf{A}_2,\\
[\mathsf{A}_1,\mathsf{B}_1]=0, & [\mathsf{A}_2,\mathsf{B}_2]=0, & [\mathsf{A}_3,\mathsf{B}_3]=0,\\
[\mathsf{A}_1,\mathsf{B}_2]=\mathsf{B}_3, & [\mathsf{A}_1,\mathsf{B}_3]=-\mathsf{B}_2, & \\
[\mathsf{A}_2,\mathsf{B}_3]=\mathsf{B}_1, & [\mathsf{A}_2,\mathsf{B}_1]=-\mathsf{B}_3, & \\
[\mathsf{A}_3,\mathsf{B}_1]=\mathsf{B}_2, & [\mathsf{A}_3,\mathsf{B}_2]=-\mathsf{B}_1. &
\end{array}\right\} \qquad (4)$$

Denoting $\mathsf{I}^{23}=\mathsf{A}_1$, $\mathsf{I}^{31}=\mathsf{A}_2$, $\mathsf{I}^{12}=\mathsf{A}_3$, and $\mathsf{I}^{01}=\mathsf{B}_1$, $\mathsf{I}^{02}=\mathsf{B}_2$, $\mathsf{I}^{03}=\mathsf{B}_3$ we can write the relations (4) in a more compact form:

$$\left[\mathsf{I}^{\mu\nu},\mathsf{I}^{\lambda\rho}\right]=\delta_{\mu\rho}\mathsf{I}^{\lambda\nu}+\delta_{\nu\lambda}\mathsf{I}^{\mu\rho}-\delta_{\nu\rho}\mathsf{I}^{\mu\lambda}-\delta_{\mu\lambda}\mathsf{I}^{\nu\rho}.$$

Let us consider the operators

$$\mathsf{X}_l=\frac{1}{2}i(\mathsf{A}_l+i\mathsf{B}_l),\quad \mathsf{Y}_l=\frac{1}{2}i(\mathsf{A}_l-i\mathsf{B}_l), \qquad (5)$$
$$(l=1,2,3).$$

Using the relations (4), we find that

$$[\mathsf{X}_k,\mathsf{X}_l]=i\varepsilon_{klm}\mathsf{X}_m,\quad [\mathsf{Y}_l,\mathsf{Y}_m]=i\varepsilon_{lmn}\mathsf{Y}_n,\quad [\mathsf{X}_l,\mathsf{Y}_m]=0. \qquad (6)$$

Further, introducing generators of the form

$$\left.\begin{array}{ll}
\mathsf{X}_+=\mathsf{X}_1+i\mathsf{X}_2, & \mathsf{X}_-=\mathsf{X}_1-i\mathsf{X}_2,\\
\mathsf{Y}_+=\mathsf{Y}_1+i\mathsf{Y}_2, & \mathsf{Y}_-=\mathsf{Y}_1-i\mathsf{Y}_2,
\end{array}\right\} \qquad (7)$$

[1]Other designation of this group is $SU(1,1)$ known also as three-dimensional Lorentz group, representations of which was studied by Bargmann [6].

[2]The hyperspherical functions (or hyperspherical harmonics) are known in mathematics for a long time (see, for example, [8]). These functions are generalizations of the three-dimensional spherical functions on the case of n-dimensional euclidean spaces. For that reason we retain this name (hyperspherical functions) for the case of pseudo-euclidean spaces.

we see that in virtue of commutativity of the relations (6) a space of an irreducible finite–dimensional representation of the group $\mathfrak{G}_+$ can be spanned on the totality of $(2l+1)(2\dot{l}+1)$ basis vectors $\mid l,m;\dot{l},\dot{m}\rangle$, where $l,m,\dot{l},\dot{m}$ are integer or half–integer numbers, $-l \leq m \leq l$, $-\dot{l} \leq \dot{m} \leq \dot{l}$. Therefore,

$$
\begin{aligned}
&\mathsf{X}_- \mid l,m;\dot{l},\dot{m}\rangle = \sqrt{(l+m)(l-m+1)} \mid l,m-1,\dot{l},\dot{m}\rangle \quad (m>-l),\\
&\mathsf{X}_+ \mid l,m;\dot{l},\dot{m}\rangle = \sqrt{(l-m)(l+m+1)} \mid l,m+1;\dot{l},\dot{m}\rangle \quad (m<l),\\
&\mathsf{X}_3 \mid l,m;\dot{l},\dot{m}\rangle = m \mid l,m;\dot{l},\dot{m}\rangle,\\
&\mathsf{Y}_- \mid l,m;\dot{l},\dot{m}\rangle = \sqrt{(\dot{l}+\dot{m})(\dot{l}-\dot{m}+1)} \mid l,m;\dot{l},\dot{m}-1\rangle \quad (\dot{m}>-\dot{l}),\\
&\mathsf{Y}_+ \mid l,m;\dot{l},\dot{m}\rangle = \sqrt{(\dot{l}-\dot{m})(\dot{l}+\dot{m}+1)} \mid l,m;\dot{l},\dot{m}+1\rangle \quad (\dot{m}<\dot{l}),\\
&\mathsf{Y}_3 \mid l,m;\dot{l},\dot{m}\rangle = \dot{m} \mid l,m;\dot{l},\dot{m}\rangle.
\end{aligned}
\tag{8}
$$

From the relations (6) it follows that each of the sets of infinitisimal operators X and Y generates the group $SU(2)$ and these two groups commute with each other. Thus, from the relations (6) and (8) it follows that the group $\mathfrak{G}_+$, in essence, is equivalent to the group $SU(2)\otimes SU(2)$. In contrast to the Gel'fand–Naimark representation for the Lorentz group [25, 47], which does not find a broad application in physics, a representation (8) is a most useful in theoretical physics (see, for example, [1, 56, 54, 55]). This representation for the Lorentz group was first given by Van der Waerden in his brilliant book [79]. It should be noted here that the representation basis, defined by the formulae (5)–(8), has an evident physical meaning. For example, in the case of $(1,0)\oplus(0,1)$–representation space there is an analogy with the photon spin states. Namely, the operators X and Y correspond to the right and left polarization states of the photon. For that reason we will call the canonical basis consisting of the vectors $\mid lm;\dot{l}\dot{m}\rangle$ as *a helicity basis*.

As known, a double covering of the proper orthochronous Lorentz group $\mathfrak{G}_+$, the group $SL(2,\mathbb{C})$, is isomorphic to the Clifford–Lipschitz group $\mathbf{Spin}_+(1,3)$, which, in turn, is completely defined within a biquaternion algebra $\mathbb{C}_2$, since

$$
\mathbf{Spin}_+(1,3) \simeq \left\{ \begin{pmatrix} \alpha & \beta \\ \gamma & \delta \end{pmatrix} \in \mathbb{C}_2 : \ \det \begin{pmatrix} \alpha & \beta \\ \gamma & \delta \end{pmatrix} = 1 \right\} = SL(2,\mathbb{C}).
$$

Thus, a fundamental representation of the group $\mathfrak{G}_+$ is realized in a spinspace $\mathbb{S}_2$. The spinspace $\mathbb{S}_2$ is a complexification of the minimal left ideal of the algebra $\mathbb{C}_2$: $\mathbb{S}_2 = \mathbb{C}\otimes I_{2,0} = \mathbb{C}\otimes \mathcal{C}\ell_{2,0}e_{20}$ or $\mathbb{S}_2 = \mathbb{C}\otimes I_{1,1} = \mathbb{C}\otimes\mathcal{C}\ell_{1,1}e_{11}$ ($\mathbb{C}\otimes I_{0,2} = \mathbb{C}\otimes\mathcal{C}\ell_{0,2}e_{02}$), where $\mathcal{C}\ell_{p,q}$ $(p+q=2)$ is a real subalgebra of $\mathbb{C}_2$, $I_{p,q}$ is the minimal left ideal of the algebra $\mathcal{C}\ell_{p,q}$, e_{pq} is a primitive idempotent.

Linear transformations of 'vectors' (spinors and cospinors) of the spinspaces $\mathbb{S}_2$

and $\dot{\mathbb{S}}_2$ have the form

$$\begin{array}{rclcrcl} {}'\xi^1 & = & \alpha\xi^1+\beta\xi^2, & \quad & {}'\xi^{\dot{1}} & = & \dot{\alpha}\xi^{\dot{1}}+\dot{\beta}\xi^{\dot{2}}, \\ {}'\xi^2 & = & \gamma\xi^1+\delta\xi^2, & & {}'\xi^{\dot{2}} & = & \dot{\gamma}\xi^{\dot{1}}+\dot{\delta}\xi^{\dot{2}}, \\ & \sigma = & \begin{pmatrix} \alpha & \beta \\ \gamma & \delta \end{pmatrix} & & & \dot{\sigma} = & \begin{pmatrix} \dot{\alpha} & \dot{\beta} \\ \dot{\gamma} & \dot{\delta} \end{pmatrix}. \end{array} \tag{9}$$

Transformations (9) form the group $SL(2,\mathbb{C})$. The expressions (9) compose a base of the 2–spinor van der Waerden formalism [78, 53], in which the spaces $\mathbb{S}_2$ and $\dot{\mathbb{S}}_2$ are called correspondingly spaces of *undotted and dotted spinors.* The each of the spaces $\mathbb{S}_2$ and $\dot{\mathbb{S}}_2$ is homeomorphic to an extended complex plane $\mathbb{C}\cup\infty$ representing an absolute (the set of infinitely distant points) of a Lobatchevskii space $S^{1,2}$. At this point, a group of fractional linear transformations of the plane $\mathbb{C}\cup\infty$ is isomorphic to a motion group of $S^{1,2}$ [52]. Besides, in accordance with [39], the Lobatchevskii space $S^{1,2}$ is an absolute of the Minkowski world $\mathbb{R}^{1,3}$ and, therefore, the group of fractional linear transformations of the plane $\mathbb{C}\cup\infty$ (motion group of $S^{1,2}$) twice covers a 'rotation group' of the space–time $\mathbb{R}^{1,3}$, that is the proper Lorentz group.

The tensor product $\mathbb{C}_2\otimes\mathbb{C}_2\otimes\cdots\otimes\mathbb{C}_2\simeq\mathbb{C}_{2k}$ of the k algebras $\mathbb{C}_2$ induces a tensor product of the k spinspaces $\mathbb{S}_2$:

$$\mathbb{S}_2\otimes\mathbb{S}_2\otimes\cdots\otimes\mathbb{S}_2=\mathbb{S}_{2^k}.$$

Vectors of the spinspace $\mathbb{S}_{2^k}$ (or elements of the minimal left ideal of $\mathbb{C}_{2k}$) are spintensors of the following form

$$\xi^{\alpha_1\alpha_2\cdots\alpha_k}=\sum\xi^{\alpha_1}\otimes\xi^{\alpha_2}\otimes\cdots\otimes\xi^{\alpha_k}, \tag{10}$$

where summation is produced on all the index collections $(\alpha_1\ldots\alpha_k)$, $\alpha_i=1,2$. In virtue of (9) for each spinor ξ^{α_i} from (10) we have a transformation rule ${}'\xi^{\alpha_i'}=\sigma^{\alpha_i'}_{\alpha_i}\xi^{\alpha_i}$. Therefore, in general case we obtain

$${}'\xi^{\alpha_1'\alpha_2'\cdots\alpha_k'}=\sum\sigma^{\alpha_1'}_{\alpha_1}\sigma^{\alpha_2'}_{\alpha_2}\cdots\sigma^{\alpha_k'}_{\alpha_k}\xi^{\alpha_1\alpha_2\cdots\alpha_k}. \tag{11}$$

A representation (11) is called *undotted spintensor representation of the proper Lorentz group of the rank k.*

Further, let $\overset{*}{\mathbb{C}}_2$ be a biquaternion algebra, the coefficients of which are complex conjugate. Let us show that the algebra $\overset{*}{\mathbb{C}}_2$ can be obtained from $\mathbb{C}_2$ under action of the automorphism $\mathcal{A}\to\mathcal{A}^\star$ or antiautomorphism $\mathcal{A}\to\widetilde{\mathcal{A}}$. Indeed, in virtue of an isomorphism $\mathbb{C}_2\simeq C\!\ell_{3,0}$ a general element

$$\mathcal{A}=a^0\mathbf{e}_0+\sum_{i=1}^{3}a^i\mathbf{e}_i+\sum_{i=1}^{3}\sum_{j=1}^{3}a^{ij}\mathbf{e}_{ij}+a^{123}\mathbf{e}_{123}$$

of the algebra $\mathcal{C}\ell_{3,0}$ can be written in the form

$$\mathcal{A} = (a^0 + \omega a^{123})\mathbf{e}_0 + (a^1 + \omega a^{23})\mathbf{e}_1 + (a^2 + \omega a^{31})\mathbf{e}_2 + (a^3 + \omega a^{12})\mathbf{e}_3, \quad (12)$$

where $\omega = \mathbf{e}_{123}$. Since ω belongs to a center of the algebra $\mathcal{C}\ell_{3,0}$ (commutes with all the basis elements) and $\omega^2 = -1$, then we can to suppose $\omega \equiv i$. The action of the automorphism $\star$ on the homogeneous element $\mathcal{A}$ of a degree k is defined by a formula $\mathcal{A}^\star = (-1)^k\mathcal{A}$. In accordance with this, the action of the automorphism $\mathcal{A} \to \mathcal{A}^\star$, where $\mathcal{A}$ is the element (12), has a form

$$\mathcal{A} \longrightarrow \mathcal{A}^\star = -(a^0 - \omega a^{123})\mathbf{e}_0 - (a^1 - \omega a^{23})\mathbf{e}_1 - (a^2 - \omega a^{31})\mathbf{e}_2 - (a^3 - \omega a^{12})\mathbf{e}_3. \quad (13)$$

Therefore, $\star : \mathbb{C}_2 \to -\overset{*}{\mathbb{C}}_2$. Correspondingly, the action of the antiautomorphism $\mathcal{A} \to \widetilde{\mathcal{A}}$ on the homogeneous element $\mathcal{A}$ of a degree k is defined by a formula $\widetilde{\mathcal{A}} = (-1)^{\frac{k(k-1)}{2}}\mathcal{A}$. Thus, for the element (12) we obtain

$$\mathcal{A} \longrightarrow \widetilde{\mathcal{A}} = (a^0 - \omega a^{123})\mathbf{e}_0 + (a^1 - \omega a^{23})\mathbf{e}_1 + (a^2 - \omega a^{31})\mathbf{e}_2 + (a^3 - \omega a^{12})\mathbf{e}_3, \quad (14)$$

that is, $\widetilde{\ } : \mathbb{C}_2 \to \overset{*}{\mathbb{C}}_2$. This allows us to define an algebraic analog of the Wigner's representation doubling: $\mathbb{C}_2 \oplus \overset{*}{\mathbb{C}}_2$. Further, from (12) it follows that $\mathcal{A} = \mathcal{A}_1 + \omega\mathcal{A}_2 = (a^0\mathbf{e}_0 + a^1\mathbf{e}_1 + a^2\mathbf{e}_2 + a^3\mathbf{e}_3) + \omega(a^{123}\mathbf{e}_0 + a^{23}\mathbf{e}_1 + a^{31}\mathbf{e}_2 + a^{12}\mathbf{e}_3)$. In general case, in virtue of an isomorphism $\mathbb{C}_{2k} \simeq \mathcal{C}\ell_{p,q}$, where $\mathcal{C}\ell_{p,q}$ is a real Clifford algebra with a division ring $\mathbb{K} \simeq \mathbb{C}$, $p - q \equiv 3, 7 \pmod 8$, we have for a general element of $\mathcal{C}\ell_{p,q}$ an expression $\mathcal{A} = \mathcal{A}_1 + \omega\mathcal{A}_2$, here $\omega^2 = \mathbf{e}^2_{12\ldots p+q} = -1$ and, therefore, $\omega \equiv i$. Thus, from $\mathbb{C}_{2k}$ under action of the automorphism $\mathcal{A} \to \mathcal{A}^\star$ we obtain a general algebraic doubling

$$\mathbb{C}_{2k} \oplus \overset{*}{\mathbb{C}}_{2k}. \quad (15)$$

Correspondingly, a tensor product $\overset{*}{\mathbb{C}}_2 \otimes \overset{*}{\mathbb{C}}_2 \otimes \cdots \otimes \overset{*}{\mathbb{C}}_2 \simeq \overset{*}{\mathbb{C}}_{2r}$ of r algebras $\overset{*}{\mathbb{C}}_2$ induces a tensor product of r spinspaces $\dot{\mathbb{S}}_2$:

$$\dot{\mathbb{S}}_2 \otimes \dot{\mathbb{S}}_2 \otimes \cdots \otimes \dot{\mathbb{S}}_2 = \dot{\mathbb{S}}_{2^r}.$$

The vectors of the spinspace $\dot{\mathbb{S}}_{2^r}$ have the form

$$\xi^{\dot{\alpha}_1\dot{\alpha}_2\cdots\dot{\alpha}_r} = \sum \xi^{\dot{\alpha}_1} \otimes \xi^{\dot{\alpha}_2} \otimes \cdots \otimes \xi^{\dot{\alpha}_r}, \quad (16)$$

where the each cospinor $\xi^{\dot{\alpha}_i}$ from (16) in virtue of (9) is transformed by the rule $'\xi^{\dot{\alpha}'_i} = \sigma^{\dot{\alpha}'_i}_{\dot{\alpha}_i}\xi^{\dot{\alpha}_i}$. Therefore,

$$'\xi^{\dot{\alpha}'_1\dot{\alpha}'_2\cdots\dot{\alpha}'_r} = \sum \sigma^{\dot{\alpha}'_1}_{\dot{\alpha}_1}\sigma^{\dot{\alpha}'_2}_{\dot{\alpha}_2}\cdots\sigma^{\dot{\alpha}'_r}_{\dot{\alpha}_r}\xi^{\dot{\alpha}_1\dot{\alpha}_2\cdots\dot{\alpha}_r}. \quad (17)$$

A representation (17) is called *a dotted spintensor representation of the proper Lorentz group of the rank r.*

In general case we have a tensor product of k algebras $\mathbb{C}_2$ and r algebras $\overset{*}{\mathbb{C}}_2$:

$$\mathbb{C}_2 \otimes \mathbb{C}_2 \otimes \cdots \otimes \mathbb{C}_2 \otimes \overset{*}{\mathbb{C}}_2 \otimes \overset{*}{\mathbb{C}}_2 \otimes \cdots \otimes \overset{*}{\mathbb{C}}_2 \simeq \mathbb{C}_{2k} \otimes \overset{*}{\mathbb{C}}_{2r},$$

which induces a spinspace

$$\mathbb{S}_2 \otimes \mathbb{S}_2 \otimes \cdots \otimes \mathbb{S}_2 \otimes \dot{\mathbb{S}}_2 \otimes \dot{\mathbb{S}}_2 \otimes \cdots \otimes \dot{\mathbb{S}}_2 = \mathbb{S}_{2^{k+r}} \tag{18}$$

with the vectors

$$\xi^{\alpha_1\alpha_2\cdots\alpha_k\dot{\alpha}_1\dot{\alpha}_2\cdots\dot{\alpha}_r} = \sum \xi^{\alpha_1} \otimes \xi^{\alpha_2} \otimes \cdots \otimes \xi^{\alpha_k} \otimes \xi^{\dot{\alpha}_1} \otimes \xi^{\dot{\alpha}_2} \otimes \cdots \otimes \xi^{\dot{\alpha}_r}. \tag{19}$$

In this case we have a natural unification of the representations (11) and (17):

$$'\xi^{\alpha'_1\alpha'_2\cdots\alpha'_k\dot{\alpha}'_1\dot{\alpha}'_2\cdots\dot{\alpha}'_r} = \sum \sigma^{\alpha'_1}_{\alpha_1}\sigma^{\alpha'_2}_{\alpha_2}\cdots\sigma^{\alpha'_k}_{\alpha_k}\sigma^{\dot{\alpha}'_1}_{\dot{\alpha}_1}\sigma^{\dot{\alpha}'_2}_{\dot{\alpha}_2}\cdots\sigma^{\dot{\alpha}'_r}_{\dot{\alpha}_r}\xi^{\alpha_1\alpha_2\cdots\alpha_k\dot{\alpha}_1\dot{\alpha}_2\cdots\dot{\alpha}_r}. \tag{20}$$

So, a representation (20) is called *a spintensor representation of the proper Lorentz group of the rank* (k, r).

In a general case, the representations defined by the formulas (11), (17) and (20), are reducible, that is, there exists possibility of decomposition of the initial spinspace $\mathbb{S}_{2^{k+r}}$ (correspondingly, spinspaces $\mathbb{S}_{2^k}$ and $\mathbb{S}_{2^r}$) into a direct sum of invariant (with respect to transformations of the group $\mathfrak{G}_+$) spinspaces $\mathbb{S}_{2^{\nu_1}} \oplus \mathbb{S}_{2^{\nu_2}} \oplus \cdots \oplus \mathbb{S}_{2^{\nu_s}}$, where $\nu_1 + \nu_2 + \ldots + \nu_s = k + r$. The algebras $\mathbb{C}_2$ ($\overset{*}{\mathbb{C}}_2$) and the spinspaces $\mathbb{S}_2$ ($\dot{\mathbb{S}}_2$) correspond to fundamental represesentations $\boldsymbol{\tau}_{\frac{1}{2},0}$ ($\boldsymbol{\tau}_{0,\frac{1}{2}}$) of the Lorentz group $\mathfrak{G}_+$. In general case the spinspace (18) is reducible, that is, there exists a decomposition of the original spinspace $\mathbb{S}_{2^{k+r}}$ into a direct sum of irreducible subspaces with respect to a representation

$$\underbrace{\boldsymbol{\tau}_{\frac{1}{2},0} \otimes \boldsymbol{\tau}_{\frac{1}{2},0} \otimes \cdots \otimes \boldsymbol{\tau}_{\frac{1}{2},0}}_{k \text{ times}} \otimes \underbrace{\boldsymbol{\tau}_{0,\frac{1}{2}} \otimes \boldsymbol{\tau}_{0,\frac{1}{2}} \otimes \cdots \otimes \boldsymbol{\tau}_{0,\frac{1}{2}}}_{r \text{ times}}. \tag{21}$$

The full representation space $\mathbb{S}_{2^{k+r}}$ contains both symmetric and antisymmetric spintensors (19).

The decomposition of the spinspace with respect to $SL(2, \mathbb{C})$ is a simplest case of the Weyl scheme. Every irreducible representation of the group $SL(2, \mathbb{C})$ is defined by the Young tableau consisting of only one row. Thus, all the possible irreducible representations of $SL(2, \mathbb{C})$ correspond to the following Young tableaux:

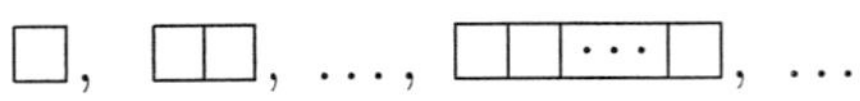

For that reason the representation $\boldsymbol{\tau}_{\frac{m}{2},0}$ is realized in the space $\mathrm{Sym}_{(m,0)}$ of all symmetric spintensors of the rank m. Dimension of $\mathrm{Sym}_{(m,0)}$ is equal to $m + 1$.

In turn, every element of the spinspace (18), related with the representation (21), corresponds to an element of $\mathbb{S}_{2^k} \otimes \mathbb{S}_{2^r}$ (representations $\boldsymbol{\tau}_{\frac{k}{2},0} \otimes \boldsymbol{\tau}_{\frac{r}{2},0}$ and $\boldsymbol{\tau}_{\frac{k}{2},0} \otimes \boldsymbol{\tau}_{0,\frac{r}{2}}$ are equivalent). This equivalence can be described as follows

$$\varphi \otimes \psi \longrightarrow \varphi \otimes \psi I, \tag{22}$$

where $\varphi, \psi \in \mathbb{S}_{2^k}$, $\psi I \in \mathbb{S}_{2^r}$ and

$$I = \lambda \begin{pmatrix} 0 & & -1 \\ & \cdot^{\cdot^{\cdot}} & \\ (-1)_{\frac{r+k}{2}} & & 0 \end{pmatrix}$$

is the matrix of a bilinear form (this matrix is symmetric if $\frac{r+k}{2} \equiv 0 \pmod 2$ and skewsymmetric if $\frac{r+k}{2} \equiv 1 \pmod 2$). In such a way, the representation (21) is realized in a symmetric space $\mathrm{Sym}_{(k,r)}$ of dimension $(k+1)(r+1)$ (or $(2l+1)(2\dot{l}+1)$ if suppose $l = k/2$ and $\dot{l} = r/2$). The decomposition of (21) is given by a Clebsh-Gordan formula

$$\boldsymbol{\tau}_{l_1\dot{l}_1} \otimes \boldsymbol{\tau}_{l_2\dot{l}_2} = \sum_{|l_1-l_2|\le k\le l_1+l_2; |\dot{l}_1-\dot{l}_2|\le \dot{k}\le \dot{l}_1+\dot{l}_2} \boldsymbol{\tau}_{k\dot{k}}.$$

where the each $\boldsymbol{\tau}_{k\dot{k}}$ acts in the space $\mathrm{Sym}_{(k,\dot{k})}$. In turn, every space $\mathrm{Sym}_{(k,r)}$ can be represented by a space of polynomials

$$p(z_0, z_1, \bar{z}_0, \bar{z}_1) = \sum_{\substack{(\alpha_1,\ldots,\alpha_k) \\ (\dot{\alpha}_1,\ldots,\dot{\alpha}_r)}} \frac{1}{k!\,r!} a^{\alpha_1\cdots\alpha_k\dot{\alpha}_1\cdots\dot{\alpha}_r} z_{\alpha_1}\cdots z_{\alpha_k}\bar{z}_{\dot{\alpha}_1}\cdots\bar{z}_{\dot{\alpha}_r}. \tag{23}$$

$$(\alpha_i, \dot{\alpha}_i = 0, 1)$$

where the numbers $a^{\alpha_1\cdots\alpha_k\dot{\alpha}_1\cdots\dot{\alpha}_r}$ are unaffected at the permutations of indices. The expressions (23) can be understood as *functions on the Lorentz group*. Later on, we will find an Euler parametrization of these functions (see section 3). When the coefficients $a^{\alpha_1\cdots\alpha_k\dot{\alpha}_1\cdots\dot{\alpha}_r}$ in (23) are depend on the variables x^α ($\alpha = 0, 1, 2, 3$), then we have

$$p(x, z, \bar{z}) = \sum_{\substack{(\alpha_1,\ldots,\alpha_k) \\ (\dot{\alpha}_1,\ldots,\dot{\alpha}_r)}} \frac{1}{k!\,r!} a^{\alpha_1\cdots\alpha_k\dot{\alpha}_1\cdots\dot{\alpha}_r}(x) z_{\alpha_1}\cdots z_{\alpha_k}\bar{z}_{\dot{\alpha}_1}\cdots\bar{z}_{\dot{\alpha}_r}. \tag{24}$$

$$(\alpha_i, \dot{\alpha}_i = 0, 1)$$

The functions (24) should be considered as *the functions on the Poincaré group.* Some applications of these functions contained in [26]. Representations of the Poincaré group $SL(2,\mathbb{C}) \odot T(4)$ are realized via the functions (24), here $T(4)$ is a subgroup of 4-dimensional translations.

Infinitesimal operators of $\mathfrak{G}_+$ in the helicity basis have a very simple form

$$\begin{aligned}
\mathsf{A}_1 \mid l,m;\dot{l},\dot{m}\rangle &= -\frac{i}{2}\boldsymbol{\alpha}^l_m \mid l,m-1;\dot{l},\dot{m}\rangle - \frac{i}{2}\boldsymbol{\alpha}^l_{m+1} \mid l,m+1;\dot{l}\dot{m}\rangle,\\
\mathsf{A}_2 \mid l,m;\dot{l},\dot{m}\rangle &= \frac{1}{2}\boldsymbol{\alpha}^l_m \mid l,m-1;\dot{l},\dot{m}\rangle - \frac{1}{2}\boldsymbol{\alpha}^l_{m+1} \mid l,m+1;\dot{l},\dot{m}\rangle,\\
\mathsf{A}_3 \mid l,m;\dot{l},\dot{m}\rangle &= -im \mid l,m;\dot{l},\dot{m}\rangle,
\end{aligned} \tag{25}$$

$$\begin{aligned}
\mathsf{B}_1 \mid l,m;\dot{l},\dot{m}\rangle &= -\frac{1}{2}\boldsymbol{\alpha}^l_m \mid l,m-1;\dot{l},\dot{m}\rangle - \frac{1}{2}\boldsymbol{\alpha}^l_{m+1} \mid l,m+1;\dot{l},\dot{m}\rangle,\\
\mathsf{B}_2 \mid l,m;\dot{l},\dot{m}\rangle &= -\frac{i}{2}\boldsymbol{\alpha}^l_m \mid l,m-1;\dot{l},\dot{m}\rangle + \frac{i}{2}\boldsymbol{\alpha}^l_{m+1} \mid l,m+1;\dot{l},\dot{m}\rangle,\\
\mathsf{B}_3 \mid l,m;\dot{l},\dot{m}\rangle &= -m \mid l,m;\dot{l},\dot{m}\rangle,
\end{aligned} \tag{26}$$

$$\begin{aligned}
\widetilde{\mathsf{A}}_1 \mid l,m;\dot{l},\dot{m}\rangle &= -\frac{i}{2}\boldsymbol{\alpha}^{\dot{l}}_{\dot{m}} \mid l,m;\dot{l},\dot{m}-1\rangle - \frac{i}{2}\boldsymbol{\alpha}^{\dot{l}}_{\dot{m}+1} \mid l,m;\dot{l},\dot{m}+1\rangle,\\
\widetilde{\mathsf{A}}_2 \mid l,m;\dot{l},\dot{m}\rangle &= \frac{1}{2}\boldsymbol{\alpha}^{\dot{l}}_{\dot{m}} \mid l,m;\dot{l},\dot{m}-1\rangle - \frac{1}{2}\boldsymbol{\alpha}^{\dot{l}}_{\dot{m}+1} \mid l,m;\dot{l},\dot{m}+1\rangle,\\
\widetilde{\mathsf{A}}_3 \mid l,m;\dot{l},\dot{m}\rangle &= -i\dot{m} \mid l,m;\dot{l},\dot{m}\rangle,
\end{aligned} \tag{27}$$

$$\begin{aligned}
\widetilde{\mathsf{B}}_1 \mid l,m;\dot{l},\dot{m}\rangle &= \frac{1}{2}\boldsymbol{\alpha}^{\dot{l}}_{\dot{m}} \mid l,m;\dot{l},\dot{m}-1\rangle + \frac{1}{2}\boldsymbol{\alpha}^{\dot{l}}_{\dot{m}+1} \mid l,m;\dot{l},\dot{m}+1\rangle,\\
\widetilde{\mathsf{B}}_2 \mid l,m;\dot{l},\dot{m}\rangle &= \frac{i}{2}\boldsymbol{\alpha}^{\dot{l}}_{\dot{m}} \mid l,m;\dot{l},\dot{m}-1\rangle - \frac{i}{2}\boldsymbol{\alpha}^{\dot{l}}_{\dot{m}+1} \mid l,m;\dot{l},\dot{m}+1\rangle,\\
\widetilde{\mathsf{B}}_3 \mid l,m;\dot{l},\dot{m}\rangle &= -\dot{m} \mid l,m;\dot{l},\dot{m}\rangle,
\end{aligned} \tag{28}$$

where

$$\boldsymbol{\alpha}^l_m = \sqrt{(l+m)(l-m+1)}.$$

In the matrix notation for the operators A_i we have

$$\mathsf{A}^j_1 = -\frac{i}{2}\begin{bmatrix}
0 & \boldsymbol{\alpha}_{-l_j+1} & 0 & \ldots & 0 & 0\\
\boldsymbol{\alpha}_{-l_j+1} & 0 & \boldsymbol{\alpha}_{-l_j+2} & \ldots & 0 & 0\\
0 & \boldsymbol{\alpha}_{-l_j+2} & 0 & \ldots & 0 & 0\\
\cdots & \cdots & \cdots & \cdots & \cdots & \cdots\\
\cdots & \cdots & \cdots & \cdots & \cdots & \cdots\\
0 & 0 & 0 & \ldots & 0 & \boldsymbol{\alpha}_{l_j}\\
0 & 0 & 0 & \ldots & \boldsymbol{\alpha}_{l_j} & 0
\end{bmatrix}, \tag{29}$$

$$\mathsf{A}^j_2 = \frac{1}{2}\begin{bmatrix}
0 & \boldsymbol{\alpha}_{-l_j+1} & 0 & \ldots & 0 & 0\\
-\boldsymbol{\alpha}_{-l_j+1} & 0 & \boldsymbol{\alpha}_{-l_j+2} & \ldots & 0 & 0\\
0 & -\boldsymbol{\alpha}_{-l_j+2} & 0 & \ldots & 0 & 0\\
\cdots & \cdots & \cdots & \cdots & \cdots & \cdots\\
\cdots & \cdots & \cdots & \cdots & \cdots & \cdots\\
0 & 0 & 0 & \ldots & 0 & \boldsymbol{\alpha}_{l_j}\\
0 & 0 & 0 & \ldots & -\boldsymbol{\alpha}_{l_j} & 0
\end{bmatrix}, \tag{30}$$

$$\mathsf{A}_3^j = \begin{bmatrix} il_j & 0 & 0 & \dots & 0 & 0 \\ 0 & i(l_j-1) & 0 & \dots & 0 & 0 \\ 0 & 0 & i(l_j-2) & \dots & 0 & 0 \\ \dots & \dots & \dots & \dots & \dots & \dots \\ \dots & \dots & \dots & \dots & \dots & \dots \\ 0 & 0 & 0 & \dots & -i(l_j-1) & 0 \\ 0 & 0 & 0 & \dots & 0 & -il_j \end{bmatrix}, \qquad (31)$$

and so on.

2.1 Gel'fand-Naimark basis

There exists another representation basis for the Lorentz group:

$$\begin{aligned}
H_3\xi_{lm} &= m\xi_{lm}, \\
H_+\xi_{lm} &= \sqrt{(l+m+1)(l-m)}\xi_{l,m+1}, \\
H_-\xi_{lm} &= \sqrt{(l+m)(l-m+1)}\xi_{l,m-1}, \\
F_3\xi_{lm} &= C_l\sqrt{l^2-m^2}\xi_{l-1,m} - A_l m\xi_{l,m} - \\
&\quad -C_{l+1}\sqrt{(l+1)^2-m^2}\xi_{l+1,m}, \\
F_+\xi_{lm} &= C_l\sqrt{(l-m)(l-m-1)}\xi_{l-1,m+1} - \\
&\quad -A_l\sqrt{(l-m)(l+m+1)}\xi_{l,m+1} + \\
&\quad +C_{l+1}\sqrt{(l+m+1)(l+m+2)}\xi_{l+1,m+1}, \\
F_-\xi_{lm} &= -C_l\sqrt{(l+m)(l+m-1)}\xi_{l-1,m-1} - \\
&\quad -A_l\sqrt{(l+m)(l-m+1)}\xi_{l,m-1} - \\
&\quad -C_{l+1}\sqrt{(l-m+1)(l-m+2)}\xi_{l+1,m-1},
\end{aligned}$$

$$A_l = \frac{il_0l_1}{l(l+1)}, \quad C_l = \frac{i}{l}\sqrt{\frac{(l^2-l_0^2)(l^2-l_1^2)}{4l^2-1}},$$

$$m = -l, -l+1, \dots, l-1, l,$$

$$l = l_0, l_0+1, \dots,$$

where l_0 is positive integer or half-integer number, l_1 is an arbitrary complex number. These formulas define a finite–dimensional representation of the group $\mathfrak{G}_+$ when $l_1^2 = (l_0+p)^2$, p is some natural number. In the case $l_1^2 \neq (l_0+p)^2$ we have an infinite–dimensional representation of $\mathfrak{G}_+$. The operators $H_3, H_+, H_-, F_3, F_+, F_-$ are

$$H_+ = i\mathsf{A}_1 - \mathsf{A}_2, \quad H_- = i\mathsf{A}_1 + \mathsf{A}_2, \quad H_3 = i\mathsf{A}_3,$$
$$F_+ = i\mathsf{B}_1 - \mathsf{B}_2, \quad F_- = i\mathsf{B}_1 + \mathsf{B}_2, \quad F_3 = i\mathsf{B}_3.$$

This basis was first given by Gel'fand in 1944 (see also [31, 23, 47]). The following relations between generators $\mathsf{Y}_\pm$, $\mathsf{X}_\pm$, Y_3, X_3 and $H_\pm$, $F_\pm$, H_3, F_3 define a relationship between the helicity (Van der Waerden) and Gel'fand-Naimark bases

$$\begin{aligned}
\mathsf{Y}_+ &= -\frac{1}{2}(F_+ + iH_+), & \mathsf{X}_+ &= \frac{1}{2}(F_+ - iH_+),\\
\mathsf{Y}_- &= -\frac{1}{2}(F_- + iH_-), & \mathsf{X}_- &= \frac{1}{2}(F_- - iH_-), \cdot\\
\mathsf{Y}_3 &= -\frac{1}{2}(F_3 + iH_3), & \mathsf{X}_3 &= \frac{1}{2}(F_3 - iH_3).
\end{aligned}$$

The relation between the numbers l_0, l_1 and the number k of the factors $\mathbb{C}_2$ in the product $\mathbb{C}_2 \otimes \mathbb{C}_2 \otimes \cdots \otimes \mathbb{C}_2$ is given by a following formula

$$(l_0, l_1) = \left(\frac{k}{2}, \frac{k}{2} + 1\right),$$

whence it immediately follows that $k = l_0 + l_1 - 1$. Thus, we have *a complex representation* $\mathfrak{C}^{l_0+l_1-1,0}$ *of the proper Lorentz group* $\mathfrak{G}_+$ *in the spinspace* $\mathbb{S}_{2^k}$. In accordance with [25] a representation conjugated to $\mathfrak{C}^{l_0+l_1-1,0}$ is defined by a pair

$$(l_0, l_1) = \left(-\frac{r}{2}, \frac{r}{2} + 1\right),$$

that is, this representation has a form $\mathfrak{C}^{0,l_0-l_1+1}$. In turn, a representation conjugated to fundamental representation $\mathfrak{C}^{1,0}$ is $\mathfrak{C}^{0,-1}$. As known [25], if an irreducible representation of the proper Lorentz group $\mathfrak{G}_+$ is defined by the pair (l_0, l_1), then a conjugated representation is also irreducible and defined by a pair $\pm(l_0, -l_1)$.

2.2 One-parameter subgroups

The representation of the group $\mathfrak{G}_+$ in the space $\operatorname{Sym}(k, r)$ has a form

$$\begin{aligned}
T_g q(\mathfrak{z}, \bar{\mathfrak{z}}) &= \frac{1}{z_1^k \bar{z}_1^r} T_g \left[z_1^k \bar{z}_1^r q\left(\frac{z_0}{z_1}, \frac{\bar{z}_0}{\bar{z}_1}\right)\right] = \\
&= (\gamma\mathfrak{z} + \delta)^k (\overset{*}{\gamma}\bar{\mathfrak{z}} + \overset{*}{\delta})^r q\left(\frac{\alpha\mathfrak{z} + \beta}{\gamma\mathfrak{z} + \delta}, \frac{\overset{*}{\alpha}\bar{\mathfrak{z}} + \overset{*}{\beta}}{\overset{*}{\gamma}\bar{\mathfrak{z}} + \overset{*}{\delta}}\right),
\end{aligned} \tag{32}$$

where

$$\mathfrak{z} = \frac{z_0}{z_1}, \quad \bar{\mathfrak{z}} = \frac{\bar{z}_0}{\bar{z}_1}.$$

It is easy to see that for the group $SU(2) \subset SL(2, \mathbb{C})$ the formulae (23) and (32) reduce to the following

$$p(z_0, z_1) = \sum_{(\alpha_1, \ldots, \alpha_k)} \frac{1}{k!} a^{\alpha_1 \cdots \alpha_k} z_{\alpha_1} \cdots z_{\alpha_k}, \tag{33}$$

$$T_g q(\mathfrak{z}) = (\gamma\mathfrak{z} + \delta)^k q\left(\frac{\alpha\mathfrak{z} + \beta}{\gamma\mathfrak{z} + \delta}\right), \tag{34}$$

and the representation space Sym(k,r) reduces to Sym$(k,0)$. One–parameter subgroups of $SU(2)$ are defined by the matrices

$$a_1(t)=\begin{pmatrix}\cos\frac{t}{2} & i\sin\frac{t}{2}\\ i\sin\frac{t}{2} & \cos\frac{t}{2}\end{pmatrix},\quad a_2(t)=\begin{pmatrix}\cos\frac{t}{2} & -\sin\frac{t}{2}\\ \sin\frac{t}{2} & \cos\frac{t}{2}\end{pmatrix},$$

$$a_3(t)=\begin{pmatrix}e^{\frac{it}{2}} & 0\\ 0 & e^{-\frac{it}{2}}\end{pmatrix}. \tag{35}$$

An arbitrary matrix $u\in SU(2)$ written via Euler angles has a form

$$u=\begin{pmatrix}\alpha & \beta\\ -\overset{*}{\beta} & \overset{*}{\alpha}\end{pmatrix}=\begin{pmatrix}\cos\frac{\theta}{2}e^{\frac{i(\varphi+\psi)}{2}} & i\sin\frac{\theta}{2}e^{\frac{i(\varphi-\psi)}{2}}\\ i\sin\frac{\theta}{2}e^{\frac{i(\psi-\varphi)}{2}} & \cos\frac{\theta}{2}e^{-\frac{i(\varphi+\psi)}{2}}\end{pmatrix}, \tag{36}$$

where $0\le\varphi<2\pi$, $0<\theta<\pi$, $-2\pi\le\psi<2\pi$, $\det u=1$. Hence it follows that $|\alpha|=\cos\frac{\theta}{2}$, $|\beta|=\sin\frac{\theta}{2}$ and

$$\cos\theta = 2|\alpha|^2-1, \tag{37}$$

$$e^{i\varphi} = -\frac{\alpha\beta i}{|\alpha|\,|\beta|}, \tag{38}$$

$$e^{\frac{i\psi}{2}} = \frac{\alpha e^{-\frac{i\varphi}{2}}}{|\alpha|}. \tag{39}$$

Diagonal matrices $\begin{pmatrix}e^{\frac{i\varphi}{2}} & 0\\ 0 & e^{-\frac{i\varphi}{2}}\end{pmatrix}$ form one–parameter subgroup in the group $SU(2)$. Therefore, each matrix $u\in SU(2)$ belongs to a bilateral adjacency class containing the matrix

$$\begin{pmatrix}\cos\frac{\theta}{2} & i\sin\frac{\theta}{2}\\ i\sin\frac{\theta}{2} & \cos\frac{\theta}{2}\end{pmatrix}.$$

The matrix element $t^l_{mn}=e^{-i(m\varphi+n\psi)}\langle T_l(\theta)\psi_n,\psi_m\rangle$ of the group $SU(2)$ in the polynomial basis

$$\psi_n(\mathfrak{z})=\frac{\mathfrak{z}^{l-n}}{\sqrt{\Gamma(l-n+1)\Gamma(l+n+1)}},\quad -l\le n\le l,$$

where

$$T_l(\theta)\psi(\mathfrak{z})=\left(i\sin\frac{\theta}{2}\mathfrak{z}+\cos\frac{\theta}{2}\right)^{2l}\psi\left(\frac{\cos\frac{\theta}{2}\mathfrak{z}+i\sin\frac{\theta}{2}}{i\sin\frac{\theta}{2}\mathfrak{z}+\cos\frac{\theta}{2}}\right),$$

has a form

$$t^l_{mn}(g) = e^{-i(m\varphi+n\psi)}\langle T_l(\theta)\psi_n,\psi_m\rangle =$$

$$\frac{e^{-i(m\varphi+n\psi)}\langle T_l(\theta)\mathfrak{z}^{l-n}\mathfrak{z}^{l-m}\rangle}{\sqrt{\Gamma(l-m+1)\Gamma(l+m+1)\Gamma(l-n+1)\Gamma(l+n+1)}} =$$

$$e^{-i(m\varphi+n\psi)} i^{m-n}\sqrt{\Gamma(l-m+1)\Gamma(l+m+1)\Gamma(l-n+1)\Gamma(l+n+1)}\times$$

$$\cos^{2l}\frac{\theta}{2}\tan^{m-n}\frac{\theta}{2}\times$$

$$\sum_{j=\max(0,n-m)}^{\min(l-n,l+n)}\frac{i^{2j}\tan^{2j}\dfrac{\theta}{2}}{\Gamma(j+1)\Gamma(l-m-j+1)\Gamma(l+n-j+1)\Gamma(m-n+j+1)}. \tag{40}$$

Further, using the formula

$${}_2F_1\left(\begin{matrix}\alpha,\beta\\ \gamma\end{matrix}\middle|\, z\right) = \frac{\Gamma(\gamma)}{\Gamma(\alpha)\Gamma(\beta)}\sum_{k\geq 0}\frac{\Gamma(\alpha+k)\Gamma(\beta+k)}{\Gamma(\gamma+k)}\frac{z^k}{k!} \tag{41}$$

we can express the matrix element (40) via the hypergeometric function:

$$t^l_{mn}(g) = \frac{i^{m-n}e^{-i(m\varphi+n\psi)}}{\Gamma(m-n+1)}\sqrt{\frac{\Gamma(l+m+1)\Gamma(l-n+1)}{\Gamma(l-m+1)\Gamma(l+n+1)}}\times$$

$$\cos^{2l}\frac{\theta}{2}\tan^{m-n}\frac{\theta}{2}\,{}_2F_1\left(\begin{matrix}m-l+1,1-l-n\\ m-n+1\end{matrix}\middle|\, i^2\tan^2\frac{\theta}{2}\right), \tag{42}$$

where $m \geq n$. At $m < n$ in the right part of (42) it needs to replace m and n by $-m$ and $-n$, respectively. Since l, m and n are finite numbers, then the hypergeometric series is interrupted.

Further, replacing in the one–parameter subgroups (35) the parameter t by $-it$, we obtain

$$b_1(t) = \begin{pmatrix}\cosh\frac{t}{2} & \sinh\frac{t}{2}\\ \sinh\frac{t}{2} & \cosh\frac{t}{2}\end{pmatrix},\quad b_2(t) = \begin{pmatrix}\cosh\frac{t}{2} & i\sinh\frac{t}{2}\\ -i\sinh\frac{t}{2} & \cosh\frac{t}{2}\end{pmatrix},$$

$$b_3(t) = \begin{pmatrix}e^{\frac{t}{2}} & 0\\ 0 & e^{-\frac{t}{2}}\end{pmatrix}. \tag{43}$$

These subgroups correspond to hyperbolic rotations.

3 Hyperspherical functions

As known [28], a root subgroup of a semisimple Lie group O_4 (a rotation group of the 4-dimensional space) is a normal divisor of O_4. For that reason the 6-parameter group O_4 is semisimple, and is represented by a direct product of the two 3-parameter unimodular groups. By analogy with the group O_4, a double covering $SL(2,\mathbb{C})$ of the proper orthochronous Lorentz group $\mathfrak{G}_+$ (a rotation group of the 4-dimensional spacetime continuum) is semisimple, and is represented by a direct product of the two 3-parameter special unimodular groups, $SL(2,\mathbb{C}) \simeq SU(2)\otimes SU(2)$. An explicit form of this isomorphism can be obtained by means of a complexification of the group $SU(2)$, that is, $SL(2,\mathbb{C}) \simeq \mathsf{complex}(SU(2)) \simeq SU(2)\otimes SU(2)$ [67].

3.1 Complexification of $SU(2)$

The group $SL(2,\mathbb{C})$ of all complex matrices

$$\begin{pmatrix} \alpha & \beta \\ \gamma & \delta \end{pmatrix}$$

of 2-nd order with the determinant $\alpha\delta - \gamma\beta = 1$, is a *complexification* of the group $SU(2)$. The group $SU(2)$ is one of the real forms of $SL(2,\mathbb{C})$. The transition from $SU(2)$ to $SL(2,\mathbb{C})$ is realized via the complexification of three real parameters φ, θ, ψ (Euler angles). Let $\theta^c = \theta - i\tau$, $\varphi^c = \varphi - i\epsilon$, $\psi^c = \psi - i\varepsilon$ be complex Euler angles, where

$$\begin{array}{rclcl} 0 & \leq & \operatorname{Re}\theta^c = \theta & \leq & \pi, \\ 0 & \leq & \operatorname{Re}\varphi^c = \varphi & < & 2\pi, \\ -2\pi & \leq & \operatorname{Re}\psi^c = \psi & < & 2\pi, \end{array} \quad \begin{array}{rclcl} -\infty & < & \operatorname{Im}\theta^c = \tau & < & +\infty, \\ -\infty & < & \operatorname{Im}\varphi^c = \epsilon & < & +\infty, \\ -\infty & < & \operatorname{Im}\psi^c = \varepsilon & < & +\infty. \end{array} \tag{44}$$

Replacing in (36) the angles φ, θ, ψ by the complex angles $\varphi^c, \theta^c, \psi^c$, we come to the following matrix

$$\mathfrak{g} = \begin{pmatrix} \cos\frac{\theta^c}{2} e^{\frac{i(\varphi^c+\psi^c)}{2}} & i\sin\frac{\theta^c}{2} e^{\frac{i(\varphi^c-\psi^c)}{2}} \\ i\sin\frac{\theta^c}{2} e^{\frac{i(\psi^c-\varphi^c)}{2}} & \cos\frac{\theta^c}{2} e^{-\frac{i(\varphi^c+\psi^c)}{2}} \end{pmatrix} =$$
$$\begin{pmatrix} \left[\cos\frac{\theta}{2}\cosh\frac{\tau}{2} + i\sin\frac{\theta}{2}\sinh\frac{\tau}{2}\right] e^{\frac{\epsilon+\varepsilon+i(\varphi+\psi)}{2}} & \left[\cos\frac{\theta}{2}\sinh\frac{\tau}{2} + i\sin\frac{\theta}{2}\cosh\frac{\tau}{2}\right] e^{\frac{\epsilon-\varepsilon+i(\varphi-\psi)}{2}} \\ \left[\cos\frac{\theta}{2}\sinh\frac{\tau}{2} + i\sin\frac{\theta}{2}\cosh\frac{\tau}{2}\right] e^{\frac{\varepsilon-\epsilon+i(\psi-\varphi)}{2}} & \left[\cos\frac{\theta}{2}\cosh\frac{\tau}{2} + i\sin\frac{\theta}{2}\sinh\frac{\tau}{2}\right] e^{\frac{-\epsilon-\varepsilon-i(\varphi+\psi)}{2}} \end{pmatrix}, \tag{45}$$

since $\cos\frac{1}{2}(\theta - i\tau) = \cos\frac{\theta}{2}\cosh\frac{\tau}{2} + i\sin\frac{\theta}{2}\sinh\frac{\tau}{2}$, and $\sin\frac{1}{2}(\theta - i\tau) = \sin\frac{\theta}{2}\cosh\frac{\tau}{2} - i\cos\frac{\theta}{2}\sinh\frac{\tau}{2}$. It is easy to verify that the matrix (45) coincides with a matrix of the fundamental representation of the group $SL(2,\mathbb{C})$ (in Euler parametrization):

$$\mathfrak{g}(\varphi,\,\epsilon,\,\theta,\,\tau,\,\psi,\,\varepsilon)=$$

$$\begin{pmatrix} e^{i\frac{\varphi}{2}} & 0\\ 0 & e^{-i\frac{\varphi}{2}}\end{pmatrix}\begin{pmatrix} e^{\frac{\epsilon}{2}} & 0\\ 0 & e^{-\frac{\epsilon}{2}}\end{pmatrix}\begin{pmatrix}\cos\frac{\theta}{2} & i\sin\frac{\theta}{2}\\ i\sin\frac{\theta}{2} & \cos\frac{\theta}{2}\end{pmatrix}\begin{pmatrix}\cosh\frac{\tau}{2} & \sinh\frac{\tau}{2}\\ \sinh\frac{\tau}{2} & \cosh\frac{\tau}{2}\end{pmatrix}\begin{pmatrix} e^{i\frac{\psi}{2}} & 0\\ 0 & e^{-i\frac{\psi}{2}}\end{pmatrix}\begin{pmatrix} e^{\frac{\varepsilon}{2}} & 0\\ 0 & e^{-\frac{\varepsilon}{2}}\end{pmatrix}. \tag{46}$$

Moreover, the complexification of $SU(2)$ gives us the most simple and direct way for calculation of matrix elements of the Lorentz group. It is known that these elements have a great importance in quantum field theory and widely used at the study of relativistic amplitudes.

The matrix element $t^l_{mn} = e^{-m(\epsilon+i\varphi)-n(\varepsilon+i\psi)}\langle T_l(\theta,\tau)\psi_\lambda,\psi_{\dot\lambda}\rangle$ of the finite–dimensional representation of $SL(2,\mathbb{C})$ at $l=\dot l$ in the polynomial basis

$$\psi_\lambda(\mathfrak{z},\bar{\mathfrak{z}})=\frac{\mathfrak{z}^{l-n}\bar{\mathfrak{z}}^{l-m}}{\sqrt{\Gamma(l-n+1)\Gamma(l+n+1)\Gamma(l-m+1)\Gamma(l+m+1)}},$$

has a form

$$t^l_{mn}(\mathfrak{g})=e^{-m(\epsilon+i\varphi)-n(\varepsilon+i\psi)}Z^l_{mn}=e^{-m(\epsilon+i\varphi)-n(\varepsilon+i\psi)}\times$$

$$\sum^{l}_{k=-l} i^{m-k}\sqrt{\Gamma(l-m+1)\Gamma(l+m+1)\Gamma(l-k+1)\Gamma(l+k+1)}\times$$

$$\cos^{2l}\frac{\theta}{2}\tan^{m-k}\frac{\theta}{2}\times$$

$$\sum^{\min(l-m,l+k)}_{j=\max(0,k-m)}\frac{i^{2j}\tan^{2j}\dfrac{\theta}{2}}{\Gamma(j+1)\Gamma(l-m-j+1)\Gamma(l+k-j+1)\Gamma(m-k+j+1)}\times$$

$$\sqrt{\Gamma(l-n+1)\Gamma(l+n+1)\Gamma(l-k+1)\Gamma(l+k+1)}\cosh^{2l}\frac{\tau}{2}\tanh^{n-k}\frac{\tau}{2}\times$$

$$\sum^{\min(l-n,l+k)}_{s=\max(0,k-n)}\frac{\tanh^{2s}\dfrac{\tau}{2}}{\Gamma(s+1)\Gamma(l-n-s+1)\Gamma(l+k-s+1)\Gamma(n-k+s+1)}. \tag{47}$$

We will call the functions Z^l_{mn} in (47), as *hyperspherical functions*. Using (41) we can write the hyperspherical functions Z^l_{mn} via the hypergeometric series:

$$Z^l_{mn} = \cos^{2l}\frac{\theta}{2}\cosh^{2l}\frac{\tau}{2}\sum_{k=-l}^{l} i^{m-k}\tan^{m-k}\frac{\theta}{2}\tanh^{n-k}\frac{\tau}{2}\times$$

$$ {}_2F_1\left(\begin{array}{c} m-l+1, 1-l-k \\ m-k+1 \end{array}\middle| i^2\tan^2\frac{\theta}{2}\right) {}_2F_1\left(\begin{array}{c} n-l+1, 1-l-k \\ n-k+1 \end{array}\middle| \tanh^2\frac{\tau}{2}\right). \quad (48)$$

Therefore, matrix elements can be expressed by means of the function (*a generalized hyperspherical function*)

$$\mathfrak{M}^l_{mn}(\mathfrak{g}) = e^{-m(\epsilon+i\varphi)}Z^l_{mn}e^{-n(\varepsilon+i\psi)}, \quad (49)$$

where

$$Z^l_{mn}(\cos\theta^c) = \sum_{k=-l}^{l} P^l_{mk}(\cos\theta)\mathfrak{P}^l_{kn}(\cosh\tau), \quad (50)$$

here $P^l_{mn}(\cos\theta)$ is a generalized spherical function on the group $SU(2)$ (see [25]), and $\mathfrak{P}^l_{mn}$ is an analog of the generalized spherical function for the group $QU(2)$ (so–called Jacobi function [76]). $QU(2)$ is a group of quasiunitary unimodular matrices of second order. As well as the group $SU(2)$, the group $QU(2)$ is one of the real forms of $SL(2,\mathbb{C})$ ($QU(2)$ is noncompact).

3.2 Appell functions

From (48) we see that the function Z^l_{mn} depends on two variables θ and τ. Therefore, using Bateman factorization we can express the hyperspherical functions Z^l_{mn} via Appell functions F_1–F_4 (hypergeometric series of two variables [3, 7]). Appell functions are defined by the following expressions:

$$\begin{aligned}
F_1(\alpha,\beta,\beta';\gamma;x,y) &= \sum_{m,n}^{\infty}\frac{(\alpha)_{m+n}(\beta)_m(\beta')_n}{(\gamma)_{m+n}m!n!}x^my^n,\\
F_2(\alpha,\beta,\beta';\gamma,\gamma';x,y) &= \sum_{m,n}^{\infty}\frac{(\alpha)_m(\beta)_m(\beta')_n}{(\gamma)_m(\gamma')_nm!n!}x^my^n,\\
F_3(\alpha,\alpha',\beta,\beta';\gamma;x,y) &= \sum_{m,n}^{\infty}\frac{(\alpha)_m(\alpha')_n(\beta)_m(\beta')_n}{(\gamma)_{m+n}m!n!}x^my^n,\\
F_4(\alpha,\beta;\gamma,\gamma';x,y) &= \sum_{m,n}^{\infty}\frac{(\alpha)_{m+n}(\beta)_{m+n}}{(\gamma)_m(\gamma')_nm!n!}x^my^n,
\end{aligned}$$

where $(a)_n = \Gamma(a+n)/\Gamma(a)$. For example, for the function F_4 there exists a following factorization (see [10, 12])

$$
{}_2F_1\left(\begin{matrix}\alpha,\beta\\ \gamma\end{matrix}\,\middle|\,x\right){}_2F_1\left(\begin{matrix}\alpha,\beta\\ \gamma'\end{matrix}\,\middle|\,y\right)=
$$
$$
=\sum_{r=0}^{\infty}\frac{(\alpha)_r(\beta)_r(\gamma+\gamma'-\alpha-\beta-1)_r}{r!(\gamma)_r(\gamma')_r}x^r y^r\times
$$
$$
\times F_4(\alpha+r,\beta+r;\gamma+r,\gamma'+r;x-xy,y-xy).
$$

Then, using this formula we can express the hyperspherical functions Z^l_{mn}, defining the matrix elements of the main diagonal ($m=n$), via the Appell function F_4:

$$
Z^l_{mm}=\cos^{2l}\frac{\theta}{2}\cosh^{2l}\frac{\tau}{2}\sum_{k=-l}^{l}\sum_{r\geq 0}i^{m-k}(-1)^r\times
$$
$$
\frac{(m-l+1)_r(1-l-k)_r(m-k+2l-1)_r}{\Gamma(r+1)(m-k+1)^2_r}\tan^{m-k}\frac{\theta}{2}\tanh^{m-k}\frac{\tau}{2}\tan^{2r}\frac{\theta}{2}\tanh^{2r}\frac{\tau}{2}\times
$$
$$
F_4\left(m-l+r+1,1-l-k+r;m-k+r+1,m-k+r+1;-\tan^2\frac{\theta}{2}+\right.
$$
$$
\left.+\tan^2\frac{\theta}{2}\tanh^2\frac{\tau}{2},\tanh^2\frac{\tau}{2}+\tan^2\frac{\theta}{2}\tanh^2\frac{\tau}{2}\right). \quad (51)
$$

Since l and m are finite numbers, then the series standing in the right part of (51) is interrupted.

In turn, for the function F_2 there exists a following decomposition [10, 7]:

$$
{}_2F_1\left(\begin{matrix}\alpha,\beta\\ \gamma\end{matrix}\,\middle|\,x\right){}_2F_1\left(\begin{matrix}\alpha,\beta'\\ \gamma'\end{matrix}\,\middle|\,y\right)=
$$
$$
=\sum_{r=0}^{\infty}(-1)^r\frac{(\alpha)_r(\beta)_r(\beta')_r}{r!(\gamma)_r(\gamma')_r}x^r y^r\times
$$
$$
\times F_2(\alpha+r,\beta+r,\beta'+r;\gamma+r,\gamma'+r;x,y).
$$

Thus, the hyperspherical functions of the main diagonal are expressed via the Appell function F_2 as follows:

$$Z^l_{mm}=\cos^{2l}\frac{\theta}{2}\cosh^{2l}\frac{\tau}{2}\sum_{k=-l}^{l}\sum_{r\geq 0}i^{m-k}\times$$
$$\frac{(m-l+1)_r(1-l-k)^2_r}{\Gamma(r+1)(m-k+1)^2_r}\tan^{m-k}\frac{\theta}{2}\tanh^{m-k}\frac{\tau}{2}\tan^{2r}\frac{\theta}{2}\tanh^{2r}\frac{\tau}{2}\times$$
$$F_2\left(m-l+r+1, 1-l-k+r, 1-l-k+r;\right.$$
$$\left.m-k+r+1, m-k+r+1; -\tan^2\frac{\theta}{2}, \tanh^2\frac{\tau}{2}\right). \quad (52)$$

In [10], Burchnall and Chaundy obtained 15 pairs of decompositions containing the Appell functions and usual hypergeometric functions. A detailed consideration of the relationship between the hyperspherical functions Z^l_{mn} and the Appell functions F_1-F_4 (and also Horn functions [32]) comes beyond the framework of the present work and will be considered in a future paper.

3.3 Integral representations of $Z^l_{mn}(\theta,\tau)$

Let us choose in the space $\mathfrak{D}_\chi$ of the representation $T_\chi(\mathfrak{g})$ of $SU(2)\otimes SU(2)$ the basis consisting of the functions $\left\{e^{-in\vartheta}\right\}$, then

$$T_\chi(\mathfrak{g})f(e^{i\vartheta})=(\alpha e^{i\vartheta}+\gamma)^{l+o}(\beta e^{i\vartheta}+\delta)^{l-o}f\left(\frac{\alpha e^{i\vartheta}+\gamma}{\beta e^{i\vartheta}+\delta}\right). \quad (53)$$

Therefore,

$$T_\chi(\mathfrak{g})e^{-in\vartheta}=(\alpha e^{i\vartheta}+\gamma)^{l-n-o}(\beta e^{i\vartheta}+\delta)^{l+n+o}e^{-in\vartheta}.$$

The matrix elements $t^\chi_{mn}(\mathfrak{g})$ of the representation $T_\chi(\mathfrak{g})$ in the basis $\left\{e^{-in\vartheta}\right\}$ are Fourier coefficients in the decomposition of the functions $T_\chi(\mathfrak{g})e^{-in\vartheta}$ on the system $\left\{e^{-im\vartheta}\right\}$:

$$T_\chi(\mathfrak{g})e^{-in\vartheta}=\sum_{m=-\infty}^{\infty}t^\chi_{mn}(\mathfrak{g})e^{-im\vartheta}.$$

From the formula for the Fourier coefficients we obtain

$$t^\chi_{mn}(\mathfrak{g})=\frac{1}{2\pi}\int\limits_0^{2\pi}(\alpha e^{i\vartheta}+\gamma)^{l-n-o}(\beta e^{i\vartheta}+\delta)^{l+n+o}e^{i(m-n)\vartheta}d\vartheta. \quad (54)$$

In such a way, we have an integral representation for the matrix elements. Making the substitution $e^{i\vartheta}=z$ we come to the following representation:

$$t^\chi_{mn}(\mathfrak{g})=\frac{1}{2\pi i}\oint\limits_\Gamma(\alpha z+\gamma)^{l-n-o}(\beta z+\delta)^{l+n+o}z^{m-l+o-1}dz, \quad (55)$$

where $\Gamma:\ |z|=1$ is an unit circle. In the basis $\{e^{-im\vartheta}\}$ the matrices of the operators $T_\chi(h)$ have a very simple form, where

$$h=\begin{pmatrix} e^{\frac{it}{2}} & 0\\ 0 & e^{-\frac{it}{2}}\end{pmatrix}$$

is the diagonal matrix. Then from the formula (53) we see that the operator $T_\chi(h)$ has a form

$$T_\chi(h)f(e^{i\vartheta})=e^{-i\vartheta}f(e^{i(\vartheta+t)})$$

and, therefore,

$$T_\chi(h)e^{-im\vartheta}=e^{-i(m+o)t}e^{-im\vartheta}.$$

Thus, the matrix of $T_\chi(h)$ in the basis $\{e^{-im\vartheta}\}$ is an infinite diagonal matrix, on the main diagonal of which we have the numbers $e^{-i(m+o)t}$.

As it has been shown previously (see (46)), the element $\mathfrak{g}$ of the fundamental representation of $SU(2)\otimes SU(2)$ has a form

$$\mathfrak{g}(\varphi^c,\theta^c,\psi^c)=\begin{pmatrix} e^{\frac{i\varphi^c}{2}} & 0\\ 0 & e^{-\frac{i\varphi^c}{2}}\end{pmatrix}\begin{pmatrix}\cos\frac{\theta^c}{2} & i\sin\frac{\theta^c}{2}\\ i\sin\frac{\theta^c}{2} & \cos\frac{\theta^c}{2}\end{pmatrix}\begin{pmatrix} e^{\frac{i\psi^c}{2}} & 0\\ 0 & e^{-\frac{i\psi^c}{2}}\end{pmatrix},$$

where φ^c, θ^c, ψ^c are the complex Euler angles. Since the matrix $T_\chi(\mathfrak{g})$ for the diagonal matrices has been found, then it is remain to find a matrix of the operator $T_\chi(\mathfrak{g}(\theta,\tau))$ corresponding to the element

$$\mathfrak{g}(\theta,\tau)=\begin{pmatrix}\cos\frac{\theta^c}{2} & i\sin\frac{\theta^c}{2}\\ i\sin\frac{\theta^c}{2} & \cos\frac{\theta^c}{2}\end{pmatrix}=\begin{pmatrix}\cos\frac{\theta}{2}\cosh\frac{\tau}{2}+i\sin\frac{\theta}{2}\sinh\frac{\tau}{2} & \cos\frac{\theta}{2}\sinh\frac{\tau}{2}+i\sin\frac{\theta}{2}\cosh\frac{\tau}{2}\\ \cos\frac{\theta}{2}\sinh\frac{\tau}{2}+i\sin\frac{\theta}{2}\cosh\frac{\tau}{2} & \cos\frac{\theta}{2}\cosh\frac{\tau}{2}+i\sin\frac{\theta}{2}\sinh\frac{\tau}{2}\end{pmatrix}$$

Then from the integral representation (54), we obtain

$$t^\chi_{mn}(\mathfrak{g}(\theta,\tau))=\frac{1}{2\pi}\int\limits_0^{2\pi}\left(\cos\frac{\theta^c}{2}e^{i\vartheta}+i\sin\frac{\theta^c}{2}\right)^{l-n-o}\left(i\sin\frac{\theta^c}{2}e^{i\vartheta}+\cos\frac{\theta^c}{2}\right)^{l+n+o}e^{i(m-n)\vartheta}d\vartheta.$$

Therefore, an integral representation for the hyperspherical function $Z^l_{mn}(\theta,\tau)$ has a form

$$Z^l_{mn}(\theta,\tau)=\frac{1}{2\pi}\int\limits_0^{2\pi}\left(\cos\frac{\theta^c}{2}e^{i\vartheta}+i\sin\frac{\theta^c}{2}\right)^{l-n}\left(i\sin\frac{\theta^c}{2}e^{i\vartheta}+\cos\frac{\theta^c}{2}\right)^{l+n}e^{i(m-n)\vartheta}d\vartheta=$$

$$\frac{1}{2\pi}\int\limits_0^{2\pi}\left(\left[\cos\frac{\theta}{2}\cosh\frac{\tau}{2}+i\sin\frac{\theta}{2}\sinh\frac{\tau}{2}\right]e^{i\vartheta}+\cos\frac{\theta}{2}\sinh\frac{\tau}{2}+i\sin\frac{\theta}{2}\cosh\frac{\tau}{2}\right)^{l-n}\times$$

$$\left(\left[\cos\frac{\theta}{2}\sinh\frac{\tau}{2}+i\sin\frac{\theta}{2}\cosh\frac{\tau}{2}\right]e^{i\vartheta}+\cos\frac{\theta}{2}\cosh\frac{\tau}{2}+i\sin\frac{\theta}{2}\sinh\frac{\tau}{2}\right)^{l+n}e^{i(m-n)\vartheta}d\vartheta. \tag{56}$$

Or, using the integral representation (55), we obtain

$$Z^l_{mn}(\theta,\tau)=\frac{1}{2\pi i}\oint\limits_{\Gamma}\left(\cos\frac{\theta^c}{2}z+i\sin\frac{\theta^c}{2}\right)^{l-n}\left(i\sin\frac{\theta^c}{2}z+\cos\frac{\theta^c}{2}\right)^{l+n}z^{m-l-1}dz=$$

$$\frac{1}{2\pi i}\oint\limits_{\Gamma}\left(\left[\cos\frac{\theta}{2}\cosh\frac{\tau}{2}+i\sin\frac{\theta}{2}\sinh\frac{\tau}{2}\right]z+\cos\frac{\theta}{2}\sinh\frac{\tau}{2}+i\sin\frac{\theta}{2}\cosh\frac{\tau}{2}\right)^{l-n}\times$$

$$\left(\left[\cos\frac{\theta}{2}\sinh\frac{\tau}{2}+i\sin\frac{\theta}{2}\cosh\frac{\tau}{2}\right]z+\cos\frac{\theta}{2}\cosh\frac{\tau}{2}+i\sin\frac{\theta}{2}\sinh\frac{\tau}{2}\right)^{l+n}z^{m-l-1}dz. \tag{57}$$

3.4 Zonal hyperspherical functions

Let $o=0$, then in the space $\mathfrak{D}_l$ there is a function which invariant with respect to all the operators $T_l(h)$, where h is the diagonal matrix from the group $SL(2,\mathbb{C})\sim SU(2)\otimes SU(2)$:

$$h=\begin{pmatrix} e^{\frac{it}{2}} & 0\\ 0 & e^{-\frac{it}{2}}\end{pmatrix}.$$

For example, the basis element 1 is such a function. The matrix element $t^l_{00}(\mathfrak{g})$, corresponding to such a basis element, we will call *a zonal hyperspherical function* of the representation $T_l(\mathfrak{g})$ with respect to the subgroup Ω of the diagonal matrices.

So, at $o=0$ the representation $T_l(\mathfrak{g})$ has a zonal hyperspherical function satisfying the following equation

$$t^l_{00}(h_1\mathfrak{g}h_2)=t^l_{00}(\mathfrak{g}),$$

where $h_1,h_2\in\Omega$. Hence it immediately follows that $t^l_{00}(\mathfrak{g})$ depends only on the Euler angles θ and τ. From (47) we obtain

$$t^l_{00}(\mathfrak{g})=Z^l_{00}(\theta,\tau).$$

We will denote the function $Z^l_{00}(\theta,\tau)$ via $Z_l(\theta,\tau)$. Thus,

$$Z_l(\theta,\tau)=t^l_{00}(0,0,\theta,\tau,0,0)=Z^l_{00}(\theta,\tau).$$

From (47) it follows an explicit expression for the zonal hypersperical function:

$$Z_l(\theta,\tau)=\sum_{k=-l}^{l} i^{-k}\Gamma(l+1)\sqrt{\Gamma(l-k+1)\Gamma(l+k+1)}\times$$
$$\cos^{2l}\frac{\theta}{2}\tan^{-k}\frac{\theta}{2}\times$$
$$\sum_{j=\max(0,k)}^{\min(l,l+k)}\frac{i^{2j}\tan^{2j}\frac{\theta}{2}}{\Gamma(j+1)\Gamma(l-j+1)\Gamma(l+k-j+1)\Gamma(j-k+1)}\times$$
$$\Gamma(l+1)\sqrt{\Gamma(l-k+1)\Gamma(l+k+1)}\cosh^{2l}\frac{\tau}{2}\tanh^{-k}\frac{\tau}{2}\times$$
$$\sum_{s=\max(0,k)}^{\min(l,l+k)}\frac{\tanh^{2s}\frac{\tau}{2}}{\Gamma(s+1)\Gamma(l-s+1)\Gamma(l+k-s+1)\Gamma(s-k+1)}.$$

Further, from (48), (51) and (52) we obtain corresponding expressions for $Z_l(\theta,\tau)$ via the hypergeometric function ${}_2F_1$ and the Appell functions F_4 and F_2:

$$Z^l_{mn}=\cos^{2l}\frac{\theta}{2}\cosh^{2l}\frac{\tau}{2}\sum_{k=-l}^{l} i^{-k}\tan^{-k}\frac{\theta}{2}\tanh^{-k}\frac{\tau}{2}\times$$
$${}_2F_1\left(\begin{matrix}-l+1,1-l-k\\ -k+1\end{matrix}\,\middle|\, i^2\tan^2\frac{\theta}{2}\right){}_2F_1\left(\begin{matrix}-l+1,1-l-k\\ -k+1\end{matrix}\,\middle|\,\tanh^2\frac{\tau}{2}\right),$$

$$Z^l_{mm}=\cos^{2l}\frac{\theta}{2}\cosh^{2l}\frac{\tau}{2}\sum_{k=-l}^{l}\sum_{r\geq 0} i^{-k}(-1)^r\times$$
$$\frac{(-l+1)_r(1-l-k)_r(2l-k-1)_r}{\Gamma(r+1)(-k+1)^2_r}\tan^{-k}\frac{\theta}{2}\tanh^{-k}\frac{\tau}{2}\tan^{2r}\frac{\theta}{2}\tanh^{2r}\frac{\tau}{2}\times$$
$$F_4\left(r-l+1,1-l-k+r;r-k+1,r-k+1;-\tan^2\frac{\theta}{2}+\right.$$
$$\left.+\tan^2\frac{\theta}{2}\tanh^2\frac{\tau}{2},\tanh^2\frac{\tau}{2}+\tan^2\frac{\theta}{2}\tanh^2\frac{\tau}{2}\right),$$

$$Z^l_{mm}=\cos^{2l}\frac{\theta}{2}\cosh^{2l}\frac{\tau}{2}\sum^{l}_{k=-l}\sum_{r\geq 0} i^{-k}\times$$
$$\frac{(-l+1)_r(1-l-k)^2_r}{\Gamma(r+1)(-k+1)^2_r}\tan^{-k}\frac{\theta}{2}\tanh^{-k}\frac{\tau}{2}\tan^{2r}\frac{\theta}{2}\tanh^{2r}\frac{\tau}{2}\times$$
$$F_2\left(r-l+1,1-l-k+r,1-l-k+r;r-k+1,r-k+1;-\tan^2\frac{\theta}{2},\tanh^2\frac{\tau}{2}\right).$$

Integral representations (56) and (57) have in this case the following form

$$Z_l(\theta,\tau)=\frac{1}{2\pi}\int\limits^{2\pi}_{0}\left(\cos\frac{\theta^c}{2}e^{i\vartheta}+i\sin\frac{\theta^c}{2}\right)^l\left(i\sin\frac{\theta^c}{2}e^{i\vartheta}+\cos\frac{\theta^c}{2}\right)^l d\vartheta=$$
$$\frac{1}{2\pi}\int\limits^{2\pi}_{0}(\cos\theta^c+i\sin\theta^c\cos\vartheta)d\vartheta=$$
$$\frac{1}{2\pi}\int\limits^{2\pi}_{0}(\cos\theta\cosh\tau+i\sin\theta\sinh\tau+i[\sin\theta\cosh\tau-i\cos\theta\sinh\tau]\cos\vartheta)d\vartheta,$$

$$Z_l(\theta,\tau)=\frac{1}{2\pi i}\oint\limits_{\Gamma}\left(\cos\frac{\theta^c}{2}z+i\sin\frac{\theta^c}{2}\right)^l\left(i\sin\frac{\theta^c}{2}z+\cos\frac{\theta^c}{2}\right)^l z^{-l-1}dz=$$
$$\frac{i^l\sin^l\theta^c}{2^{l+1}\pi i}\oint\limits_{\Gamma}(z^2-2iz\cot\theta^c+1)^l z^{-l-1}dz=$$
$$\frac{i^l(\sin\theta\cosh\tau-i\cos\theta\sinh\tau)^l}{2^{l+1}\pi i}\oint\limits_{\Gamma}(z^2-2iz\frac{\cot\theta\coth\tau+1}{\coth\tau-\cot\theta}+1)z^{-l-1}dz.$$

3.5 Associated hyperspherical functions

Let us consider now associated hyperspherical functions of the representation $T_\chi(\mathfrak{g})$, $\chi=(l,0)$, that is, the matrix elements $t^l_{m0}(\mathfrak{g})$ standing in one column with the function $t^l_{00}(\mathfrak{g})$. In this case from (47) we have

$$t^l_{m0}(\mathfrak{g})=e^{-m(\epsilon+i\varphi)}Z^l_{m0}(\theta,\tau).$$

Hence it follows that matrix elements $t^l_{m0}(\mathfrak{g})$ do not depend on the Euler angles ε and ψ, that is, $t^l_{m0}(\mathfrak{g})$ are constant on the left adjacency classes formed by the subgroup Ω^c_ψ of the diagonal matrices $\begin{pmatrix} e^{\frac{i\psi^c}{2}} & 0 \\ 0 & e^{-\frac{i\psi^c}{2}}\end{pmatrix}$. Therefore,

$$t^l_{m0}(\mathfrak{g}h)=t^l_{m0}(\mathfrak{g}),\quad h\in\Omega^c_\psi.$$

We will denote the functions $Z^{m0}(\theta,\tau)$ via $Z^m_l(\theta,\tau)$. From (47) we obtain an explicit expression for the *associated hyperspherical function* $Z^m_l(\theta,\tau)$:

$$Z^m_l(\theta,\tau)=\sum_{k=-l}^{l} i^{m-k}\sqrt{\Gamma(l-m+1)\Gamma(l+m+1)\Gamma(l-k+1)\Gamma(l+k+1)}\times$$

$$\cos^{2l}\frac{\theta}{2}\tan^{m-k}\frac{\theta}{2}\times$$

$$\sum_{j=\max(0,k-m)}^{\min(l-m,l+k)}\frac{i^{2j}\tan^{2j}\dfrac{\theta}{2}}{\Gamma(j+1)\Gamma(l-m-j+1)\Gamma(l+k-j+1)\Gamma(m-k+j+1)}\times$$

$$\Gamma(l+1)\sqrt{\Gamma(l-k+1)\Gamma(l+k+1)}\cosh^{2l}\frac{\tau}{2}\tanh^{-k}\frac{\tau}{2}\times$$

$$\sum_{s=\max(0,k)}^{\min(l,l+k)}\frac{\tanh^{2s}\dfrac{\tau}{2}}{\Gamma(s+1)\Gamma(l-s+1)\Gamma(l+k-s+1)\Gamma(s-k+1)}. \tag{58}$$

Further, from (48) it follows that

$$Z^l_{mn}=\cos^{2l}\frac{\theta}{2}\cosh^{2l}\frac{\tau}{2}\sum_{k=-l}^{l} i^{m-k}\tan^{m-k}\frac{\theta}{2}\tanh^{-k}\frac{\tau}{2}\times$$

$${}_2F_1\left(\begin{matrix}m-l+1,1-l-k\\ m-k+1\end{matrix}\middle| i^2\tan^2\frac{\theta}{2}\right){}_2F_1\left(\begin{matrix}-l+1,1-l-k\\ -k+1\end{matrix}\middle|\tanh^2\frac{\tau}{2}\right). \tag{59}$$

Corresponding integral representations for the functions $Z^m_l(\theta,\tau)$ have the form:

$$Z^m_l(\theta,\tau)=\frac{1}{2\pi}\int_0^{2\pi}(\cos\theta^c+i\sin\theta^c\cos\vartheta)e^{im\vartheta}d\vartheta=$$

$$\frac{1}{2\pi}\int_0^{2\pi}(\cos\theta\cosh\tau+i\sin\theta\sinh\tau+i[\sin\theta\cosh\tau-i\cos\theta\sinh\tau]\cos\vartheta)e^{im\vartheta}d\vartheta,$$

$$Z^m_l(\theta,\tau)=\frac{i^l\sin^l\theta^c}{2^{l+1}\pi i}\oint_\Gamma(z^2-2iz\cot\theta^c+1)^l z^{m-l-1}dz=$$

$$\frac{i^l(\sin\theta\cosh\tau-i\cos\theta\sinh\tau)^l}{2^{l+1}\pi i}\oint_\Gamma(z^2-2iz\frac{\cot\theta\coth\tau+1}{\coth\tau-\cot\theta}+1)z^{m-l-1}dz.$$

Associated hyperspherical functions admit a very elegant geometric interpretation, namely, they are the functions on the surface of a two-dimensional complex sphere. Indeed, let us construct in $\mathbb{C}^3$ a two–dimensional complex sphere from the quantities $z_k = x_k + iy_k$, $\overset{*}{z}_k = x_k - iy_k$ as follows (see Figure 1)

$$\mathbf{z}^2 = z_1^2 + z_2^2 + z_3^2 = \mathbf{x}^2 - \mathbf{y}^2 + 2i\mathbf{x}\mathbf{y} = r^2 \tag{60}$$

and its complex conjugate (dual) sphere

$$\overset{*}{\mathbf{z}}{}^2 = \overset{*}{z}_1{}^2 + \overset{*}{z}_2{}^2 + \overset{*}{z}_3{}^2 = \mathbf{x}^2 - \mathbf{y}^2 - 2i\mathbf{x}\mathbf{y} = \overset{*}{r}{}^2. \tag{61}$$

For more details about the two-dimensional complex sphere see [33, 34, 60]. It is well-known that both quantities $\mathbf{x}^2 - \mathbf{y}^2$, $\mathbf{x}\mathbf{y}$ are invariant with respect to the Lorentz transformations, since a surface of the complex sphere is invariant (Casimir operators of the Lorentz group are constructed from such quantities, see also (101)). It is easy to see that three–dimensional complex space $\mathbb{C}^3$ is isometric to a real space $\mathbb{R}^{3,3}$ with a basis $\{i\mathbf{e}_1, i\mathbf{e}_2, i\mathbf{e}_3, \mathbf{e}_4, \mathbf{e}_5, \mathbf{e}_6\}$. At this point a metric tensor of $\mathbb{R}^{3,3}$ has the form

$$g_{ab} = \begin{pmatrix} -1 & 0 & 0 & 0 & 0 & 0 \\ 0 & -1 & 0 & 0 & 0 & 0 \\ 0 & 0 & -1 & 0 & 0 & 0 \\ 0 & 0 & 0 & 1 & 0 & 0 \\ 0 & 0 & 0 & 0 & 1 & 0 \\ 0 & 0 & 0 & 0 & 0 & 1 \end{pmatrix}.$$

Hence it immediately follows that $\mathbb{C}^3$ is isometric to the bivector space $\mathbb{R}^6$.

3.6 Symmetry relations for the functions $Z^l_{mn}(\theta, \tau)$

The hyperspherical functions $Z^l_{mn}(\theta, \tau)$ satisfy some symmetry relations with respect to the indices l, m, n. Let us show that these functions satisfy the relation

$$Z^l_{mn}(\theta, \tau) = Z^l_{-m,-n}(\theta, \tau). \tag{62}$$

Consider the operator S transforming $f(e^{i\vartheta})$ into $e^{2io\vartheta} f(e^{-i\vartheta})$. It is easy to verify that S commutes with an operator $T_\chi(\mathfrak{g}(\theta, \tau))$, where

$$\mathfrak{g}(\theta, \tau) = \begin{pmatrix} \cos\frac{\theta}{2}\cosh\frac{\tau}{2} + i\sin\frac{\theta}{2}\sinh\frac{\tau}{2} & \cos\frac{\theta}{2}\sinh\frac{\tau}{2} + i\sin\frac{\theta}{2}\cosh\frac{\tau}{2} \\ \cos\frac{\theta}{2}\sinh\frac{\tau}{2} + i\sin\frac{\theta}{2}\cosh\frac{\tau}{2} & \cos\frac{\theta}{2}\cosh\frac{\tau}{2} + i\sin\frac{\theta}{2}\sinh\frac{\tau}{2} \end{pmatrix},$$

that is,

$$ST_\chi(\mathfrak{g}(\theta, \tau)) = T_\chi(\mathfrak{g}(\theta, \tau))S. \tag{63}$$

Matrix elements s_{mn} of the operator S in the basis $\{e^{-im\vartheta}\}$ equal to zero if $m+n \neq -2o$, and equal to the unit if $m+n = -2o$. Multiplying the matrices in (63) and comparing the corresponding elements, we obtain

$$t^\chi_{-2o-m,n}(\mathfrak{g}(\theta, \tau)) = t^\chi_{m,-2o-n}(\mathfrak{g}(\theta, \tau)).$$

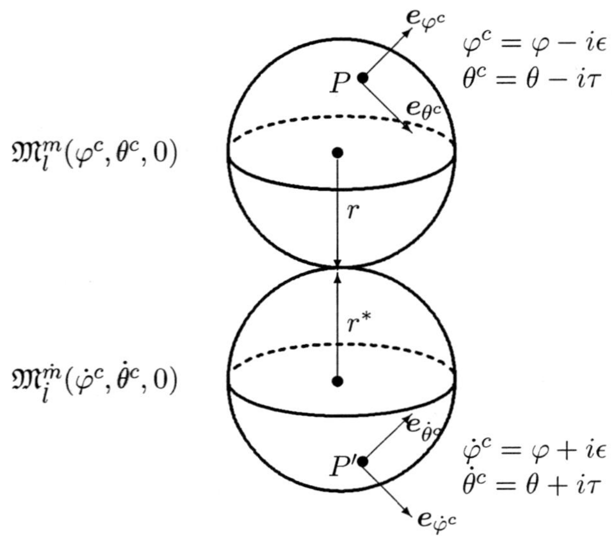

Figure 1 Two–dimensional complex sphere $z_1^2 + z_2^2 + z_3^2 = r^2$ in three–dimensional complex space $\mathbb{C}^3$. The space $\mathbb{C}^3$ is isometric to the bivector space $\mathbb{R}^6$. The dual (complex conjugate) sphere $\overset{*}{z}_1{}^2 + \overset{*}{z}_2{}^2 + \overset{*}{z}_3{}^2 = \overset{*}{r}{}^2$ is a mirror image of the complex sphere with respect to the hyperplane. The associated hyperspherical functions $\mathfrak{M}_l^m(\varphi^c, \theta^c, 0)$ ($\mathfrak{M}_l^{\dot{m}}(\dot{\varphi}^c, \dot{\theta}^c, 0)$) are defined on the surface of the complex (dual) sphere.

Since $t^{\chi}_{mn}(\mathfrak{g}(\theta,\tau)) = Z^l_{m',n'}(\theta,\tau)$, where $m' = m + o$, $n' = n + o$, then

$$Z^l_{-m-o,n+o}(\theta,\tau) = Z^l_{m+o,-n-o}(\theta,\tau).$$

Hence it follows that

$$Z^l_{mn}(\theta,\tau) = Z^l_{-m,-n}(\theta,\tau)$$

for all the complex values of l and all integer or half-integer values of m and n. Further, replacing in the expression (47) m by $-n$, and n by $-m$, we obtain

$$Z^l_{-n,-m}(\theta,\tau) = Z^l_{m,n}(\theta,\tau)$$

or, in virtue of the relation (62),

$$Z^l_{nm}(\theta,\tau) = Z^l_{mn}(\theta,\tau). \tag{64}$$

Therefore, the hyperspherical functions $Z^l_{mn}(\theta,\tau)$ are symmetric.

3.7 Matrices $T_l(\mathfrak{g})$

Using the formula (47), let us find explicit expressions for the matrices $T_l(\mathfrak{g})$ of the finite–dimensional representations of $\mathfrak{G}_+$ at $l = 0, \frac{1}{2}, 1$:

$$T_0(\theta,\tau) = 1,$$

$$T_{\frac{1}{2}}(\theta,\tau) = \begin{pmatrix} Z^{\frac{1}{2}}_{-\frac{1}{2}-\frac{1}{2}} & Z^{\frac{1}{2}}_{\frac{1}{2}-\frac{1}{2}} \\ Z^{\frac{1}{2}}_{-\frac{1}{2}\frac{1}{2}} & Z^{\frac{1}{2}}_{\frac{1}{2}\frac{1}{2}} \end{pmatrix} =$$

$$\begin{pmatrix} \cos\frac{\theta}{2}\cosh\frac{\tau}{2} + i\sin\frac{\theta}{2}\sinh\frac{\tau}{2} & \cos\frac{\theta}{2}\sinh\frac{\tau}{2} + i\sin\frac{\theta}{2}\cosh\frac{\tau}{2} \\ \cos\frac{\theta}{2}\sinh\frac{\tau}{2} + i\sin\frac{\theta}{2}\cosh\frac{\tau}{2} & \cos\frac{\theta}{2}\cosh\frac{\tau}{2} + i\sin\frac{\theta}{2}\sinh\frac{\tau}{2} \end{pmatrix}, \tag{65}$$

$$T_1(\theta,\tau) = \begin{pmatrix} Z^1_{-1-1} & Z^1_{-10} & Z^1_{-11} \\ Z^1_{0-1} & Z^1_{00} & Z^1_{01} \\ Z^1_{1-1} & Z^1_{10} & Z^1_{11} \end{pmatrix} =$$

$$\begin{pmatrix} \cos^2\frac{\theta}{2}\cosh^2\frac{\tau}{2}+\frac{i\sin\theta\sinh\tau}{2}-\sin^2\frac{\theta}{2}\sinh^2\frac{\tau}{2} & \frac{1}{\sqrt{2}}(\cos\theta\sinh\tau+i\sin\theta\cosh\tau) & \cos^2\frac{\theta}{2}\sinh^2\frac{\tau}{2}+\frac{i\sin\theta\sinh\tau}{2}-\sin^2\frac{\theta}{2}\cosh^2\frac{\tau}{2} \\ \frac{1}{\sqrt{2}}(\cos\theta\sinh\tau+i\sin\theta\cosh\tau) & \cos\theta\cosh\tau+i\sin\theta\sinh\tau & \frac{1}{\sqrt{2}}(\cos\theta\sinh\tau+i\sin\theta\cosh\tau) \\ \cos^2\frac{\theta}{2}\sinh^2\frac{\tau}{2}+\frac{i\sin\theta\sinh\tau}{2}-\sin^2\frac{\theta}{2}\cosh^2\frac{\tau}{2} & \frac{1}{\sqrt{2}}(\cos\theta\sinh\tau+i\sin\theta\cosh\tau) & \cos^2\frac{\theta}{2}\cosh^2\frac{\tau}{2}+\frac{i\sin\theta\sinh\tau}{2}-\sin^2\frac{\theta}{2}\sinh^2\frac{\tau}{2} \end{pmatrix}. \quad (66)$$

3.8 Addition Theorem

Let $\mathfrak{g} = of\mathfrak{g}_1 of\mathfrak{g}_2$ be the product of two matrices $\mathfrak{g}_1$, $\mathfrak{g}_2 \in SL(2,\mathbb{C})$. Let us denote the Euler angles of the matrix $\mathfrak{g}$ via $\varphi^c, \theta^c, \psi^c$, the matrix $\mathfrak{g}_1$ via $\varphi^c_1, \theta^c_1, \psi^c_1$ and the matrix $\mathfrak{g}_2$ via $\varphi^c_2, \theta^c_2, \psi^c_2$. Expressing now the Euler angles of the matrix $\mathfrak{g}$ via the Euler angles of the factors $\mathfrak{g}_1$, $\mathfrak{g}_2$, we consider at first the particular case $\varphi^c_1 = \psi^c_1 = \psi^c_2 = 0$:

$$\mathfrak{g} = \begin{pmatrix} \cos\frac{\theta^c_1}{2} & i\sin\frac{\theta^c_1}{2} \\ i\sin\frac{\theta^c_1}{2} & \cos\frac{\theta^c_1}{2} \end{pmatrix}\begin{pmatrix} \cos\frac{\theta^c_2}{2}e^{\frac{i\varphi^c_2}{2}} & i\sin\frac{\theta^c_2}{2}e^{\frac{i\varphi^c_2}{2}} \\ i\sin\frac{\theta^c_2}{2}e^{-\frac{i\varphi^c_2}{2}} & \cos\frac{\theta^c_2}{2}e^{-\frac{i\varphi^c_2}{2}} \end{pmatrix}.$$

Multiplying the matrices in the right part of this equality and using a complex analog of the formulae (37)–(39), we obtain

$$\cos\theta^c = \cos\theta^c_1\cos\theta^c_2 - \sin\theta^c_1\sin\theta^c_2\cos\varphi^c_2, \quad (67)$$

$$e^{i\varphi^c} = \frac{\sin\theta^c_1\cos\theta^c_2 + \cos\theta^c_1\sin\theta^c_2\cos\varphi^c_2 + i\sin\theta^c_2\sin\varphi^c_2}{\sin\theta^c}, \quad (68)$$

$$e^{\frac{i(\varphi^c+\psi^c)}{2}} = \frac{\cos\frac{\theta^c_1}{2}\cos\frac{\theta^c_2}{2}e^{\frac{i\varphi^c_2}{2}} - \sin\frac{\theta^c_1}{2}\sin\frac{\theta^c_2}{2}e^{-\frac{i\varphi^c_2}{2}}}{\cos\frac{\theta^c}{2}}. \quad (69)$$

It is not difficult to obtain a general case. Indeed, in virtue of (46) the matrix $\mathfrak{g} \in SL(2,\mathbb{C})$ admits a representation

$$\mathfrak{g}(\varphi^c,\theta^c,\psi^c) = \begin{pmatrix} e^{\frac{i\varphi^c}{2}} & 0 \\ 0 & e^{-\frac{i\varphi^c}{2}} \end{pmatrix}\begin{pmatrix} \cos\frac{\theta^c}{2} & i\sin\frac{\theta^c}{2} \\ i\sin\frac{\theta^c}{2} & \cos\frac{\theta^c}{2} \end{pmatrix}\begin{pmatrix} e^{\frac{i\psi^c}{2}} & 0 \\ 0 & e^{-\frac{i\psi^c}{2}} \end{pmatrix} \equiv$$
$$\equiv \mathfrak{g}(\varphi^c,0,0)\mathfrak{g}(0,\theta^c,0)\mathfrak{g}(0,0,\psi^c).$$

Therefore,

$$\mathfrak{g}(\varphi^c_1,\theta^c_1,\psi^c_1)\mathfrak{g}(\varphi^c_2,\theta^c_2,\psi^c_2) =$$
$$\mathfrak{g}(\varphi^c_1,0,0)\mathfrak{g}(0,\theta^c_1,0)\mathfrak{g}(0,0,\psi^c_1)\mathfrak{g}(\varphi^c_2,0,0)\mathfrak{g}(0,\theta^c_2,0)\mathfrak{g}(0,0,\psi^c_2). \quad (70)$$

It is obvious that

$$\mathfrak{g}(0,0,\psi_1^c)\mathfrak{g}(\varphi_2^c,0,0)=\mathfrak{g}(\varphi_2^c+\psi_1^c,0,0).$$

Besides, if we multiply the matrix $\mathfrak{g}(\varphi^c,\theta^c,\psi^c)$ at the left by the matrix $\mathfrak{g}(\varphi_1^c,0,0)$, the Euler angle φ^c increases by φ_1^c, and other Euler angles remain unaltered. Analogously, if we multiply at the right the matrix $\mathfrak{g}(\varphi^c,\theta^c,\psi^c)$ by $\mathfrak{g}(0,0,\psi_2^c)$, the angle ψ^c increases by ψ_2^c. Hence it follows that in general case the angle φ_2^c should be replaced by $\varphi_2^c+\psi_1^c$, and the angles φ^c and ψ^c should be replaced by $\varphi^c-\varphi_1^c$ and $\psi^c-\psi_2^c$, that is,

$$\begin{aligned}
\cos\theta^c &= \cos\theta_1^c\cos\theta_2^c-\sin\theta_1^c\sin\theta_2^c\cos(\varphi_2^c+\psi_1^c),\\
e^{i(\varphi^c-\varphi_1^c)} &= \frac{\sin\theta_1^c\cos\theta_2^c+\cos\theta_1^c\sin\theta_2^c\cos(\varphi_2^c+\psi_1^c)+i\sin\theta_2^c\sin(\varphi_2^c+\psi_1^c)}{\sin\theta^c},\\
e^{\frac{i(\varphi^c+\psi^c-\varphi_1^c-\psi_2^c)}{2}} &= \frac{\cos\frac{\theta_1^c}{2}\cos\frac{\theta_2^c}{2}e^{\frac{i(\varphi_2^c+\psi_1^c)}{2}}-\sin\frac{\theta_1^c}{2}\sin\frac{\theta_2^c}{2}e^{-\frac{i(\varphi_2^c+\psi_1^c)}{2}}}{\cos\dfrac{\theta^c}{2}}.
\end{aligned}\tag{71}$$

Addition Theorem for hyperspherical functions Z^l_{mn} follows from the relation

$$T_l(\mathfrak{g}_1\mathfrak{g}_2)=T_l(\mathfrak{g}_1)T_l(\mathfrak{g}_2).$$

Hence it follows that

$$t^l_{mn}(\mathfrak{g}_1\mathfrak{g}_2)=\sum_{k=-l}^{l}t^l_{mk}(\mathfrak{g}_1)t^l_{kn}(\mathfrak{g}_2).$$

Let us apply this equality to the matrices $\mathfrak{g}_1$ and $\mathfrak{g}_2$ with the Euler angles $0,0,\theta_1,\tau_1,0,0$ and $\varphi_2,\epsilon_2,\theta_2,\tau_2,0,0$, respectively. Using the formula (47), we obtain

$$\begin{aligned}
t^l_{mk}(\mathfrak{g}_1) &= Z^l_{mk}(\cos\theta_1,\cosh\tau_1),\\
t^l_{kn}(\mathfrak{g}_2) &= e^{-k(\epsilon_2+i\varphi_2)}Z^l_{kn}(\cos\theta_2,\cosh\tau_2)
\end{aligned}$$

and

$$t^l_{mn}(\mathfrak{g}_1\mathfrak{g}_2)=e^{-m(\epsilon+i\varphi)-n(\varepsilon+i\psi)}Z^l_{mn}(\cos\theta,\cosh\tau),$$

where $\epsilon,\varphi,\theta,\tau,\varepsilon,\psi$ are the Euler angles of the matrix $\mathfrak{g}_1\mathfrak{g}_2$. In accordance with (67)–(69) these angles are expressed via the factor angles $0,0,\theta_1,\tau_1,0,0$ and $\varphi_2,\epsilon_2,\theta_2,\tau_2,0,0$. Thus, in this case the functions Z^l_{mn} satisfy the following addition theorem:

$$e^{-m(\epsilon+i\varphi)-n(\varepsilon+i\psi)}Z^l_{mn}(\cos\theta^c)=\sum_{k=-l}^{l}e^{-k(\epsilon_2+i\varphi_2)}Z^l_{mk}(\cos\theta_1^c)Z^l_{kn}(\cos\theta_2^c).\tag{72}$$

In general case when the Euler angles are related by the formulae (71) we obtain

$$e^{-m[\epsilon+\epsilon_1+i(\varphi_1-\varphi)]-n[\varepsilon+\varepsilon_2-i(\psi_2-\psi)]}Z^l_{mn}(\cos\theta^c)=$$

$$\sum_{k=-l}^{l}e^{-k[\epsilon_2+\varepsilon_1+i(\varphi_2+\psi_1)]}Z^l_{mk}(\cos\theta_1^c)Z^l_{kn}(\cos\theta_2^c).$$

Addition theorems for the associated and zonal hyperspherical functions follow as particular cases from the proved theorem for the functions $Z^l_{mn}(\theta,\tau)$. In the subsections 3.4 and 3.5 these functions have been defined by the formulas

$$Z_l(\cos\theta^c)=Z^l_{00}(\cos\theta^c)$$

and

$$Z^m_l(\cos\theta^c)=Z^l_{m0}(\cos\theta^c).$$

Supposing $n=0$ in the formula (72), we obtain an addition theorem for the associated hyperspherical functions:

$$e^{-m(\epsilon+i\varphi)}Z^m_l(\cos\theta^c)=\sum_{k=-l}^{l}e^{-k(\epsilon_2+i\varphi_2)}Z^l_{mk}(\cos\theta^c_1)Z^k_l(\cos\theta^c_2),$$

where the angles φ^c, φ^c_2, θ^c, θ^c_1, θ^c_2 are related by (67)–(69). Supposing $m=0$, $n=0$, we obtain

$$Z_l(\cos\theta^c)=\sum_{k=-l}^{l}e^{-k(\epsilon_2+i\varphi_2)}Z^k_l(\cos\theta^c_1)Z^k_l(\cos\theta^c_2).$$

3.9 Matrix elements of the principal series representations of the Lorentz group

As it has been shown in [47], for the case of principal series representations there exists an analog of the spinor representation formula (32):

$$V_af(z)=(a_{12}z+a_{22})^{\frac{\lambda}{2}+i\frac{\rho}{2}-1}\overline{(a_{12}z+a_{22})}^{-\frac{\lambda}{2}+i\frac{\rho}{2}-1}f\left(\frac{a_{11}z+a_{21}}{a_{12}z+a_{22}}\right), \qquad (73)$$

where $f(z)$ is a measurable functions of the Hilbert space $L_2(Z)$, satisfying the condition $\int|f(z)|^2dz<\infty$, $z=x+iy$. At this point, the numbers l_0, l_1 and λ, ρ are related by the formulas

$$l_0=\left|\frac{\lambda}{2}\right|,\quad l_1=-i(\operatorname{sign}\lambda)\frac{\rho}{2}\quad\text{if } m\neq 0,$$
$$l_0=0,\quad l_1=\pm i\frac{\rho}{2}\quad\text{if } m=0.$$

A totality of all representations $a\to V_a$, corresponding to all possible pairs λ, ρ, is called a principal series of representations of the group $SL(2,\mathbb{C})$. At this point, a comparison of (73) with the formula (32) for the spinor representation $\mathfrak{S}_l$ shows that the both formulas have the same structure; only the exponents at the factors $(a_{12}z+a_{22})$, $\overline{(a_{12}z+a_{22})}$ and the functions $f(z)$ are different. In the case of spinor representations the functions $f(z)$ are polynomials $p(z,\bar{z})$ in the spaces $\operatorname{Sym}_{(k,r)}$, and in the case of a representation $\mathfrak{S}_{\lambda,\rho}$ of the principal series $f(z)$ are functions from the Hilbert space $L_2(Z)$.

As known, a representation S_l of the group $SU(2)$ is realized in terms of the functions $P^l_{mn}(\cos\theta)$.

Theorem 1 (Naimark [47]). *The representation S_l is contained in $\mathfrak{S}_{\lambda,\rho}$ no more then one time. At this point, S_l is contained in $\mathfrak{S}_{\lambda,\rho}$, when $\frac{\lambda}{2}$ is one from the numbers $-l, -l+1, \ldots, l$.*

Therefore, matrix elements of the principal series representations of the Lorentz group, making infinite-dimensional matrix, have the form (see also [20]):

$$t^{-\frac{1}{2}+i\rho}_{mn}(\mathfrak{g}) = e^{-m(\epsilon+i\varphi)-n(\varepsilon+i\psi)}\,Z^{-\frac{1}{2}+i\rho}_{mn} = e^{-m(\epsilon+i\varphi)-n(\varepsilon+i\psi)}\times$$

$$\sum^{[\frac{\lambda}{2}]}_{k=-\frac{\lambda}{2}} i^{m-k}\sqrt{\Gamma(\frac{\lambda}{2}-m+1)\Gamma(\frac{\lambda}{2}+m+1)\Gamma(\frac{\lambda}{2}-k+1)\Gamma(\frac{\lambda}{2}+k+1)}\times$$

$$\cos^{\lambda}\frac{\theta}{2}\tan^{m-k}\frac{\theta}{2}\times$$

$$\sum^{[\min(\frac{\lambda}{2}-m,\frac{\lambda}{2}+k)]}_{j=\max(0,k-m)} \frac{i^{2j}\tan^{2j}\dfrac{\theta}{2}}{\Gamma(j+1)\Gamma(\frac{\lambda}{2}-m-j+1)\Gamma(\frac{\lambda}{2}+k-j+1)\Gamma(m-k+j+1)}\times$$

$$\sqrt{\Gamma(\frac{1}{2}+i\rho-n)\Gamma(\frac{1}{2}+i\rho+n)\Gamma(\frac{1}{2}+i\rho-k)\Gamma(\frac{1}{2}+i\rho+k)}\cosh^{-1+2i\rho}\frac{\tau}{2}\tanh^{n-k}\frac{\tau}{2}\times$$

$$\sum^{\infty}_{s=\max(0,k-n)} \frac{\tanh^{2s}\dfrac{\tau}{2}}{\Gamma(s+1)\Gamma(\frac{1}{2}+i\rho-n-s)\Gamma(\frac{1}{2}+i\rho+k-s)\Gamma(n-k+s+1)}. \qquad (74)$$

Thus, the matrix elements of the principal series representations of the group $\mathfrak{G}_+$ are expressed via the function

$$\mathfrak{M}^{-\frac{1}{2}+i\rho}_{mn}(\mathfrak{g}) = e^{-m(\epsilon+i\varphi)}\,Z^{-\frac{1}{2}+i\rho}_{mn}(\cos\theta^c)e^{-n(\varepsilon+i\psi)}, \qquad (75)$$

where

$$Z^{-\frac{1}{2}+i\rho}_{mn}(\cos\theta^c) = \sum^{[\frac{\lambda}{2}]}_{k=-\frac{\lambda}{2}} P^{\frac{\lambda}{2}}_{mk}(\cos\theta)\mathfrak{P}^{-\frac{1}{2}+i\rho}_{kn}(\cosh\tau).$$

In the case of associated functions ($n = 0$) we obtain

$$Z^{m}_{-\frac{1}{2}+i\rho}(\cos\theta^c) = \sum^{[\frac{\lambda}{2}]}_{k=-\frac{\lambda}{2}} P^{\frac{\lambda}{2}}_{mk}(\cos\theta)\mathfrak{P}^{k}_{-\frac{1}{2}+i\rho}(\cosh\tau), \qquad (76)$$

where $\mathfrak{P}^k_{-\frac{1}{2}+i\rho}(\cosh\tau)$ are *conical functions* (see [7]). In this case our result agrees with the paper [20], where matrix elements (eigenfunctions of Casimir operators) of noncompact rotation groups are expressed in terms of conical and spherical functions (see also [76]).

Further, at $\lambda=0$ and $\rho=i\sigma$ from (73) it follows that

$$V_a f(z) = |a_{12}z+a_{22}|^{-2-\sigma} f\left(\frac{a_{11}z+a_{21}}{a_{12}z+a_{22}}\right).$$

This formula defines an unitary representation $a\rightarrow V_a$ of supplementary series $\mathfrak{D}_\sigma$ of the group $SL(2,\mathbb{C})$. At this point, for the supplementary series the relations

$$l_0=0,\quad l_1=\pm\frac{\sigma}{2}$$

hold. In turn, the representation S_l of the group $SU(2)$ is contained in the representation $\mathfrak{D}_\sigma$ of supplementary series when l is an integer number. In this case S_l is contained in $\mathfrak{D}_\sigma$ exactly one time and the number $\frac{\lambda}{2}=0$ is one from the set $-l,-l+1,\ldots,l$ [47].

Thus, matrix elements of supplementary series appear as a particular case of the matrix elements of principal series at $\lambda=0$ and $\rho=i\sigma$:

$$t^{-\frac{1}{2}-\sigma}_{mn}(\mathfrak{g}) = e^{-m(\epsilon+i\varphi)-n(\varepsilon+i\psi)} Z^{-\frac{1}{2}-\sigma}_{mn} = e^{-m(\epsilon+i\varphi)-n(\varepsilon+i\psi)}\times$$

$$\sqrt{\Gamma(\tfrac{1}{2}-\sigma-n)\Gamma(\tfrac{1}{2}-\sigma+n)\Gamma(\tfrac{1}{2}-\sigma-k)\Gamma(\tfrac{1}{2}-\sigma+k)}\cosh^{-1-2\sigma}\frac{\tau}{2}\tanh^{n-k}\frac{\tau}{2}\times$$

$$\sum^{\infty}_{s=\max(0,k-n)}\frac{\tanh^{2s}\frac{\tau}{2}}{\Gamma(s+1)\Gamma(\frac{1}{2}-\sigma-n-s)\Gamma(\frac{1}{2}-\sigma+k-s)\Gamma(n-k+s+1)}. \tag{77}$$

Or

$$\mathfrak{M}^{-\frac{1}{2}-\sigma}_{mn}(\mathfrak{g}) = e^{-m(\epsilon+i\varphi)}\mathfrak{P}^{-\frac{1}{2}-\sigma}_{mn}(\cosh\tau)e^{-n(\varepsilon+i\psi)},$$

that is, the hyperspherical function $Z^{-\frac{1}{2}+i\rho}_{mn}(\cos\theta^c)$ in the case of supplementary series is degenerated to the Jacobi function $\mathfrak{P}^{-\frac{1}{2}-\sigma}_{mn}(\cosh\tau)$. For the associated functions of supplementary series we obtain

$$\mathfrak{P}^m_{-\frac{1}{2}-\sigma}(\mathfrak{g}) = e^{-m(\epsilon+i\varphi)}\mathfrak{P}^m_{-\frac{1}{2}-\sigma}(\cosh\tau).$$

4 Infinitesimal operators of $SU(2)\otimes SU(2)$

Let $\omega^c(t)$ be the one–parameter subgroup of $SL(2,\mathbb{C})$. The operators of the right regular representation of $SU(2)\otimes SU(2)$, corresponded to the elements of this subgroup, transfer complex functions $f(\mathfrak{g})$ into $R(\omega^c(t))f(\mathfrak{g}) = f(\mathfrak{g}\omega^c(t))$. By this reason the infinitesimal operator of the right regular representation $R(\mathfrak{g})$, associated with one–parameter subgroup $\omega^c(t)$, transfers the function $f(\mathfrak{g})$ into $\frac{df(\mathfrak{g}\omega^c(t))}{dt}$ at $t=0$.

Let us denote Euler angles of the element $\mathfrak{g}\omega^c(t)$ via $\varphi^c(t),\theta^c(t),\psi^c(t)$. Then there is an equality

$$\left.\frac{df(\mathfrak{g}\omega^c(t))}{dt}\right|_{t=0}=\frac{\partial f}{\partial\varphi^c}\left(\varphi^c(0)\right)'+\frac{\partial f}{\partial\theta^c}\left(\theta^c(0)\right)'+\frac{\partial f}{\partial\psi^c}\left(\psi^c(0)\right)'.$$

The infinitesimal operator A^c_ω, corresponded to the subgroup $\omega^c(t)$, has a form

$$\mathsf{A}^c_\omega=\mathsf{A}_\omega-i\mathsf{B}_\omega=\left(\varphi^c(0)\right)'\frac{\partial}{\partial\varphi^c}+\left(\theta^c(0)\right)'\frac{\partial}{\partial\theta^c}+\left(\psi^c(0)\right)'\frac{\partial}{\partial\psi^c}.$$

Let us calculate infinitesimal operators A^c_1, A^c_2, A^c_3 corresponding the complex subgroups Ω^c_1, Ω^c_2, Ω^c_3. The subgroup Ω^c_3 consists of the matrices

$$\omega_3(t^c)=\begin{pmatrix}e^{\frac{it^c}{2}} & 0\\ 0 & e^{-\frac{it^c}{2}}\end{pmatrix}.$$

Let $\mathfrak{g}=\mathfrak{g}(\varphi^c,\theta^c,\psi^c)$ be a matrix with complex Euler angles $\varphi^c=\varphi-i\epsilon$, $\theta^c=\theta-i\tau$, $\psi^c=\psi-i\varepsilon$. Therefore, Euler angles of the matrix $\mathfrak{g}\omega_3(t^c)$ equal to φ^c, θ^c, ψ^c+t-it. Hence it follows that

$$\varphi'(0)=0,\;\;\epsilon'(0)=0,\;\;\theta'(0)=0,\;\;\tau'(0)=0,\;\;\psi'(0)=1,\;\;\varepsilon'(0)=-i.$$

So, the operator A^c_3, corresponded to the subgroup Ω^c_3, has a form

$$\mathsf{A}^c_3=\frac{\partial}{\partial\psi}-i\frac{\partial}{\partial\varepsilon}.$$

Whence

$$\mathsf{A}_3=\frac{\partial}{\partial\psi},\qquad(78)$$

$$\mathsf{B}_3=\frac{\partial}{\partial\varepsilon}.\qquad(79)$$

Let us calculate the infinitesimal operator A^c_1 corresponded the complex subgroup Ω^c_1. The subgroup Ω^c_1 consists of the following matrices

$$\omega_1(t^c)=\begin{pmatrix}\cos\frac{t^c}{2} & i\sin\frac{t^c}{2}\\ i\sin\frac{t^c}{2} & \cos\frac{t^c}{2}\end{pmatrix}.$$

The Euler angles of these matrices equal to 0, $t^c=t-it$, 0. Let us represent the matrix $\mathfrak{g}\omega_1(t^c)$ by the product $\mathfrak{g}_1\mathfrak{g}_2$, the Euler angles of which are described by the formulae (71). Then the Euler angles of the matrix $\omega_1(t^c)$ equal to $\varphi_2^c = 0$, $\theta_2^c = t - it$, $\psi_2^c = 0$, and the Euler angles of the matrix $\mathfrak{g}$ equal to $\varphi_1^c = \varphi^c$, $\theta_1^c = \theta^c$, $\psi_1^c = \psi^c$. Thus, from the general formulae (71) we obtain that Euler angles $\varphi^c(t)$, $\theta^c(t)$, $\psi^c(t)$ of the matrix $\mathfrak{g}\omega_1(t^c)$ are defined by the following relations:

$$\cos\theta^c(t) = \cos\theta^c\cos t^c - \sin\theta^c\sin t^c\cos\psi^c, \tag{80}$$

$$e^{i\varphi^c(t)} = e^{i\varphi^c}\frac{\sin\theta^c\cos t^c + \cos\theta^c\sin t^c\cos\psi^c + i\sin t^c\sin\psi^c}{\sin\theta^c(t)}, \tag{81}$$

$$e^{\frac{i[\varphi^c(t)+\psi^c(t)]}{2}} = e^{\frac{i\varphi^c}{2}}\frac{\cos\frac{\theta^c}{2}\cos\frac{t^c}{2}e^{\frac{i\psi^c}{2}} - \sin\frac{\theta^c}{2}\sin\frac{t^c}{2}e^{-\frac{i\psi^c}{2}}}{\cos\frac{\theta^c(t)}{2}}. \tag{82}$$

For calculation of derivatives $\varphi'(t)$, $\epsilon'(t)$, $\theta'(t)$, $\tau'(t)$, $\psi'(t)$, $\varepsilon'(t)$ at $t = 0$ we differentiate on t the both parts of the each equality from (80)–(82) and take $t = 0$. At this point we have $\varphi(0) = \varphi$, $\epsilon(0) = \epsilon$, $\theta(0) = \theta$, $\tau(0) = \tau$, $\psi(0) = \psi$, $\varepsilon(0) = \varepsilon$.

So, let us differentiate the both parts of (80). In the result we obtain

$$\theta'(t) - i\tau'(t) = (1 - i)\cos\psi^c.$$

Taking $t = 0$, we find that

$$\theta'(0) = \cos\psi^c, \quad \tau'(0) = \cos\psi^c.$$

Differentiating now the both parts of (81), we obtain

$$\varphi'(0) - i\epsilon'(0) = \frac{(1-i)\sin\psi^c}{\sin\theta^c}.$$

Therefore,

$$\varphi'(0) = \frac{\sin\psi^c}{\sin\theta^c}, \quad \epsilon'(0) = \frac{\sin\psi^c}{\sin\theta^c}.$$

Further, differentiating the both parts of (82), we find that

$$\psi'(0) - i\varepsilon'(0) = -(1+i)\cot\theta^c\sin\psi^c$$

and

$$\psi'(0) = -\cot\theta^c\sin\psi^c, \quad \varepsilon'(0) = -\cot\theta^c\sin\psi^c.$$

In such a way, we obtain the following infinitesimal operators:

$$\mathsf{A}_1 = \cos\psi^c\frac{\partial}{\partial\theta} + \frac{\sin\psi^c}{\sin\theta^c}\frac{\partial}{\partial\varphi} - \cot\theta^c\sin\psi^c\frac{\partial}{\partial\psi}, \tag{83}$$

$$\mathsf{B}_1 = \cos\psi^c\frac{\partial}{\partial\tau} + \frac{\sin\psi^c}{\sin\theta^c}\frac{\partial}{\partial\epsilon} - \cot\theta^c\sin\psi^c\frac{\partial}{\partial\varepsilon}. \tag{84}$$

Let us calculate now an infinitesimal operator A_2^c corresponded to the complex subgroup Ω_2^c. The subgroup Ω_2^c consists of the following matrices

$$\omega_2(t^c) = \begin{pmatrix} \cos\frac{t^c}{2} & -\sin\frac{t^c}{2} \\ \sin\frac{t^c}{2} & \cos\frac{t^c}{2} \end{pmatrix},$$

where the Euler angles equal correspondingly to 0, $t^c = t - it$, 0. It is obvious that the matrix $\mathfrak{g}\omega_2(t^c)$ can be represented by the product

$$\mathfrak{g}_1\mathfrak{g}_2 = \begin{pmatrix} \cos\frac{\theta_1^c}{2} & i\sin\frac{\theta_1^c}{2} \\ i\sin\frac{\theta_1^c}{2} & \cos\frac{\theta_1^c}{2} \end{pmatrix}\begin{pmatrix} \cos\frac{\theta_2^c}{2}e^{\frac{i\varphi_2^c}{2}} & -\sin\frac{\theta_2^c}{2}e^{\frac{i\varphi_2^c}{2}} \\ \sin\frac{\theta_2^c}{2}e^{-\frac{i\varphi_2^c}{2}} & \cos\frac{\theta_2^c}{2}e^{-\frac{i\varphi_2^c}{2}} \end{pmatrix}.$$

Multiplying the matrices in the right part of this equality, we obtain that Euler angles of the product $\mathfrak{g}_1\mathfrak{g}_2$ are related by formulae

$$\cos\theta^c = \cos\theta_1^c\cos\theta_2^c + \sin\theta_1^c\sin\theta_2^c\sin\varphi_2^c, \tag{85}$$

$$e^{i\varphi^c} = \frac{\sin\theta_1^c\cos\theta_2^c - \cos\theta_1^c\sin\theta_2^c\sin\varphi_2^c + i\sin\theta_2^c\cos\varphi_2^c}{\sin\theta^c}, \tag{86}$$

$$e^{\frac{i(\varphi^c+\psi^c)}{2}} = \frac{\cos\frac{\theta_1^c}{2}\cos\frac{\theta_2^c}{2}e^{\frac{i\varphi_2^c}{2}} + i\sin\frac{\theta_1^c}{2}\sin\frac{\theta_2^c}{2}e^{-\frac{i\varphi_2^c}{2}}}{\cos\frac{\theta^c}{2}}. \tag{87}$$

Or, repeating the calculations as in the case of (71), we obtain in general case

$$\begin{aligned}
\cos\theta^c &= \cos\theta_1^c\cos\theta_2^c + \sin\theta_1^c\sin\theta_2^c\sin(\varphi_2^c + \psi_1^c), \\
e^{i(\varphi^c-\varphi_1^c)} &= \frac{\sin\theta_1^c\cos\theta_2^c - \cos\theta_1^c\sin\theta_2^c\sin(\varphi_2^c+\psi_1^c) + i\sin\theta_2^c\cos(\varphi_2^c+\psi_1^c)}{\sin\theta^c}, \\
e^{\frac{i(\varphi^c+\psi^c-\varphi_1^c-\psi_2^c)}{2}} &= \frac{\cos\frac{\theta_1^c}{2}\cos\frac{\theta_2^c}{2}e^{\frac{i(\varphi_2^c+\psi_1^c)}{2}} + \sin\frac{\theta_1^c}{2}\sin\frac{\theta_2^c}{2}e^{-\frac{i(\varphi_2^c+\psi_1^c)}{2}}}{\cos\frac{\theta^c}{2}}.
\end{aligned} \tag{88}$$

Therefore, Euler angles of the matrix $\omega_2(t^c)$ equal to $\varphi_2^c = 0$, $\theta_2^c = t - it$, $\psi_2^c = 0$, and Euler angles of the matrix $\mathfrak{g}$ equal to $\varphi_1^c = \varphi^c$, $\theta_1^c = \theta^c$, $\psi_1^c = \psi^c$. Then from the formulae (88) we obtain that Euler angles $\varphi^c(t)$, $\theta^c(t)$, $\psi^c(t)$ of the matrix $\mathfrak{g}\omega_2(t^c)$ are defined by relations

$$\cos\theta^c(t) = \cos\theta^c\cos t^c + \sin\theta^c\sin t^c\sin\psi^c, \tag{89}$$

$$e^{i\varphi^c(t)} = e^{i\varphi^c}\frac{\sin\theta^c\cos t^c - \cos\theta^c\sin t^c\sin\psi^c + i\sin t^c\cos\psi^c}{\sin\theta^c(t)}, \tag{90}$$

$$e^{\frac{i[\varphi^c(t)+\psi^c(t)]}{2}} = e^{\frac{i\varphi^c}{2}}\frac{\cos\frac{\theta^c}{2}\cos\frac{t^c}{2}e^{\frac{i\psi^c}{2}} + i\sin\frac{\theta^c}{2}\sin\frac{t^c}{2}e^{-\frac{i\psi^c}{2}}}{\cos\frac{\theta^c(t)}{2}}. \tag{91}$$

Differentiating on t the both parts of the each equalities (89)–(91) and taking $t = 0$, we obtain

$$\begin{aligned}\theta'(0) &= \tau'(0) = -\sin\psi^c,\\ \varphi'(0) &= \epsilon'(0) = \frac{\cos\psi^c}{\sin\theta^c},\\ \psi'(0) &= \varepsilon'(0) = -\cot\theta^c\cos\psi^c.\end{aligned} \tag{92}$$

Therefore, for the subgroup Ω_2^c we have the following infinitesimal operators

$$\mathsf{A}_2 = -\sin\psi^c\frac{\partial}{\partial\theta} + \frac{\cos\psi^c}{\sin\theta^c}\frac{\partial}{\partial\varphi} - \cot\theta^c\cos\psi^c\frac{\partial}{\partial\psi}, \tag{93}$$

$$\mathsf{B}_2 = -\sin\psi^c\frac{\partial}{\partial\tau} + \frac{\cos\psi^c}{\sin\theta^c}\frac{\partial}{\partial\epsilon} - \cot\theta^c\cos\psi^c\frac{\partial}{\partial\varepsilon}. \tag{94}$$

It is easy to verify that operators A_i, B_i, defined by the formulae (78), (79), (83), (84) and (93), (94), are satisfy the commutation relations (4).

4.1 Casimir operators and differential equations for hyperspherical functions

Taking into account the expressions (78), (79), (83), (84) and (93), (94) we can write the operators (5) in the form

$$\mathsf{X}_1 = \cos\psi^c\frac{\partial}{\partial\theta^c} + \frac{\sin\psi^c}{\sin\theta^c}\frac{\partial}{\partial\varphi^c} - \cot\theta^c\sin\psi^c\frac{\partial}{\partial\psi^c}, \tag{95}$$

$$\mathsf{X}_2 = -\sin\psi^c\frac{\partial}{\partial\theta^c} + \frac{\cos\psi^c}{\sin\theta^c}\frac{\partial}{\partial\varphi^c} - \cot\theta^c\cos\psi^c\frac{\partial}{\partial\psi^c}, \tag{96}$$

$$\mathsf{X}_3 = \frac{\partial}{\partial\psi^c}, \tag{97}$$

$$\mathsf{Y}_1 = \cos\dot{\psi}^c\frac{\partial}{\partial\dot{\theta}^c} + \frac{\sin\dot{\psi}^c}{\sin\dot{\theta}^c}\frac{\partial}{\partial\dot{\varphi}^c} - \cot\dot{\theta}^c\sin\dot{\psi}^c\frac{\partial}{\partial\dot{\psi}^c}, \tag{98}$$

$$\mathsf{Y}_2 = -\sin\dot{\psi}^c\frac{\partial}{\partial\dot{\theta}^c} + \frac{\cos\dot{\psi}^c}{\sin\dot{\theta}^c}\frac{\partial}{\partial\dot{\varphi}^c} - \cot\dot{\theta}^c\cos\dot{\psi}^c\frac{\partial}{\partial\dot{\psi}^c}, \tag{99}$$

$$\mathsf{Y}_3 = \frac{\partial}{\partial\dot{\psi}^c}, \tag{100}$$

where

$$\frac{\partial}{\partial\theta^c} = \frac{1}{2}\left(\frac{\partial}{\partial\theta} + i\frac{\partial}{\partial\tau}\right), \quad \frac{\partial}{\partial\varphi^c} = \frac{1}{2}\left(\frac{\partial}{\partial\varphi} + i\frac{\partial}{\partial\epsilon}\right), \quad \frac{\partial}{\partial\psi^c} = \frac{1}{2}\left(\frac{\partial}{\partial\psi} + i\frac{\partial}{\partial\varepsilon}\right),$$

$$\frac{\partial}{\partial\dot{\theta}^c} = \frac{1}{2}\left(\frac{\partial}{\partial\theta} - i\frac{\partial}{\partial\tau}\right), \quad \frac{\partial}{\partial\dot{\varphi}^c} = \frac{1}{2}\left(\frac{\partial}{\partial\varphi} - i\frac{\partial}{\partial\epsilon}\right), \quad \frac{\partial}{\partial\dot{\psi}^c} = \frac{1}{2}\left(\frac{\partial}{\partial\psi} - i\frac{\partial}{\partial\varepsilon}\right),$$

As known, for the Lorentz group there are two independent Casimir operators

$$\begin{aligned} \mathsf{X}^2 &= \mathsf{X}_1^2 + \mathsf{X}_2^2 + \mathsf{X}_3^2 = \frac{1}{4}(\mathsf{A}^2 - \mathsf{B}^2 + 2i\mathsf{A}\mathsf{B}), \\ \mathsf{Y}^2 &= \mathsf{Y}_1^2 + \mathsf{Y}_2^2 + \mathsf{Y}_3^2 = \frac{1}{4}(\widetilde{\mathsf{A}}^2 - \widetilde{\mathsf{B}}^2 - 2i\widetilde{\mathsf{A}}\widetilde{\mathsf{B}}). \end{aligned} \tag{101}$$

Substituting (95)-(100) into (101), we obtain for the Casimir operators the following expressions

$$\begin{aligned} \mathsf{X}^2 &= \frac{\partial^2}{\partial \theta^{c2}} + \cot\theta^c \frac{\partial}{\partial \theta^c} + \frac{1}{\sin^2\theta^c}\left[\frac{\partial^2}{\partial \varphi^{c2}} - 2\cos\theta^c \frac{\partial}{\partial \varphi^c}\frac{\partial}{\partial \psi^c} + \frac{\partial^2}{\partial \psi^{c2}}\right], \\ \mathsf{Y}^2 &= \frac{\partial^2}{\partial \dot{\theta}^{c2}} + \cot\dot{\theta}^c \frac{\partial}{\partial \dot{\theta}^c} + \frac{1}{\sin^2\dot{\theta}^c}\left[\frac{\partial^2}{\partial \dot{\varphi}^{c2}} - 2\cos\dot{\theta}^c \frac{\partial}{\partial \dot{\varphi}^c}\frac{\partial}{\partial \dot{\psi}^c} + \frac{\partial^2}{\partial \dot{\psi}^{c2}}\right]. \end{aligned} \tag{102}$$

Matrix elements of unitary irreducible representations of the Lorentz group are eigenfunctions of the operators (102):

$$\begin{aligned} \left[\mathsf{X}^2 + l(l+1)\right]\mathfrak{M}^l_{mn}(\varphi^c, \theta^c, \psi^c) &= 0, \\ \left[\mathsf{Y}^2 + \dot{l}(\dot{l}+1)\right]\mathfrak{M}^{\dot{l}}_{\dot{m}\dot{n}}(\dot{\varphi}^c, \dot{\theta}^c, \dot{\psi}^c) &= 0, \end{aligned} \tag{103}$$

where

$$\begin{aligned} \mathfrak{M}^l_{mn}(\varphi^c, \theta^c, \psi^c) &= e^{-i(m\varphi^c + n\psi^c)} Z^l_{mn}(\theta^c), \\ \mathfrak{M}^{\dot{l}}_{\dot{m}\dot{n}}(\dot{\varphi}^c, \dot{\theta}^c, \dot{\psi}^c) &= e^{-i(\dot{m}\dot{\varphi}^c + \dot{n}\dot{\varphi}^c)} Z^{\dot{l}}_{\dot{m}\dot{n}}(\dot{\theta}^c). \end{aligned} \tag{104}$$

Substituting the hyperspherical functions (104) into (103) and taking into account the operators (102), we obtain

$$\begin{aligned} \left[\frac{d^2}{d\theta^{c2}} + \cot\theta^c \frac{d}{d\theta^c} - \frac{m^2 + n^2 - 2mn\cos\theta^c}{\sin^2\theta^c} + l(l+1)\right] Z^l_{mn}(\theta^c) &= 0, \\ \left[\frac{d^2}{d\dot{\theta}^{c2}} + \cot\dot{\theta}^c \frac{d}{d\dot{\theta}^c} - \frac{\dot{m}^2 + \dot{n}^2 - 2\dot{m}\dot{n}\cos\dot{\theta}^c}{\sin^2\dot{\theta}^c} + \dot{l}(\dot{l}+1)\right] Z^{\dot{l}}_{\dot{m}\dot{n}}(\dot{\theta}^c) &= 0. \end{aligned}$$

Finally, after substitutions $z = \cos\theta^c$ and $\overset{*}{z} = \cos\dot{\theta}^c$, we come to the following differential equations

$$\begin{aligned} \left[(1-z^2)\frac{d^2}{dz^2} - 2z\frac{d}{dz} - \frac{m^2 + n^2 - 3mnz}{1 - z^2} + l(l+1)\right] Z^l_{mn}(\arccos z) &= 0, \\ \left[(1-\overset{*}{z}{}^2)\frac{d^2}{d\overset{*}{z}{}^2} - 2\overset{*}{z}\frac{d}{d\overset{*}{z}} - \frac{\dot{m}^2 + \dot{n}^2 - 2\dot{m}\dot{n}\overset{*}{z}}{1 - \overset{*}{z}{}^2} + \dot{l}(\dot{l}+1)\right] Z^{\dot{l}}_{\dot{m}\dot{n}}(\arccos \overset{*}{z}) &= 0. \end{aligned}$$

The latter equations have three singular points -1, $+1$, ∞.

Further, Casimir operators on the 2-dimensional complex sphere (correspondingly, on the dual sphere) have the form

$$\begin{aligned}\mathsf{X}^2 &= \frac{\partial^2}{\partial\theta^{c2}} + \cot\theta^c\frac{\partial}{\partial\theta^c} + \frac{1}{\sin^2\theta^c}\frac{\partial^2}{\partial\varphi^{c2}},\\ \mathsf{Y}^2 &= \frac{\partial^2}{\partial\dot{\theta}^{c2}} + \cot\dot{\theta}^c\frac{\partial}{\partial\dot{\theta}^c} + \frac{1}{\sin^2\dot{\theta}^{c2}}\frac{\partial^2}{\partial\dot{\varphi}^{c2}}.\end{aligned}\tag{105}$$

Associated hyperspherical functions $\mathfrak{M}_l^m(\varphi^c,\theta^c,0)$ and $\mathfrak{M}_{\dot{l}}^{\dot{m}}(\dot{\varphi}^c,\dot{\theta}^c,0)$, defined on the surface of the two-dimensional complex sphere, are eigenfunctions of the operators X^2 and Y^2:

$$\begin{aligned}\left[\mathsf{X}^2 + l(l+1)\right]\mathfrak{M}_l^m(\varphi^c,\theta^c,0) &= 0,\\ \left[\mathsf{Y}^2 + \dot{l}(\dot{l}+1)\right]\mathfrak{M}_{\dot{l}}^{\dot{m}}(\dot{\varphi}^c,\dot{\theta}^c,0) &= 0\end{aligned}\tag{106}$$

Substituting the functions $\mathfrak{M}_l^m(\varphi^c,\theta^c,0) = e^{-im\varphi^c}Z_l^m(\theta^c)$, $\mathfrak{M}_{\dot{l}}^{\dot{m}}(\dot{\varphi}^c,\dot{\theta}^c,0) = e^{-i\dot{m}\dot{\varphi}^c}Z_{\dot{l}}^{\dot{m}}(\dot{\theta}^c)$ into (106) and taking into account the operators (105), we obtain the following equations

$$\begin{aligned}\left[\frac{d^2}{d\theta^{c2}} + \cot\theta^c\frac{d}{d\theta^c} - \frac{m^2}{\sin^2\theta^c} + l(l+1)\right]Z_l^m(\theta^c) &= 0,\\ \left[\frac{d^2}{d\dot{\theta}^{c2}} + \cot\dot{\theta}^c\frac{d}{d\dot{\theta}^c} - \frac{m^2}{\sin^2\dot{\theta}^c} + \dot{l}(\dot{l}+1)\right]Z_{\dot{l}}^{\dot{m}}(\dot{\theta}^c) &= 0.\end{aligned}$$

Or, introducing the substitutions $z = \cos\theta^c$, $\overset{*}{z} = \cos\dot{\theta}^c$ we find that

$$\begin{aligned}\left[(1-z^2)\frac{d^2}{dz^2} - 2z\frac{d}{dz} - \frac{m^2}{1-z^2} + l(l+1)\right]Z_l^m(\arccos z) &= 0,\\ \left[(1-\overset{*}{z}{}^2)\frac{d^2}{d\overset{*}{z}{}^2} - 2\overset{*}{z}\frac{d}{d\overset{*}{z}} - \frac{\dot{m}^2}{1-\overset{*}{z}{}^2} + \dot{l}(\dot{l}+1)\right]Z_{\dot{l}}^{\dot{m}}(\arccos\overset{*}{z}) &= 0.\end{aligned}$$

Analogously, Casimir operators, corresponding to zonal hyperspherical functions $Z_l(\theta^c)$, have the form

$$\begin{aligned}\mathsf{X}^2 &= \frac{\partial^2}{\partial\theta^{c2}} + \cot\theta^c\frac{\partial}{\partial\theta^c},\\ \mathsf{Y}^2 &= \frac{\partial^2}{\partial\dot{\theta}^{c2}} + \cot\dot{\theta}^c\frac{\partial}{\partial\dot{\theta}^c}.\end{aligned}\tag{107}$$

And the equations for Z_l are

$$\begin{aligned}\left[(1-z^2)\frac{d^2}{dz^2} - 2z\frac{d}{dz} + l(l+1)\right]Z_l(\arccos z) &= 0,\\ \left[(1-\overset{*}{z}{}^2)\frac{d^2}{d\overset{*}{z}{}^2} - 2\overset{*}{z}\frac{d}{d\overset{*}{z}} + \dot{l}(\dot{l}+1)\right]Z_{\dot{l}}(\arccos\overset{*}{z}) &= 0.\end{aligned}$$

5 Recurrence relations between hyperspherical functions

Between generalized hyperspherical functions $\mathfrak{M}^l_{mn}$ (and also the hyperspherical functions Z^l_{mn}) there exists a wide variety of recurrence relations. Part of them relates the hyperspherical functions of one and the same order (with identical l), other part relates the functions of different orders.

In virtue of the Van der Waerden representation (8) the recurrence formulae for the hyperspherical functions of one and the same order follow from the equalities

$$\mathsf{X}_-\mathfrak{M}^l_{mn} = \boldsymbol{\alpha}_n\mathfrak{M}^l_{m,n-1}, \quad \mathsf{X}_+\mathfrak{M}^l_{mn} = \boldsymbol{\alpha}_{n+1}\mathfrak{M}^l_{m,n+1}, \tag{108}$$

$$\mathsf{Y}_-\mathfrak{M}^{\dot{l}}_{\dot{m}\dot{n}} = \boldsymbol{\alpha}_{\dot{n}}\mathfrak{M}^{\dot{l}}_{\dot{m},\dot{n}-1}, \quad \mathsf{Y}_+\mathfrak{M}^{\dot{l}}_{\dot{m}\dot{n}} = \boldsymbol{\alpha}_{\dot{n}+1}\mathfrak{M}^{\dot{l}}_{\dot{m},\dot{n}+1}, \tag{109}$$

where

$$\boldsymbol{\alpha}_n = \sqrt{(l+n)(l-n+1)}, \quad \boldsymbol{\alpha}_{\dot{n}} = \sqrt{(\dot{l}+\dot{n})(\dot{l}-\dot{n}+1)}.$$

From (5) and (7) it follows that

$$\begin{aligned}
\mathsf{X}_+ &= \frac{1}{2}\left(i\mathsf{A}_1 - \mathsf{A}_2 - \mathsf{B}_1 - i\mathsf{B}_2\right), \\
\mathsf{X}_- &= \frac{1}{2}\left(i\mathsf{A}_1 + \mathsf{A}_2 - \mathsf{B}_1 + i\mathsf{B}_2\right), \\
\mathsf{Y}_+ &= \frac{1}{2}\left(i\widetilde{\mathsf{A}}_1 - \widetilde{\mathsf{A}}_2 + \widetilde{\mathsf{B}}_1 + i\widetilde{\mathsf{B}}_2\right), \\
\mathsf{Y}_- &= \frac{1}{2}\left(i\widetilde{\mathsf{A}}_1 + \widetilde{\mathsf{A}}_2 + \widetilde{\mathsf{B}}_1 - i\widetilde{\mathsf{B}}_2\right).
\end{aligned} \tag{110}$$

Using the formulae (83), (84) and (93), (94), we obtain

$$\mathsf{X}_+ = \frac{e^{-i\psi^c}}{2}\left[i\frac{\partial}{\partial\theta} - \frac{1}{\sin\theta^c}\frac{\partial}{\partial\varphi} + \cot\theta^c\frac{\partial}{\partial\psi} - \frac{\partial}{\partial\tau} - \frac{i}{\sin\theta^c}\frac{\partial}{\partial\epsilon} + i\cot\theta^c\frac{\partial}{\partial\varepsilon}\right], \tag{111}$$

$$\mathsf{X}_- = \frac{e^{i\psi^c}}{2}\left[i\frac{\partial}{\partial\theta} + \frac{1}{\sin\theta^c}\frac{\partial}{\partial\varphi} - \cot\theta^c\frac{\partial}{\partial\psi} - \frac{\partial}{\partial\tau} + \frac{i}{\sin\theta^c}\frac{\partial}{\partial\epsilon} - i\cot\theta^c\frac{\partial}{\partial\varepsilon}\right], \tag{112}$$

$$\mathsf{Y}_+ = \frac{e^{-i\dot{\psi}^c}}{2}\left[i\frac{\partial}{\partial\theta} - \frac{1}{\sin\dot{\theta}^c}\frac{\partial}{\partial\varphi} + \cot\dot{\theta}^c\frac{\partial}{\partial\psi} + \frac{\partial}{\partial\tau} + \frac{i}{\sin\dot{\theta}^c}\frac{\partial}{\partial\epsilon} - i\cot\dot{\theta}^c\frac{\partial}{\partial\varepsilon}\right], \tag{113}$$

$$\mathsf{Y}_- = \frac{e^{i\dot{\psi}^c}}{2}\left[i\frac{\partial}{\partial\theta} + \frac{1}{\sin\dot{\theta}^c}\frac{\partial}{\partial\varphi} - \cot\dot{\theta}^c\frac{\partial}{\partial\psi} + \frac{\partial}{\partial\tau} - \frac{i}{\sin\dot{\theta}^c}\frac{\partial}{\partial\epsilon} + i\cot\dot{\theta}^c\frac{\partial}{\partial\varepsilon}\right]. \tag{114}$$

Further, substituting the function $\mathfrak{M}^l_{mn} = e^{-m(\epsilon-i\varphi)}Z^l_{mn}(\theta,\tau)e^{-n(\varepsilon-i\psi)}$ into the relations (108) and taking into account the operators (111) and (112), we find that

$$i\frac{\partial \dot{Z}^l_{mn}}{\partial\theta} - \frac{\partial \dot{Z}^l_{mn}}{\partial\tau} - \frac{2i(m-n\cos\theta^c)}{\sin\theta^c}\dot{Z}^l_{mn} = 2\boldsymbol{\alpha}_n\dot{Z}^l_{m,n-1}, \tag{115}$$

$$i\frac{\partial \dot{Z}^l_{mn}}{\partial\theta} - \frac{\partial \dot{Z}^l_{mn}}{\partial\tau} + \frac{2i(m-n\cos\theta^c)}{\sin\theta^c}\dot{Z}^l_{mn} = 2\boldsymbol{\alpha}_{n+1}\dot{Z}^l_{m,n+1}. \tag{116}$$

Since the functions $\dot{Z}^l_{mn}(\theta,\tau)$ are symmetric, that is, $\dot{Z}^l_{mn}(\theta,\tau)=\dot{Z}^l_{nm}(\theta,\tau)$, then substituting $\dot{Z}^l_{nm}(\theta,\tau)$ in lieu of $\dot{Z}^l_{mn}$ into the formulae (115)–(116) and replacing m by n, and n by m, we obtain

$$
\begin{aligned}
i\frac{\partial Z^l_{mn}}{\partial\theta}-\frac{\partial Z^l_{mn}}{\partial\tau}-\frac{2i(n-m\cos\theta^c)}{\sin\theta^c}Z^l_{mn} &= 2\boldsymbol{\alpha}_m Z^l_{m-1,n}, &(117)\\
i\frac{\partial Z^l_{mn}}{\partial\theta}-\frac{\partial Z^l_{mn}}{\partial\tau}+\frac{2i(n-m\cos\theta^c)}{\sin\theta^c}Z^l_{mn} &= 2\boldsymbol{\alpha}_{m+1} Z^l_{m+1,n}. &(118)
\end{aligned}
$$

Analogously, substituting the function $\mathfrak{M}^{\dot{l}}_{\dot{m}\dot{n}}=e^{-\dot{m}(\epsilon-i\varphi)}Z^{\dot{l}}_{\dot{m}\dot{n}}(\theta,\tau)e^{-\dot{n}(\varepsilon-i\psi)}$ into the relations (109), we obtain

$$
\begin{aligned}
i\frac{\partial Z^{\dot{l}}_{\dot{m}\dot{n}}}{\partial\theta}+\frac{\partial Z^{\dot{l}}_{\dot{m}\dot{n}}}{\partial\tau}+\frac{2i(\dot{m}-\dot{n}\cos\dot{\theta}^c)}{\sin\dot{\theta}^c}Z^{\dot{l}}_{\dot{m}\dot{n}} &= 2\boldsymbol{\alpha}_{\dot{n}} Z^{\dot{l}}_{\dot{m},\dot{n}-1}, &(119)\\
i\frac{\partial Z^{\dot{l}}_{\dot{m}\dot{n}}}{\partial\theta}+\frac{\partial Z^{\dot{l}}_{\dot{m}\dot{n}}}{\partial\tau}-\frac{2i(\dot{m}-\dot{n}\cos\dot{\theta}^c)}{\sin\dot{\theta}^c}Z^{\dot{l}}_{\dot{m}\dot{n}} &= 2\boldsymbol{\alpha}_{\dot{n}+1} Z^{\dot{l}}_{\dot{m},\dot{n}+1}. &(120)
\end{aligned}
$$

Further, using the symmetry of the functions $Z^{\dot{l}}_{\dot{m}\dot{n}}$ we obtain

$$
\begin{aligned}
i\frac{\partial Z^{\dot{l}}_{\dot{m}\dot{n}}}{\partial\theta}+\frac{\partial Z^{\dot{l}}_{\dot{m}\dot{n}}}{\partial\tau}+\frac{2i(\dot{n}-\dot{m}\cos\dot{\theta}^c)}{\sin\dot{\theta}^c}Z^{\dot{l}}_{\dot{m}\dot{n}} &= 2\boldsymbol{\alpha}_{\dot{m}} Z^{\dot{l}}_{\dot{m}-1,\dot{n}}, &(121)\\
i\frac{\partial Z^{\dot{l}}_{\dot{m}\dot{n}}}{\partial\theta}+\frac{\partial Z^{\dot{l}}_{\dot{m}\dot{n}}}{\partial\tau}-\frac{2i(\dot{n}-\dot{m}\cos\dot{\theta}^c)}{\sin\dot{\theta}^c}Z^{\dot{l}}_{\dot{m}\dot{n}} &= 2\boldsymbol{\alpha}_{\dot{m}+1} Z^{\dot{l}}_{\dot{m}+1,\dot{n}}. &(122)
\end{aligned}
$$

Supposing $n=0$ ($\dot{n}=0$) in the formulas (117)–(118) and (121)–(122), we obtain recurrence relations for the associated hyperspherical functions:

$$
\begin{aligned}
i\frac{\partial Z^m_l}{\partial\theta}-\frac{\partial Z^m_l}{\partial\tau}+2im\cot\theta^c Z^m_l &= 2\boldsymbol{\alpha}_m Z^{m-1}_l,\\
i\frac{\partial Z^m_l}{\partial\theta}-\frac{\partial Z^m_l}{\partial\tau}-2im\cot\theta^c Z^m_l &= 2\boldsymbol{\alpha}_{m+1} Z^{m+1}_l,
\end{aligned}
$$

and

$$
\begin{aligned}
i\frac{\partial Z^{\dot{m}}_{\dot{l}}}{\partial\theta}+\frac{\partial Z^{\dot{m}}_{\dot{l}}}{\partial\tau}-2i\dot{m}\cot\dot{\theta}^c Z^{\dot{m}}_{\dot{l}} &= 2\boldsymbol{\alpha}_{\dot{m}} Z^{\dot{m}-1}_{\dot{l}},\\
i\frac{\partial Z^{\dot{m}}_{\dot{l}}}{\partial\theta}+\frac{\partial Z^{\dot{m}}_{\dot{l}}}{\partial\tau}+2i\dot{m}\cot\dot{\theta}^c Z^{\dot{m}}_{\dot{l}} &= 2\boldsymbol{\alpha}_{\dot{m}+1} Z^{\dot{m}+1}_{\dot{l}}.
\end{aligned}
$$

Let us consider now recurrence relations between hyperspherical functions with different order. These recurrence formulae are related with the tensor products of irreducible representations of the Lorentz group. Indeed, in accordance with Van der Waerden representation (8) an arbitrary finite–dimensional representation of the group $\mathfrak{G}_+$ has a form $\boldsymbol{\tau}_{l0}\otimes\boldsymbol{\tau}_{0\dot{l}}\sim\boldsymbol{\tau}_{l\dot{l}}$, where $\boldsymbol{\tau}_{l0}$ and $\boldsymbol{\tau}_{0\dot{l}}$ are representations of the group $SU(2)$. Then a product of the two representations $\boldsymbol{\tau}_{l_1\dot{l}_1}$ and $\boldsymbol{\tau}_{l_2\dot{l}_2}$ of the Lorentz group is defined by an expression

$$\boldsymbol{\tau}_{l_1\dot{l}_1}\otimes\boldsymbol{\tau}_{l_2\dot{l}_2}=\sum_{|l_1-l_2|\le m\le l_1+l_2;|\dot{l}_1-\dot{l}_2|\le\dot{m}\le\dot{l}_1+\dot{l}_2}\boldsymbol{\tau}_{m\dot{m}}. \tag{123}$$

The vectors $\zeta_{lm;\dot{l}\dot{m}}=\mid lm;\dot{l}\dot{m}\rangle$ of the helicity basis have the form

$$\zeta_{lm;\dot{l}\dot{m}}=\sum_{\substack{m_1+m_2=m,\\ \dot{m}_1+\dot{m}_2=\dot{m}}}C(l_1,l_2,l;m_1,m_2,m)C(\dot{l}_1,\dot{l}_2,\dot{l};\dot{m}_1,\dot{m}_2,\dot{m})\zeta_{l_1m_1;\dot{l}_1\dot{m}_1}\otimes\zeta_{l_2m_2;\dot{l}_2\dot{m}_2}, \tag{124}$$

where

$$C(l_1,l_2,l;m_1,m_2,m)C(\dot{l}_1,\dot{l}_2,\dot{l};\dot{m}_1,\dot{m}_2,\dot{m})=B^{l_1,l_2,l;m_1,m_2,m}_{\dot{l}_1,\dot{l}_2,\dot{l};\dot{m}_1,\dot{m}_2,\dot{m}}$$

are the Clebsch–Gordan coefficients of the group $SL(2,\mathbb{C})$. Expressing the Clebsch–Gordan coefficients $C(l_1,l_2,l;m_1,m_2,m_1+m_2)$ of the group $SU(2)$ via a generalized hypergeometric function ${}_3F_2$ (see, for example, [51, 77, 74]) we see that CG–coefficients of $SL(2,\mathbb{C})$ have the form

$$\begin{aligned}B^{l_1,l_2,l;m_1,m_2,m}_{\dot{l}_1,\dot{l}_2,\dot{l};\dot{m}_1,\dot{m}_2,\dot{m}}&=(-1)^{l_1+\dot{l}_1-m_1-\dot{m}_1}\times\\ &\frac{\Gamma(l_1+l_2-m+1)\Gamma(\dot{l}_1+\dot{l}_2-\dot{m}+1)}{\Gamma(l_2-l_1+m+1)\Gamma(\dot{l}_2-\dot{l}_1+\dot{m}+1)}\times\\ &\left(\frac{(l-m)!(l+l_2-l_1)!(l_1-m_1)!(l_2+m_2)!(l+m)!(2l+1)}{(l_1-l_2+l)!(l_1+l_2-l)!(l_1+l_2+l)!(l_1-m_1)!(l_2-m_2)!}\right)^{\frac{1}{2}}\times\\ &\left(\frac{(\dot{l}-\dot{m})!(\dot{l}+\dot{l}_2-\dot{l}_1)!(\dot{l}_1-\dot{m}_1)!(\dot{l}_2+\dot{m}_2)!(\dot{l}+\dot{m})!(2\dot{l}+1)}{(\dot{l}_1-\dot{l}_2+\dot{l})!(\dot{l}_1+\dot{l}_2-\dot{l})!(\dot{l}_1+\dot{l}_2+\dot{l})!(\dot{l}_1-\dot{m}_1)!(\dot{l}_2-\dot{m}_2)!}\right)^{\frac{1}{2}}\times\\ {}_3F_2&\left(\left.\begin{matrix}l+m+1,-l+m,-l_1+m_1\\ -l_1-l_2+m,l_2-l_1+m+1\end{matrix}\right|1\right){}_3F_2\left(\left.\begin{matrix}\dot{l}+\dot{m}+1,-\dot{l}+\dot{m},-\dot{l}_1+\dot{m}_1\\ -\dot{l}_1-\dot{l}_2+\dot{m},\dot{l}_2-\dot{l}_1+\dot{m}+1\end{matrix}\right|1\right),\end{aligned} \tag{125}$$

where $m=m_1+m_2$, $\dot{m}=\dot{m}_1+\dot{m}_2$. In virtue of the orthogonality of the Clebsch–Gordan coefficients from (124) it follows that

$$\begin{aligned}\zeta_{l_1m_1;\dot{l}_1\dot{m}_2}\otimes\zeta_{l_2m_2;\dot{l}_2\dot{m}_2}&=\sum_{\substack{m_1+m_2=m,\\ \dot{m}_1+\dot{m}_2=\dot{m}}}\overline{C(l_1,l_2,l;m_1,m_2,m)C(\dot{l}_1,\dot{l}_2,\dot{l};\dot{m}_1,\dot{m}_2,\dot{m})}\zeta_{lm;\dot{l}\dot{m}}\\ &=\sum_{\substack{m_1+m_2=m,\\ \dot{m}_1+\dot{m}_2=\dot{m}}}\bar{B}^{l_1,l_2,l;m_1,m_2,m}_{\dot{l}_1,\dot{l}_2,\dot{l};\dot{m}_1,\dot{m}_2,\dot{m}}\zeta_{lm;\dot{l}\dot{m}}.\end{aligned} \tag{126}$$

Further, assume that $l_1=1$ and $\dot{l}_1=1$, then at $l_2\ge 1$ and $\dot{l}_2\ge 1$ the numbers l and m (correspondingly $\dot{l}$ and $\dot{m}$) take the values $l=l_2-1,\ l_2,\ l_2+1,\ m=$

m_2-1, m_2, m_2+1 (correspondingly $\dot{l}=\dot{l}_2-1$, $\dot{l}_2$, $\dot{l}_2+1$, $\dot{m}=\dot{m}_2-1$, $\dot{m}_2$, $\dot{m}_2+1$). In this case the system (126) can be rewritten as follows

$$\begin{aligned}
\zeta_{1,-1;1,-1}\otimes\zeta_{l_2,m_2+1;\dot{l}_2,\dot{m}_2+1} &= \bar{b}^m_{11}\zeta_{l+1,m;\dot{l}+1,\dot{m}}+\bar{b}^m_{12}\zeta_{lm;\dot{l}\dot{m}}+\bar{b}^m_{13}\zeta_{l-1,m;\dot{l}-1,\dot{m}},\\
\zeta_{1,0;1,0}\otimes\zeta_{l_2m_2;\dot{l}_2\dot{m}_2} &= \bar{b}^m_{21}\zeta_{l+1,m;\dot{l}+1,\dot{m}}+\bar{b}^m_{22}\zeta_{lm;\dot{l}\dot{m}}+\bar{b}^m_{23}\zeta_{l-1,m;\dot{l}-1,\dot{m}},\\
\zeta_{1,1;1,1}\otimes\zeta_{l_2,m_2-1;\dot{l}_2,\dot{m}_2-1} &= \bar{b}^m_{31}\zeta_{l+1,m;\dot{l}+1,\dot{m}}+\bar{b}^m_{32}\zeta_{lm\dot{l}\dot{m}}+\bar{b}^m_{33}\zeta_{l-1,m;\dot{l}-1,\dot{m}}
\end{aligned}\tag{127}$$

where

$$\bar{b}^{(m)}=\begin{pmatrix}
\bar{B}^{1,l_2,l_2-1;1,m_2,m}_{1,\dot{l}_2,\dot{l}_2-1;1,\dot{m}_2,\dot{m}} & \bar{B}^{1,l_2,l_2-1;0,m_2,m}_{1,\dot{l}_2,\dot{l}_2-1;1,\dot{m}_2,\dot{m}} & \bar{B}^{1,l_2,l_2-1;-1,m_2,m}_{1,\dot{l}_2,\dot{l}_2-1;-1,\dot{m}_2,\dot{m}}\\
\bar{B}^{1,l_2,l_2;1,m_2,m}_{1,\dot{l}_2,\dot{l}_2;1,\dot{m}_2,\dot{m}} & \bar{B}^{1,l_2,l_2;0,m_2,m}_{1,\dot{l}_2,\dot{l}_2;0,\dot{m}_2,\dot{m}} & \bar{B}^{1,l_2,l_2;-1,m_2,m}_{1,\dot{l}_2,\dot{l}_2;-1,\dot{m}_2,\dot{m}}\\
\bar{B}^{1,l_2,l_2+1;1,m_2,m}_{1,\dot{l}_2,\dot{l}_2+1;1,\dot{m}_2,\dot{m}} & \bar{B}^{1,l_2,l_2+1;0,m_2,m}_{1,\dot{l}_2,\dot{l}_2+1;0,\dot{m}_2,\dot{m}} & \bar{B}^{1,l_2,l_2+1;-1,m_2,m}_{1,\dot{l}_2,\dot{l}_2+1;-1,\dot{m}_2,\dot{m}}
\end{pmatrix}=$$

$$\begin{pmatrix}
\sqrt{\frac{(l_2-m)(l_2-m+1)(\dot{l}_2-\dot{m})(\dot{l}_2-\dot{m}+1)}{(2l_2+1)(2l_2+2)(2\dot{l}_2+1)(2\dot{l}_2+2)}} & \sqrt{\frac{(l_2+m+1)(l_2-m)(\dot{l}_2+\dot{m}+1)(\dot{l}_2-\dot{m}}{4l_2(l_2+1)\dot{l}_2(\dot{l}_2+1)}} & \sqrt{\frac{(l_2+m)(l_2+m+1)(\dot{l}_2+\dot{m})(\dot{l}_2+\dot{m}+1)}{4l_2(2l_2+1)\dot{l}_2(\dot{l}_2+1)}}\\
\sqrt{\frac{(l_2+m+1)(l_2-m+1)(\dot{l}_2+\dot{m}+1)(\dot{l}_2-\dot{m}+1)}{(2l_2+1)(l_2+1)(2\dot{l}_2+1)(\dot{l}_2+1)}} & \sqrt{\frac{m\dot{m}}{l_2(l_2+1)\dot{l}_2(\dot{l}_2+1)}} & \sqrt{\frac{(l_2+m_2)(l_2-m_2)(\dot{l}_2+\dot{m}_2)(\dot{l}_2-\dot{m}_2)}{l_2(2l_2+1)\dot{l}_2(2\dot{l}_2+1)}}\\
\sqrt{\frac{(l_2+m)(l_2+m+1)(\dot{l}_2+\dot{m})(\dot{l}_2+\dot{m}+1)}{(2l_2+1)(2l_2+2)(2\dot{l}_2+1)(2\dot{l}_2+2)}} & \sqrt{\frac{(l_2+m)(l_2-m+1)(\dot{l}_2+\dot{m})(\dot{l}_2-\dot{m}+1)}{4l_2(l_2+1)\dot{l}_2(\dot{l}_2+1)}} & \sqrt{\frac{(l_2-m)(l_2-m+1)(\dot{l}_2-\dot{m})(\dot{l}_2-\dot{m}+1)}{4l_2(2l_2+1)\dot{l}_2(\dot{l}_2+1)}}
\end{pmatrix}.\tag{128}$$

Let $T^l_{\mathfrak{g}}$ be a matrix of the irreducible representation of the weight l in the helicity basis. Let us apply the transformation $T_{\mathfrak{g}}$ to the left and right parts of the each equalities (127). In the left part we have

$$\begin{gathered}
T_{\mathfrak{g}}\zeta_{1,k;1,\dot{k}}\otimes\zeta_{l_2,m_2-k;\dot{l}_2-\dot{k}}=T^1_{\mathfrak{g}}\zeta_{1,k;1,\dot{k}}\otimes T^{l_2}_{\mathfrak{g}}\zeta_{l_2,m_2-k;\dot{l}_2-\dot{k}}=\\
\bar{b}^m_{k+2,1}T^{l+1}_{\mathfrak{g}}\zeta_{l+1,m;\dot{l}+1}+\bar{b}^m_{k+2,2}T^l_{\mathfrak{g}}\zeta_{lm;\dot{l}\dot{m}}+\bar{b}^m_{k+2,3}T^{l-1}_{\mathfrak{g}}\zeta_{l-1,m;\dot{l}-1,\dot{m}},
\end{gathered}$$

where $k,\dot{k}=-1,0,1$. Denoting the elements of $T^l_{\mathfrak{g}}$ via $\mathfrak{M}^l_{mn}$ (generalized hyperspherical functions) we find

$$\begin{gathered}
\left(\mathfrak{M}^1_{-1,k}\zeta_{1,-1;1,-1}+\mathfrak{M}^1_{0,k}\zeta_{1,0;1,0}+\mathfrak{M}^1_{1,k}\zeta_{1,1;1,1}\right)\sum\mathfrak{M}^l_{j,m-k}\zeta_{l_2,m_2-j;\dot{l}_2-\dot{j}}=\\
\sum\left(\bar{b}^m_{k+2,1}\mathfrak{M}^{l+1}_{jm}\zeta_{l+1,j;\dot{l}+1,\dot{j}}+\bar{b}^m_{k+2,2}\mathfrak{M}^l_{jm}\zeta_{lj;\dot{l}\dot{j}}+\bar{b}^m_{k+2,3}\mathfrak{M}^{l-1}_{jm}\zeta_{l-1,j;\dot{l}-1;\dot{j}}\right).
\end{gathered}$$

Replacing in the right part the vectors $\zeta_{l+1,j;\dot{l}+1,\dot{j}}$, $\zeta_{lj;\dot{l}\dot{j}}$, $\zeta_{l-1,j;\dot{l}-1,\dot{j}}$ via $\zeta_{1,-1;1,-1}\otimes\zeta_{l_2,j+1;\dot{l}_2,\dot{j}+1}$, $\zeta_{1,0;1,0}\otimes\zeta_{l_2j;\dot{l}_2\dot{j}}$, $\zeta_{1,1;1,1}\otimes\zeta_{l_2,j-1;\dot{l}_2,\dot{j}-1}$ and comparing the coefficients at $\zeta_{1,-1;1,-1}\otimes\zeta_{l_2,j+1;\dot{l}_2,\dot{j}+1}$, $\zeta_{1,0;1,0}\otimes\zeta_{l_2j;\dot{l}_2\dot{j}}$, $\zeta_{1,1;1,1}\otimes\zeta_{l_2,j-1;\dot{l}_2,\dot{j}-1}$ in the left and right parts, we obtain three relations depending on k. Giving in these relations three possible values $-1, 0, 1$ to the number k and substituting the functions $\mathfrak{M}^1_{mn}(\varphi,\epsilon,\theta,\tau,\psi,\varepsilon)$ (the matrix (66)), we find the following nine recurrence relations:

$$\bar{b}^m_{11}\mathfrak{M}^{l+1}_{jm}\bar{b}^j_{11}+\bar{b}^m_{12}\mathfrak{M}^l_{jm}\bar{b}^j_{12}+\bar{b}^m_{13}\mathfrak{M}^{l-1}_{jm}\bar{b}^j_{13}=$$
$$\left(\cos^2\frac{\theta}{2}\cosh^2\frac{\tau}{2}+\frac{i\sin\theta\sinh\tau}{2}-\sin^2\frac{\theta}{2}\sinh^2\frac{\tau}{2}\right)e^{\epsilon+i\varphi+\varepsilon+i\psi}\mathfrak{M}^l_{j+1,m+1},$$
$$\bar{b}^m_{11}\mathfrak{M}^{l+1}_{jm}\bar{b}^j_{21}+\bar{b}^m_{12}\mathfrak{M}^l_{jm}\bar{b}^j_{22}+\bar{b}^m_{13}\mathfrak{M}^{l-1}_{jm}\bar{b}^j_{23}=$$
$$\frac{1}{\sqrt{2}}(\cos\theta\sinh\tau+i\sin\theta\cosh\tau)e^{-\varepsilon-i\psi}\mathfrak{M}^l_{j,m+1},$$
$$\bar{b}^m_{11}\mathfrak{M}^{l+1}_{jm}\bar{b}^j_{31}+\bar{b}^m_{12}\mathfrak{M}^l_{jm}\bar{b}^j_{32}+\bar{b}^m_{13}\mathfrak{M}^{l-1}_{jm}\bar{b}^j_{33}=$$
$$\left(\cos^2\frac{\theta}{2}\sinh^2\frac{\tau}{2}+\frac{i\sin\theta\sinh\tau}{2}-\sin^2\frac{\theta}{2}\cosh^2\frac{\tau}{2}\right)e^{\epsilon+i\varphi-\varepsilon-i\psi}\mathfrak{M}^l_{j-1,m+1},$$
$$\bar{b}^m_{21}\mathfrak{M}^{l+1}_{jm}\bar{b}^j_{11}+\bar{b}^m_{22}\mathfrak{M}^l_{jm}\bar{b}^j_{12}+\bar{b}^m_{23}\mathfrak{M}^{l-1}_{jm}\bar{b}^j_{13}=$$
$$\frac{1}{\sqrt{2}}(\cos\theta\sinh\tau+i\sin\theta\cosh\tau)e^{\varepsilon+i\psi}\mathfrak{M}^l_{j+1,m},$$
$$\bar{b}^m_{21}\mathfrak{M}^{l+1}_{jm}\bar{b}^j_{21}+\bar{b}^m_{22}\mathfrak{M}^l_{jm}\bar{b}^j_{22}+\bar{b}^m_{23}\mathfrak{M}^{l-1}_{jm}\bar{b}^j_{23}=(\cos\theta\cosh\tau+i\sin\theta\sinh\tau)\mathfrak{M}^l_{j,m},$$
$$\bar{b}^m_{21}\mathfrak{M}^{l+1}_{jm}\bar{b}^j_{31}+\bar{b}^m_{22}\mathfrak{M}^l_{jm}\bar{b}^j_{32}+\bar{b}^m_{23}\mathfrak{M}^{l-1}_{jm}\bar{b}^j_{33}=$$
$$\frac{1}{\sqrt{2}}(\cos\theta\sinh\tau+i\sin\theta\cosh\tau)e^{-\varepsilon-i\psi}\mathfrak{M}^l_{j-1,m},$$
$$\bar{b}^m_{31}\mathfrak{M}^{l+1}_{jm}\bar{b}^j_{11}+\bar{b}^m_{32}\mathfrak{M}^l_{jm}\bar{b}^j_{12}+\bar{b}^m_{33}\mathfrak{M}^{l-1}_{jm}\bar{b}^i_{13}=$$
$$\left(\cos^2\frac{\theta}{2}\sinh^2\frac{\tau}{2}+\frac{i\sin\theta\sinh\tau}{2}-\sin^2\frac{\theta}{2}\cosh^2\frac{\tau}{2}\right)e^{-\epsilon-i\varphi+\epsilon+i\psi}\mathfrak{M}^l_{j+1,m-1},$$
$$\bar{b}^m_{31}\mathfrak{M}^{l+1}_{jm}\bar{b}^j_{21}+\bar{b}^m_{32}\mathfrak{M}^l_{jm}\bar{b}^j_{22}+\bar{b}^m_{33}\mathfrak{M}^{l-1}_{jm}\bar{b}^j_{23}=$$
$$\frac{1}{\sqrt{2}}(\cos\theta\sinh\tau+i\sin\theta\cosh\tau)e^{-\epsilon-i\varphi}\mathfrak{M}^l_{j,m-1},$$
$$\bar{b}^m_{31}\mathfrak{M}^{l+1}_{jm}\bar{b}^j_{31}+\bar{b}^m_{32}\mathfrak{M}^l_{jm}\bar{b}^j_{32}+\bar{b}^m_{33}\mathfrak{M}^{l-1}_{jm}\bar{b}^j_{33}=$$
$$\left(\cos^2\frac{\theta}{2}\cosh^2\frac{\tau}{2}+\frac{i\sin\theta\sinh\tau}{2}-\sin^2\frac{\theta}{2}\sinh^2\frac{\tau}{2}\right)e^{-\epsilon-i\varphi-\varepsilon-i\psi}\mathfrak{M}^l_{j-1,m-1}.$$

Let us find recurrence relations between the functions $\mathfrak{M}^l_{mn}$, where the weight l changed by $\frac{1}{2}$. Thus, at $l_1=1/2$, $\dot{l}_2=1/2$ and $l_1\geq 1/2$, $\dot{l}_2\geq 1/2$ by analogy with

(127) we obtain

$$\begin{aligned} \zeta_{\frac{1}{2},\frac{1}{2};\frac{1}{2},\frac{1}{2}} \otimes \zeta_{l_2,m_2-\frac{1}{2};\dot{l}_2,\dot{m}_2-\frac{1}{2}} &= \bar{b}^m_{00}\zeta_{l+\frac{1}{2},m;\dot{l}+\frac{1}{2},\dot{m}} + \bar{b}^m_{01}\zeta_{l-\frac{1}{2},m;\dot{l}-\frac{1}{2},\dot{m}}, \\ \zeta_{\frac{1}{2},-\frac{1}{2};\frac{1}{2},-\frac{1}{2}} \otimes \zeta_{l_2,m_2+\frac{1}{2};\dot{l}_2,\dot{m}_2+\frac{1}{2}} &= \bar{b}^m_{10}\zeta_{l+\frac{1}{2},m;\dot{l}+\frac{1}{2},\dot{m}} + \bar{b}^m_{11}\zeta_{l-\frac{1}{2},m;\dot{l}-\frac{1}{2},\dot{m}}, \end{aligned}$$

where

$$\bar{b}^{(m)} = \begin{pmatrix} \bar{B}^{\frac{1}{2},l_2,l_2+\frac{1}{2};-\frac{1}{2},m_2,m}_{\frac{1}{2},\dot{l}_2,\dot{l}_2+\frac{1}{2};-\frac{1}{2},\dot{m}_2,\dot{m}} & \bar{B}^{\frac{1}{2},l_2,l_2-\frac{1}{2};-\frac{1}{2},m_2,m}_{\frac{1}{2},\dot{l}_2,\dot{l}_2-\frac{1}{2};-\frac{1}{2},\dot{m}_2,\dot{m}} \\ \bar{B}^{\frac{1}{2},l_2,l_2+\frac{1}{2};\frac{1}{2},m_2,m}_{\frac{1}{2},\dot{l}_2,\dot{l}_2+\frac{1}{2};\frac{1}{2},\dot{m}_2,\dot{m}} & \bar{B}^{\frac{1}{2},l_2,l_2-\frac{1}{2};\frac{1}{2},m_2,m}_{\frac{1}{2},\dot{l}_2,\dot{l}_2-\frac{1}{2};\frac{1}{2},\dot{m}_2,\dot{m}} \end{pmatrix} =$$

$$\begin{pmatrix} \sqrt{\frac{(l_2-m+\frac{1}{2})(\dot{l}_2-\dot{m}+\frac{1}{2})}{(2l_2+1)(2\dot{l}_2+1)}} & \sqrt{\frac{(l_2+m+\frac{1}{2})(\dot{l}_2+\dot{m}+\frac{1}{2})}{(2l_2+1)(2\dot{l}_2+1)}} \\ \sqrt{\frac{(l_2+m+\frac{1}{2})(\dot{l}_2+\dot{m}+\frac{1}{2})}{(2l_2+1)(2\dot{l}_2+1)}} & \sqrt{\frac{(l_2-m+\frac{1}{2})(\dot{l}_2-\dot{m}+\frac{1}{2})}{(2l_2+1)(2\dot{l}_2+1)}} \end{pmatrix}.$$

Carrying out the analogous calculations as for the case $l = 1$ and using the matrix (65), we come to the following recurrence relations

$$\begin{aligned} \bar{b}^m_{00}\mathfrak{M}^{l+\frac{1}{2}}_{jm}\bar{b}^j_{00} + \bar{b}^m_{01}\mathfrak{M}^{l-\frac{1}{2}}_{jm}\bar{b}^j_{01} &= \left(\cos\frac{\theta}{2}\cosh\frac{\tau}{2} + i\sin\frac{\theta}{2}\sinh\frac{\tau}{2}\right)e^{\frac{\epsilon+i\varphi+\varepsilon+i\psi}{2}}\mathfrak{M}^l_{j+\frac{1}{2},m+\frac{1}{2}}, \\ \bar{b}^m_{00}\mathfrak{M}^{l+\frac{1}{2}}_{jm}\bar{b}^j_{10} + \bar{b}^m_{01}\mathfrak{M}^{l-\frac{1}{2}}_{jm}\bar{b}^j_{11} &= \left(\cos\frac{\theta}{2}\sinh\frac{\tau}{2} + i\sin\frac{\theta}{2}\cosh\frac{\tau}{2}\right)e^{\frac{\epsilon+i\varphi-\varepsilon-i\psi}{2}}\mathfrak{M}^l_{j-\frac{1}{2},m+\frac{1}{2}}, \\ \bar{b}^m_{10}\mathfrak{M}^{l+\frac{1}{2}}_{jm}\bar{b}^j_{00} + \bar{b}^m_{11}\mathfrak{M}^{l-\frac{1}{2}}_{jm}\bar{b}^j_{01} &= \left(\cos\frac{\theta}{2}\sinh\frac{\tau}{2} + i\sin\frac{\theta}{2}\cosh\frac{\tau}{2}\right)e^{\frac{-\epsilon-i\varphi+\varepsilon+i\psi}{2}}\mathfrak{M}^l_{j+\frac{1}{2},m-\frac{1}{2}}, \\ \bar{b}^m_{10}\mathfrak{M}^{l+\frac{1}{2}}_{jm}\bar{b}^j_{10} + \bar{b}^m_{11}\mathfrak{M}^{l-\frac{1}{2}}_{jm}\bar{b}^j_{11} &= \left(\cos\frac{\theta}{2}\cosh\frac{\tau}{2} + i\sin\frac{\theta}{2}\sinh\frac{\tau}{2}\right)e^{\frac{-\epsilon-i\varphi-\varepsilon-i\psi}{2}}\mathfrak{M}^l_{j-\frac{1}{2},m-\frac{1}{2}}. \end{aligned}$$

6 Harmonic analysis on the group $SU(2)\otimes SU(2)$

Since $SU(2)\otimes SU(2)$ is locally compact, then there exists an invariant measure $d\mathfrak{g}$ (Haar measure) on this group, that is, such a measure that for any finite continuous function $f(\mathfrak{g})$ we have

$$\int f(\mathfrak{g})d\mathfrak{g} = \int f(\mathfrak{g}_0\mathfrak{g})d\mathfrak{g} = \int f(\mathfrak{g}\mathfrak{g}_0)d\mathfrak{g} = \int f(\mathfrak{g}^{-1})d\mathfrak{g}.$$

Applying the equations (95)–(100), we come to a following expression for the Haar measure in terms of the parameters (44):

$$d\mathfrak{g} = \sin\theta^c \sin\dot{\theta}^c d\theta d\varphi d\psi d\tau d\epsilon d\varepsilon. \tag{129}$$

Thus, an invariant integration on the group $SU(2)\otimes SU(2)$ is defined by the formula

$$\int\limits_{SU(2)\otimes SU(2)} f(g)d\mathfrak{g} = \frac{1}{32\pi^4}\int\limits_{-\infty}^{+\infty}\int\limits_{-\infty}^{+\infty}\int\limits_{-\infty}^{+\infty}\int\limits_{-2\pi}^{2\pi}\int\limits_{0}^{2\pi}\int\limits_{0}^{\pi} f(\theta,\varphi,\psi,\tau,\epsilon,\varepsilon)\sin\theta^c\sin\dot{\theta}^c d\theta d\varphi d\psi d\tau d\epsilon d\varepsilon.$$

Since a dimension of the spinor representation $T_{\mathfrak{g}}$ of $SU(2)\otimes SU(2)$ is equal to $(2l+1)(2\dot{l}+1)$, then the functions $\sqrt{(2l+1)(2\dot{l}+1)}t^{l}_{mn}(\mathfrak{g})$ form a full orthogonal normalized system on this group with respect to the invariant measure $d\mathfrak{g}$. At this point, the index l runs all possible integer or half-integer non-negative values, and the indices m and n run the values $-l,-l+1,\ldots,l-1,l$. In virtue of (47) the matrix elements t^{l}_{mn} are expressed via the generalized hyperspherical function $t^{l}_{mn}(\mathfrak{g})=\mathfrak{M}^{l}_{mn}(\varphi,\epsilon,\theta,\tau,\psi,\varepsilon)$. Therefore,

$$\int\limits_{SU(2)\otimes SU(2)}\mathfrak{M}^{l}_{mn}(\mathfrak{g})\overline{\mathfrak{M}^{l}_{mn}(\mathfrak{g})}d\mathfrak{g}=\frac{32\pi^{4}}{(2l+1)(2\dot{l}+1)}\delta(\mathfrak{g}'-\mathfrak{g}), \qquad (130)$$

where $\delta(\mathfrak{g}'-\mathfrak{g})$ is a δ-function on the group $SU(2)\otimes SU(2)$. An explicit form of δ-function is

$$\delta(\mathfrak{g}'-\mathfrak{g})=\delta(\varphi'-\varphi)\delta(\epsilon'-\epsilon)\delta(\cos\theta'\cosh\tau'-\cos\theta\cosh\tau)\times$$
$$\times\,\delta(\sin\theta'\sinh\tau'-\sin\theta\sinh\tau)\delta(\psi'-\psi)\delta(\varepsilon'-\varepsilon).$$

Substituting into (130) the expression

$$\mathfrak{M}^{l}_{mn}(\mathfrak{g})=e^{-m(\epsilon+i\varphi)}Z^{l}_{mn}e^{-n(\varepsilon+i\psi)}$$

and taking into account (129), we obtain

$$\int\limits_{-\infty}^{+\infty}\int\limits_{-\infty}^{+\infty}\int\limits_{-\infty}^{+\infty}\int\limits_{-2\pi}^{2\pi}\int\limits_{0}^{2\pi}\int\limits_{0}^{\pi}Z^{l}_{mn}\overline{Z^{s}_{pq}}e^{-(m+p)\epsilon}e^{-i(m-p)\varphi}\times$$
$$\times\,e^{-(n+q)\varepsilon}e^{-i(n-q)\psi}\sin\theta^{c}\sin\dot{\theta}^{c}d\theta d\varphi d\psi d\tau d\epsilon d\varepsilon=\frac{32\pi^{4}\delta_{ls}\delta_{mp}\delta_{nq}\delta(\mathfrak{g}'-\mathfrak{g})}{(2l+1)(2\dot{l}+1)}.$$

Since the hyperspherical function of the principal series has the form

$$Z^{-\frac{1}{2}+i\rho}_{mn}(\cos\theta^{c})=\sum_{k=-\frac{\lambda}{2}}^{[\frac{\lambda}{2}]}P^{\frac{\lambda}{2}}_{mk}(\cos\theta)\mathfrak{P}^{-\frac{1}{2}+i\rho}_{kn}(\cosh\tau),$$

then any function $f(\mathfrak{g})$ on the group $SU(2)\otimes SU(2)$, such that $\int|f(\mathfrak{g})|^{2}d\mathfrak{g}<+\infty$, is expanded on the matrix elements of the principal series

$$\mathfrak{M}^{-\frac{1}{2}+i\rho}_{mn}(\mathfrak{g})=e^{-m(\epsilon+i\varphi)-n(\varepsilon+i\psi)}\sum_{k=-l}^{[\frac{\lambda}{2}]}P^{\frac{\lambda}{2}}_{mk}(\cos\theta)\mathfrak{P}^{-\frac{1}{2}+i\rho}_{kn}(\cosh\tau)$$

Since the Lorentz group is noncompact, then an expansion should be run on the conical functions $\mathfrak{P}^{-\frac{1}{2}+i\rho}_{kn}(\cosh\tau)$, where the parameter τ changes in the limits $0\leq\tau<\infty$. In other words, this problem can be formulated as follows.

Let m and n be simultaneously integer or half-integer numbers, and let $F(x)$ be the function such that

$$\int_1^\infty |F(x)|^2 dx < +\infty.$$

It takes to expand the function $F(x)$ via the functions $\mathfrak{P}^l_{mn}(x)$, where l is an expansion parameter and $1 \leq x < \infty$.

As it shown in [76], the functions $\mathfrak{P}^l_{mn}(x)$ satisfy the self-conjugate differential equation

$$\frac{d}{dx}(x^2-1)\frac{du}{dx} - \frac{m^2+n^2-2mnx}{x^2-1} = l(l+1)u.$$

The functions $\mathfrak{P}^l_{mn}(x)$ are continuous at the point $x=1$ corresponding to $\tau = 0$. In other words, $\mathfrak{P}^l_{mn}(x)$ are eigenfunctions of the self-conjugate operator

$$\frac{d}{dx}(x^2-1)\frac{du}{dx} - \frac{m^2+n^2-2mnx}{x^2-1}, \quad 1 \leq x < \infty.$$

Using the standard expansion technique on eigenfunctions of self-conjugate operators (see, for example, [43, 46]), Vilenkin [76] derived the following result.

Theorem 2 (Vilenkin [76]). *If m and n are integer numbers, then any function $F(x)$, such that $\int\limits_1^\infty |F(x)|^2 dx < +\infty$, has an expansion*

$$F(x) = \frac{1}{4\pi^2}\int_0^\infty a(\rho)\mathfrak{P}^{-\frac{1}{2}+i\rho}_{mn}(x)\rho\tanh\pi\rho d\rho + \frac{1}{4\pi^2}\sum_{l=1}^{M}\left(l-\frac{1}{2}\right)b(l)\mathfrak{P}^l_{mn}(x),$$

where

$$M = \begin{cases} \min(|m|,|n|) & \text{if } mn \geq 0, \\ 0 & \text{if } mn < 0. \end{cases}$$

The summation is produced via integer values l. The coefficients $a(\rho)$ and $b(l)$ in this expansion are expressed by the formulas:

$$a(\rho) = \int_1^\infty F(x)\mathfrak{P}^{-\frac{1}{2}-i\rho}_{mn}(x)dx \equiv \int_1^\infty F(x)\overline{\mathfrak{P}^{-\frac{1}{2}+i\rho}_{mn}(x)}dx$$

and

$$b(l) = (-1)^{m-n}\int_1^\infty F(x)\mathfrak{P}^{-l-1}_{mn}(x)dx \equiv$$

$$\equiv (-1)^{m-n}\frac{\Gamma(l+m+1)\Gamma(l-m+1)}{\Gamma(l+n+1)\Gamma(l-n+1)}\int_1^\infty F(x)\overline{\mathfrak{P}^l_{mn}(x)}dx.$$

There is an analog of the Plancherel formula:

$$\int\limits_{1}^{\infty} |F(x)|^2 dx = \frac{1}{4\pi^2} \int\limits_{0}^{\infty} |a(\rho)|^2 \rho \tanh \pi\rho d\rho + \\ + \frac{(-1)^{n-m}}{4\pi^2} \sum_{l=1}^{M} \left(l - \frac{1}{2}\right) \frac{\Gamma(l+n+1)\Gamma(l-n+1)}{\Gamma(l+m+1)\Gamma(l-m+1)} |b(l)|^2.$$

Analogously, if m and n are half-integer numbers, then

$$F(x) = \frac{1}{4\pi^2} \int\limits_{0}^{\infty} a(\rho) \mathfrak{P}_{mn}^{-\frac{1}{2}+i\rho}(x) \rho \coth \pi\rho d\rho + \frac{1}{4\pi^2} \sum_{l=\frac{1}{2}}^{M} \left(l - \frac{1}{2}\right) b(l) \mathfrak{P}_{mn}^{l}(x),$$

where

$$M = \begin{cases} \min(|m|, |n|) & \text{if } mn > 0, \\ 0 & \text{if } mn < 0. \end{cases}$$

The summation is produced via half-integer values l. The coefficients $a(\rho)$ and $b(l)$ are expressed by the same formulas that take place for integer m and n. In this case, the Plancherel formula has a following form

$$\int\limits_{1}^{\infty} |F(x)|^2 dx = \frac{1}{4\pi^2} \int\limits_{0}^{\infty} |a(\rho)|^2 \rho \coth \pi\rho d\rho + \\ + \frac{(-1)^{m-n}}{4\pi^2} \sum_{l=\frac{1}{2}}^{M} \left(l - \frac{1}{2}\right) \frac{\Gamma(l+n+1)\Gamma(l-n+1)}{\Gamma(l+m+1)\Gamma(l-m+1)} |b(l)|^2.$$

Let us apply the Vilenkin Theorem to an expansion of the functions $f(\mathfrak{g})$ on the Lorentz group, such that $\int |f(\mathfrak{g})|^2 d\mathfrak{g} < +\infty$. Then, taking into account that matrix elements of the principal series representations have the form

$$\mathfrak{M}_{mn}^{-\frac{1}{2}+i\rho}(\mathfrak{g}) = e^{-m(\epsilon+i\varphi)-n(\varepsilon+i\psi)} \sum_{k=-\frac{\lambda}{2}}^{[\frac{\lambda}{2}]} P_{mk}^{\frac{\lambda}{2}}(\cos\theta) \mathfrak{P}_{kn}^{-\frac{1}{2}+i\rho}(\cosh\tau),$$

we obtain

$$f(\mathfrak{g}) = \frac{(2l_0+1)(2\dot{l}_0+1)}{32\pi^4} \sum_{m,n} \sum_{k=-\frac{\lambda}{2}}^{[\frac{\lambda}{2}]} \left[\int\limits_{0}^{\infty} a_{mn}(\rho) e^{-m(\epsilon+i\varphi)-n(\varepsilon+i\psi)} \times \right. \\ \times P_{mk}^{\frac{\lambda}{2}}(\cos\theta) \mathfrak{P}_{kn}^{-\frac{1}{2}+i\rho}(\cosh\tau) \rho \tanh \pi\rho d\rho + \\ \left. + \sum_{l_0=1}^{\infty} \left(l_0 - \frac{1}{2}\right) b_{mn}(l_0) e^{-m(\epsilon+i\varphi)-n(\varepsilon+i\psi)} P_{mk}^{l_0}(\cos\theta) \mathfrak{P}_{kn}^{l_0}(\cosh\tau) \right]. \quad (131)$$

The values of the coefficients $a_{mn}(\rho)$ and $b_{mn}(l_0)$ are expressed by the formulas

$$a_{mn}(\rho)=\sum_{k=-\frac{\lambda}{2}}^{[\frac{\lambda}{2}]}\int f(\mathfrak{g})e^{-m(\epsilon+i\varphi)-n(\varepsilon+i\psi)}P^{\frac{\lambda}{2}}_{mk}(\cos\theta)\mathfrak{P}^{-\frac{1}{2}-i\rho}_{kn}(\cosh\tau)d\mathfrak{g}, \tag{132}$$

$$b_{mn}(l_0)=\frac{(-1)^{m-n}\Gamma(l_0+m+1)\Gamma(l_0-m+1)}{\Gamma(l_0+n+1)\Gamma(l_0-n+1)}\int f(\mathfrak{g})\mathfrak{M}^{l_0}_{mn}(\mathfrak{g})d\mathfrak{g}, \tag{133}$$

where $d\mathfrak{g}$ is the Haar measure on the Lorentz group in Euler parameters:

$$d\mathfrak{g}=\sin\theta^c\sin\dot{\theta}^c d\theta d\varphi d\psi d\tau d\epsilon d\varepsilon.$$

In the case of discrete series of representations, the expansion takes a form

$$f(\mathfrak{g})=\frac{(2l_0+1)(2\dot{l}_0+1)}{32\pi^4}\sum_{m,n}\sum_{k=-\frac{\lambda}{2}}^{[\frac{\lambda}{2}]}\left[\int\limits_0^\infty a_{mn}(\rho)e^{-m(\epsilon+i\varphi)-n(\varepsilon+i\psi)}\times\right.$$
$$\times P^{\frac{\lambda}{2}}_{mk}(\cos\theta)\mathfrak{P}^{-\frac{1}{2}+i\rho}_{kn}(\cosh\tau)\rho\tanh\pi\rho d\rho+$$
$$\left.+\sum_{l_0=1}^{M}\left(l_0-\frac{1}{2}\right)b_{mn}(l_0)e^{-m(\epsilon+i\varphi)-n(\varepsilon+i\psi)}P^{l_0}_{mk}(\cos\theta)\mathfrak{P}^{l_0}_{kn}(\cosh\tau)\right]. \tag{134}$$

where

$$M=\begin{cases}\min(|m|,|n|) & \text{if } mn\geq 0,\\ 0 & \text{if } mn<0.\end{cases}$$

The coefficients $a_{mn}(\rho)$ and $b_{mn}(l)$ have the form (132) and (133). Analogously, if m and n are half-integer numbers, then

$$f(\mathfrak{g})=\frac{(2l_0+1)(2\dot{l}_0+1)}{32\pi^4}\sum_{m,n}\sum_{k=-\frac{\lambda}{2}}^{[\frac{\lambda}{2}]}\left[\int\limits_0^\infty a_{mn}(\rho)e^{-m(\epsilon+i\varphi)-n(\varepsilon+i\psi)}\times\right.$$
$$\times P^{\frac{\lambda}{2}}_{mk}(\cos\theta)\mathfrak{P}^{-\frac{1}{2}+i\rho}_{kn}(\cosh\tau)\rho\coth\pi\rho d\rho+$$
$$\left.+\sum_{l_0=\frac{1}{2}}^{M}\left(l_0-\frac{1}{2}\right)b_{mn}(l_0)e^{-m(\epsilon+i\varphi)-n(\varepsilon+i\psi)}P^{l_0}_{mk}(\cos\theta)\mathfrak{P}^{l_0}_{kn}(\cosh\tau)\right]. \tag{135}$$

where

$$M=\begin{cases}\min(|m|,|n|) & \text{if } mn>0,\\ 0 & \text{if } mn<0.\end{cases}$$

The coefficients $a_{mn}(\rho)$ and $b_{mn}(l_0)$ have the same form as in the case of integer m and n.

Since

$$\coth \pi\rho = \tanh \pi\left(\rho + \frac{i}{2}\right),$$

then integral terms in the expansions (134) and (135) can be written uniformly if we replace $\tanh \pi\rho$ and $\coth \pi\rho$ by $\tanh \pi(\rho + oi)$, where $o = 0$ in the integer case and $o = 1/2$ in the half-integer case. The following expansion is an unification of the expansions (134) and (135):

$$f(\mathfrak{g}) = \frac{(2l_0+1)(2\dot{l}_0+1)}{32\pi^4}\sum_{m,n}\sum_{k=-\frac{\lambda}{2}}^{[\frac{\lambda}{2}]}\left[\int\limits_0^\infty a^o_{mn}(\rho)e^{-m(\epsilon+i\varphi)-n(\varepsilon+i\psi)}\times\right.$$
$$\times P^{\frac{\lambda}{2}}_{mk}(\cos\theta)\mathfrak{P}^{(-\frac{1}{2}+i\rho,o)}_{kn}(\cosh\tau)\rho\tanh\pi(\rho+oi)d\rho+$$
$$\left.+\sum_{l_0=1-o}^{M}\left(l_0-\frac{1}{2}\right)b^o_{mn}(l_0)e^{-m(\epsilon+i\varphi)-n(\varepsilon+i\psi)}P^{l_0}_{mk}(\cos\theta)\mathfrak{P}^{l_0}_{kn}(\cosh\tau)\right], \quad (136)$$

where

$$a^o_{mn}(\rho) = \sum_{k=-\frac{\lambda}{2}}^{[\frac{\lambda}{2}]}\int f(\mathfrak{g})e^{-m(\epsilon+i\varphi)-n(\varepsilon+i\psi)}P^{\frac{\lambda}{2}}_{mk}(\cos\theta)\mathfrak{P}^{(-\frac{1}{2}+i\rho,o)}_{kn}(\cosh\tau)d\mathfrak{g}, \quad (137)$$

$$b^o_{mn}(l_0) = \frac{(-1)^{m-n}\Gamma(l_0+m+o+1)\Gamma(l_0-m-o+1)}{\Gamma(l_0+n+o+1)\Gamma(l_0-n-o+1)}\int f(\mathfrak{g})\mathfrak{M}^{l_0}_{mn}(\mathfrak{g})d\mathfrak{g}, \quad (138)$$

$$d\mathfrak{g} = \sin\theta^c\sin\dot{\theta}^c d\theta d\varphi d\psi d\tau d\epsilon d\varepsilon.$$

There is an analog of the Plancherel formula:

$$\int|f(\mathfrak{g})|^2 d\mathfrak{g} = \frac{(2l_0+1)(2\dot{l}_0+1)}{32\pi^4}\sum_{m,n,o}\left[\int\limits_0^\infty |a^o_{mn}(\rho)|^2\rho\tanh\pi(\rho+oi)d\rho+\right.$$
$$\left.+(-1)^{m-n}\sum_{l_0=1-o}^{M}\frac{\Gamma(l_0+n+o+1)\Gamma(l_0-n-o+1)}{\Gamma(l_0+m+o+1)\Gamma(l_0-m-o+1)}\left(l_0-\frac{1}{2}\right)|b^o_{mn}(l_0)|^2\right].$$

Thus, the expansion of square integrable functions $f(\mathfrak{g})$ on the group $SL(2,\mathbb{C})$ has only matrix elements of the principal series of representations. Representations of supplementary series do not participate in the expansion.

An expansion of the functions $f(\mathfrak{g})$ on the Lorentz group in terms of associated hyperspherical functions, that is, an expansion on the two-dimensional complex sphere, has an important meaning in physical applications. Using the explicit expression (76) for the associated hyperspherical functions of the principal series, we find the following expansion:

$$f(\mathfrak{g})=\frac{(2l_0+1)(2\dot{l}_0+1)}{32\pi^4}\sum_m\sum_{k=-\frac{\lambda}{2}}^{[\frac{\lambda}{2}]}\left[\int\limits_0^{\infty}a^o_m(\rho)e^{-m(\epsilon+i\varphi)}\times\right.$$
$$\times P^{\frac{\lambda}{2}}_{mk}(\cos\theta)\mathfrak{P}^k_{(-\frac{1}{2}+i\rho,o)}(\cosh\tau)\rho\tanh\pi(\rho+oi)d\rho+$$
$$\left.+\sum_{l_0=1-o}^{M}\left(l_0-\frac{1}{2}\right)b^o_m(l_0)e^{-m(\epsilon+i\varphi)}P^{l_0}_{mk}(\cos\theta)\mathfrak{P}^k_{l_0}(\cosh\tau)\right],\qquad(139)$$

where

$$a^o_m(\rho)=\sum_{k=-\frac{\lambda}{2}}^{[\frac{\lambda}{2}]}\int f(\mathfrak{g})e^{-m(\epsilon+i\varphi)}P^{\frac{\lambda}{2}}_{mk}(\cos\theta)\mathfrak{P}^k_{(-\frac{1}{2}+i\rho,o)}(\cosh\tau)d\mathfrak{g},\qquad(140)$$

$$b^o_m(l_0)=\frac{(-1)^m\Gamma(l_0+m+o+1)\Gamma(l_0-m-o+1)}{\Gamma(l_0+o+1)\Gamma(l_0-o+1)}\int f(\mathfrak{g})\mathfrak{M}^m_{l_0}(\mathfrak{g})d\mathfrak{g}\qquad(141)$$

and

$$d\mathfrak{g}=\sin\theta^c\sin\dot{\theta}^c d\theta d\varphi d\tau d\epsilon.$$

is a Haar measure on the surface of the two-dimensional complex sphere.

In turn, physical fields, describing particles with an arbitrary spin (both integer and half-integer), are defined in terms of finite-dimensional (spinor) representations of the group $\mathfrak{G}_+$ via the expansions on associated hyperspherical functions realized on the surface of the two-dimensional complex sphere. At this point, the expansion (139) takes a form

$$f(\mathfrak{g})=\frac{(2l+1)(2\dot{l}+1)}{32\pi^4}\sum_{k=-l}^{l}\sum_{l=1-o}^{M}\left(l-\frac{1}{2}\right)b^o_m(l)e^{-m(\epsilon+i\varphi)}P^l_{mk}(\cos\theta)\mathfrak{P}^k_l(\cosh\tau),\qquad(142)$$

where

$$b^o_m(l)=\frac{(-1)^m\Gamma(l+m+o+1)\Gamma(l-m-o+1)}{\Gamma(l+o+1)\Gamma(l-o+1)}\int f(\mathfrak{g})\mathfrak{M}^m_l(\mathfrak{g})d\mathfrak{g}.\qquad(143)$$

An expansion on the cone for the square integrable function (the wave function of free particle with the null spin) was first given by I. S. Shapiro [58, 59]. Later on, Chou Kuang-chao and Zastavenko [13] refined the Shapiro expansion for the particles with non-null spin (see also [15, 49]). From mathematical viewpoint the functions obtained in [58, 13] present an integral transformation, which allows us to obtain an expansion of the function, defined on the hyperboloid, via the conical functions. Such expansions with the use of integral geometry have been further studied in the Gel'fand-Graev works [24] and later have been used by Vilenkin and Smorodinsky [75] for a definition of the formulas of direct and inverse expansions on degenerate representations of the Lorentz group in different coordinate systems. Further, in sequel of the work [75] the authors of [81, 41] studied the questions about relation between different subgroups of the Lorentz group and coordinate systems on the hyperboloid and also the questions concerning convergence and asymptotic expansions. The following step in this direction was became in [44, 42], where the authors constructed irreducible unitary representations of the Lorentz group, realized on the space of functions defined on the direct product of two spaces – the hyperboloid (with the infinite-dimensional representation) and the sphere (with the finite-dimensional spinor representation). These functions, forming the basis for integral representations of scattering amplitudes, are represented by the product of spherical functions (Legendre functions) and conical functions (see also[48]). In the work [42] it has been shown that a realization of the Lorentz group representations on the cone is closely related with the formulas of helicity expansions [37]. Basis functions on the cone and relativistically-invariant expansions of the spiral scattering amplitudes have been obtained by Verdiev [73, 72].

Example. By way of example let us consider a decomposition of the functions on the group $SU(2)\otimes SU(2)$, defining solutions for the Dirac field $(1/2,0)\oplus(0,1/2)$. In [68, 70] it has been shown that these solutions are defined in terms of associated hyperspherical functions:

$$\begin{aligned}
\psi_1(r,\varphi^c,\theta^c) &= \boldsymbol{f}^l_{\frac{1}{2},\frac{1}{2}}(\operatorname{Re} r)\mathfrak{M}^{\frac{1}{2}}_l(\varphi,\epsilon,\theta,\tau,0,0),\\
\psi_2(r,\varphi^c,\theta^c) &= \pm\boldsymbol{f}^l_{\frac{1}{2},\frac{1}{2}}(\operatorname{Re} r)\mathfrak{M}^{-\frac{1}{2}}_l(\varphi,\epsilon,\theta,\tau,0,0),\\
\dot{\psi}_1(r^*,\dot{\varphi}^c,\dot{\theta}^c) &= \mp\boldsymbol{f}^{\dot{l}}_{\frac{1}{2},-\frac{1}{2}}(\operatorname{Re} r^*)\mathfrak{M}^{\frac{1}{2}}_{\dot{l}}(\varphi,\epsilon,\theta,\tau,0,0),\\
\dot{\psi}_2(r^*,\dot{\varphi}^c,\dot{\theta}^c) &= \boldsymbol{f}^{\dot{l}}_{\frac{1}{2},-\frac{1}{2}}(\operatorname{Re} r^*)\mathfrak{M}^{-\frac{1}{2}}_{\dot{l}}(\varphi,\epsilon,\theta,\tau,0,0),
\end{aligned}$$

where

$$l=\frac{1}{2},\ \frac{3}{2},\ \frac{5}{2},\ldots;$$
$$\dot{l}=\frac{1}{2},\ \frac{3}{2},\ \frac{5}{2},\ldots;$$

$$\mathfrak{M}^{\pm\frac{1}{2}}_l(\varphi,\epsilon,\theta,\tau,0,0)=e^{\mp\frac{1}{2}(\epsilon+i\varphi)}Z^{\pm\frac{1}{2}}_l(\theta,\tau),$$

$$Z^{\pm\frac{1}{2}}_l(\theta,\tau)=\cos^{2l}\frac{\theta}{2}\cosh^{2l}\frac{\tau}{2}\sum^{l}_{k=-l}i^{\pm\frac{1}{2}-k}\tan^{\pm\frac{1}{2}-k}\frac{\theta}{2}\tanh^{-k}\frac{\tau}{2}\times$$
$${}_2F_1\left(\begin{array}{c}\pm\frac{1}{2}-l+1,1-l-k\\ \pm\frac{1}{2}-k+1\end{array}\middle|\, i^2\tan^2\frac{\theta}{2}\right){}_2F_1\left(\begin{array}{c}-l+1,1-l-k\\ -k+1\end{array}\middle|\,\tanh^2\frac{\tau}{2}\right),$$

$$\mathfrak{M}_{\dot{l}}^{\pm\frac{1}{2}}(\varphi,\epsilon,\theta,\tau,0,0)=e^{\mp\frac{1}{2}(\epsilon-i\varphi)}Z_{\dot{l}}^{\pm\frac{1}{2}}(\theta,\tau),$$

$$Z_{\dot{l}}^{\pm\frac{1}{2}}(\theta,\tau)=\cos^{2\dot{l}}\frac{\theta}{2}\cosh^{2\dot{l}}\frac{\tau}{2}\sum_{\dot{k}=-\dot{l}}^{\dot{l}}i^{\pm\frac{1}{2}-\dot{k}}\tan^{\pm\frac{1}{2}-\dot{k}}\frac{\theta}{2}\tanh^{-\dot{k}}\frac{\tau}{2}\times$$
$${}_2F_1\left(\begin{array}{c}\pm\frac{1}{2}-\dot{l}+1,1-\dot{l}-\dot{k}\\ \pm\frac{1}{2}-\dot{k}+1\end{array}\middle|\,i^2\tan^2\frac{\theta}{2}\right){}_2F_1\left(\begin{array}{c}-\dot{l}+1,1-\dot{l}-\dot{k}\\ -\dot{k}+1\end{array}\middle|\,\tanh^2\frac{\tau}{2}\right).$$

The radial components $\boldsymbol{f}^{l}_{\frac{1}{2},\frac{1}{2}}(\operatorname{Re}r)$ and $\boldsymbol{f}^{\dot{l}}_{\frac{1}{2},-\frac{1}{2}}(\operatorname{Re}r^*)$, where r is the radius of the two-dimensional complex sphere, are expressed via the Bessel functions of half-integer order:

$$\begin{aligned}\boldsymbol{f}^{l}_{\frac{1}{2},\frac{1}{2}}(\operatorname{Re}r) &= C_1\sqrt{\kappa^c\dot{\kappa}^c}\operatorname{Re}r J_l\left(\sqrt{\kappa^c\dot{\kappa}^c}\operatorname{Re}r\right)+C_2\sqrt{\kappa^c\dot{\kappa}^c}\operatorname{Re}r J_{-l}\left(\sqrt{\kappa^c\dot{\kappa}^c}\operatorname{Re}r\right),\\ \boldsymbol{f}^{\dot{l}}_{\frac{1}{2},-\frac{1}{2}}(\operatorname{Re}r^*) &= \frac{C_1}{2}\sqrt{\frac{\dot{\kappa}^c}{\kappa^c}}\operatorname{Re}r^* J_{l+1}\left(\sqrt{\kappa^c\dot{\kappa}^c}\operatorname{Re}r^*\right)-\frac{C_2}{2}\sqrt{\frac{\dot{\kappa}^c}{\kappa^c}}\operatorname{Re}r^* J_{-l-1}\left(\sqrt{\kappa^c\dot{\kappa}^c}\operatorname{Re}r^*\right).\end{aligned}$$

Then the decomposition for the field $(1/2,0)\oplus(0,1/2)$ takes a form:

$$\psi_1=\frac{(2l+1)(2\dot{l}+1)}{32\pi^4}\boldsymbol{f}^{l}_{\frac{1}{2},\frac{1}{2}}(\operatorname{Re}r)\sum_{k=-l}^{l}\sum_{l=\frac{1}{2}}^{M}\left(l-\frac{1}{2}\right)b_{\frac{1}{2}}(l)e^{-\frac{1}{2}(\epsilon+i\varphi)}P^{l}_{\frac{1}{2},k}(\cos\theta)\mathfrak{P}^{k}_{l}(\cosh\tau),$$

$$\psi_2=\pm\frac{(2l+1)(2\dot{l}+1)}{32\pi^4}\boldsymbol{f}^{l}_{\frac{1}{2},\frac{1}{2}}(\operatorname{Re}r)\sum_{k=-l}^{l}\sum_{l=\frac{1}{2}}^{M}\left(l-\frac{1}{2}\right)b_{-\frac{1}{2}}(l)e^{\frac{1}{2}(\epsilon+i\varphi)}P^{l}_{-\frac{1}{2},k}(\cos\theta)\mathfrak{P}^{k}_{l}(\cosh\tau),$$

$$\dot{\psi}_1=\mp\frac{(2l+1)(2\dot{l}+1)}{32\pi^4}\boldsymbol{f}^{\dot{l}}_{\frac{1}{2},-\frac{1}{2}}(\operatorname{Re}r^*)\sum_{\dot{k}=-\dot{l}}^{\dot{l}}\sum_{\dot{l}=\frac{1}{2}}^{\dot{M}}\left(\dot{l}-\frac{1}{2}\right)b_{\frac{1}{2}}(\dot{l})e^{-\frac{1}{2}(\epsilon-i\varphi)}P^{\dot{l}}_{\frac{1}{2},\dot{k}}(\cos\theta)\mathfrak{P}^{\dot{k}}_{\dot{l}}(\cosh\tau)$$

$$\dot{\psi}_2=\frac{(2l+1)(2\dot{l}+1)}{32\pi^4}\boldsymbol{f}^{\dot{l}}_{\frac{1}{2},-\frac{1}{2}}(\operatorname{Re}r^*)\sum_{\dot{k}=-\dot{l}}^{\dot{l}}\sum_{\dot{l}=\frac{1}{2}}^{\dot{M}}\left(\dot{l}-\frac{1}{2}\right)b_{-\frac{1}{2}}(\dot{l})e^{\frac{1}{2}(\epsilon-i\varphi)}P^{\dot{l}}_{-\frac{1}{2},\dot{k}}(\cos\theta)\mathfrak{P}^{\dot{k}}_{\dot{l}}(\cosh\tau),$$

where

$$b_{\pm\frac{1}{2}}(l)=\frac{(-1)^{\pm\frac{1}{2}}\Gamma(l\pm\frac{1}{2}+1)\Gamma(l\mp\frac{1}{2}+1)}{\Gamma(l+1)\Gamma(l+1)}\int\left[\mathfrak{M}_{l}^{\pm\frac{1}{2}}(\varphi,\epsilon,\theta,\tau,0,0)\right]^2 d\mathfrak{g},$$

$$b_{\pm\frac{1}{2}}(\dot{l})=\frac{(-1)^{\pm\frac{1}{2}}\Gamma(\dot{l}\pm\frac{1}{2}+1)\Gamma(\dot{l}\mp\frac{1}{2}+1)}{\Gamma(\dot{l}+1)\Gamma(\dot{l}+1)}\int\left[\mathfrak{M}_{\dot{l}}^{\pm\frac{1}{2}}(\varphi,\epsilon,\theta,\tau,0,0)\right]^2 d\mathfrak{g},$$

here $d\mathfrak{g}$ is a Haar measure on the surface of the two-dimensional complex sphere:

$$d\mathfrak{g}=\sin\theta^c\sin\dot{\theta}^c d\theta d\varphi d\tau d\epsilon.$$

In conclusion, it should be noted that such a description corresponds to a quantum field theory on the Poincaré group introduced by Lurçat [45] (see also [5, 40, 9, 4, 63, 17, 26] and references therein). Moreover, it allows us to widely use a harmonic analysis on the Poincaré group [50, 29, 30] (or, on the product $SU(2) \otimes SU(2)$) at the study of relativistic amplitudes. Harmonic analysis on the Poincaré group in terms of hyperspherical functions will be considered in the following work.

References

[1] A. I. Akhiezer, V. B. Berestetskii, *Quantum Electrodynamics* (John Wiley & Sons, New York, 1965).

[2] M. Andrews, J. Gunson, Complex Angular Momenta and Many-Particle States. I. Properties of Local Representations of the Rotation Group, *J. Math. Phys.* **5**, 1391–1400 (1964).

[3] P. Appell, M. J. Kampé de Fériet, Fonctions hypégeométriques et hypersphéques. *Polynomes d'Hermite* (Gauthier–Villars, 1926).

[4] H. Arodź, Metric tensors, Lagrangian formalism and Abelian gauge field on the Poincaré group, *Acta Phys. Pol., Ser.* **B7**, 177–190 (1976).

[5] H. Bacry, A. Kihlberg, Wavefunctions on homogeneous spaces, *J. Math. Phys.* **10**, 2132–2141 (1969).

[6] V. Bargmann, Irreducible unitary representations of the Lorentz group, *Ann. of Math.* **48**, 568–640 (1947).

[7] H. Bateman, A. Erdélyi, *Higher Transcendental Functions*, vol. I (Mc Grow-Hill Book Company, New York, 1953).

[8] H. Bateman, A. Erdélyi, *Higher Transcendental Functions*, vol. II (Mc Grow-Hill Book Company, New York, 1953).

[9] C. P. Boyer, G. N. Fleming, Quantum field theory on a seven-dimensional homogeneous space of the Poincaré group, *J. Math. Phys.* **15**, 1007–1024 (1974).

[10] J. L. Burchnall, T. W. Chaundy, Quart. *J. Math.*, Oxford Ser. **12**, 112–128 (1941).

[11] E. Cartan, Sur la détermination d'un systéme orthogonal complet dans un espace dé Riemann symétrique clos, *Rend. Circ. Mat. Palermo* **53**, 217–252 (1929).

[12] T. W. Chaundy, On Appell's fourth hypergeometric function, *Quart. J. Math.* **17**, No. 66, 81–85 (1966).

[13] Chou Kuang-chao, I. G. Zastavenko, The Shapiro integral transformation, *Zh. Ehksp. Teor. Fiz.* **35**, 1417–1425 (1958).

[14] A. Z. Dolginov, Relativistic spherical functions, *Zh. Ehksp. Teor. Fiz.* **30**, 746–755 (1956).

[15] A. Z. Dolginov, I. N. Toptygin, Relativistic spherical functions. II, *Zh. Ehksp. Teor. Fiz.* **37**, 1441–1451 (1959).

[16] A. Z. Dolginov, A. N. Moskalev, Relativistic spherical functions. III, *Zh. Ehksp. Teor. Fiz.* **37**, 1697–1707 (1959).

[17] W. Drechsler, Geometro-stohastically quantized fields with internal spin variables, *J. Math. Phys.* **38**, 5531–5558 (1997).

[18] L. D. Eskin, On the theory of relativistic spherical functions,*Nauchn. dokl. vys. shcoly* **2**, 95–97 (1959).

[19] L. D. Eskin, On the matrix elements of irreducible representations of the Lorentz group, *Izvestia vuzov, Matem.* **6**, 179–184 (1961).

[20] J. Fischer, J. Niederle, R. Raczka, Generalized Spherical Functions for the Noncompact Rotation Groups, *J. Math. Phys.* **7**, 816–821 (1966).

[21] V. A. Fock, *Zs. f. Phys.* **98**, 145 (1935).

[22] I.M. Gel'fand, Z.Ya. Shapiro, Representations of the rotation group of three–dimensional space and their applications, *Uspekhi Mat. Nauk* **7**, 3–117 (1952).

[23] I.M. Gel'fand, A.M. Yaglom, General relativistic–invariant equations and infinite–dimensional representations of the Lorentz group, *Zh. Ehksp. Teor. Fiz.* **18**, 703–733 (1948).

[24] I. M. Gel'fand, M. I. Graev, N. Ya. Vilenkin, Integral geometry and related questions of group representations (Fizmatgiz, Moskow, 1962) [in Russian].

[25] I. M. Gel'fand, R. A. Minlos, Z. Ya. Shapiro, *Representations of the Rotation and Lorentz Groups and their Applications* (Pergamon Press, Oxford, 1963).

[26] D. M. Gitman, A. L. Shelepin, Fields on the Poincaré Group: Arbitrary Spin Description and Relativistic Wave Equations, *Int. J. Theor. Phys.* **40**(3), 603–684 (2001).

[27] V. Ya. Golodets, Matrix elements of irreducible unitary and spinor representations of the homogeneous Lorentz group, *Vesti Academii Navuk Belarusskoi SSR* **1**, 19–28 (1961).

[28] M. Goto, F. Grosshans, Semisimple Lie Algebras (Marcel Dekker, New York, 1978).

[29] N. X. Hai, Harmonic analysis on the Poincaré group, I. Generalized matrix elements, *Commun. Math. Phys.* **12**, 331–350 (1969).

[30] N. X. Hai, Harmonic analysis on the Poincaré group, II. The Fourier transform, *Commun. Math. Phys.* **22**, 301–320 (1971).

[31] Harish Chandra, Infinite irreducible representations of the Lorentz group, *Proc. Royal. Soc. London* **A189**, 372–401 (1947).

[32] *J. Horn, Math. Ann.* **105**, 381–407 (1931).

[33] M. Huszar, Angular Momentum and Unitary Spinor Bases of the Lorentz Group, *Preprint JINR No. E2-5429*, Dubna (1970).

[34] M. Huszar, J. Smorodinsky, Representations of the Lorentz Group on the Two-Dimensional Complex Sphere and Two-Particle States, *Preprint JINR No. E2-5020*, Dubna (1970).

[35] M. Huszar, Spherical functions of the Lorentz group on the hyperboloids, *Acta Phys. Hung.* **58**, 175–185 (1985).

[36] M. Huszar, Addition theorems for the spherical functions of the Lorentz group, *Acta Phys. Hung.* **64**, 361–378 (1988).

[37] M. Jacob, G. C. Wick, *Ann. of Phys.* 7, 404 (1959).

[38] V. I. Kolomytsev, The reduction of the irreducible unitary representations of the group $SL(2,\mathbb{C})$ restricted to the subgroup $SU(1,1)$. The additional series., *Teor. Mat. Fiz.* **2**, 210–229 (1970).

[39] A. P. Kotel'nikov, In memorial *Lobatchevskii* **2**, 37–66 (Kazan, 1927).

[40] A. Kihlberg, Fields on a homogeneous space of the Poincaré group, *Ann. Inst. Henri Poincaré* **13**, 57–76 (1970).

[41] G. I. Kuznetsov, Ya. A. Smorodinsky, Integral representations for relativistic amplitudes and asymptotic theorems, *Yad. Fiz.* **6**, 1308–1312 (1967).

[42] G. I. Kuznetsov, M. A. Liberman, A. A. Makarov, Ya. A. Smorodinsky, Helicity and unitary representations of the Lorentz group, *Yad. Fiz.* **10**, 644–656 (1969).

[43] B. M. Levitan, Expansion in eigenfunctions of differential equations of second order (Gostehizdat, Moscow, 1950) [in Russian].

[44] M. A. Liberman, Ya. A. Smorodinsky, M. B. Sheftel, Unitary representations of the Lorentz group and functions with spin, *Yad. Fiz.* **7**, 202–214 (1968).

[45] F. Lurçat, Quantum field theory and the dynamical role of spin, *Physics* **1**, 95 (1964).

[46] M. A. Naimark, *Linear Differential Operators* (Gostehizdat, Moscow, 1954) [in Russian].

[47] M. A. Naimark, *Linear Representations of the Lorentz Group* (Pergamon, London, 1964).

[48] P. Pajas, P. Winternitz, Representations of the Lorentz Group: New Integral Relations between Legendre Functions, *J. Math. Phys.* **11**, 1505–1510 (1970).

[49] V. S. Popov, On the theory of relativistic transformations of the wave functions and the density matrix of particles with spin, *Zh. Ehksp. Teor. Fiz.* **37**, 1116–1126 (1959).

[50] G. Rideau, On the reduction of the regular representation of the Poincaré group,*Commun. Math. Phys.* **3**, 218–227 (1966).

[51] M. E. Rose, *Multipole Fields* (John Wiley & Sons, New York, 1955).

[52] B. A. Rozenfel'd, *Non–Euclidean Geometries* (Moscow, 1955) [in Russian].

[53] Yu. B. Rumer, *Spinorial Analysis* (Moscow, 1936) [in Russian].

[54] Yu. B. Rumer, A. I. Fet, *Group Theory and Quantized Fields* (Moscow, 1977) [in Russian].

[55] L. Ryder, Quantum Field Theory (Cambridge University Press, Cambridge, 1985).

[56] S. S. Schweber, *An Introduction to Relativistic Quantum Field Theory* (Harper & Row, New York, 1961).

[57] A. Sciarrino, M. Toller, *J. Math. Phys.* **8**, 1252 (1967).

[58] I. S. Shapiro, Expansion of wave function in irreducible representations of the Lorentz group, *Doklady AN SSSR* **106**, 647–649 (1956).

[59] I. S. Shapiro, Expansion of scattering amplitude in relativistic spherical functions, *Zh. Ehksp. Teor. Fiz.* **43**, 1727–1730 (1962).

[60] Ya.A. Smorodinsky, M. Huszar, Representations of the Lorentz group and the generalization of helicity states, *Teor. Mat. Fiz.* **4**, 3, 328–340 (1970).

[61] S. Ström, On the matrix elements of a unitary representation of the homogeneous Lorentz group, *Arkiv för Fysik* **29**, 467–483 (1965).

[62] S. Ström, A note on the matrix elements of a unitary representation of the homogeneous Lorentz group, *Arkiv för Fysik* **33**, 465–469 (1967).

[63] M. Toller, Free quantum fields on the Poincaré group, *J. Math. Phys.* **37**, 2694–2730 (1996).

[64] V. V. Varlamov, Fundamental Automorphisms of Clifford Algebras and an Extension of Dąbrowski Pin Groups, *Hadronic Journal* **22**, 497–535 (1999).

[65] V. V. Varlamov, Discrete Symmetries and Clifford Algebras, *Int. J. Theor. Phys.* **40**, No. 4, 769–805 (2001).

[66] V. V. Varlamov, Clifford Algebras and Discrete Transformations of Spacetime, *Proceedings of Third Siberian Conference on Mathematical Problems of Space-time Physics of Complex Systems*, Novosibirsk, June 20–22 2000. Publishing House of the Institute of Mathematics, Novosibirsk, pp. 97–135, 2001.

[67] V. V. Varlamov, Hyperspherical Functions and Linear Representations of the Lorentz Group, *Hadronic Journal* **25**, 481–508 (2002).

[68] V. V. Varlamov, General Solutions of Relativistic Wave Equations, *Int. J. Theor. Phys.* **42**, No. 3, 583–633 (2003).

[69] V. V. Varlamov, Relativistic Wave Equations in the Helicity Basis, *preprint math-ph/0211027* (2002); *Hadronic Journal* **26**, 275-298 (2003).

[70] V. V. Varlamov, Fields on the Lorentz Group: Helicity Basis and Relativistic Wave Equations, Invited contribution to *Progress in Quantum Physics Research* (Nova Science Publishers, New York), to appear.

[71] I. A. Verdiev, L. A. Dadashev, Matrix elements of the Lorentz group unitary representation, *Yad. Fiz.* **6**, 1094–1099 (1967).

[72] I. A. Verdiev, Relativistically invariant expansion of spiral scattering amplitude, *Zh. Ehksp. Teor. Fiz.* **55**, 1771–1783 (1968).

[73] I. A. Verdiev, *Yad. Fiz.* **9**, 1310 (1969).

[74] I. A. Verdiev, G. A. Kerimov, Ya. A. Smorodinsky, Clebsh-Gordan coefficients of the Lorentz group, *Yad. Fiz.* **21**, 1351–1361 (1975).

[75] N. Ya. Vilenkin, Ya. A. Smorodinsky, Invariant expansions of relativistic amplitudes, *Zh. Ehksp. Teor. Fiz.* **46**, 1793–1808 (1964).

[76] N. Ya. Vilenkin, *Special Functions and the Theory of Group Representations* (AMS, Providence, 1968).

[77] N. Ya. Vilenkin, A. U. Klimyk, *Representations of Lie Groups and Special Functions*, vols. 1–3. (Dordrecht: Kluwer Acad. Publ., 1991–1993).

[78] B. L. van der Waerden, *Spinoranalyse*, Nachr. d. Ces. d. Wiss. Göttingen, 100–109 (1929).

[79] B. L. van der Waerden, *Die Gruppentheoretische Methode in der Quantenmechanik* (Springer, Berlin, 1932).

[80] H. Weyl, Classical Groups (Princeton University Press, New York, 1946).

[81] P. Winternitz, I. Fris, Invariant expansions of relativistic amplitudes and subgroups of the proper Lorentz group, *Yad. Fiz.* **1**, 889–901 (1965).

In: Mathematical Physics Research at the Cutting Edge
Editor: C.V. Benton, pp. 247-268
ISBN 1-59033-939-8

The Next Stage: Quantum Game Theory

Edward W. Piotrowski
Institute of Theoretical Physics, University of Białystok,
Lipowa 41, Pl 15424 Białystok, Poland
e-mail: ep@alpha.uwb.edu.pl
Jan Sładkowski
Institute of Physics, University of Silesia,
Uniwersytecka 4, Pl 40007 Katowice, Poland
e-mail: sladk@us.edu.pl

Abstract

Recent development in quantum computation and quantum information theory allows to extend the scope of game theory for the quantum world. The paper presents the history, basic ideas and recent development in quantum game theory. On grounds of the discussed material, we reason about possible future development of quantum game theory and its impact on information processing and the emerging information society.

PACS Classification: 02.50.Le, 03.67.Lx, 05.50.+q, 05.30.d
Mathematics Subject Classification: 81-02, 91-02, 91A40, 81S99
Keywords and phrases: quantum games, quantum strategies, quantum information theory, quantum computations

1 Introduction

The emerging of global information infrastructure caused one of the main paradigm shifts in human history: information is becoming a crucial if not the most important resource. Recently the scientific community has became more and more aware that information processing is a physical phenomenon and that information theory is inseparable from both applied and fundamental physics. Attention to the very physical aspects of information processing revealed new perspectives of computation, cryptography and communication methods. In most of the cases quantum description of the system provides advantages over the classical situation. Game theory, the study of (rational) decision making in conflict situations, seems to ask for a quantum version. For example, games against nature [1] include those for which nature is quantum mechanical. Does quantum theory offer more subtle ways of playing games? Game theory considers strategies that are probabilistic mixtures of pure strategies. Why cannot they be intertwined in a more complicated way, for example interfered or entangled? Are there situations in which quantum theory can enlarge the set of possible strategies? Can quantum strategies be more successful than classical ones? And if the answer is yes are they of any practical value? John von Neumann is one of the founders of both game theory [2] and quantum theory, is that a meaningful coincidence? In this paper we would like to convince the reader that the research on quantum game theory cannot be neglected because present technological development suggest that sooner or later someone would take full advantage of quantum theory and may use quantum strategies to beat us at some game. Cryptography and communication methods seem to be the more probable battle fields but who can be sure? The paper is organized as follows. We will begin by presenting a detailed analysis of a simple example given by David A. Meyer [5] that will illustrate the general idea of a quantum game and methods of gaining an advantage over "classical opponent". Then we will attempt at giving a definition of a quantum game and review problems that have already been discussed in the literature. Finally we will try to show some problems that should be addressed in the near future. In the following discussion we will use quantum theory as a language but the broadcasted message would be that it can be used as a weapon.

2 Quantum game prehistory and history

It is not easy to give the precise date of birth of quantum game theory. Quantum games have probably been camouflaged since the very beginning of the quantum era because a lot of experiments can be reformulated in terms of game theory. Quantum game theory began with works of Wiesner on quantum money [3], Vaidman, who probably first used the term game in quantum context [4], and Meyer [5] and Eisert et al [6] who first formulated their problems in game theory formalism. Possible applications of quantum games in biology were discussed by Iqbal and Toor [7], in economics by Piotrowski and Sładkowski [8, 9]. Flitney and Abbott quantized Parrondo's paradox [10]. David Meyer put forward a fabulous argument for research on quantum game theory that we are going to retell here [5]. He describes a game that is likely to be played by two characters of the popular TV series *Star Trek: The Next Generation*, Captain Picard and Q. Suppose they play the modern version of the penny flip game that is implemented as a *spin–flip game* (there probably are no coins on a starship). Picard is to set an electron in the spin up state, whereupon they will take turns (Q, then Picard, then Q) flipping the spin or not, without being able to see it. Q wins if the spin is up when they measure the electron's state. This is a two–person *zero–sum strategic game* which might be analyzed using the payoff matrix:

	NN	NF	FN	FF
N	-1	1	1	-1
F	1	-1	-1	1

where the rows and columns are labelled by Picard's and Q's *pure strategies* (moves), respectively; F denotes a flip and N denotes no flip; and the numbers in the matrix are Picard's payoffs: 1 indicating a win and -1 a loss of a one currency unit. Q's payoffs can be obtained by reversing the signs in the above matrix (this is the defining feature of a zero sum game).

Example: Q's strategy is to flip the spin on his first turn and then not flip it on his second, while Picard's strategy is to not flip the spin on his turn. The result is that the state of the spin is, successively: U, D, D, D, so Picard wins.

It is natural to define a two dimensional vector space V with basis (U, D) and to represent players' strategies by sequences of 2×2 matrices. That is, the matrices

$$F := \begin{array}{c} \\ {\scriptstyle U} \\ {\scriptstyle D} \end{array}\!\!\begin{array}{c} {\scriptstyle U \quad D} \\ \begin{pmatrix} 0 & 1 \\ 1 & 0 \end{pmatrix} \end{array} \qquad \text{and} \qquad N := \begin{array}{c} \\ {\scriptstyle U} \\ {\scriptstyle D} \end{array}\!\!\begin{array}{c} {\scriptstyle U \quad D} \\ \begin{pmatrix} 1 & 0 \\ 0 & 1 \end{pmatrix} \end{array}$$

correspond to flipping and not flipping the spin, respectively, since we define them to act by left multiplication on the vector representing the state of the spin. A general *mixed strategy* consists in a linear combination of F and N, which acts as a 2×2 matrix:

$$\begin{array}{c} \\ {\scriptstyle U} \\ {\scriptstyle D} \end{array}\!\!\begin{array}{c} {\scriptstyle U \qquad\quad D} \\ \begin{pmatrix} 1-p & p \\ p & 1-p \end{pmatrix} \end{array}$$

if the player flips the spin with probability $p\in[0, 1]$. A sequence of mixed actions puts the state of the electron into a convex linear combination $a\,U + (1{-}a)\,D$, $0 \le a \le 1$, which means that if the spin is measured the electron will be in the spin–up state with probability a. Q, having studied quantum theory, is utilizing a *quantum strategy*, implemented as a sequence of unitary, rather than stochastic, matrices. In standard Dirac notation the basis of V is written $(|U\rangle, |D\rangle)$. A *pure* quantum state for the electron is a linear combination $a\,|U\rangle + b\,|D\rangle$, a, $b \in \mathbb{C}$, $a\,\overline{a} + b\,\overline{b} = 1$, which means that if the spin is measured, the electron will be in the spin–up state with probability $a\,\overline{a}$. Since the electron starts in the state $|U\rangle$, this is the state of the electron if Q's first action is the unitary operation

$$U_1 = U(a, b) := \begin{array}{c} \\ {\scriptstyle U} \\ {\scriptstyle D} \end{array}\!\!\begin{array}{c} {\scriptstyle U \quad\ D} \\ \begin{pmatrix} a & b \\ \overline{b} & -\overline{a} \end{pmatrix} \end{array}.$$

Captain Picard is utilizing a *classical mixed strategy* (probabilistic) in which he flips the spin with probability p (has he preferred drill to studying quantum theory?).

After his action the electron is in a mixed quantum state, i.e., it is in the pure state $b\,|U\rangle + a\,|D\rangle$ with probability p and in the pure state $a\,|U\rangle + b\,|D\rangle$ with probability $1-p$. Mixed states are conveniently represented as *density matrices*, elements of $V \otimes V^{\dagger}$ with trace 1; the diagonal entry (k,k) is the probability that the system is observed to be in the state $|\psi_k\rangle$. The density matrix for a pure state $|\psi\rangle \in V$ is the projection matrix $|\psi\rangle\langle\psi|$ and the density matrix for a mixed state is the corresponding convex linear combination of pure density matrices. Unitary transformations act on density matrices by conjugation: the electron starts in the pure state $\rho_0 |U\rangle\langle U|$ and Q's first action puts it into the pure state:

$$\rho_1 = U_1 \rho_0 U_1^{\dagger} = \begin{pmatrix} a\,\overline{a} & a\,\overline{b} \\ b\,\overline{a} & b\,\overline{b} \end{pmatrix}.$$

Picard's mixed action acts on this density matrix, not as a stochastic matrix on a probabilistic state, but as a convex linear combination of unitary (deterministic) transformations:

$$\rho_2 = p\,F \rho_1 F^{\dagger} + (1-p)\,N \rho_1 N^{\dagger}$$

$$\begin{pmatrix} p\,b\,\overline{b} + (1-p)\,a\,\overline{a} & p\,b\,\overline{a} + (1-p)\,a\,\overline{b} \\ p\,a\,\overline{b} + (1-p)\,b\,\overline{a} & p\,a\,\overline{a} + (1-p)\,b\,\overline{b} \end{pmatrix}.$$

For $p = \frac{1}{2}$ the diagonal elements of ρ_2 are equal to $\frac{1}{2}$. If the game were to end here, Picard's strategy would ensure him the expected payoff of 0, independently of Q's strategy. In fact, if Q were to employ any strategy for which $a\,\overline{a} \neq b\,\overline{b}$, Picard could obtain the expected payoff of $|a\,\overline{a} - b\,\overline{b}| > 0$ by setting $p = 0, 1$ according to whether $b\,\overline{b} > a\,\overline{a}$, or the reverse. Similarly, if Picard were to choose $p \neq \frac{1}{2}$, Q could obtain the expected payoff of $|2p - 1|$ by setting $a=1$ or $b=1$ according to whether $p < \frac{1}{2}$, or the reverse. Thus the mixed/quantum equilibria for the two–move game are pairs $\big([\frac{1}{2}F + \frac{1}{2}N], [U(a,b)]\big)$ for which $a\,\overline{a} = b\,\overline{b} = \frac{1}{2}$ and the outcome is the same as if both players utilize optimal mixed strategies. But Q has another move at his disposal (U_3) which again transforms the state of the electron by conjugation to $\rho_3 U_3 \rho_2 U_3^{\dagger}$. If Q's strategy consists of $U_1 = U(1/\sqrt{2}, 1/\sqrt{2}) = U_3$, his first action puts the electron into a simultaneous eigenstate of both F and N (eigenvalue 1), which is therefore invariant under any mixed strategy $p\,F + (1-p)N$ of Picard. His second move inverts his first move and produces $\rho_3 |U\rangle\langle U|$. That is, with probability 1 the electron spin is up! Since Q can do no better than to win with probability 1, this is an optimal quantum strategy for him. All the pairs

$$\big([p\,F + (1-p)N], [U(1/\sqrt{2}, 1/\sqrt{2}), U(1/\sqrt{2}, 1/\sqrt{2})]\big)$$

are mixed/quantum equilibria, with value -1 to Picard; this is why he loses every game. We think that this hypothetical story convinces the reader that quantum games should be studied thoroughly in order to prevent analogous events from shaping his/her destiny let alone other aspects. The practical lesson that the above example teaches is that quantum theory may offer strategies that at least in some cases give advantage over classical strategies. Therefore physicist and game theorists should find answers to the following five questions.

- Is the idea of quantum game feasible?
- Under what conditions some players may be able to take the advantage of quantum phenomena?
- Are there genuine quantum games that have no classical counterparts or origin?
- Are protocols for playing quantum game against human player secure against cheating?
- Can the formalism be generalized to include other non–Boolean logic based systems?

Finding answers to the above questions is challenging and intriguing. It is anticipated that answers to these questions will have a profound impact on the development of quantum theory, quantum information processing and technology. Unfortunately, at this stage it we are not able to give any definite answer and, in fact, we have no idea in what direction we should look to find them. Nevertheless one can present some strong arguments for developing quantum theory of games. Modern technologies are developed mostly due to investigation into the quantum nature of matter. The results of recent experiments in nanotechnology, quantum dots and molecular physics are very promising. This means that we sooner or later may face situations analogous to captain Picard's if we are not on alert. Many cryptographic and information processing problems can be reformulated in game–like setting. Therefore quantum information and quantum cryptography should provide us with cases in point. It is obvious that some classical games can be implemented in such a way that the set of possible strategies would include strategies that certainly deserve the adjective quantum [11, 12]. Such games can certainly be played in a laboratory. This process is often referred to as quantization of the respective standard game. But this is an abuse of language: we are in fact defining a new game. In the classical setting the problems of security and honesty are usually well defined. Realistic quantum cryptography systems and quantum networks (BBN, Harvard and Boston Universities are already building the DARPA Quantum Network [13]) will certainly provide us with examples of genuine quantum games and strategies. Unlike, in quantum game theory the problem is much more involved. In many cases it can be settled in the "classical way" (e.g. by selecting arbiters or sort of clearinghouses) but if you admit quantum strategies in less definite setting of actually being developed technologies it may be even difficult to name dishonesty. If quantum games should ever be applied outside physical laboratories a lot of technical problems must be solved. Security of quantum games is only one of them but it already involves error corrections, quantum state tomography and methods of communications and preparations of quantum systems forming the "quantum board" and the necessary "quantum memory". We envisage that critical analysis of already proposed quantum information processing protocols must be done to this end. One of the main objectives would be a definition of (possibly universal) primitives necessary for realistic quantum games. Quantum phenomena probably play important role in biological and other complex systems and, although this point of view is not commonly accepted, quantum games may turn out to be an important tool for the analysis of various complex systems. Genetic algorithms and DNA computation can also be used to implement games and quantum games may be the most promising field [14]. Massive parallel DNA processing would allow to play simultaneously trillions of games. Noncommutative propositions are characteristic of various situations not necessary associated with quantum systems. In fact, the richness of possible structures is immense. There are suggestions that quantum–like description of market phenomena may be more accurate than the classical (probabilistic) one [15]. The quantum morphogenesis [16] shows one possible way of generalization of the formalism that may find application in social sciences.

3 Quantum game theory

Basically, any quantum system that can be manipulated by at least one party and where the utility of the moves can be reasonably defined, quantified and ordered may be conceived as a quantum game. The quantum system may be referred to as a *quantum board* although the term *universum of the game* seems to be more appropriate [17]. We will suppose that all players know the state of the game at the beginning and at some crucial stages that may depend an the game being played. This is a subtle point because it is not always possible to identify the state of a quantum system let alone the technical problems with actual identification of the state (one can easily give examples of systems that are only partially accessible to some players [18]). A "realistic" quantum game should include measuring apparatuses or information channels that provide information on the state of the game at crucial stages and specify the way of its termination. We will neglect these nontrivial issues here. Therefore we will suppose that a *two–player quantum game* $\Gamma=(\mathcal{H},\rho,S_A,S_B,P_A,P_B)$ is completely specified by the underlying Hilbert space $\mathcal{H}$ of the physical system, the initial state $\rho\in\mathcal{S}(\mathcal{H})$, where $\mathcal{S}(\mathcal{H})$ is the associated state space, the sets S_A and S_B of permissible quantum operations of the two players, and the pay–off (utility) functions P_A and P_B, which specify the pay–off for each player. A *quantum strategy* $s_A\in S_A$, $s_B\in S_B$ is a collection of admissible quantum operations, that is the mappings of the space of states onto itself. One usually supposes that they are completely positive trace–preserving maps. The quantum game's definition may also include certain additional rules, such as the order of the implementation of the respective quantum strategies or restriction on the admissible communication channels, methods of stopping the game etc. We also exclude the alteration of the pay–off during the game. The generalization for the N players case is obvious. Schematically we have:

$$\rho \mapsto (s_A, s_B) \mapsto \sigma \Rightarrow (P_A, P_B)\,.$$

The following concepts will be used in the remainder of this paper. These definitions are completely analogous to the corresponding definitions in standard game theory [19, 20]. The adjective quantum gives no extra meaning to them. A strategy s_A is called a *dominant strategy* of Alice if

$$P_A(s_A, s'_B) \;\geq\; P_A(s'_A, s'_B)$$

for all $s'_A \in S_A$, $s'_B \in S_B$. Analogously we can define a dominant strategy for Bob. A pair (s_A, s_B) is said to be an *equilibrium in dominant strategies* if s_A and s_B are the players' respective dominant strategies. A combination of strategies (s_A, s_B) is called a *Nash equilibrium* if

$$\begin{aligned} P_A(s_A, s_B) \;&\geq\; P_A(s'_A, s_B)\,, \\ P_B(s_A, s_B) \;&\geq\; P_B(s_A, s'_B)\,. \end{aligned}$$

A pair of strategies (s_A, s_B) is called *Pareto optimal*, if it is not possible to increase one player's pay–off without lowering the pay–off of the other player. A solution in dominant strategies is the strongest solution concept for a non–zero sum game. For example, in the popular Prisoner's Dilemma game [19, 20]:

	Bob : C	Bob : D
Alice : C	$(3, 3)$	$(0, 5)$
Alice : D	$(5, 0)$	$(1, 1)$

where the numbers in parentheses represent the row (Alice) and column (Bob) player's payoffs, respectively. Defection (D) is the dominant strategy, as it is favorable regardless what strategy the other party chooses.

In general the optimal strategy depends on the strategy chosen by the other party. A Nash equilibrium implies that neither player has a motivation to unilaterally alter his/her strategy from this kind of equilibrium solution, as this action will lower his/her pay–off. Given that the other player will stick to the strategy corresponding to the equilibrium, the best result is achieved by also playing the equilibrium solution. The concept of Nash equilibria is therefore of paramount importance to studies of non–zero–sum games. It is, however, only an acceptable solution concept if the Nash equilibrium is not unique (this happens very often). For games with multiple Nash equilibria we have to find a way to eliminate all but one of them. Therefore a Nash equilibrium is not necessarily an efficient and satisfactory one. We say that an equilibrium is Pareto optimal if there is no other outcome which would make both players better off. But usually there are no incentives to adopt the Pareto optimal strategies. In the Prisoner's Dilemma the Pareto equilibrium is reached if both players adopt the strategy C, but they are afraid of being outwitted by the opponent's playing D. If the same game is repeated many times the situation changes because the players may communicate by changing strategies and learning is possible. To this end both players should adopt mixed strategies. One can prove that any game has a Nash equilibrium in the class of mixed strategies [19, 20].

4 Quantum games in action: a review recent results

Quantum game theory attracted much attention since the prescription for quantization of games has been put forward by Eisert, Wilkens and Lewenstein [6]. It was subsequently generalized by Marinatto and Weber [21]. This general setting was described above. Actually, it can be applied to any $2 \times n$ games (each player has n strategies and the players' actions are represented by $U(n)$ or $SU(n)$ operators). This prescription has been used for "quantizing" various classical games (Prisoner's Dilemma [6, 22], The Monty Hall Problem [23, 24], Battle of Sexes [25, 26, 27], Stag Hunt Game [28], Rock, Scissors and Paper [29, 30], Coordination Problem [31], Duopoly Problem [32], duels [33] etc. The results show that, in general, the "quantization process" and relations to the background classical problems are not unique. Nash equilibria can be found but, as in the classical problems, in most cases they are not Pareto optimal. Lee and Johnson have shown that playing games quantum mechanically can be more efficient and giving a saturation of the upper bound on the efficiency [34]. From their work it can be deduced that there are quantum versions of the minimax theorem for zero sum quantum games and the Nash equilibrium theorem for general static quantum games. There are many unexplored connections between quantum information theory and other scientific models. Quantum game theory offers tools in analysis of phenomena that usually are not considered as physical processes. Theory of information can be used for analysis of algorithms that describe player's strategies and tactics but classical games form only a small? subclass of games that can be played in quantum information media. If we ignore technological problem then we can extend this subclass so that exploration of quantum phenomena is possible. There are two obvious modifications of classical simulation games.

1 – prequantization: Redefine the game so that it became a reversal operation on qubits representing player's strategies. This allows for quantum coherence of strategies[1].

2 – quantization: Reduce the number of qubits and allow arbitrary unitary[2] trans-

[1] This may result from nonclassical strategies or classically forbidden measurements of the state of the game

[2] At least one of the performed operations should not be equivalent to a classical one

formation so that the basic feature of the classical game are preserved.

Any game modified in this way is in fact a quantum algorithm that usually allows for more effective information processing than the starting game. Actually, any quantum computation is a potential quantum game if we manage to reinterpret it in game–theoretical terms. To illustrate the second method let us consider Wiesner's counterfeit–proof banknote [3]. This is the first quantum secrecy method (elimination of effective eavesdropping). As a quantum game it consists in a finite series of sub–games presented in Fig. 1. An arbiter Trent produces a pair of random qubits $|\psi_T\rangle$ and $|\psi_{T'}\rangle$. The polarization of the qubit (strategy) $|\psi_T\rangle$ is known to Trent and is kept secret. The qubit $|\psi_{T'}\rangle$ is ancillary. Alice qubit $|\psi_A\rangle$ describes her strategies $|\mathrm{I}\rangle$ and $|0\rangle$. The first move is performed by Alice. Her strategy $|\mathrm{I}\rangle$ consists in switching the Trent's qubits $|\psi_T\rangle$ and $|\psi_{T'}\rangle$. The strategy $|0\rangle$ consists in leaving the Trent's qubits intact. These moves form the controlled–swap gate [35]. Her opponent Bob wins only if after the game Trent learns that his qubit $|\psi_T\rangle$ has not been changed.

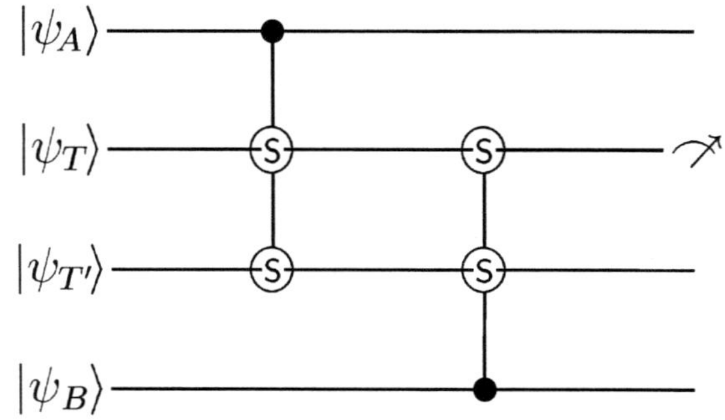

Figure 1: Quantum identification game constructed from two controlled–swap gates (Wiesner's money).

To win, Bob must always begin with a strategy identical to the one used by Alice. If there is no coordination of moves between Alice and Bob the probability of Bob's success exponentially decreases with growing number of sub–games being played and is negligible even for a small number of sub–games. Alice and Bob's strategies are classical but due to the prequantization process eavesdropping is not possible if Trent uses arbitrary polarizations $|\psi_T\rangle|0\rangle + z\,|\mathrm{I}\rangle$, $z \in \overline{\mathcal{C}} \simeq S_2$ (in the projective nonhomogeneous coordinates). This game can be quantized by elimination of the ancillary qubit $|\psi_{T'}\rangle$. Then Alice and Bob strategies should be equivalent to controlled–Hadamard gates [35]. In this case Trent's qubit is changed only if Alice adopts the strategy $|\mathrm{I}\rangle$ that result in $|\psi_T\rangle|0\rangle + z\,|\mathrm{I}\rangle \longrightarrow |0\rangle + \frac{1-z}{1+z}\,|\mathrm{I}\rangle$ (quantum Fourier transform), see Fig. 2. The actual Wiesner's idea was to encode the secret values of $|\psi_T\rangle$ that result from Alice moves in the series of sub–games on an otherwise numbered banknote. In addition, the issuer Trent takes over the role of

Alice and records the values of $|\psi_T\rangle$ and $|\psi_A\rangle$ with the label being the number of the banknote. The authentication of the banknote is equivalent to a success in the game when Bob's strategy is used against that recorded by Trent (if Bob wins then his forgery is successful).

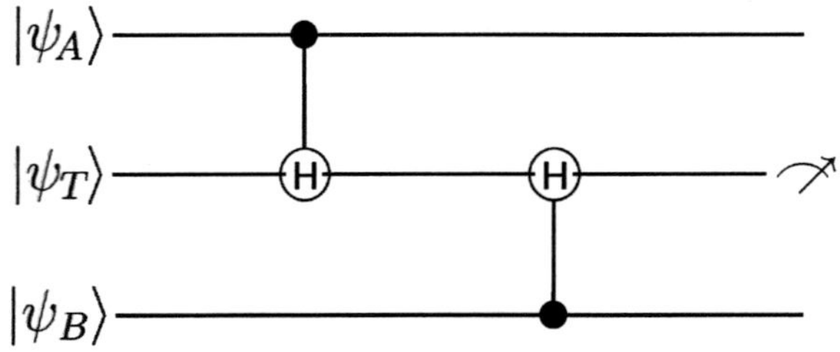

Figure 2: Quantum identification game constructed from two controlled–Hadamard gates.

The introduction of classically impossible strategies results in better security against quantum attack (pretending to be Alice). Eavesdropping of the state $|\psi_T\rangle$ modified by Alice's strategy is ineffective even if Trend limits himself to polarizations from the set $\{|0\rangle, |I\rangle\}$. It is possible that an analogous reduction of qubits allows to exponentially reduce the complexity of quantum algorithms. Therefore quantum games may sometimes be the only feasible alternatives if the classical problems are computationally to complex to be ever implemented. Description of games against Nature is far more complicated. It is not easy to show that they do not contradict known natural laws or are actually being played. For example, let us consider a prequantized version of the Maxwell's Demon game against Nature [36]. Demon acting in accord with physical laws tries to build a Szilard's engine. The Demon fails because Nature erases information and this is an energy consuming process. Such arguments work also in biology and social sciences. The classical theory of interacting particles localized at nodes of crystal lattices results in quantum model of collective phenomenon known as phonon. Phonons do not exist outside the crystal lattice. May humans and animals form classical ingredients of large quantum entities? May Penrose will not be able to find consciousness at the sub–neuronic microtubular level [37] because it is localized at the complex multi–neuron level? Do we try to convince ourselves that there are living actors in TV sets?

4.1 Quantum games in economics and social sciences

Modern game theory has its roots in economics and social sciences and one should not be surprised by number of attempts at quantizing classical problems. In the "standard" quantum game theory one tries in some sense to quantize an operational description of "classical" versions of the game being analyzed. It usually enlarges the set admissible strategies in a nontrivial way. Piotrowski and Sładkowski follow a different way. Technological development will sooner or later result in construction of quantum computers. If one considers the number of active traders, the intensity of trade contemporary markets and their role in the civilization then one must admit that the *the market game* is the biggest one ever played by humans. How would look a market cleared by a quantum computer quantum network or other quantum device? They propose to describe market players strategies in terms of state vectors $|\psi\rangle$ belonging to some Hilbert space $\mathcal{H}$ [8, 9]. The probability densities of revealing the players, say Alice and Bob, intentions are described in terms of random variables p and q:

$$\frac{|\langle q|\psi\rangle_A|^2}{{}_A\langle\psi|\psi\rangle_A}\,\frac{|\langle p|\psi\rangle_B|^2}{{}_B\langle\psi|\psi\rangle_B}\,dqdp\,,$$

where $\langle q|\psi\rangle_A$ is the probability amplitude of offering the price q by Alice who wants to buy and the demand component of her state is given by $|\psi\rangle_A \in \mathcal{H}_A$. Bob's amplitude $\langle p|\psi\rangle_B$ is interpreted in an analogous way (opposite position). Of course, the "intentions" q and p not always result in the accomplishment of the transaction [8]. According to standard risk theory it seems reasonable to define the observable of *the risk inclination operator*:

$$H(\mathcal{P}_k,\mathcal{Q}_k) := \frac{(\mathcal{P}_k - p_{k0})^2}{2\,m} + \frac{m\,\omega^2(\mathcal{Q}_k - q_{k0})^2}{2}\,,$$

where $p_{k0} := \frac{{}_k\langle\psi|\mathcal{P}_k|\psi\rangle_k}{{}_k\langle\psi|\psi\rangle_k}$, $q_{k0} := \frac{{}_k\langle\psi|\mathcal{Q}_k|\psi\rangle_k}{{}_k\langle\psi|\psi\rangle_k}$, $\omega := \frac{2\pi}{\theta}$. θ denotes the characteristic time of transaction [38] which is, roughly speaking, an average time spread between two opposite moves of a player (e.g. buying and selling the same asset). The parameter $m>0$ measures the risk asymmetry between buying and selling positions. Analogies with quantum harmonic oscillator allow for the following characterization of quantum market games. The constant h_E describes the minimal inclination of the player to risk. It is equal to the product of the lowest eigenvalue of $H(\mathcal{P}_k,\mathcal{Q}_k)$ and $2\,\theta$. $2\,\theta$ is in fact the minimal interval during which it makes sense to measure the profit. Except the ground state all the adiabatic strategies $H(\mathcal{P}_k,\mathcal{Q}_k)|\psi\rangle = const|\psi\rangle$ are giffens [8, 39] that is goods that do not obey the law of demand and supply. It should be noted here that in a general case the operators $\mathcal{Q}_k$ do not commute because traders observe moves of other players and often act accordingly. One big bid can influence the market at least in a limited time spread. Therefore it is natural to apply the formalism of noncommutative quantum mechanics where one considers

$$[x^j, x^k] = \mathrm{i}\,\Theta^{jk} := \mathrm{i}\,\Theta\,\epsilon^{jk}.$$

The analysis of harmonic oscillator in more then one dimensions imply that the parameter Θ modifies the constant $\hbar_E \to \sqrt{\hbar_E^2 + \Theta^2}$ and, accordingly, the eigenvalues of $H(\mathcal{P}_k,\mathcal{Q}_k)$. This has the natural interpretation that moves performed by other players can diminish or increase one's inclination to taking risk. When a game allows a great number of players in it is useful to consider it as a two–players game:

the trader $|\psi\rangle_k$ against the Rest of the World (RW). The concrete algorithm $\mathcal{A}$ may allow for an effective strategy of RW (for a sufficiently large number of players a single player would not have much influence on the form of the RW strategy). If one considers the RW strategy it make sense to declare its simultaneous demand and supply states because for one player RW is a buyer and for another it is a seller. To describe such situation it is convenient to use the Wigner formalism. If the market continuously measures the same strategy of the player, say the demand $\langle q|\psi\rangle$, and the process is repeated sufficiently often for the whole market, then the prices given by some algorithm do not result from the supplying strategy $\langle p|\psi\rangle$ of the player. The necessary condition for determining the profit of the game is the transition of the player to the state $\langle p|\psi\rangle$. If, simultaneously, many of the players change their strategies then the quotation process may collapse due to the lack of opposite moves. In this way the quantum Zeno effects explains stock exchange crashes. Another example of the quantum market Zeno effect is the stabilization of prices of an asset provided by a monopolist.
But one does not need any sophisticated equipment or technology to apply quantum theory and quantum games in economics and social sciences. In fact, Lambertini claims that quantum mechanics and mathematical economics are isomorphic [40]. Therefore one should expect that various quantum tools as the quantum morphogenesis [16] would be invented and used to describe social phenomena. An interesting analysis was done by Arfi who proposes to use quantum game for wide spectrum of problems in political sciences [41]. Quantum game theory may help solving some philosophical paradoxes, c.f. the quantum solution to the notorious Newcomb's paradox (free will dilemma) [42].

Strategies adopted by social groups or their individual members usually seem to be unspeakable and elusive. Efforts to imitate them often fail. Impossible to clone quantum strategies have analogous properties [35]. On the other side, customs, habits and memories are so durable that possibilities of effacing them are illusory. This resembles the no deleting theorem for quantum states (strategies) [43]. Both theorems describe the same forbidden process expressed in reverse chronological order $|\psi\rangle|0\rangle \not\leftrightarrow |\psi\rangle|\psi\rangle$. An interesting thermodynamical discussion of this impossibility is given in [44]. These analogies cannot be explained in the classical paradigm.

4.2 Quantum games in biology

Living organism may in fact behave in quantum–like way. This may be caused by at least two factors. First, quantum entanglement and decoherence may affect various molecular processes. Second, quantum–like description of dynamics in a population of interacting individuals may be more accurate than the probabilistic one. Therefore a cautious speculation on the possibility that the natural world might already be exploiting the advantages of quantum games on the macroscopic scale may be in place. Maynard Smith in his book *Evolution and the Theory of Games* [45] discusses an evolutionary approach in classical game theory. The concept of evolutionary stability stimulated the development of evolutionary game theory. Iqbal and Toor showed in a series of papers [7, 29, 46, 47, 48] that the presence of entanglement, in asymmetric as well as symmetric bimatrix games, can disturb the evolutionary stability expressed by the idea of evolutionary stable strategies. Therefore evolutionary stability of a symmetric Nash equilibrium can be made to appear or disappear by controlling entanglement in symmetric and asymmetric bimatrix games. It shows that the presence of quantum mechanical effects may have a deciding role on the outcomes of evolutionary dynamics in a population of interacting entities. They suggest that a relevance of their ideas may be found in the studies of the evolution of genetic code at the dawn of life and evolutionary algorithms where interactions between individual of a population may be governed by quantum effects. The nature of these quantum effects, influencing the course of evolution, will also determine the evolutionary outcome. Therefore Darwin's idea of natural selection may be relevant even for quantum systems. Another class of problem concerns replication in biology [49]. The role of DNA and its replication still waits for explanation. Game theory and quantum game theory offer interesting and powerful tools to this end the results will probably find their applications in computation, physics, complex system analysis and cognition sciences [50, 51, 52]. Neuroeconomics [53, 54], a discipline that aims at proving that economic theory may provide an alternative to the classical Cartesian model of the brain and behavior, is a source of fascinating topics for a debate. Is there a *quantum neuroeconomics* [55]? We may expect a rich dialogue between theoretical neurobiology and quantum logic [56].

4.3 Quantum games and information processing

Quantum theory of information is certainly a serious challenge to the standard game theory and will probably stimulate the research in quantum game theory. Most of the cryptographic problems are in fact games, sometimes in camouflage. Analysis and design of cryptographic primitives can also be perceived as games so their quantum counterparts are quantum games, e.g. quantum key distribution, quantum coin tossing [57, 13] or the coordination problem in distributive computing [58]. Coin tossing protocols form an important class of cryptographic primitives. They are used to define a random bit among separated parties. Classical coin flipping can implemented by a trusted arbiter or by assuming that the players have limited computational power. If the players have unlimited computational power then no classical coin flipping protocol is possible because any such protocol represents a two player game and, according to game theory, there always is a player with a winning strategy. By contrast, in a quantum world the existence of coin flipping protocols is not ruled out even by unlimited computational power. This is because any attempt by a player to deviate (cheat) from the protocol can disturb the quantum states, and therefore be detected by the adversary. But this is far from being the whole story. There are quantum games that live across the border of our present knowledge. For example, consider some classical or quantum problem X. Let us define the game $kXcl$: you win if and only if you solve the problem (perform the task) X given access to only k bits of information. The quantum counterpart reads: solve the problem X on a quantum computer or other quantum device given access to only k bits of information. Let us call the game $kXcl$ or kXq interesting if the corresponding limited information–tasks are feasible. Let $OkhamXcl$ ($OkhamXq$) denotes the minimal k interesting game in the class $kXcl$ (kXq). Authors of the paper [55] described the game played by a market trader who gains the profit P for each bit (qubit) of information about her strategy. If we denote this game by MP then $OkhamM\frac{1}{2}cl = 2M\frac{1}{2}cl$ and for $P > \frac{1}{2}$ the game does not exist $OkhamMPcl$. They also considered the more effective game $1M\frac{2+\sqrt{2}}{4}q$ for which $OkhamM\frac{2+\sqrt{2}}{4}q \neq 1M\frac{2+\sqrt{2}}{4}q$ if the trader can operate on more then one market. This happens because there are entangled strategies that are more profitable [59]. There are a lot of intriguing questions that can be ask, for example for which X the meta–game $Okham(OkhamXq)cl$ can be solved or when, if at all, the meta–problem $Okham(OkhamXq)q$ is well defined problem. Such problems arise in quantum memory analysis [60].

Algorithmic combinatorial games, except for cellular automata, have been completely ignored by quantum physicists. This is astonishing because at least some of the important intractable problems might be attacked and solved on a quantum computer (even such a simple one player game as Minesweeper in NP–complete [61]).

4.4 Quantum games, complexity theory and decision theory

What form does the decision theory take for a quantum player? Almost all quantum acts involve preparing a system, measuring it, and then receiving some reward (in a more or less general sense) which is dependent on the outcome of the measurement. Therefore it should not be astonishing that game–theoretical analysis of quantum phenomena has far reaching consequences. Deutsch claims to have derived the Born from decision–theoretic assumptions [62, 63]. In fact he have defined a quantum game and quantum–mechanical version of decision theory. What is striking about the Deutsch game is that rational agents are so strongly constrained in their behavior that not only must they assign probabilities to uncertain events, they must assign precisely those probabilities given by the Born rule. His proof must be understood in the explicit context of the Everett interpretation, and that in this context it is acceptable [63].

Roughly speaking, one of the main goals of complexity theory is to present lower bounds on various resources needed to solve a certain computational problem. From a cryptographic viewpoint, the most demanding problem is to prove nontrivial lower bounds on the complexity of breaking concrete cryptographic systems. Query complexity on the other side, is an abstract scenario which can be thought of as a game.

The goal is to determine some information by asking as few questions as possible see e.g. quantum oracle and their interrogations [64]. A weak form of quantum interactive proof systems known as quantum Merlin–Arthur games [65, 66, 67] defines a whole class of quantum games with wide application in quantum complexity theory and cryptography. Here, powerful Merlin presents a proof and Arthur, who is the verifier, verifies its correctness. The task is to prove a statement without yielding anything beyond its validity (*zero knowledge proofs*).

There are games in which the agents' strategies do not have adequate descriptions in terms of some Boolean algebra of logic and theory of probability. They can be analyzed according to the rules of quantum theory and the result are promising, see e.g. the Wise Alice game proposed in [68, 69]. This game is a simplified version of the quantum bargaining game [70] restricted to the "quantum board" of the form $[buy, sell] \times [bid, accept]$. Quantum semantic games also belong to this class [71].

4.5 Quantum gambling

At the present stage of our technological development it already is feasible to open *quantum casinos*, where gambling at quantum games would be possible. Of course, such an enterprise would be costly but if you recall the amount of money spent on advertising various products it seems to us that it is a worthy cause. Goldenberg, Vaidman and Wiesner described the following game based on the coin tossing protocol [72]. Alice has two boxes, A and B, which can store a particle. The quantum states of the particle in the boxes are denoted by $|a\rangle$ and $|b\rangle$, respectively. Alice prepares the particle in some state and sends box B to Bob.
Bob wins in one of the two cases:

1. If he finds the particle in box B, then Alice pays him 1 monetary unit (after checking that box A is empty).

2. If he asks Alice to send him box A for verification and he finds that she initially prepared a state different from $|\psi_0\rangle = 1/\sqrt{2}\,(|a\rangle + |b\rangle)$, then Alice pays him R monetary units.

In any other case Alice wins, and Bob pays her 1 monetary unit. They have analyzed the security of the scheme, possible methods of cheating and calculated the average gain of each party as a result of her/his specific strategy. The analysis shows that the protocol allows two remote parties to play a gambling game, such that in a certain limit it becomes a fair game. No unconditionally secure classical method is known to accomplish this task. This game was implemented by Yong–Sheng Zhang et al, [73]. Other proposals based on properties of non–orthogonal states were put forward by Hwang, Ahn, and Hwang [74] and Hwang and Matsumoto [75]. Witte proposed a quantum version of the Heads or Tails game [76]. Piotrowski and Sładkowski suggested that although sophisticated technologies to put a quantum market in motion are not yet available, simulation of quantum markets and auctions can be performed in an analogous way to precision physical measurements during which classical apparatuses are used to explore quantum phenomena. People seeking after excitement would certainly not miss the opportunity to perfect their skills at using "quantum strategies". To this end an automatic game "Quantum Market" will be sufficient and such a device can be built up due to the recent advances in technology [55]. Segre published an interesting detailed analysis of quantum casinos and a Mathematica packages for simulating quantum gambling [77]. His and others considerations show that quantum gambling is closely related to quantum logic, decision theory and can be used for defining a Bayesian theory of quantum probability [78].

5 Conclusions

Games, used both for entertainment and scientific aims, are traditionally modelled as mathematical objects, and therefore are traditionally seen as mathematical disciplines. However, all processes in the real world are physical phenomena and as such involve noise, various uncertainty factors and, what concerned us here, quantum phenomena. This fact can be used both for the benefit and detriment. Works of Deutsch, Penrose and others seem to be harbingers of the dawn of a quantum game era when consistent quantum information description would be used not only in physics and natural sciences but also in social sciences and economics. The heterogeneity and fruitfulness of quantum computations will certainly stimulate such interdisciplinary studies and technological development. Quantum games broaden our horizons and offer new opportunities for the technology and economics. If human decisions can be traced to microscopic quantum events one would expect that nature would have taken advantage of quantum computation in evolving complex brains. In that sense one could indeed say that quantum computers are playing according to quantum rules. David Deutsch has proposed an interesting unification of theories of information, evolution and quanta [79]. Lambertini put forward arguments for observing Schroedinger cat like objects on real markets [40]. But why quantum social sciences should emerge just now [80]? They could have not emerged earlier because a tournament quantum computer versus classical one is not possible without technological development necessary for a construction of quantum computers. Now it seems to be feasible. Quantum–like approach to market description might turn out to be an important theoretical tool for investigation of computability problems in economics or game theory even if never implemented in real market [81, 15]. It is tempting to "quantize" Karl Popper's ideas [82] expressed in terms of language–games [83]. Such a revision would determine regions of quantum falsification of scientific theories (q–falsification). Should theories that have high falsification and low q–falsification be regarded as restraining development? If this is the case then *the quantum information processing paradigm* (see e.g. [84])

should replace the alternative platonism or mysticism [37]. Of course, as any other disciplines, quantum game theory also has its negative sides but there is no doubt that it will be a crucial discipline for the emerging information society.

Acknowledgements We are greatly indebted to prof. Zbigniew Hasiewicz for critical reading of the manuscript and helpful remarks. This paper has been supported by the **Polish Ministry of Scientific Research and Information Technology** under the (solicited) grant No **PBZ-MIN-008/P03/2003**.

References

[1] Milnor, J., Games against nature, in Thrall, R. M., Coombs, C. H., Davis, R. L., (eds.), *Decision Processes*, John Wiley & Sons, New York (1954) p. 49.

[2] von Neumann, J. and Morgenstern, O., *Theory of Games and Economic Behavior*, Princeton University Press, Princeton (1953).

[3] Wiesner, S., Conjugate coding, *SIGACT News* **15/1** (1983) 78. http://kh.bu.edu/qcl/pdf/wiesners198316024137.pdf.

[4] Vaidman, L., Variations on the theme of the Greenberger–Horne–Zeilinger proof, *Foundation of Physics* **29** (1999) 615.

[5] Meyer, D. A., Quantum strategies, *Physical Review Letters* **82** (1999) 1052.

[6] Eisert, J., Wilkens, M., Lewenstein, M., Quantum Games and Quantum Strategies, *Physical Review Letters* **83** (1999) 3077.

[7] Iqbal A., Toor A. H., Evolutionarily stable strategies in quantum games, *Physics Letters A* **280** (2001) 249.

[8] Piotrowski, E. W., Sładkowski, J., Quantum Market Games, *Physica A* **312** (2002) 208.

[9] Piotrowski, E. W., Sładkowski, J., Quantum English Auctions, *Physica A* **318** (2003) 505.

[10] Flitney A. P., Abbott D., Quantum models of Parrondo's games, *Physica A* **324** (2003) 152.

[11] Du, J. et al, Experimental realization of quantum games on a quantum computer *Physical Review Letters* **88** (2002) 137902.

[12] Pietarinen, A., Quantum logic and quantum theory in a game–theoretic perspective, *Open Systems and Information Dynamics* **9** (2002) 273.

[13] Elliott, C., Pearson, D., Troxel G., Quantum Cryptography in Practice, preprint of SIGCOMM 2003 paper; quant-ph/0307049.

[14] Wood, D., Bi, H., Kimbrough, S., Wu, D. J., Chen, J., DNA Starts to Learn Poker, in: Jonoska, N., Seeman, N. C., (eds.), *DNA Computing*, Lecture Notes in Computer Science, Springer–Verlag, Berlin (2002).

[15] Waite, S., *Quantum investing*, Texere Publishing, London (2002).

[16] Aerts, D., et al, Quantum morphogenesis: A variation on Thom's catastrophe theory, *Physical Review E* **67** (2003) 051926.

[17] Bugajski, S., Klamka, J., Quantum iterative system, quantum games, and quantum Parrondo effect, in preparation.

[18] Beltrametti, E. G., Bugajski, S., A classical extention of quantum mechanics, *Journal of Physics A* **28** (1995) 3329.

[19] Osborne, M. J., *A Course in Game Theory*, MIT Press, Boston (1994).

[20] Straffin, P. D., *Game Theory and Strategy*, AMS, Rhod Island (1993).

[21] Marinatto, L., Weber, T., A Quantum Approach To Static Games Of Complete Information, *Phsics Letters A* **272** (2000) 291.

[22] Du, J. et al, Playing Prisoner's Dilemma with Quantum Rules *Fluctuation and Noise Letters* **2** R189 (2002).

[23] Flitney, A. P., Abbott, D., Quantum version of the Monty Hall problem, *Physical Review A* **65** (2002) 062318.

[24] D'Ariano, G. M. et al, The Quantum Monty Hall Problem, *Quantum Information and Computing* **2** (2002) 355.

[25] Nawaz, A., Toor A. H., Worst–case Payoffs in Quantum Battle of Sexes Game; quant-ph/0110096.

[26] Du, J. et al, Nash Equilibrium in the Quantum Battle of Sexes Game; quant-ph/0010050.

[27] Du, J. et al, Remark On Quantum Battle of The Sexes Game; quant-ph/0103004.

[28] Toyota, N., Quantization of the stag hunt game and the Nash equilibrilum; quant-ph/0307029.

[29] Iqbal A., Toor A. H., Quantum repeated games, *Physics Letters A* **300** (2002) 541.

[30] Stohler, M., Fischbach, E., Non–Transitive Quantum Games; quant-ph/0307072.

[31] Huberman, B. A., Hogg, T., Quantum Solution of Coordination Problems; quant-ph/0306112.

[32] Iqbal A., Toor A.H., Backwards–induction outcome in a quantum game, *Physical Review A* **65** (2002) 052328.

[33] Flitney, A. P., Abbott, D., Quantum duels and truels; quant-ph/0305058.

[34] Lee, C. F., Johnson, N. F., Efficiency and formalism of quantum games, *Physical Review A* **67** (2003) 022311.

[35] Nielsen, M. A., Chuang, I. L., *Quantum Computation and Quantum Information*, Cambridge University Press, Cambridge (2000).

[36] Plenio, M. B., Vitelli, V., The physics of forgetting: Landauer's erasure principle and information theory, *Contemporary Physics* **42** (2001) 25.

[37] Penrose, R., *Shadows of the Mind*, Cambridge University Press, Cambridge (1994).

[38] Piotrowski, E. W., Sładkowski, J., The Merchandising Mathematician Model, *Physica A* **318** (2003) 496.

[39] Sładkowski, J., Giffen paradoxes in quantum market games, *Physica A* **324** (2003) 234.

[40] Lambertini, L., Quantum Mechanics and Mathematical Economics are Isomorphic; http://www.spbo.unibo.it/gopher/DSEC/370.pdf.

[41] Arfi, B., Ambivalence of Choice and "Holistic" Strategic Interaction: A Quantum Game–Theoretic Proposal; http://atticus.igs.berkeley.edu /research_programs/ppt/papers/barfi.pdf.

[42] Piotrowski, E. W., Sładkowski, J., Quantum solution to the Newcomb's paradox; quant-ph/0202074.

[43] Pati, A. K., Braunstein, S. L., Impossibility of deleting an unknown quantum state, *Nature* **404** (2000) 164.

[44] Horodecki, M., Horodecki, R., De, A. S., Sen, U., No–deleting and no–cloning principles as consequences of conservation of quantum information; quant-ph/0306044.

[45] Smith, M. J., *Evolution and the Theory of Games*, Cambridge University, New York 1982.

[46] Iqbal A., Toor A. H., Quantum mechanics gives stability to a Nash equilibrium, *Physical Review A* **65** (2002) 022306.

[47] Iqbal A., Toor A. H., Darwinism in quantum systems?, *Physics Letters A* **294** (2002) 261.

[48] Iqbal A., Toor A.H., Entanglement and Dynamic Stability of Nash Equilibria in a Symmetric Quantum Game, *Physics Letters A* **286** (2001) 245.

[49] Kauffman, L. H., Biologic; quant-ph/0204007.

[50] Patel, A., Quantum Algorithms and the Genetic Code, *Pramana* **56** (2001) 367.

[51] Patel, A., Testing Quantum Dynamics in Genetic Information Processing, *Journal of Genetics* **80** (2001) 39.

[52] Home, D., Chattopadhayaya, R., Determination of When an Outcome is Actualised in a Quantum Measurement using DNA — Photolyase System; . quant-ph/9903036.

[53] Glimcher, P. W., Decisions, Decisions, Decisions: Choosing a Biological Science of Choise, *Neuron* **36** (2002) 323.

[54] Glimcher, P. W., *Decisions, Uncertainty, and the Brain: The Science of Neuroeconomics*, MIT Press, Cambridge (2003).

[55] Piotrowski, E. W., Sładkowski, J., Quantum computer: an appliance for playing market games; quant-ph/0305017.

[56] Collum, G., Systems of logical systems: neuroscience and quantum logic, *Foundations of Science* **7** (2002) 49.

[57] Keyl, M., Fundamentals of Quantum Information Theory, *Physics Reports* **369** (2002) 431.

[58] Fitzi, M., Gisin, N., Maurer, U., A Quantum solution to the Byzantine agreement problem; quant-ph/0107127.

[59] Piotrowski, E. W., Fixed Point Theorem for Simple Quantum Strategies in Quantum Market Games, *Physica A* **324** (2003) 196.

[60] Koenig, R., Maurer, U., Renner, R., On the Power of Quantum Memory; quant-ph/0305154.

[61] see for example:
http://www.claymath.org/Popular_Lectures/Minesweeper/.

[62] Deutsch, D., Quantum Theory of Probabilty and Decisions, *Proceedings of the Royal Society of London* **A**455 (1999) 3129.

[63] Wallace, D., Quantum theory of Probabilty and Decision Theory, Revisited; quant-ph/0211104.

[64] Kashefi, E., Kent, A. Vedral, V., Banaszek, K., *Physical Review A* **65** (2002) 050304.

[65] Kobayashi, H., Matsumoto, K., Yamakami, T., Quantum Merlin–Arthur Proof Systems: Are Multiple Merlins More Helpful to Arthur?; quant-ph/0306051.

[66] Knill, E., Quantum Randomness and Nondeterminism; quant-ph/9610012.

[67] Watrous, J., Quantum statistical zero–knowledge; quant-ph/0202111.

[68] Grib, A., Parfionov, G., Can the game be quantum?; quant-ph/0206178.

[69] Grib, A., Parfionov, G., Macroscopic quantum game; quant-ph/0211068.

[70] Piotrowski, E. W., Sładkowski, J., Quantum Bargaining Games, *Physica A* **308** (2002) 391.

[71] Pietarinen, A., Quantum Logic and Quantum Theory in a Game–Theoretic Perspective, *Open Systems and Information Dynamics* **9** (2002) 273.

[72] Goldenberg, L., Vaidman, L., Wiesner, S., Quantum Gambling, *Physical Review Letters* **82** (1999) 3356.

[73] Zhang, S.-Y. et al, Optical Realization of Quantum Gambling Machine; quant-ph/0001008.

[74] Hwang, W.-Y., Ahn, D., Hwang, S. W. *Physical Review A* **64** 2001 064302.

[75] Hwang, W.-Y., Matsumoto, K., Quantum Gambling Using Three Nonorthogonal States, *Physical Review A* **66** (2002) 052311.

[76] Witte, F. M. C., Quantum 2–player gambling and correlated pay–off; quant-ph/0207085.

[77] Segre, G., Law of Excluded Quantum Gambling Strategies; quant-ph/0104080.

[78] Pitowsky, I., Betting on the Outcomes of Measurements: A Bayesian Theory of Quantum Probability, preprint quant-ph/0208121.

[79] Deutsch, D., *The Fabric of Reality*, Penguin Putnam Incorporated, New York (1998).

[80] Mendes, R. V., Quantum games and social norms; preprint quant-ph/0208167.

[81] Velupillai, K., *Computable Economics, the Arne Ryde Memorial Lectures*, Oxford University Press, Oxford (2000).

[82] Popper, K. R., *The Logic of Scientific Discovery*, Harper Torch Books, New York (1968).

[83] Hintikka, J., *Logic, language–games and information*, Clarendon Press, Oxford (1973).

[84] Horodecki, R., Horodecki, M., Horodecki, P., Quantum information isomorphism: beyond the dillemma of Scylla of ontology and Charybdis of instrumentalism, to appear in special issue of the IBM Journal of Research and Development; quant-ph/0305024.

Index

T

U

V

Z